# ODOR
# CONTROL
# and
# OLFACTION

HANDBOOK

# ODOR CONTROL and OLFACTION

*By*
J. P. COX, Ph.D

*Edited by*
RALPH B. DUCLOS

*Researched and compiled by*
FLORIE COX

*Illustrated by*
ROBERT G. JOHNSON

**POLLUTION SCIENCES PUBLISHING COMPANY**
**P.O. Box 175, Lynden, Washington 98264**

First Printing

*Library of Congress Catalog Number: 75-35291*
PRINTED IN THE UNITED STATES OF AMERICA
BY EDWARDS BROTHERS INCORPORATED ANN ARBOR, MICH

# Dedication

For better or worse, this book could not have happened without the efforts of Florie Cox, Ralph Duclos and Jeanne Cox, my wife.

Most books have numerous predecessors upon which they are to a great measure constructed, being the next logical in progression. Such is only true to a slight degree in this case. For various reasons odor control and olfaction have not been popular undertakings, and with the notable exception of Moncrieff, little has been done until recently to alter this trend. Much is owed to Moncrieff, and I hereby acknowledge this debt.

My personal gratitude to Kelly, John, Duffy and Laura for their help. Also to Bobby Nietfield and Sam Bennett, as motley a collection of freckled faces that ever made room for or gave ground to such an enterprise.

James P. Cox
Wiser Lake, Washington

CONTENTS

# INTRODUCTION

The purpose of this text is to present in a comprehensive manner the science, technology and mystery of odors and olfaction. Behind the purpose is the desire to take part in a meaningful way in the upsurge for a cleaner, safer, saner environment.

To some great extent the part that odors play in this scheme is somewhat misunderstood and downplayed by the authorities as is evidenced by the scant or ill-enforced legislation. For the most part, pollution can be encountered at all sensory levels: visual, audible, gustatory, olfactory, tactile and even more insidiously, at levels where perception plays no part: radiation, PCB's, nitrosamines, DDT, fluoride, mercury and countless other wastes that destroy or maim many living organisms. At the center of this great awakening lie the giant corporations and research houses--governmental and otherwise. They stand anxiously ready to serve the public, selling remedies to problems all too often created by themselves.

For the most part, the technology to solve the pollution problems exists in bits and pieces, here and there the legacy of the dynamic and overwhelming scientific picnic of the twentieth century--with the exception of the field of olfaction and odors. Here it is that we find a complete, or almost complete, blank. As the basic science of olfaction is pried open to view, many basic phenomenologies and curiosities become evident. It is in this fertile ground that new basic patents and means can be discovered to solve problems and probe the eternal mysteries of man's universe.

As you shall see in the forthcoming pages, the science and technology of odors is in reality little more than a repository for misunderstood and poorly researched facts, curiosities and fantasies. One must be given to wonder how important the understanding of odor is, and whether or not it is a significant factor in what we call the "quality of life."

Anyone who has had contact with persons disturbed by malodors is impressed by the almost pathological reactions displayed. When people find themselves disturbed by a foul odor, their reaction can become both hysterical and overpowering.

It was once thought that malodors caused disease. No one can now say that they do not. It is generally accepted that malodors are only associated with disease and disease causing conditions but, as with most things concerning odors, this is only a broad generality. In the past, the medical professions gave rise to supporters of the Pythogenic theory:

Dr. William Cullen, Professor of the Practice of Physic in the University of Edinburgh, in his "First Lines in the Practice of Physic," in 1789 wrote:

> "Miasmata are next to be considered. These may arise from various sources and be of different kinds; but we know little of their variety, or of their several effects. We know with certainty only one species of miasma, which can be considered as the cause of fever; and, from the universality of this, it may be doubted if there be any other.

This miasma, so universally the cause of fever, is that which arises from marshes or moist ground, acted upon by heat. So many observations have now been made with respect to this, in so many different regions of the earth, that there is neither any doubt of its being in general a cause of fevers, nor of its being very universally the cause of intermittent fevers, in all their different forms."

The distinguished Dr. Cullen in a commendable effort to explain the effect of marsh effluvia on human beings further contributes:

"To render our doctrine of fever consistent and complete, it is necessary to add here, that those remote causes of fever, human and marsh effluvia, seem to be of a debilitating or sedative quality. They arise from a putrescent matter. Their production is favored, and their power increased, by circumstances which favor putrefaction; and they often prove putrefactive ferments with respect to the animal fluids. As putrid matter, therefore, is always with respect to animal bodies, a powerful sedative, so it can hardly be doubted, that human and marsh effluvia are of the same quality: and it is confirmed by this, that the debility which is always induced, seems to be in proportion to the other marks that appear of the power of those causes.

Besides these cases of asthma excited by heat or cold, there are others in which the fits are especially excited by powers applied to the nervous system; as by passions of the mind, by particular odors, and by irritation of smoke and dust."

Dr. James Johnson, in his edition of "A Treatise on Derangements of the Liver, Internal Organs and Nervous System," published in 1820, points out that asthma's causes include:

"Hereditary conformation, atmospherical influence, certain irritations, as from dust, smoke, offensive odours, etc."

Modern theory has it that negatively charged ions are favorable to the environment while positively charged ions can cause murder and mayhem. A device is presently sold which dispenses negative ions. Retailers have been told and many believe that flooding the buying sections of retail stores with negative ions enhances sales. Hosiery treated with perfume displayed alongside identical product which had not been scented outsold the unperfumed controls by a ratio of five to one (R. W. Moncrieff, 1966). The statistics seem plausible. Moreover, positive ions may be deleterious to health while negative ions may be beneficial. Positive ions may cause mucosal irritation which in turn increases general susceptibility to viral and bacterial infections. Air pollution has a direct effect on ion content. Where pollution is heavy, the low ion density is decreased to as much as one fifth normal; the high ion concentrations increase. Furthermore, it is likely that ions impart an odor distinct in its potential for pain (cacosmia). Vinegar, hydrochloric acid and ammonia are excellent examples of this principle. Although some odors may belong distinctly to the cacosmic class and give rise to olfaction solely through ions, it is more likely that cacosmic odors are encountered as components of many other classes of odors. To what extent ionization plays a role in complete olfaction is not presently known, but almost certainly some classes of odor are strongly characterized by this factor. Unlike the other senses, olfaction is not elicited by a single, pure form of energy, but is responsive to several and combinations of several energy forms.

It is well known that atmospheric electric fields strongly influence mental equilibrium as witnessed by the results of so-called Foehn winds (ill winds). In Europe where the phenomenon is well recognized, society accomodates the criminally liable with more lenient treatment if Foehn winds were prevalent when the crime was committed.

Experiments over the past decade have proven that odors can cause increased heart rates, respiration and blood pressure (W. Neuhaus, 1963)(E. Fink, 1965). These increased biological activities are thought to be associated with reflexes resulting from perception levels of osmogenes. Under some circumstances continued exposure to an odorous environment can cause atrophy of primary and secondary olfactory apparatus. Odor perception is a result of physiochemical reactions in and/or around the olfactory apparatus. The question, therefore, of whether or not the organism is affected physically is moot, and only the degree and extent of the affect is open to consideration.

There is no proof yet that human pheromones exist that are within the context of effects of insect pheromones. There is no question, however, that odors can alter or create moods. Where pheromones result in compulsive responses among lower animals, it may be in humans at least that they are reduced by higher centers of rationalization to only tendencies or impulses. W. F. Allen (1929) demonstrated that many odorous and irritating substances introduced in the nasal cavities produced marked depression or inhibition of respiration and circulation in anesthetized animals. A. Rolandus (1948), working with rabbits and a controlled odor flow system, found that only some osmogenes were effective in lowering heart rates. M. Bassi and E. Pascucci (1942) and A. Caniggia and G. Brogi (1947) estimate that over 2,000 food odors cause alterations in the blood sugar level of man. Salivation (activation of the parotids) can be induced (A. T. Snarski, 1901)(C. A. Elsberg, H. Spotnitz, E. J. Strongin, 1940)(Chauncey, Feller, Shannon, 1963)(M. Bassi, F. Manci, 1940) or inhibited (M. Bassi, F. Manci, 1940) by odorous vapors. It is conjectured that the trigeminal activity of an osmogene is the determinant. C. Davies and G. N. Jenkins (1964) have demonstrated the relationship between increased parotid gland secretions and a concomitant increase in sodium ions.

Odors can produce striking alterations in heart rate and respiration. The intensity of effect, however, seems partly dependent on species and probably odorants selected, the rabbit being the most responsive followed by the dog, cat, guinea pig and man. In addition, the two measures do not always show parallel effects (T. Engen, L. P. Lipsitt, H. Kaye, 1963).

In testing psycho-galvanic skin responses to odors, R. W. Moncrieff (1966) found that (1) an unpleasant odor will cause a more pronounced reflex than a pleasant one, (2) the reflexes vary from one individual to another, and (3) with the same individual different kinds of response can be elicited by odorants. He states further that in all cases the reflex is due to an emotional disturbance caused by perception of the odor followed a second or two by sweating. Perception of an unpleasant odor causes not only perspiration of the hands but of the feet and other parts of the body as well. It is a fair inference that odors have a measurable physiological action on the subject who perceives them, and that this action varies not only with the nature of the odorant but also with the temperament of the observer (R. W. Moncrieff, 1966).

In experiments where sleeping infants were exposed to odorants, facial wincing, heart and respiration rates were increased (A. Genzer, 1873). Odor stimulation was found to modify sucking responses by K. Jensen (1932) and D. R. Disher (1934). Goetzl et al. (1947) found that olfactory thresholds varied in constant relation to hunger or satiety in humans. Sensitivity to the odor of coffee increased before lunch and decreased after the meal, correlating with the feeling of satiety. The omission of the principal meal led to a progressive and continuous lowering of the olfactory threshold. The level of olfactory acuity was proposed as a measure of the sensations of hunger or satiety. These results were confirmed by Goetzl et al. in 1950 and by F. J. Hammer in 1951. They were denied by H. D. Janowitz and M. I. Grossman (1949) and by K. Zilstorff-Pedersen (1955). E. Furchtgolt and M. P. Friedman (1960) and Berg et al. (1963) found, however, that the lowering of olfactory thresholds under the influence of hunger exists in some individuals, being entirely absent in others. Improved performances in problem and attention tests have been shown by R. A. Champion and R. R. Field (1963).

It would seem that certain odors have powerful effects on autonomic function while others have little or none.

## THE WORLD OF ODOR

Among the senses odor is generally considered the most primitive. Whether or not this is so remains an unsolved mystery, at least for the present. Ears, eyes, and nose all collect the necessary information through stereo receptors leaving taste and touch to fend for information without benefit of stereo reception. The sense of smell is the only sense which has associated with it a distinct and individual brain. This small brain is located at the base of the prefrontal lobe and is known as the olfactory bulb. The sense of smell is not crossed on its way to the brain as are the other senses. The ability to discern odors is considered by far the most sensitive sense. In spite of stereo receptivity, odor appears to be a non-directional phenomenon. It has been said that the sense of smell is the least specific of all the senses. It is hard to understand the meaning of such a statement since the nose can perceive more than 5,000 distinctions in odor character. The tactile sense can distinguish between a dozen or so sensations, the ear perceives the audible harmonic range, the palate and tongue recognize only four distinct sensations, and the eye is limited to the visible light spectrum. The sense of smell may well be the most specific of the senses.

The world of odors is far more vast than first thought. If we try to imagine a world without them we would find that considerable excitement--sensual and hedonic--would be eliminated from the living experience. A choice steak and a piece of rubber would taste the same as would an onion and an apple. The sweet perfumes of spring and summer would go unnoticed. A glass of chlorine and a glass of water would taste the same. Old memories locked in subconscious files would be lost along with the odor key that subtley conjured them up. Chemists would probably be out of work or in hospitals. Thousands would die or be mutilated when the smoke from fires or gas leaks (recognized by noticeable and unpleasant odorants) went unnoticed.

Odors are subtle, yet gregarious, ubiquitous and, in general, indescribable. Yet they are absolute in that they are specifically distinct.

Modern pollution technicians are wrestling with an updated question: "What is an odor?" And more specifically: "What is a good odor and what is a bad odor?" The answer of the atomic age technologist might just as well have been founded by an ancient Greek, for certainly the truth is that "odor is in the nose of the beholder," and more specifically, "a good or bad odor is whatever the perceiver believes it to be." Armed with this anachronistic answer, modern pollution technologists attempt to stave off court injunctions, develop universal solutions to malodorous pollution problems and pursue, by virtue of so-called odor panels, the esoteric business of setting things right.

Interestingly enough, many things which are odoriferously repulsive are beneficial, such as cod liver oil. On the other hand, many chemicals which are very destructive if not immediately lethal are either pleasant or have no odor associated with them such as carbon monoxide and cyanide (bitter almonds odor). This represents a strange inconsistency if Nature's purpose in providing a sensory apparatus of smell is to warn of impending danger as heralded by the volatile factors associated with chemical compounds. We must, therefore, look elsewhere for Nature's logic in the expenditure of her energies. It would seem instantly that the ability to perceive odors would fit nicely into the format of natural selection since, for example, it is obvious that the ability to discern the odor of a forest fire in the primitive state would provide a significant advantage to the specie exhibiting it. Also, many animals have specific odors associated with them. One has only to recall the experience of smelling the difference between a cave inhabited by a musk bearing animal as opposed to a cave which is uninhabited. It is fairly safe to assume that for numerous reasons of survival as interrelated to odor bearing and odor perceiving species which competed for the environment that those whose olfactory apparatus was more perfected showed a preponderance for survival.

What would happen if salmon lost their sense of smell, for it is with their fine sense of smell that they unerringly find their way home. The stream where they, and their ancestors before them, were spawned has one and only one smell, characterized by the special group of trees that live beside it and the minerals that fall into it, forming an osmic mosaic that is unmistakably individual.

How long would a fancy French restaurant stay fancy if the chef became anosmic? What about the bite of spoiled food you might be about to eat, or the smell of gas in the garage as you search for your lighter?

What imparts odor and how can the phenomenon be manipulated? Is there an odor standard of practical importance, and is there, as a matter of fact, primary odors such as primary colors from which all odors are constructed? Numerous attempts have been made to put forth a comprehensive classification. They are, for the most part, not of any practical significance.

As science has progressed, the great enlightenments have always been rooted in sensorium and yet, aside from perfumery, modern man, if he considers it at all, seems to be prepared to accept odor as a vestigal sense more or less insignificant in light of the less subtle, more dominant sensory repertoire. The sense of sight, the sense of sound, the sense of touch, the sense of taste seem to be appropriately ordered with the sense of smell following along and being accepted as an extension of taste. Undoubtedly, the most misunderstood and least consciously exciting sense of all is the sense of smell.

A bee stings, and then again another bee joins in and stings until soon, almost as if in a maddened frenzy bees swarm from hundreds of yards away to sting repeatedly.

Under the sun drenched sky, a huge circle of ants plods wearily in a never ending circle until finally the last few drop from exhaustion and starvation. All are dead.

A moth flutters its way through a forest against wind and predators unerringly to find a mute mate--no sound has passed, no eyes have seen, but the consumation takes place.

A female monkey's oestrus triggers a fertile egg into place deep inside her body and formerly disinterested suitors fight to mount her continuously. When the egg has been impregnated, the masculine suitors take up other interests.

A tiny field mouse searching for seeds is violently dispatched by a swooping barn owl. His pregnant and diminutive mate waits quietly for his return, huddled in her cozy quarters. Finally, driven by hunger, she sets out into the predatory world where she encounters the demanding attentions of a young bachelor field mouse who follows her to the nest. His agitated sexuality for her is consumated after she spontaneously aborts.

An irrate neighbor slams down the phone at 3 A.M. and the desk sergeant shrugs his shoulders. So fifteen or twenty cats are howling on his doorstep, led to the early morning glee club by the neighbor's demure but ripe, female Siamese.

A young girl at a football game falls over in the bleachers and begins uncontrolled contortions. A parent doctor kneels by her side, takes her pulse, feels her forehead and then astonishingly sniffs her breath. He smells an odor reminiscent of fingernail polish remover. A modern case of glue sniffing? Not at all. He confidently tells the ambulance driver that she is in diabetic coma.

This variety of experiences all have one common factor. The focal point of the action-reaction was an odor.

## Fantasy in the World of Odors

A troop of soldiers moves silently through a densely jungled valley, wondering if their movements are watched, if death will momentarily spew from the close jungle. The soldiers stop as a corporal opens a bag at his side and with a shiney silver probe inspects the trail, the sides of the forest. He methodically plunges the device into hollows, quietly reads and takes notes of the dancing needle on the device. "No humans through this area for at least 72 hours," he murmurs.

A doctor examining a patient with a history of hypochondria quietly analyzes the reading from a similar but more sophisticated device. Chronic hyperglycemia complicated by a slight thyroid imbalance, precursor odors of carcinoma localized near the anal area. He writes out instructions for a diet and a prescription for the thyroid imbalance, then schedules the patient for immediate rectal examination.

In the post-operating room upstairs, a warning light indicates to a nurse that a patient due for surgery is emitting high levels of adrenalin, a sure sign of extreme anxiety. She prepares medications to soothe the patient before the operation and notes that the operation schedule should be set ahead 15 minutes to be sure the anxiety is arrested.

In the psychiatric ward the same device has just informed a doctor that the middle aged business man is emitting a classic odor pattern of paranoia, in spite of apparent improvement.

Every patient in the diabetic ward is continuously monitored for signs of hypoglycemia. Recent surgery patients are monitored for odors emitted by infectious bacteria.

At the airport an alarm sounds as a handsome passenger passes the boarding gate. He is detained 10 minutes until the odor print is compared and printed out by a computer. The desk clerk in airport security rings up the boarding officer and reports that the man has an arrest history for phoned bomb threats. The odor detection unit in the luggage area has already rejected his luggage and conveyed it to a bomb disposal area. The detection unit sensed strong nitro-gel contained in the luggage.

Police officers at the scene of a robbery scan the area with a portable unit. They find a reading that is sent to headquarters. Although the suspect odor prints are not yet on record, cross comparison shows that he has been active in seven burglaries over the past year. Just a matter of time before he is scanned, perhaps at an airport or for a speeding ticket.

Newspaper headlines herald the end of the last known dope smuggling racket. The heroin was detected dispersed in flour imported from Argentina.

A large bank in New York saved $44,208.00 on Thursday when its scanners detected three forgeries, one counterfeit transaction and a $16,000.00 deposit from an extortion that had taken place two years before in New Jersey.

A food production manager in Missouri was on the carpet. The shipping sensors detected salmonella in the frozen food crates going out that afternoon. A portable scan showed that a key production area was contaminated, and the source was an unclean conveyor belt.

The air pollution authority successfully implemented a constructive monitoring system throughout the city and reported that major breakthroughs were being made daily in catalytic and other devices for cleaning up industrial pollution, thanks to the use of the new odor discriminator and detector.

These dramatized events are indicative of the real repercussions of an effective odor monitoring device. To date, no such device exists, but there are some real clues in the neglected technology that might lead to its construction in the very near future. With its advent will also come the understanding that perhaps all things possess a distinctive odor. It may even be possible to prove that a state of mind has an odor. Every disease most likely does, and in a world of cause and effect it is clear that the ability to detect and make record of such factors will revolutionize science and practical living at all levels.

## ODOR AS NATURE'S LANGUAGE

In prehistoric times, Nature spoke in many prismed tongues. No doubt one of her more lucid articulations was olfactory. Primitive man was warned of enemies and strangers by their smells and undoubtedly learned to recognize edible and inedible foods by their odors. Manifestly, as other forms of communication replaced or competed with Nature's voice, man's attention to olfactory sensitivities was dulled. No longer can he hunt by following a trail; there is no need for him to hunt. Evidence from primitive peoples does exist, however, indicating that man still could, if he wished to.

Other animals and species do continue to listen to Nature's language and specialize to such an extent that odor communications can and oft times do override basic actions of self survival. What command in language outweighs the most fundamental of all of Nature's conditionings--the will to survive? For years man marvelled at the customs and habits of insects. It was obvious that insects seemed to communicate. Bit by bit, piece by piece, the great puzzle fitted together, and the precise, abundant verbage of the insect world became evident: airborne pheromones (Greek, pherein: to bear; hormone: to urge on), super-charged odors. Ants forage, fight wars, attack enemies, mobilize, organize, propagate, store and grow food, raise and own slaves--all, it would seem, through the common insect communication language of odors.

In the species F. sanguinea, a slave making ant, when scouts encounter a slave species such as F. subsericea, they return to their own nests; not, however, before laying a strong odor trail. Columns of workers immediately emerge from the nest and following the scout trail conduct a full scale raid. Studies have shown that the trailmaking odor is an acetate discharged from the hindgut of the slavemakers. Moreover, when the nests are broken open, the workers attack intruders, discharging defensive odorous substances from a small gland known as the Dufours gland which repells and serves to identify the enemy. These same substances, taken from the crushed bodies of workers and impregnated in the end of wooden applicators and inserted into the colony causes extreme agitation in most of the workers, provoking repeated attacks to the tip of the applicators. This effect lasts for over thirty minutes. When the chemical synthetic, decyl acetate, was placed on a wooden applicator tip and inserted into the colony, the same results ensued.

It was found on investigation that discharges from slavemaker Dufours glands, when applied to slave ant colonies, caused panic reactions, disorientation and retreat. The colony nest, once treated with the extract, was deserted by the ants, never to be reoccupied (E. O. Wilson, F. E. Regnier, 1971).

Experiments with insects of all sorts now prove that reproduction, mate finding, host finding, food finding, alarm and flight responses may be elicited by application in the vicinity of the insect of the appropriate pheromone. The amounts required are staggeringly small.

Experiments with moths have proven that males are attracted by females over half a mile away. Males of the saturniid and lasiocampid families (silkworms, test caterpillers and eggars) have been lured to females at distances reported to be as great as 2.5 miles. One seductive, caged female sawfly attracted more than 11,000 males (R. H. Wright, 1964). Of course, the pheromones are highly species specific, for if they were not, ladybugs would chase after cockroaches, flies after moths, ants after beetles, and the insect population would soon be reduced, along with everything else, to chaos and extinction.

Man with his never ending cunning has conspired to synthesize these pheromones and use them against insect pests. Several such compounds are now on the market and used in traps are effectively controlling many farm pests.

Insects are not alone in their odor conditioned behavior. Dogs, cats and even primates as high as rhesus monkeys have been proven to predicate certain behavior patterns in response to pheromones. Tests with rats indicate that they appear to excrete odorants perceptible to other rats, and that the nature of the odor is emotional (R. R. Morrison, H. W. Ludvigson, 1970). Rats subjected to a maze terminating in a reward for correct response or in a shock (electric) for an incorrect response apparently left a recognizable odor behind so that rats subsequently tested were able by detecting the favorable or unfavorable odor to show considerable improvement in performance.

With this knowledge, it is interesting to speculate at the reasons for mob violence and other seemingly inexplicable and profoundly deviant behavior by otherwise normal, placid people (or lemmings). Many mental patients have claimed that they can smell fear, hostility, anxiety or other emotional moods of people. It is interesting to note that these mental patients themselves can be identified by their own peculiar odorous emanations. Could the subtle metabolic changes which result in the odor associated with schizophrenia in some way be associated with a sensitization of olfactory apparatus resulting in the ability to detect odors subliminal to normal persons?

In a recent magazine article, the author claimed that a handkerchief wiped across the scrotum and placed in the lapel resulted in strong amorous responses by otherwise normal and well behaved ladies.

Clearly, odor conveys a message while color and sound, in themselves, do not. Some of the basic messages conveyed include the following:

| | |
|---|---|
| Addresses: | Odors associated with known organisms |
| Aesthetic: | Pleasing or unpleasing, like sounds of music |
| Danger: | Fear, flight, fight |
| Edible: | Eat |
| Inedible: | Poisonous, spoiled |
| No message: | Indifference |
| Sexual: | Mating, oestrus |
| Weapon: | Physically destructive (skunk) |

The strong smell of a skunk is a message of address, warning of danger, warning of aesthetic unpleasantness and a weapon. The smell itself implies the message: "here is a skunk (address), I should get away from that bush (flight) (fear) and that awful odor (aesthetic); I would not want my eyes damaged if it sprayed me (recognition of a weapon)" (M. M. Benarie, 1973). Most people, as anyone associated with pollution knows, generally react to any definitely unknown odor as a danger or threat.

## PHYSIOLOGY

Many substances possess volatile properties that are perceived as odors. Perhaps all things possess an intrinsic quality of odor, characteristic only of the object which gives rise to the odor, and those things which seem to be odorless are merely unperceived. It is likely that odor is encountered only in that portion of a material which is in a vapor phase. There are three anatomic arrangements associated with odor perception:

1). Tissues giving rise to odor perception.

2). Vomeronasal nerve and Jacobson's organ.

3). Trigeminal nerve.

### Tissues Giving Rise to Odor Perception

Olfactory Receptors:

The location and function of olfactory receptors depends upon the aerodynamics encountered in the nasal chamber. This chamber is on the average 34 cubic centimeters for both nostrils. The mucous membrane does not take part in olfaction. The nasal cavity must condition the incoming air by acting as a heater and filter, both protecting and preparing the air for the olfactory epithelium. The olfactory epithelium is composed of approximately 500 square millimeters of yellow to yellowish-brown tissue. The cell tissue in the epithelium consists of three main types of cells: Columnar or sustentacular cells which form the matrix of the olfactory epithelium; basal cells which may be immature columnar cells; and bipolar nerve cells or ordinary olfactory rods. It is the latter which are the true odor receptors. A fourth cell encountered in the epithelium is the Bowman's gland or mucous secreting goblet cell. They are actually rare in the olfactory region.

Olfactory Bulb:

As nerve fibers leave the epithelium, they converge into large bundles high up in the nose leading to the olfactory bulb of the brain which information is transmitted to. The bulb is thought to play the role of amplification and relay since the information received by it must be infinitismal considering the amounts of odorous substance which incite sensation. In a human the olfactory bulb is about the size and shape of a small date.

Certain receptors in the nasal mucosa are sensory endings of the fifth cranial nerve and react to such odors as ammonia and chlorine by trigeminal reflex which is reflectory and prevents further breathing of the irritants. Over stimulation of any of the senses will often co-excite the trigeminus which will be interpreted by our brain as a painful sensation.

## DISEASE ODORS

Diagnosis by odor is not a modern technique. In past decades doctors specialized in diagnosing by odor but certain disorders are so obviously and characteristically associated with their odors that the diagnosis is almost automatic from first smell.

Gas gangrene is unmistakable in its characteristic odor. Some forms of cancer are heralded by a specific smell. In fact, the word malaria is derived from "mal" meaning bad and "airia" meaning air. Biomidrosis, a disease of the sweat system, is unmistakable with its highly offensive odor. A person who has breathed heavily of turpentine may find that his urine smells like violets. Toxic factors in asparagus lead to a characteristic metallic odor on urination immediately after having consumed it. Uridosis, an abnormal state wherein the urine is passed through the pores of the skin, has an unmistakable ammoniacal odor. Bacterium foetidum infection with its decomposition odor is immediately recognizable. Diphtheria, diabetes, measles, lung abscesses and mental illnesses are but a few more. It is likely that in future when sensitive and analytic odor perception equipment is available, the worst, if not all, metabolic disorders will be detected and monitored. It is even possible that patients' fear levels will be kept as record to indicate the necessity for reassurances or rescheduling of surgeries for a more appropriate time.

In 1969 Smith, Thompson and Koster isolated and identified the schizophrenic odor factor, trans-3-methyl-2-hexenoic acid. Rats were trained to discriminate between perspiration specimens of schizophrenics and controls; a human panel was also able to discriminate between the perspiration of patients and controls.

Odors Associated With Disease

| | |
|---|---|
| Apical abscess | Foetid |
| Big hemorrhage | Unmistakable |
| Burns | Characteristic |
| Cancer | Characteristic |
| Catalepsy | Cadaverous |
| Chorea | Pineapple |
| Dysentery | Djecta |
| Eczema, impetigo | Mold |
| Gangrene | Characteristic |
| Leukemia | Freshly opened corpse |
| Male hospital wards | Ammoniacal |
| Measles | Freshly plucked feathers |
| Migraine | Limburger cheese |
| Nephritis | Chaff |
| Plague | Mellow apple |
| Scarlatina | Hot bread |
| Schizophrenia | trans-3-methyl-2-hexenoic acid |
| Taenia favosa | Cat urine |
| Typhoid | Blood |
| Typhus | Mousy |
| Women & children's hospital wards | Butyric acid |

## HOW SENSITIVE IS THE NOSE?

Man is normally considered microsmatic while animals with sensitive olfaction are macrosmatic. Women, in general, are considered more perceptive of odor than men, and it has been noted that just prior to and during the menstrual period women become hyperacute to smells. Moreover, it seems that any hormone imbalance tends to result in hyperacuity, and there are many recorded cases of women in menopause who could detect subliminal odors.

Patients with untreated adrenal cortical insufficiency (Addison's disease) were tested for olfaction abnormalities against a normal group of controls. Compounds used for the test ranged from non-volatile mixtures such as sodium chloride in water to potassium chloride, sodium bicarbonate and hydrochloric acid. Not only were the Addisonians able to detect mixtures that controls were unable, for the most part, to detect, but their detection thresholds were approximately 100 times lower than the control group's. The Addisonians were treated with a salt retaining hormone, desoxycorticosterone acetate, and tested over a nine day period. There were no detectable differences between the treated and untreated Addisonians. They were then treated with various carbohydrate active steroids by oral, intramuscular and intravenous routes of administration. Detection thresholds returned to normal levels. After treatment with prednisolone and Doca was discontinued (in about 40 days) a return in hypersensitivity was noted. The sensitivity persisted as long as treatment was withheld. The increased acuity remained although treatment with Doca alone returned sodium and potassium concentrations to normal levels (R. I. Henkin, 1965)(R. I. Henkin, G. Powell, 1962).

A subject group whose taste and smell thresholds were significantly below normal and who exhibited submucous clefts of the dorsal hard palate, facial hypoplasia and physical growth retardation ranking below the third percentile were shown to exhibit hyposmia detecting thresholds of pyridine, thiophene and nitrobenzene at levels approximately 10,000 times higher than normal. Furthermore, comparisons of detection data from this group and their mothers established that the hyposmia is familial, being apparently a genetic abnormality passed maternally (R. I. Henkin, F. C. Bartter, 1966)(R. I. Henkin, I. J. Kopin, 1964)(Henkin, Christiansen, Bosma, 1966).

Sensitivity to sour taste was examined when the subject was being stimulated by a pleasant odor as well as when no test odor was present. The threshold of subjects with normally high thresholds for sour taste was lowered by the odor while those with normally low thresholds experienced the reverse effect. A third group of subjects with moderate levels of threshold showed no significant change during odor presentation (F. J. Pilgrim, H. G. Schutz, 1953).

Hyaluronidase increases human olfactory acuity markedly, even rendering odorless substances odorous. Injection of specific odorants can cause considerable sensitivity to them for up to 30 days. An osmogene inhaled by a person with normal olfactory acuity, exhaled and then inhaled by a subject suffering from anosmia for that specific odor is then perceptible. Injection of vitamin A or treatment with zinc is reported to restore olfactory perception in some cases (M. H. Briggs, R. D. Duncan, 1962). Intravenous thiopental in small doses abolished electrical responses to odors. In higher animals dextroamphetamine produces a dimunition of olfactory acuity (E. D. Adrian, 1951).

A 52 year old woman whose apartment and effects had been treated two years previously with cyanide reported a lingering odor of cyanic acid or bitter almonds in her household and personal effects. Relatives as well as representatives from the pesticide company which had treated the premises were unable to detect any odor although they had tested on several occasions when the woman claimed the odor to be worst. Excepting discussions regarding the odor, she appeared to be psychologically normal. When discussing the odor, however, she became extremely agitated, verged on hysteria, and claimed that everyone thought she was crazy. Various articles of her clothing were presented to her and she exhibited repulsion by the odor. Her household effects were treated with essential oils in thermal vapor and aired for 24 hours. She still detected the cyanide odor. Various articles of clothing, some new and some contributed, were enclosed individually in dark plastic bags and marked. She was then asked to smell in each bag and determine which was the contaminated clothing. Although tested numerous times in this way she unerringly chose the bags with her clothing. Subsequently her clothing was mixed with others and re-presented for additional testing. She still selected without fail those belonging to her. Finally, her clothing was washed through three cycles using large amounts of chlorine and then treated with essential oil of lemon and eucalyptus to mask any subliminal odor. These were detected as before, although she remarked that the cyanic odor had been reduced substantially. This is by no means the only such case known of a woman in menopause exhibiting strong osmophobia for a seemingly non-existent but probably subliminal odor.

Olfactory acuity varies with diurnal cycles as well as age, sex and species. Preferences for certain odors also vary. Licorice is an odor tolerated well by the young and old, but not in general by adults in middle age (R. W. Moncrieff, 1966). The smell of gasoline is pleasant to most children but unpleasant to adults. Musk is more appealing to women than men or children of both sexes (R. W. Moncrieff, 1966).

Perhaps no other sensation has such strong or vivid influence upon mood as does smell. Smell seems to be the golden key that can unlock and recall complete scenarios of past experiences in the warmest detail. Memories thought forgotten, people lost in distant memory are conjured to the conscious mind in detail. Past emotions are evoked of love, fear, religion and hate as well as mixtures. Those returned in detail past the threshold of recognition in what Kai Von Fieandt (1966) calls erkennemgsschwelle and those which reside below that level merely to stimulate (reizschwelle), both conscious and unconscious experiences of smell entwined in our perceptions seem to be essential in our sensory world, contributing to our enjoyment of life. We can miss them only through their loss.

Perhaps the most difficult and frustrating experience in attempting to articulate odors is the inability of our verbal expressions to convey an adequate description. We usually are reduced to making comparisons. "It smells like rotten eggs" or "skunks smell like spoiled cabbages," but direct names for specific smells are almost non-existent. One of the reasons for the difficulty in verbal objectification is that few odors are pure. Most odors are complex mixtures of several to many separate odors in varying intensity, resulting in such a specificity of character that one would have to be skilled by training in their exact identification. Tests with trained dogs have been performed where the animal had to distinguish between articles of clothing belonging to twins or to track their scents. If the twins were identical, differentiation was impossible (H. Kalmus, 1955). Dogs are generally regarded as macrosmatic. The following gives some idea of the difference in olfactory acuity between dog and man:

Minimum Identifiable Odor (MIO): Molecules Per CC

| | Dog | Man |
|---|---|---|
| Acetic acid | $2 \times 10^5$ | $5 \times 10^{13}$ |
| α-Ionone | $1 \times 10^5$ | $3 \times 10^8$ |
| Butyric acid | $9 \times 10^3$ | $7 \times 10^9$ |

Olfaction is a distance sense. The nose has characteristics which anatomically place it in a category of its own with respect to the other senses. The ability to perceive stimuli from a distance is termed projicience. Beetles and moths have been witnessed to follow the female downwind, air currents carrying all odorous molecules away from their receptors. The assumption is clear: for insects, at least, the olfactory sense can operate at a substantial distance and no molecular contact need take place. It would appear that the sense of olfaction in insects is more selective than in man, and therefore if man can respond in the same way to odor molecules at a distance, it is likely to be a rather isolated experience. It is possible, then, that there could be rare circumstances where the MIO would be zero per cc, for all practical purposes.

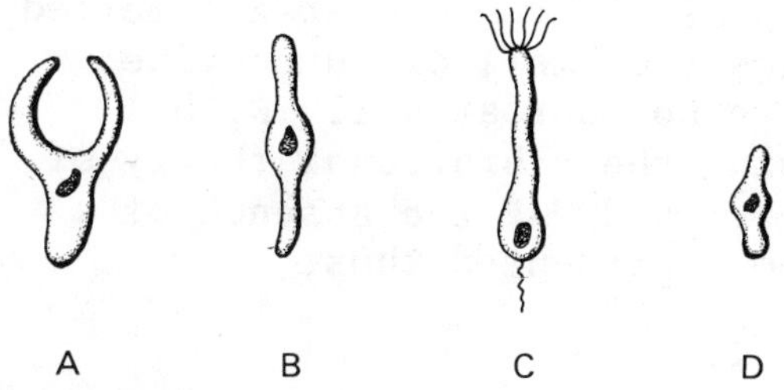


A Goblet cell
B Columnar or sustentacular cell
C Bipolar cell
D Basal or immature cell

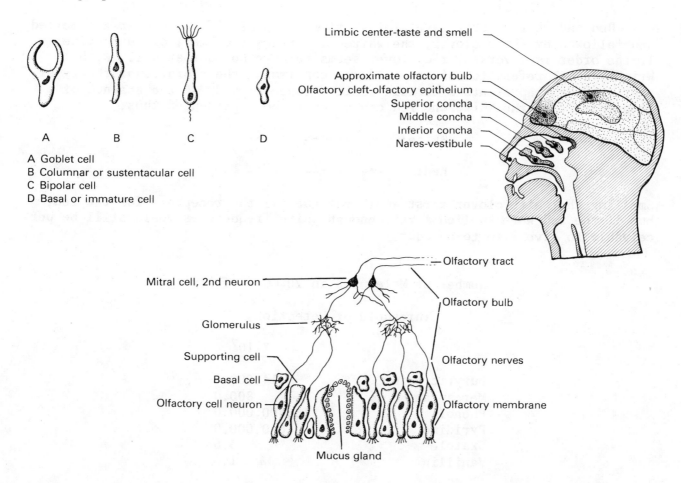

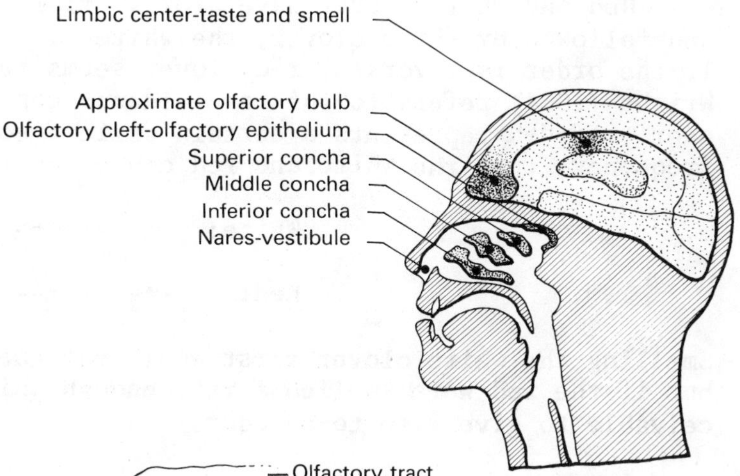


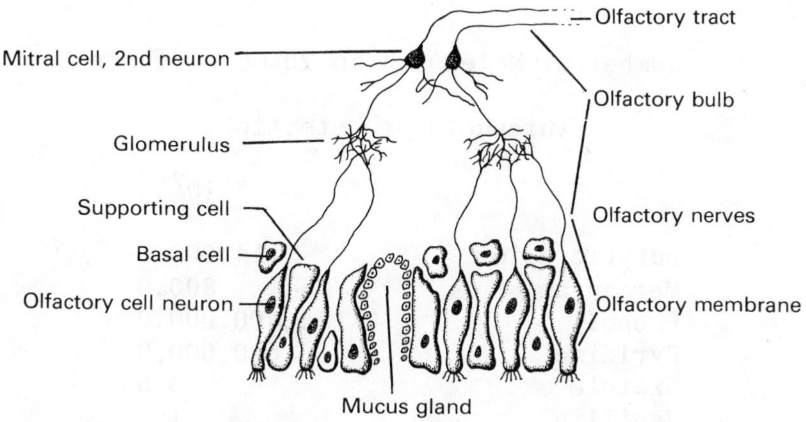

## MINIMUM STIMULUS

Ethyl alcohol has a taste independent of its odor and acts as a stimulus for the common chemical sense. Comparison of ethyl alcohol perception by each of the three senses shows:

| | |
|---|---|
| 0.44% wt/wt in air: | Smell |
| 14.00% wt/wt in water: | Taste |
| 25.00% wt/wt in water: | Chemical reaction |

Smell, then, is about 30 times as sensitive as taste and 60 times as sensitive as the common chemical sense. The sense of smell is 100,000,000 times more sensitive to the odor of methyl mercaptan than it is to that of ethyl alcohol.

Recognition Threshold Values

| | MIO per CC of Air |
|---|---|
| Butyric acid | $8.10 \times 10^{-6}$ |
| Musk | $4.10 \times 10^{-9}$ |
| Phenol | $1.20 \times 10^{-3}$ |
| Pyridine | $3.10 \times 10^{-5}$ |
| Skatole | $3.10 \times 10^{-10}$ |
| Vanillin | $1.10 \times 10^{-10}$ |

Red and white clover have similar floral odors. If red clover is smelled and followed by white clover, the white clover has the smell of turpentine. If the order is reversed, red clover seems to have no odor at all. R. H. Wright (1964) refers to this as evidence confirming the vibrational theory of odor. If "+" represents a certain osmic frequency, and "-" the absence of a frequency, then the white and red clover could be represented thus:

White: -+---+-++---+--++

Red: -+-----+-------+-

Smelling the white clover first would fatigue all the receptors for the red, but if the red were smelled first, enough white frequencies would still be perceivable to give rise to an odor.

Number of Molecules in 20 CC's of Air

Threshold of Detection

| | $\times 10^{7}$ |
|---|---|
| Butyric acid | 14,000.0 |
| Mercaptan | 800.0 |
| Phenol | 15,400,000.0 |
| Pyridine | 620,000.0 |
| Skatole | 3.6 |
| Vanillin | 1.6 |

As D. G. Moulton (1962) has pointed out, it is not true that albinos are unable to smell; however, those who have suffered trauma to the olfactory nerve normally are unable to smell. They are anosmic. Many people are incapable of smelling only certain types or certain specific odors. They are merosmic. Partial anosmia or merosmia is probably very common and may well be one of the reasons for vast taste differences and preferences between people. The concept of anosmia appears at first sight to be potentially useful for research and insight into odor. The inference that if odor blindness to certain odors exists then there are probably certain specific kinds of odor receptors, is logical. Add to this the fact that people can be made temporarily partially anosmic by continued exposure to a specific odor (odor fatigue) and the concept of primaries, primary sense receptors and primary odors becomes very appealing. Odor bearing substances in weak concentrations sometimes provoke greater odor sensations than the same materials in higher concentrations. 2,3-Butanedione, vanillin and musk are examples.

Commonly, however, when an odorous material elicits perception in extreme dilution, it is attended by two equally important phenomena. First, the odorant reaches a level of intensity where it either changes characteristics and becomes unpleasant such as indole or musk (schizosmic), or no matter how much additional material is added it does not smell stronger such as vanillin or 2,3-butanedione (peaking). Second, almost all odorous materials exhibiting schizosmic or peaking factors have the quality of insistence. Insistence means that the threshold of recognition is at very low concentrations, and the osmogene lasts for extreme periods of time. Odorants exhibiting this characteristic are among the favorites of perfumers.

## Curious Perceptions

Among the more interesting odors on record as being perceivable by certain individuals are the chastity of females as determined by the sense of smell alone (claimed by an Hungarian monk), and many recorded cases of native tribes who not only recognize their enemies by their sense of smell but track game as well. In addition, Preismann in 1877 stated that for six hours after coitus there is a peculiar odor noticeable on the breath owing to a secretion of the buccal glands. He said that this odor was most perceptable in men of 35 years of age and could be discerned at a distance of from four to six feet. He further maintained that after coitus naturally foul breath becomes sweet. There also is record of a woman suffering from chronic peritonitis who for some time prior to her death exhaled a decided odor of musk. Older literature reports that women with red hair and freckled complexions have specific odorous characteristics which modern studies bear out. Other references state that obese individuals have oleaginous odors, and that lesions of the nerves corresponding to the cutaneous area exhale the odor of stagnant water. It is said that wig makers by their sense of smell alone can tell whether hair has been cut from a living head or from combings, as hair loses all of its odor when it falls out. One woman reported that she could tell even after laundering whether it was one of her children or her husband who had used a pillowcase on their pillow since the smell from their hair was discernable to her. Aside from the highly specific odor of each individual, there is the famous "herald of death" odor.

Through revealing and apocryphal experiments performed recently is the mystery encountered in attempting to understand the nose and the "nose behind the nose." Dr. Kirk, director of Johns Hopkins Hospital in Baltimore, reported to the National Academy of Sciences that when the organs of smell are removed the internal clock regulating the time schedules of activity and rest is thrown completely out of kilter. Another recent experiment has shown that rats which had been conditioned by electric shock to avoid certain circumstances, upon impairment or removal of their olfactory apparatus would lose their conditioning and return repeatedly to be shocked.

## PROPERTIES OF ODORS

Not only has the understanding of olfaction been limited by the lack of a functional or comprehensive theory, but perhaps equally important is the lack of any relevant system of classification. In order to better understand those theories and classifications offered, a general understanding of the properties of odorants is necessary. It has also been the vogue among those interested in this field of listing phenomenon in a sort of intellectual shadow-boxing contest. It is not intended to ignore the state of the art nor to deprive the erstwhile student, and therefore an expanded list of phenomenology of odor precedes theories and classifications.

### Interesting Facts About Odors

1. All normal land mammals can smell.
2. All normal people can smell.
3. All normal insects can smell.
4. Odors are communicants between most, if not all, mammals and insects.
5. Some people cannot smell certain odors (persons suffering from brain lesions, injured olfactory nerves, obstructed nasal passages, or genetic differences), referred to as anosmic or merosmic.
6. Some people smell odors that only they can perceive (menopausal females, mentally ill persons and persons with hormone imbalances), referred to as obosmic.
7. All animals and insects respond to selective odorants which may be subliminal or imperceptible to others of the same order.
8. Some substances are universally odorous, others do not seem to be odorous at all; but odor is probably a universal property of all matter. The ability of the senses to perceive odor is not universal, but selective.
9. It is possible that odor corpuscles must contact receptors. It is unlikely the sole means of olfactory stimulation.
10. Smell is apparent on inhalation, not readily during exhalation.
11. Different substances normally exhibit different and highly characteristic odors.
12. Different substances sometimes exhibit different and highly characteristic odors.
13. Similar substances normally have similar odors.
14. Similar substances sometimes have very different odors, including isomers and even stereoisomers.
15. Some substances have several possible odors although this normally depends on the concentration of the substance.
16. Substances of high molecular weight are usually not perceptibly odorous and are often non-volatile and insoluble.
17. Perception is triggered by molecules in a vapor-gas transition phase in an excited state. Excitation may be initiated by any form of energy, i.e., chemical, light, heat.
18. Excitation results in transmission of electromagnetic waves.
19. Reception probably is accomplished in many instances by attenuated resonators which trigger chemical and/or electrical brain impulses of specific or multi-specific intensity and duration.
20. Odors could, therefore, vary for similar substances depending on the state of excitation.
21. Sensations of odor are perceived in areas besides the olfactory epithelium.

22. The quality as well as intensity of an odor can change when diluted.
23. The sense of smell is rapidly fatigued by some odorants but not by all.
24. Fatigue for one odor will not affect the perception of other dissimilar odors, but will interfere with perception of similar odors.
25. Two or more odors can cancel each other. Both mixed together can be imperceptible (Zwaardemaker pairs).
26. Odor travels downwind (some moths excluded).
27. Many odors of single substances seem to be tone or complex odors, containing numerous to several odors complexed (hues and shades).
28. Some odors seem to occur commonly, singly, and as odor components, i.e., musk, camphor.
29. Some odors are pure and not reminiscent of any other odor or odor complex.
30. Odors can cause spontaneous, compelling reactions in some, perhaps all, living things.
31. Odors can be neutralized, i.e., vinegar and ammonia, chlorine and vanilla.
32. Some odors, especially pH dependent, seem to arise as a pain sensation and not as odors at all (cacosmic odors).
33. Odors are competitive sensorially with other odorants (masked).
34. Malodors and pleasant odors can be built from each other by selective additions and concentrations (reodorizing).
35. Odors can be imprinted psychologically and often are.
36. A phenomenon of odors is "after odor," similar to "after image."
37. Colors are highly odor selective adsorbants.
38. Many organic and metallic materials adsorb odors selectively, i.e., hay, platinum, meerschaum, charcoal, lithium, fats, oils, etc.
39. Many diseases, if not all, have odors associated with them.
40. Odors can stimulate or depress the appetite.
41. There are some substances that can anesthetize or paralyze the ability to smell, i.e., formaldehyde.
42. Odors are subject to popularity stylistically, some being more popular at different times.
43. Smell (olfaction) is the only sense not crossed subcortically, i.e., the left nostril stimulates the left hemisphere.
44. Most people discriminate odors with their left nostril better than with the right when tested monorhinically.
45. The absolute and recognition thresholds are lower for dirhine than monorhine experiments.
46. Polymerization arrests or cancels odors.
47. Many depolymerized breakdown products are acutely malodorous, i.e., trimethylamine, skatole, etc.
48. Many odors can be arrested or dramatically worsened, cancelled or neutralized by oxidation or reduction, i.e., afterburners, potassium permanganate etc.
49. Odors can be altered by exposure to radiation, ultraviolet, infrared, gamma, etc.
50. Odors can be altered by harmonic interruption, microwaves, ultrasound, etc.
51. Humidity supports odors in persistence and perception.
52. Odors are subject to catalytic reactions.
53. Importance of odors varies consciously over a wide range from individual to individual.
54. Odor preferences vary depending on sex, age and specie.

As may be determined from the foregoing list, odors are at once more ubiquitous and subtle than one is given to admit at first glance. To what extent is our practical life governed by odor?

# PROPERTIES OF ODOROUS MATERIALS

## Vapor Pressure

In order to be odorous, any material must be in the vapor state. It follows that materials with vapor pressures are therefore potentially odorous. The higher the vapor pressure, the more molecules given off, and therefore the greater likelihood of odorous perception. Whereas all odorants must be in a vapor phase, not all materials in a vapor form are perceived as odorous. This may be limited to the particular limitations of perception rather than the lack of odor in a vapor form.

Vapor Pressures of Common Substances*

At 100 Mm Hg

| | |
|---|---|
| Anisaldehyde | 176.7 |
| Carbon dioxide | -100.2 |
| Chlorobenzene | 70.7 |
| 2-Chlorophenol | 106.0 |
| Citronellol | 159.8 |
| Iso-Amyl acetate | 83.2 |
| Methane | -181.4 |
| Toluene | 51.9 |
| Vanillin | 214.5 |

## Infrared Adsorption and Raman Shift

From first scientific access to infrared equipment, it has been anxiously anticipated that a correlation between odorous materials and infrared adsorption could be found. G. M. Dyson (1939) predicted early in the game that "osmic frequencies" to which the nose is sensitive would be found corresponding to wave numbers between 1400 and 3500. R. H. Wright (1964) revised Dyson's early predictions to an osmic frequency range between 50 and 500 wave numbers. To date, no proof has been forthcoming to substantiate Wright's hypothesis.

## Ultraviolet

Odor reduction of some odorous compounds can be attained by exposure to ultraviolet radiation. Valeric acid was reduced in odor intensity by half when exposed to ultraviolet wave length for 10 seconds. Trimethylamine was reduced by half when exposed 30 seconds, skatole by half when exposed 50 seconds, and vanillin by half when exposed for two minutes. Deodorization occurs as a result of the formation of ozone during the passage of ultraviolet through the atmosphere. Odorants are thereby destructively reduced by contact oxidation. Ozone in high concentrations is very toxic (two to ten PPM). However, in low concentrations, 0.005 to 0.015 PPM, it has a tonic effect, contributing greatly to the empathetic (Greek: empatheo = feeling well, being comfortable) qualities of the atmosphere. Ultraviolet is discussed further under STENCH CONTROL, Decomposition.

* See Osmogene Index

## ADSORPTION

It is no secret to anyone who has worked around odors that clothing and other materials soon adsorb and carry odor. Just how important this phenomenon is and how universal it is to all odorous materials has been overlooked.

In general, the surface coarseness, porosity, the composition of the adsorbant and color will determine the degree of adsorption and tenacity. Although adsorption is very common to odor volatiles it does not appear to be a universal property. Normally the darker colors ranging from black to white will show a decreasing propensity for adsorption. A. A. Ouchakov (1930) found that adsorption increased with the molecular weight of the osmogene. H. G. Schutz (1964) stated that substances with strong adhering properties to surfaces usually have weak odors.

When odorous materials are so volatile, why is it that they tend to linger? Actually they should, if rate of diffusion through the atmosphere was the only factor, rapidly dilute. In practice they often do not dilute, but seem to cling and permeate the areas where they are evolved. They may be extremely selective in the preference and affinity for specific adsorbants or they may be more catholic in their requirements.

Although the more common gas adsorbants are well known, little elucidation has been forthcoming on the more uncommon forms.

### Well Known Gas and Vapor Adsorbants

Carbons (charcoal, char, activated charcoal)
Platinum
Palladium
Silica, silica gel
Aluminosilicate
Iron oxide

Adsorption (Latin: sorbere = to suck up) means to take up a gas vapor or liquid by a surface or interface. The technical meaning of the word then means that when there is no doubt that the matter is held at the surface or interface of the adsorbant, adsorption has occurred. If, on the other hand, the matter is collected throughout the solid, the takeup is known as sorption or absorption. The surface may include internal pores that are large enough to permit entry of molecules of the adsorbate. Types of adsorption include the following:

### Physical Adsorption

Physical adsorption occurs when molecules are held, probably by Van der Waal's forces of attraction. The Van der Waal's forces vary as the inverse seventh power of the distance. They are the forces encountered between molecules in gases.

## Chemisorption

Chemisorption occurs when the bonds to the adsorbant result from an exchange or sharing of electrons.

## Condensorption

Condensorption occurs when the adsorbant is a cooler surface and the adsorbate is condensed to its liquid or solid phase.

## Chromosorption

Chromosorption occurs when gases or vapors are attracted to a material because of its color. It is generally accepted that odorous gases and vapors are chromosorbed in a specific and non-varying order, black being the most adsorbant followed by blue, green, red, yellow and white. Tests with a variety of subjects bear this out (J. Cox, 1973).

## Odor Vectors

Odor vectors may be air borne particles or stationary objects which exhibit some degree of adsorbability for vapors. Odor vectors under many circumstances are significant factors in malodorous pollution.

## Osmogenes and Odor Vectors

Osmogenes and odor vectors may both be active in all three states: gas, solid, liquid. Particles may either then generate odors inherently characteristic of the particle or adsorb and then regenerate the adsorbed odors. The forces causing regeneration may be photic, ionic, humidity variations or vector competitors with stronger affinities (replacement).

## Liquid Odor Vector--Osmogenes

Air borne liquid matter in the form of drops will conform to surface tension forces. The pressure (p) due to surface tension (t) on a drop of diameter (d) in centimeters is: $p = 4t/d$ where t is expressed in dynes/cm, and p is expressed in dynes/cm$^3$. Water drops less than 1μ in diameter will remain in the atmosphere indefinitely, but those greater than 1μ will gravitate. Coalescence will eventually occur until the drops increase in size and are precipitated from the atmosphere. Therefore, droplets are often vectors, not only adsorbing and absorbing, but in addition exerting weak polar forces for osmogenes.

## Adsorption Specificity of Odorants

Another interesting phenomenon of odor adsorption is the specificity of adsorbants and adsorbates for each other.

## Odor Affinity Examples

### Adsorbant: Paraffin

Pyridine adsorbed, driven out by lemonine
Lemonine driven out by methyl salicylate
Smoke driven out by camphor
Xylene driven out by orthodichlorobenzene
Orthodichlorobenzene driven out by ammonia

### Adsorbant: Char Treated Paraffin

Ammonia adsorbed, driven out by xylene
Xylene driven out by orthodichlorobenzene
Lemonine driven out by xylene

Tests on chromospecificity as well as combinations of chromolipospecificity and chromoproteinspecificity indicate there is a high degree of specificity between many adsorbants and adsorbates.

Adsorption is such a common occurance among osmogenes that many investigators attribute to this phenomenon the underlying forces endowing odorous properties to substances, Ouchakov, Dervichian, Jones, Schutz, Le Magnen and Amoore, to name a few. Actually, many volatiles are adsorbed which exhibit no odor and there is every reason to believe that many exhibit odors which are not adsorbed at all. This is not to say that adsorption does not play an important role in olfaction. It is too common a phenomenon to discount so easily. Adsorption and solubility are undoubtedly key factors in very many osmogenes. However, chemicals such as dimethyl sulfoxide, which is volatile, soluble and adsorbs readily, has such a faint odor that many observers report it as odorless. Adsorbed odors are often encountered in odor control work and at least one important odor control method, activated charcoal, depends upon this phenomenon.

Frequently process manufacturers receive complaints when they have not been in operation throughout the day. What often has happened is that osmogenes have collected on surfaces around the process property and have stored until conditions were favorable for their release. Therefore malodors can exist from previous operations and become responsible for seemingly unfair and incomprehensible complaints. The addition to the stack off-gases of small amounts (one to two PPM) of alcohols will in most cases effectively purge the stored vectors and prevent accumulation. The colors selected for the immediate buildings' exteriors and interiors can also be of considerable benefit. In general, the lighter the color, the less likely vectoring will occur.

## CHROMOSPECIFICITY

Tests with color blanks (J. P. Cox, 1973 - 1974) to establish color preferences of a variety of osmogenes verified the general tendency of osmogenes to adsorb on darker through lighter colors. This was only a tendency, however, and not predetermined as prescribed in earlier literature (W. Ogle, 1870) (Dr. Stark, 1872) (R. W. Moncrieff, 1946). Many osmogenes were not adsorbed until an oil was added to the color blanks. Finally, some osmogenes would not adsorb at all on colored paper blanks or oil impregnated colored paper blanks. It is interesting that 2,3-butanedione and vanillin, osmogenes exhibiting extraordinarily low levels of threshold, were not adsorbed. If adsorption and/or lipid solubility are relevant to olfaction, then it would be expected that those osmogenes toward which the olfactory apparatus is the most sensitive would display strong, definite adsorption characteristics. On the other hand, olfaction elicited by molecular vibrations at a distance would be irrelevant.

### Chromospecificity Index

For Selected Odorants
(Colored Paper Blanks)

Key

B: Black
O: Orange
G: Green
R: Red
Y: Yellow
L: Blue
W: White

/: Equal intensity
>: Greater than
Intensity: Arbitrary value of 1 to 9 (strength of odor) when adsorbed.

| Odorant | Order | Retention Time | Intensity |
|---|---|---|---|
| Acetic acid | R>B>W | 30 - 45 min. | 5 |
| Anisette | R/G>B>W/L | 3 - 4 hr. | 9 |
| Benzaldehyde | B>L>W/G>R | 30 - 45 min. | 6 |
| Cinnamon | B/W>L/G>R | 2 - 3 hr. | 5 |
| Floral | W>B>G>R>O>L | 4 - 5 hr. | 7 |
| Garlic | W>B>R>G | 30 - 45 min. | 4 |
| Lemon | L>B/G>W>R | 1 - 2 hr. | 5 |
| Methyl salicylate | R>W>B>G | 1 - 2 hr. | 6 |
| Musk | W>B>L>G>R | 1 - 1.5 hr. | 5 |
| Naphthalene | B>L>G/R>W | 30 - 45 min. | 5 |
| 2-Octanol | L>B/G>W/R | 1 - 2 hr. | 9 |
| Orange | L>G>W>B>R | 30 - 45 min. | 4 |
| Phenol | B/G>W>L>Y | 30 - 45 min. | 5 |
| Pyridine | L>R>G>B>W | 2 - 3 hr. | 9 |
| Smoke | W>B/R/G/L | 3 - 4 hr. | 8 |
| Thymol | W>L>G>B/R | 1 - 2 hr. | 5 |

Vanillin, 2,3-butanedione, orthodichlorobenzene, paradichlorobenzene, cod liver oil, xylene, naphthalene were either adsorbed very weakly or not at all by untreated color blanks. When, however, two cc's of peanut oil was added to each square, all but 2,3-butanedione and vanillin were adsorbed very strongly.

Lipochromospecificity Index

For Selected Odorants
(Peanut Oil Treated Colored Paper Blanks)

| Odorant | Order | Retention Time | Intensity |
|---|---|---|---|
| Cod liver oil | W G R/B L | 30 - 45 min. | 7 |
| Naphthalene | B/L G W R | 30 - 45 min. | 5 |
| Orthodichlorobenzene | B/L R G W | 30 - 45 min. | 7 |
| Paradichlorobenzene | B/L R | 30 - 45 min. | 5 |
| Xylene | L W B/R G | 30 - 45 min. | 7 |

The readiness with which many odorants are adsorbed by colored materials and the high degree of specificity shown by most tests certainly indicate that selective adsorption and the forces giving rise to it may represent a fundamental and, if not singular, perhaps underlying relationship with olfaction. It has been stated that moisture and probably a lipid layer are necessary to olfaction. Certainly for many odorants neither are required for evident and specific color adsorption. Although the addition of oils or fats may underlie adsorption for some odorants, they still exhibit a strong order of chromoadsorbent preference. Insects, which are notariously gifted in odor dissemination and recognition, do not exhibit mucous moisture or lipid layers on the surface of their antennae. Numerous micrographic studies have failed to give evidence of any moisture or fat layer. To the contrary, antennae are invariably of a highly chitinous nature covered with sensing hairs and follicles. The fluid often contained inside the antennae exhibits characteristics of a highly volatile liquor, often evaporating from the internal segments within moments of slide mounting.

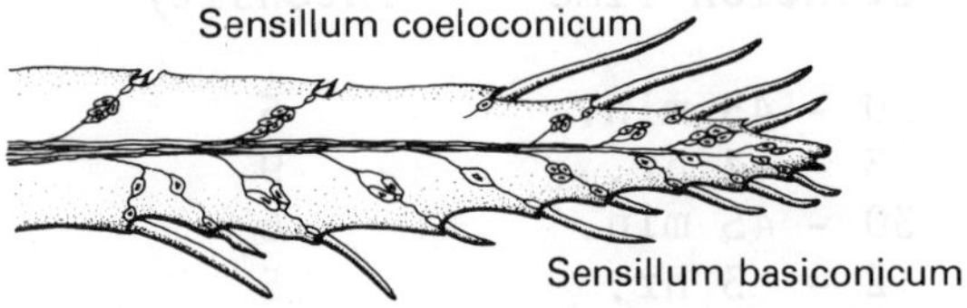


Fig. A

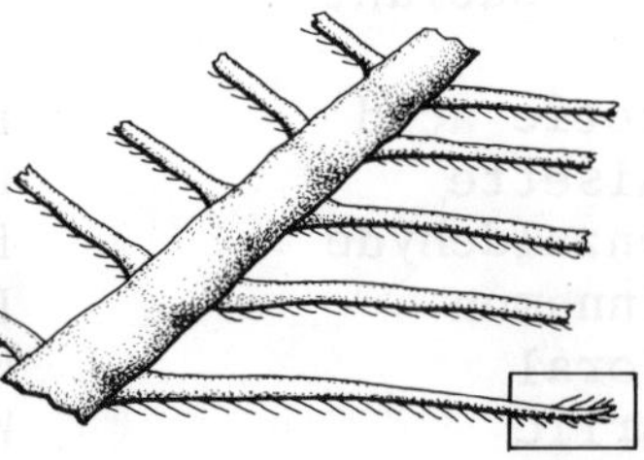

Fig. A

*ANTENNA:* (Both possible chemoreceptors. All antenna, however, do not display chemoreceptor possibilities).

All evidence seems to indicate that the phenomenology of olfaction is caused by several effects of odoriferous substances and that no single property is in general responsible for olfaction. Certain conditions or combinations are probably responsible for olfaction. They are in all probability distinct conditions, but an odorant may possess one or more of the necessary properties to elicit olfaction. An odorant molecule which possesses the condition of olfactory range vibrations might also possess the appropriate condition of chromospecificity or other olfactory activating factors such as solubility and chemical activity (ionic, polar or Van der Waal's). This would at once explain how an odorant could have two distinct odors (schizosmogenes), depending on concentration and the odor differences of chiral isomers. Furthermore, there seem to be several distinct types of odor recognition which are discussed in the chapter on taxonomy.

## THEORIES

### Some Theories and Classification of Odors

Before proceeding further to discuss the merits of the various procedures available for reduction or elimination of stench, it is appropriate to review some theories and ideas governing the technology.

Among the major hurdles a working theory must overcome and explain is why enantiomers have different odors. If chiral isomers, which are chemicals with the same structure and formula differing only in right handedness and left handedness, do smell differently, then neither the vibrational theory nor the stereochemical theory can hold up. Right (-) and sinister (+) carvone smell like oil of spearmint and oil of caraway, respectively (L. Friedman, J. G. Miller, 1971) (G. F. Russell, J. I. Hills, 1971). Additional chromatographic purifications of other enantiomeric isomers, trans-dihydrocarvone, cis-dihydrocarvone, r-lemonene and s-lemonene, are examples although not all enantiomeric isomer pairs smell differently (G. Ohloff, 1972) (M. Stoll, 1965). The following are among those which do differ in odor (G. Ohloff, 1972):

Enantiomorphic Differences in Odor

| Chiraloptical Isomers | Odor |
|---|---|
| (-)-R-4-methylcaproic acid | Caproic, more fatty and more powerful |
| (+)-S-4-methylcaproic acid | Caproic type |
| (-)-3S-citronellol | Geranium type and more powerful |
| (+)-3R-citronellol | Citronella oil type |
| (+)-Cis-rose oxide<br>(-)-Cis-rose oxide<br>(+)-Trans-rose oxide<br>(-)-Trans-rose oxide | Green, geranium type odor; cis derivatives more powerful than corresponding trans; (+) compounds sweeter and less herbal than (-) compounds; (-)-cis-rose oxide most powerful of the whole series |
| (-)-3R-Linalool | Woody lavender-like (Ho oil type) and more powerful |
| (+)-3S-Linalool | Sweet shade of lavender-like odor, more reminiscent of petitgrain oil |
| (-)-S-7-hydroxy citronellal | Reminiscent of lily-of-the-valley with a fresh green and minty shade |
| (+)-S-7-hydroxy citronellal | Strong sweet lily-of-the-valley like odor and more powerful |

It has been said that the stereochemical theory of odor can be modified to accomodate these findings (G. F. Russell, J. I. Hills, 1971), but considering the seemingly endless "primaries" recent and past searches have uncovered, it must be obvious that the stereochemical theory of odors can, at best, be only an extension of a major, unified theory of odor. That molecular shape can play a role in olfaction is unquestionably true (J. E. Amoore, 1970) (J. Timmermans, 1954) (L. J. Mullins, 1953) (R. W. Moncrieff, 1951); whether or not that role is a result of physical molecular shape, the vibrations resulting from the stresses thereof, or other factors remains to be seen. Considering the minute amounts of odorant which can elicit response and the lack of any elucidation or analogy in nature of a molecule clearing mechanism in the olfactory epithelium, action at a distance more readily explains the phenomenon of olfaction.

The fact that deuteration of an odorant shifts its far infrared adsorption maxima to lower frequencies and yet does not alter the odor (Doolittle, Beroza, Keisler, Schneider, 1968) would seem to discredit the vibrational hypothesis, if not the stereochemical. The vibrational theory alone cannot account for the powerful odors of certain small molecules such as hydrogen sulfide, ammonia, cyanic acid, etc. (H. L. Klopping, 1971) (R. H. Wright, 1957), which have no low frequency vibrational modes at all. Another hurdle for any incumbent theory is why musk odorants belonging to macrocyclic, nitro benzene, indane, and tetraline musk structural classes and numerous non-musk compounds with distinctive odors and well defined adsorption bands in the 100 to 500 $cm^{-1}$ range show no simple relationships with the presence of the musk odor and the far infrared bands (R. E. Burgess, R. H. Wright, 1968). Another general difficulty is the explanation of perception in enormously small quantities which would in the strictest sense of conditional probability exclude the site-filling or stereochemical hypothesis.

A virtual cornucopia of theories, ideas and speculations concerning olfaction are recorded. They may best be analyzed by separating them into various general categories:

## Theories of Odors

The following are among the general types of proposed theories:

### The Corpuscular Mechanical Theory of Odor:

1. Odorants are particles.
2. The particles are independent of the mass.
3. The particles are air borne.
4. The particles must be inhaled.
5. The particles must physically come into contact with the receptor.
    a. The particles all have a specific molecular shape.
    b. The receptor must be made up of template sites into which only the specific molecular shape peculiar to a given odor will fit.
    c. That once fitted into place the interreaction of particle receptor site transmits necessary perceptual information.
6. Sub-theory arguments:
    a. The interreaction is chemical.
    b. The interreaction is harmonic.

### The Wave Theory of Odor:

1. Odorants emit waves.
2. The waves stimulate olfactory response.
3. Specific wave impulses elicit specific responses.

## Specific Theories

The Undulatory Theory of Smell (W. Ogle, 1870):

1. Odors are a function of waves.
2. Olfactory pigmentation, both in degree of darkness and quantity, is of considerable importance for reception.
3. The receptor pigment absorbs and converts harmonic waves (odorants) to heat which is detected by olfactory nerves.

A Chemical Theory of Odor (G. Woker, 1906):

1. Chemical saturation or unsaturation is principally responsible for smell.
2. Chemical linkage is also important.
   Note: This theory attempts no explanation of reception.

A Wave Theory of Odor (J. H. Fabre, 1911):

1. Odor is distinctly of two types:
   a. Air-soluble particles.
   b. Waves.
2. The air-soluble particle type is perceptible, and the wave type is imperceptible (humanly).
   Note: Fabre apparently identified what we now think of as subliminal odors as imperceptible and was unquestionably thinking of the sensory apparatus of the moth and other insects.

An Harmonic Theory of Odor (A. Heyninx, 1917):

1. Odors are comprised of molecules vibrating.
2. The period of vibration corresponds to the ultraviolet light they absorb.
3. Perception might not depend on actual contact with receptors.
4. Differences between odors are due to differences in frequency of vibration.
   Note: No speculation was made with respect to mode of receptor reaction.

A Chemical Theory of Perfume Odors (L. Marchand, 1915):

1. Perfume odors are dependent on valencies.
2. Odor depends on unsaturation.

A Chemical Structure Theory of Odor (H. Henning, 1916):

1. Chemical structures are the significant factor.
2. The order of arrangement of the structure is a condition of odor.

A Mechanical-chemical Theory of Odors (E. L. Backman, 1917):

1. The physical molecules of the odorant must be in contact with the receptor area.
2. Once in contact, the odorant must dissolve
   a. First, in watery mucous and
   b. Second, in the lipoid tissues.

A Wave Theory of Odors (H. Teudt, 1919):

1. Harmonics of valence electrons within the molecule of each substance emits a characteristic frequency which is specifically perceptible.
   a. Odor does not originate at the atomic level.
2. Perception is due to resonant phenomenon between receptors and odorants.
   a. Air might amplify resonant effect.
   b. Metallic atoms, due to detaching free electrons, are not suited to production of odors.

A Residual Affinity Odor Theory (T. H. Durrans, 1920):

1. Odorants frequently possess free residual affinity, i.e., the ease with which they form double or addition compounds.
   a. Some so-called odors are sternutatory or destructive of receptors and not odors at all per se: ammonia, glacial acetic acid.
2. Odorant molecules are air borne.
3. Odorant molecules must be trapped in the mucosal receptor site.
4. Odorant molecules are dissolved in the aqueous mucous layer.
5. Dissolved odorant molecules are then passed in part to the lipid layer.
   a. Conditions being that only that part passed depends upon the partition coefficient of the substance in oil and water.
6. An additional reaction takes place in the fat layer and
   a. This reaction causes a measurable change of energy state to be registered by receptor nerves as a specific odor.

A Solubility-chemical Theory of Odor (A. Tschirch, 1921):

1. Odors are air soluble.
2. They are odorous to the degree that they are soluble.
3. Depending on the partition coefficient (the degree of solubility in lipoids), they are odorous.

A Mechanical-chemical Theory of Odor (H. Heller, 1920):

1. Odorants are discrete and air borne.
2. Odorants must contact the olfactory mucosa.
3. Once embedded in the olfactory mucosa, the odorant exerts a direct chemical action on the olfactory neurons.

A Chemical-vibrational Theory of Odor (H. Zwaardemaker, 1922):

1. Odorants are discrete, air borne particles.
2. Odorant molecules are lodged and then diffuse through the olfactory mucosa.
3. Odorants lower the surface tension of water so that they are readily absorbed as a surface layer in the watery mucous.
4. Odorants then dissolve in the lipoids.

   Note: Zwaardemaker does not speculate as to the causatives resulting in the listed conditions, nor does he speculate with regard to transmission phenomenon by receptors.

A Wave Theory of Odor (W. G. Ungerer, R. B. Stoddard, 1922):

1. Odor is caused by intermolecular vibrations which affect the olfactory nerves.
2. The vibrations are too delicate to detect with instrumentation.
3. Each pure substance has a characteristic frequency and thereby a characteristic odor.
4. The frequency can lay outside the range of olfactory sensitivity, being both too long and too short.
5. Many odorants combined are synergistic.

A Mechanical-neurochemical Theory of Odor (Lucretius, 47 B.C.)(J. T. Davies, 1953):

1. Odorant particles must impinge and
2. Penetrate a cell plasma membrane of a bimolecular lipid structure found in the nasal mucosa.
3. The penetration or puncturing results in disruption of a concentration gradient of potassium and sodium, thereby initiating excitation of the sensory nerve.

An Atomic Structure-vibrational Theory of Odor (G. M. Dyson, 1937)(R. H. Wright, 1954, 1964, 1966)(A. Demardache, R. H. Wright, 1967):

1. All molecules emit characteristic atomic frequencies.
2. Some atomic frequencies are "osmic frequencies" which give rise to smell.
3. Osmic frequencies will correspond to infrared adsorption bands.
4. Molecules exhibiting osmic frequencies, in order to be perceived, must also have sufficient volatility and "right" solubility characteristics.

A Stereochemical Theory of Odor (R. W. Moncrieff, 1951)(J. E. Amoore, 1952) (L. J. Mullins, 1955)(J. Timmermans, 1954):

1. To be odorous a molecule must exhibit a prescribed shape.
2. Certain sites are olfactory receptors and correspond to only prescribed shapes.
3. Receptor sites are limited to certain basic configurations.
4. All odors are a composite of basic olfactory receptor site stimulations.

   Note: Amoore postulates seven primary odors and seven receptor site configurations (see page 34).

A Profile Function Group Odor Theory (L. Ruzicka, 1920)(M. G. J. Beets, 1957):

1. The odor of a molecule is determined by the form and bulk of the molecule from its functional group or groups.

The differences between many of the foregoing theories is more imaginary than real. One thing is certain: to date, none seems to explain or predict various phenomenologies of odor and olfaction. Since rational explanation and prediction are two cardinal tests of any theory, it may safely be assumed that none of the theories is the general theory of olfaction, although certain of them may be partially correct. It seems clear that a workable classification may precede a working general theory, and it is likely that contrary to accepted scientific procedure it will be necessary to ask "why" animals smell before the "how" can be considered.

M. M. Mozell and M. Jagodowicz (1973), using the gas chromatograph in which the column was replaced with an in vivo frog olfactory sac, found that molecules of different odorants migrate at different rates across the olfactory mucosa. The results of these experiments indicate adsorption/desorption rates to be implicated in olfactory discrimination at the level of the olfactory mucosa. The tests demonstrated additionally that retention time of odorants on the mucosa was independent of the concentration of odorant in most cases, butyl acetate and heptaldehyde being exceptions. Whether or not adsorption/desorption phenomenon are universal to all olfactorily active molecules remains to be proven. It is, however, unlikely that this phenomenon represents anything but one of a number of support systems resulting in olfaction.

D. F. Matthews (1972) claims to verify the existence in rats of at least two distinct receptor types. The work is supported by test results achieved by T. Shibuya and D. Tucker (1967) with the vulture. Experiments with rabbit receptors led to the conclusion that if primaries do exist, there must be a great number of them (E. D. Adrian, 1926, 1946, 1971).

Receptors composed of peptides, which have ample capacity for forming hydrogen bonds, are proposed by R. E. Randebrock (1968) as the principal odor receptor. The assumption is that the α-helix is the sole receptor of odor, that the peptide chains in the α-helix are vibrating and that a single odorant molecule attaching itself to an end of a peptide chain modulates or dampens this vibration. The modified or null vibration is then transferred to a nerve cell by the other end of the helix.

G. B. Kistiakowski (1950) states that at specific sites various enzymes are involved in sensory nerves related to a number of basic primaries. The odorant inhibits one or more enzymes leading to a metabolic change which initiates a nervous impulse. A. F. Baradi and G. H. Bourne (1951) demonstrated that enzymes were localized in the nasal mucosa of rabbits, different enzymes being found in different areas. In 1972, L. H. Bannister and A. Cuschieri reported finding the enzymes acid phosphatase, alkaline phosphatase, cytochrome oxidase, succinic dehydrogenase, $Ca^{++}$-ATPase and non-specific esterase from Anguis fragilis and neonate and adult mice vomeronasal organs. A. Dravnieks (1966) disagrees that enzymes are the likely primary sensing elements, pointing out the disparity in size and shape of various osmogenes which exhibit the same odor as well as the overall sensitivity of enzyme systems to pH and ionic strength; odor characteristics are more or less independent of these factors.

## A Unified Theory of Olfaction

1. Olfaction is a complex sense dependent upon specific, multi-specific and/or composite stimuli of diverse natures.
2. Osmogenes give rise to the olfactory sensation by neurological stimulation including trigeminal reflex.
3. Trigeminal reflex may be an almost purely cacosmic reaction or act in part as an overall composite sensation elicited by co-osmogenic forces inherent in a specific osmogene.
4. Olfactory epithelium is responsive to osmogenes exhibiting a variety of

energies by

a. A series of extended resonators tuned to a range of osmic frequencies,
b. Potentiometric sensitivity between the lipo-mucosal layers and by chemical reactivity on active sites.

5. Osmogenes elicit response by exhibiting polar, ionic, Van der Waal's, catalytic and vibrational energies.
6. Adsorption via multi-specific active adsorption sites, functional group placement, ionic conditions, structure, Van der Waal's forces, osmic frequencies and potentiated reaction active sites all elicit specific forms of response and may elicit simultaneous and corresponding responses.
7. All osmogenes exhibit one or more of these forces, singly, or more often compositely.

Indole, which cannot presently be explained by any theory can be explained if it is assumed that there is a vibrational frequency in the osmic range which is detectable at low concentrations eliciting only the characteristic odor of the osmic frequency. As the concentration of indole is increased, the molecular concentration becomes sufficient to elicit a second, purely chemical, response. The osmic frequency resonators are all in an active state at low concentration levels, and the addition of more resonators elicits no additional response, while it does elicit more and more response to the reagent qualities of the osmogene. One distinctive odor is suddenly replaced by another. The osmogenic frequency is now but one component of a complex odor. The electromagnetic "action at a distance" characteristic was noticeable first and in extremely small amounts. Indole is not singular in displaying this phenomenon.

The presence of the quality of insistence in an osmogene is probably an excellent guideline for whether the osmogene results from chemical or electromagnetic energies. If the osmogene is vibrating strongly on a frequency to which the receptor sites are tuned, then most will respond simultaneously and sharply. No further addition of molecules vibrating at the same frequency will cause amplification; most or all are already resonating. This quality would indicate the almost pure vibrational mode of the osmogene for if, as the concentration of osmogenes built up, they inherently possessed any additional osmogenic capacity, it would become readily apparent by a shift in intensity or character of odor. The consequence of low and high notes to odors are probably due in no small measure to the vibrational frequency.

The explanation for different odors between chiral isomers may be the delicate equilibrium between osmogenic properties in these molecules in which any change favors one factor over another, and the result is a shift in osmogenic property.

The fact that deuteration shifts the infrared adsorption maxima would have no effect on osmogenes which exhibit infrared spectra of a non-osmogenic frequency or where the frequency was inconsequential to the other overriding osmogenic factors. Considering olfaction as a complex sense with all that it implies also explains the lack of correlation between musks.

Small molecules of the cyanic acid type rely on factors other than vibrational characteristics for olfactory perception. Color, metallic ion content, size and situation within the potentiometric lipo-neural matrix are significant factors of receptor sites within the olfactory epithelium. It is likely that some potentiated reactants are catalyzed in the receptors and/or diffuse, resulting in "active transport" via the cell membranes (A. L. Hodgkin, B. Katz, 1949)(J. T. Davies, 1953). These reactions would exhibit early fatigue while resonant receptors probably would not.

It is likely that, as in other respects, the sense of olfaction is a distinctive and specialized sense, being archaic and sensitive to diverse forms of energy. This is consistent with the fact that more primitive life forms rely substantially on olfaction for life pursuits, and the dependence predominately on a single, pure sense would quickly lead to extirpation. There are reported cases of colors being smelled in levels of so-called higher consciousness. While olfaction is dependent on energies encountered in volatiles, it is not unlikely that those energies are shared to some extent by other sense stimulating phenomena.

Olfaction may well be a motivational response, to a great extent, or perhaps even more of a refined and subtly perfect means of communication than modern man is willing to consider.

Floral Receptor Site

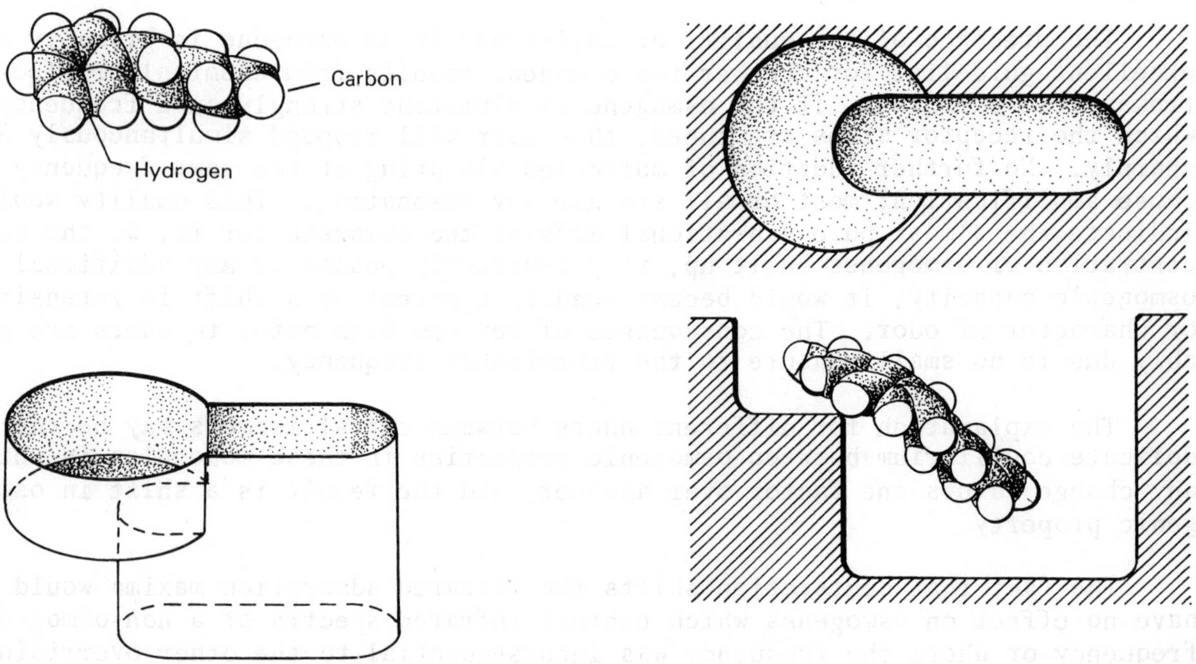


Floral, one of seven basic sites proposed by Amoore; others include oblate (ethereal), dish (camphoraceous), ring segment (musky), oblate with a recession (pepperminty).

## CLASSIFICATION

It is not surprising that classification systems have attempted to conform odors with the characteristics of sound (harmonics), light (primaries), mechanics and chemistry. It is increasingly obvious that olfaction is distinctively its own phenomenon:

| | |
|---|---|
| Vision: | Light/quantum |
| Audition: | Sound/wave |
| Touch: | Tactile pressure/heat energy |
| Taste: | Chemical/chemical energy |
| Olfaction: | ? |

Many attempts have been made to classify odors. None have proven functional because none have been comprehensive nor easily expressed. Perfumers, food chemists and even psychologists have attempted organizing classification systems. The classifications thus produced have all been indelibly characterized by the profession of their authors. In general, all the proposed systems may be categorized as:

1. Octavoid (octaves).
2. Chromatoid (primaries).
3. Subjective/empirical (it seemed like a good way).

### Classifications of Interest

E. Rimmel's Classification (1865): Subjective/empirical

| | Class | Typical Odor | Odors in Same Class |
|---|---|---|---|
| 1. | Rose | Rose | Geranium, sweetbriar, rosewood |
| 2. | Jasmine | Jasmine | Lilly-of-the-valley |
| 3. | Orange flower | Orange flower | Acacia, syringa, orange leaves |
| 4. | Tuberose | Tuberose | Lily, narcissus, jonquil, hyacinth |
| 5. | Violet | Violet | Orris-root, cassia, mignonette |
| 6. | Balsamic | Vanilla | Benzoin, storax, tonka bean, heliotrope, balsams of Peru and Tolu |
| 7. | Spice | Cinnamon | Cassia, nutmeg, mace, pimento |
| 8. | Clove | Clove | Carnation, clove pink |
| 9. | Camphor | Camphor | Patchouli, rosemary |
| 10. | Sandal | Sandalwood | Vetivert, cedarwood |
| 11. | Citrine | Lemon | Bergamot, orange |
| 12. | Lavender | Lavender | Spike lavender, thyme, marjoram |
| 13. | Mint | Peppermint | Spearmint, balm, rue, sage |
| 14. | Aniseed | Aniseed | Caraway, dill, coriander, fennel |
| 15. | Almond | Bitter almonds | Laurel, peach kernels, mirabane |
| 16. | Musk | Musk | Civet |
| 17. | Ambergris | Ambergris | Oak moss |
| 18. | Fruit | Pear | Apple, pineapple, quince |

This system is obviously designed for the perfumer and aside from its historical interest is of little, if any, value.

H. Zwaardemaker's Classification (1895): Chromatoid and Subjective/empirical

| Class | Sub-divisions |
|---|---|
| 1. Ethereal | Fruits, beeswax, ethers |
| 2. Aromatic | Camphor, cloves, lavender, lemon, bitter almonds |
| 3. Balsamic or fragrant | Flowers, violet, vanilla and coumarin |
| 4. Ambrosial | Amber, musk |
| 5. Alliaceous | Sulfuretted hydrogen, arsine, chlorine |
| 6. Empyreumatic | Roast coffee, benzene |
| 7. Caprylic | Cheese, rancid fat |
| 8. Repulsive | Deadly nightshade, bedbug |
| 9. Nauseating or foetid | Carrion, feces |

Zwaardemaker's system attempted a comprehensive approach and was founded to some extent on experimentation. Various odors were tested by Zwaardemaker in pairs, and odors which caused anosmia or partial anosmia for others were considered primary dominant.

H. Henning's Classification (1915): Chromatoid and Subjective/empirical

1. Spicy, e.g. cloves, fennel, anise.
2. Flowery, e.g. heliotrope, coumarin, geranium.
3. Fruity, e.g. oil of orange, oil of bergamot, citronellal.
4. Resinous of balsamic, e.g. turpentine, eucalyptus oil, Canada balsam.
5. Burnt, e.g. pyridine, tar.
6. Foul, e.g. sulfuretted hydrogen, carbon bisulfide.

Henning's system is principally a perfumer's system. Nevertheless, it expresses clearly certain definite categories of odor through the use of descriptive class headings. The system also failed to provide a means of quantification for simple expression.

Hennings Olfactory Prism:

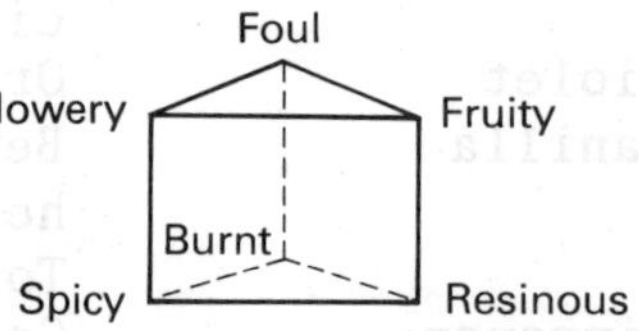


A. Heynix's Spectral Arrangement (1917): Octavoid and Chromatoid

Acrid
Rotten
Foetid
Burning
Spicy
Vanilla
Ethereal
Garlicky

Heynix's arrangement is a mixture of class, genus and factors without ready means of expression and is principally of interest only historically.

E. C. Crocker and L. F. Henderson's Arrangement (1927): Chromatoid and Subjective/empirical

Rose odor: 6423:

| | |
|---|---|
| Fragrant: | Stimulated to a degree of 6 |
| Acid: | Stimulated to a degree of 4 |
| Burnt: | Stimulated to a degree of 2 |
| Caprylic: | Stimulated to a degree of 3 |

Crocker and Henderson perhaps approached the closest to a functional system. Principally because they provided a handy scale for expressing classifications quantitatively. In practice, the system fails not only because it is a considerable over-simplification, but due to the mixing of class headings with genus and factors.

Fragrant is too broadly descriptive. It can mean anything perceived as odorous. Acid is a specific factor shared by some members of all classes of osmogenes. Caprylic is a specific sub-class and is therefore too narrow in meaning to be of comprehensive value.

The Crocker and Henderson arrangement used a numerical value of 0 to 8 to denote the occurance and intensity of the particular class heading. The odor of rose being stated numerically 6 4 2 3. This means fragrant is present and intense to a degree of 6/8th, acid is present and intense to a degree of 4/8th, burnt is present and intense to a degree of 2/8th, and caprylic is present and intense to a degree of 3/8th. In spite of its failure, the arrangement is of considerable significance.

R. C. Erb's Classification (1927): Chromatoid and Subjective/empirical

1. Infra-odors which by their strength and pungency produce distracting sensations (probably common chemical reactions).
2. Fragrant odors.
3. Empyreumatic odors.
4. Caprylic odors
5. Acid or sour odors.
6. Ultra-odors, feeble non-registering smells.

Erb's classification is essentially the same as Crocker and Henderson's with the inclusion of infra-odors and ultra-odors. The system lacks means of expression and suffers in general the deficiencies of all former classification systems.

J. E. Amoore's Primary Odors (1952 to 1965): Chromatoid

Seven odor receptor sites, therefore seven basic or primary-type smells:

Camphoraceous
Musky
Floral
Peppermint
Ethereal
Pungent
Putrid

Amoore's system, ostensibly based on chemical configuration and odor constants, is descriptive of both class headings and factors. Amoore's primaries represent a classification which at present is highly specific. As it stands, there is little new over R. W. Moncrieff (1951).

Harper, Bate-Smith, Land's Odor Character Descriptor (1968):

Intensity expressed on a scale of 0 to 5:

1. Fragrant
2. Sweaty
3. Almond-like
4. Burnt-smoky
5. Herbal-green, cut grass, etc.
6. Etherish, anaesthetic
7. Sour, acrid, vinegar, etc.
8. Blood-like, raw meat
9. Dry, powdery
10. Ammonia-like
11. Disinfectant, carbolic
12. Oily, fatty
13. Like mothballs
14. Like solvents, gasoline
15. Cooked vegetables
16. Sweet
17. Fishy
18. Spicy
19. Paint-like
20. Rancid
21. Minty, peppermint
22. Sulfidic
23. Aromatic
24. Meaty (cooked)
25. Sickening
26. Musty, earthy, moldy
27. Sharp, pungent, acid
28. Camphor-like
29. Light
30. Heavy
31. Cool, cooling
32. Warm
33. Metallic
34. Fruit (citrus)
35. Fruity (others)
36. Putrid, foul, decayed
37. Woody, resinous
38. Musk-like
39. Soapy
40. Garlic, onion
41. Animal
42. Vanilla-like
43. Fecal (manure-like)
44. Floral

This system has been used in sensory panels and because of the many possible terms has proven of some aid. It can only loosely be called a classification and deserves mention here only because of practical use by several investigators as hedonic support for gas chromatograph analysis.

## PROTO-FUNCTIONAL OSMOGENIC TAXONOMY

The perception of odor is a phenomenon singular to living organisms exhibiting olfactory apparatus. This definition excluded within the limits of present knowledge all plants. In order to find a rational basis for classification, some underlying cause or irreducible factor common to all components of the classification must be sought. With respect to the phenomenon of odor perception and what is presently known of the laws governing osmogenic essence, there is only one rational basis sufficiently common to serve as taxonomic foundation for classification.

The capacity to perceive odor results essentially from natural selection. The origins of smell are primeval and simple: survival and procreation. The range of osmogenes perceived is unquestionably related in any species to these activities, within their ecological context. Man, and the primates in general, would not enjoy extensive osmogenic repertoires in areas not directly pertinent to their procreation or survival. The survival sub-factors of fight, flight and nourishment are similar but with respect to osmogenic classification there is a difference, albeit slight. The exception to these functional causes for olfaction are a class of osmogenes which, due to similarity of properties if not biological context, are within the inherited range of perception. Casusosmic odors often connotate nothing and are of only aesthetic or malaesthetic value. In this class of osmogene the limit of the smell sense must be attributed. The osmogene may lure the organism fatally, or repell it unfortunately. since casusosmic osmogenes share properties common to biologically functional osmogenes, they can be expressed by classification common to both. Four basic prime categories can be devised within which all osmogenic substances relevant to perception can be fitted: Animalia, Thallophyta, Planta and Elementa. In addition, there are numerous factors which in themselves may be considered osmogenic, but more frequently are modifier components of osmogenes. Casusosmogenes may be classified by organoleptically determining the olfactory similarities to functional osmogenic types or appropriate combinations of factors. Intensity of the osmogene category and proportion may be stated numerically:

Prime: 0 - 9
Class: 0 - 9
Genus: 0 - 9
Specie: 0 - 9
Variety: 0

Unquestionably, this taxonomy is a first attempt and as such will exhibit inconsistencies, errors and oversights. It is hoped that constructive improvements can be implemented in light of close scrutiny by advocates of different disciplines. Although the taxonomy finds its basis in the function of natural selection and not in irreducible laws governing the physiology of olfaction, it may serve greatly in determining what those laws are. For example, the taxonomy will ultimately make possible groupings of odorants which may exhibit common chemical properties.

### Prime A: Animalia

Among primates osmogenic knowledge of animals would be a requirement of cardinal importance. Special glands necessary for procreation if osmically perceptible would give considerable advantage through natural selection to one possessing the ability to perceive, not only through mate finding and higher probabilities of fertilization at optimum time, but through detection and avoidance of ecological antagonists, potential antagonists or edible game. Carried further, increased osmogenic acuity and repertoire would give decidedly favorable survival chances. What an animal eats must be metabolized, certain specific odors are characteristic of metabolism and, additionally, what is being metabolized will be characteristically superimposed on the metabolites normal to the organism. Wastes will be found deposited near the living area, and urine and feces will mark the area of game or foe, male or female, young or old of the specie responsible for them. The animal's body is composed of carbohydrates, proteins and fats. When living or freshly killed, these materials exude characteristic odors. However, when decay and decomposition have set in, or unnatural death through disease has contaminated these constituents, they become unpleasant, even sickening and nauseating odors. Osmogenes associated with these aspects of animalia would unquestionably be the olfactory legacy of ancestors perfecting this sense in accord with the imperative of natural selection and a broad classification can be based on these characteristics.

Prime Animalia: A (Organic): 0 - 9

(Class) A. Skatend (Sk): 0 - 9
(Genus) a. Fecoid (Fec): 0 - 9
(Specie) 1. Indolic (Indo): 0 - 9 )
(Variety) a) Indole )
2. Skatolic (Skat): 0 - 9 ) Like
a). Cycloheptadecalone )
3. α-Naphthylaminic (α-Naph): 0 - 9)

b. Uroid (Uro): 0 - 9
1. Aminoic (Amin): 0 - 9
2. β-Cyclohexene-1-oneic [urinodic] (β-Cycl): 0 - 9
3. Ureaic (Urea): 0 - 9
4. p-Cresylic (p-Cres): 0 - 9

c. Bileoid (Bil): 0 - 9
1. Vomitic (Vomi): 0 - 9
2. Ambergric (Ambe): 0 - 9

B. Putrend [prior to, partial, or total decomposition of body constituents] (Pu): 0 - 9
a. Aminoid (Ami): 0 - 9
1. Trimethylaminic [amines in general] (Trim): 0 - 9
2. Cadaverinic-putrescinic (Capu): 0 - 9

b. Lipoid (Lip): 0 - 9
1. Fattic [stearic] (Stea): 0 - 9
a). Nonyl alcohol
2. Rancidic (Ranc): 0 - 9
a). Octaldehyde
3. Ketoic (Keto): 0 - 9
a). Butanol

c. Carbohydroid (Car): 0 - 9
1. Honeyic (Hone): 0 - 9
a). Benzyl phenylacetate
b). Phenyl acetic acid and esters

C. Muskend (Mu): 0 - 9
   a. Muscoid [endocrine gland] (Mus): 0 - 9
      1. Muskic (Musk): 0 - 9
         a). Amber
         b). Musk
      2. Civetic (Cive): 0 - 9
         a). Civet
         b). Castor
         c). Crotyl mercaptan
   b. Sebacoid [apocrine gland] (Seb): 0 - 9
      1. Sebacoic [mammacoid] (Seba): 0 - 9
         a). Acetylmethylcarbinol
         b). 2,3-Butanedione
         c). Acetoin
         d). β-Methylmercaptopropionaldehyde
   c. Butyroid [exocrine gland] (But): 0 - 9
      1. Butyroic (Buty): 0 - 9
         a). Butyric, isobutyric, crotonic
         b). Caproic, caprylic

## Prime T: Thallophyta

Edible fungus, ponds polluted by stagnation and reeking of aquatic fungus, the heady enjoyment of fermented fruit or grapes, bread leavened by Saccharomyces cerevisiae, food spoiled by mildew and mold are all a result of the activities of Thallophytes. In many respects, this is a prime of lesser importance to primates, but one of decided survival advantage. As far as can be determined, however, the taxonomic subkingdom Thallophyta is of considerable more advantage olfactorily than the kingdom of the lesser, more obscure life form Protista.

### Prime Thallophyta: T (Organic): 0 - 9

(Class) A. Moldend [basidic] (Mo): 0 - 9
(Genus) a. Mildewoid (Mil): 0 - 9
(Specie) 1. Mycelecic (Myce): 0 - 9
(Variety) a). Polyporous cryptarium [mildewy]
   b. Fungi aromaticoid (Far): 0 - 9
      1. Carpophoric [mushroomy] (Carp): 0 - 9
   c. Moldoid (Mol): 0 - 9
      1. Mycelic (Mycl): 0 - 9
         a). Penicillium
         b). Rhizopus
         c). Mucor
      2. Phenolic (Phen): 0 - 9
B. Actinomycend (Ac): 0 - 9
   a. Earthoid (Ear): 0 - 9
      1. Earthic (Eart): 0 - 9
         a). Soil
         b). Clay
   b. Aquaticoid (Aqu): 0 - 9
      1. Swampic (Swam): 0 - 9
         a). Streptomyces, geosmin

b). Mucidone
2. Algaeic (Alga): 0 - 9
c. Mossoid (Mos): 0 - 9
1. Mossic (Moss): 0 - 9
a). Peat
b). Irish moss
c). Oak moss
2. Lichenic (Lich): 0 - 9
C. Yeastend [spore] (Ye): 0 - 9
a. Furfuroid (Fur): 0 - 9
1. Saccharomyces cerevisiaeic (Sach): 0 - 9
2. Furfurylic (Furf): 0 - 9
a). Furfural
b. Fermentoid (Fer): 0 - 9
1. Acetoacetic (Acto): 0 - 9
a). Mycoderma aceti
c. Mustoid (Mst): 0 - 9
1. Mustic (Must): 0 - 9
a). Candida pseudotropicalis

Prime P: Planta

An overwhelmingly significant survival advantage to olfactory prototypes, especially under primitive circumstances, would be the olfactory capacity to differentiate edible from inedible plants. For homing and tracking, what better guide than indigenous flora? As season markers for timely migrations, what better indicator than the subtle cast of odor changes from flowers?

Prime Planta: P (Organic): 0 - 9

(Class) A. Herbend (He): 0 - 9
(Genus) a. Spicoid (Spi): 0 - 9
(Specie) 1. Piperonalic (Pipe): 0 - 9
(Variety) a). Piperidine
2. Cinnamonic (Cinn): 0 - 9
a). Cinnamic aldehyde
b). Eugenol [clove]
3. Ginger (Ging): 0 - 9
a). Cumin aldehyde
b). Zingiber
c). d-Linalool
b. Alliacoid (All): 0 - 9
1. Garlic [onionic] (Garl): 0 - 9
a). Diallyl disulfide
2. Alliaic (Alli): 0 - 9
a). Mustard
b). Allyl isothiocyanate
c. Herboid (Her): 0 - 9
1. Anisic (Anis): 0 - 9
a). Licorice
b). Tarragon
c). Tea
d). Turmeric

2. Sagic (Sagi): 0 - 9
   a). Thujone
3. Saffronic (Saff): 0 - 9
   a). Picrocrocin

B. Camphaltend (Ca): 0 - 9
   a. Nutoid [caryopic] (Nut): 0 - 9
      1. Nuttic (Nutt): 0 - 9
         a). Benzaldehyde
         b). Almond [cyanide]
   b. Woodoid (Woo): 0 - 9
      1. Camphoric (Camp): 0 - 9
         a). Eucalyptus
         b). Menthol
         c). Carvone
      2. Sandalwoodic (Sand): 0 - 9
      3. Tannic (Tann): 0 - 9
      4. Turpenic [resonic] (Turp): 0 - 9
         a). Pinene
         b). Guiac
         c). Cedar
   c. Balsamoid (Bal): 0 - 9
      1. Vanillic (Vani): 0 - 9
      2. Chocolatic (Choc): 0 - 9

C. Estrend (Es): 0 - 9
   a. Floroid (Flo): 0 - 9
      1. Rosic (Rosi): 0 - 9
         a). Rose
         b). Geranium
      2. Jasic (Jasi): 0 - 9
         a). Jasmine
      3. Violic (Viol): 0 - 9
         a). Violet
         b). Ionone
         c). Irone
   b. Ensiloid (Ens): 0 - 9
      1. Greenic (Gree): 0 - 9
         a). Heptyl hexyl ether, hops [green]
         b). Phenyl ethyl aldehyde
         c). Phenylacetaldehyde dimethylacetal, hexanal
   c. Fruitoid (Fru): 0 - 9
      1. Citralic (Citr): 0 - 9
         a). Amyl acetate, butyl acetate, propyl acetate, lemon oil, mandarin oil, elemi oil

## Prime E: Elementa

There are seven elements which represent prime or fundamental osmogenes, and six which are in combination probably essential or basic osmogenic elements. Many of these elements singularly or in combination are found incorporated in osmogenes from other primes. It is not surprising that most all are rather unpleasant since environments natural to primal ancestors were often associated with lethal atmospheres of these elemental vapors.

Prime Elementa: E (Inorganic): 0 - 9

(Class) A. Cacodylend (Cc): 0 - 9
(Genus) a. Osmoid (Osm): 0 - 9
(Specie) 1. Osmium tetraoxidic (Osmi): 0 - 9
b. Silicoselenoid (Sse): 0 - 9
1. Silicic (Sili): 0 - 9
(Variety) a). Silicon tetrafluoride
b). Silane
2. Selenic (Sele): 0 - 9
a). Selenium bromide
b). Selenium oxide
c. Arsenoid (Ars): 0 - 9
1. Arsenic (Arse): 0 - 9
a) Arsenic trioxide

B. Alliumend (Al): 0 - 9
a. Phosphoid (Pho): 0 - 9
1. Phosphic (Phos): 0 - 9
a). Tetraphosphorus trisulfide
b. Sulfoid (Sul): 0 - 9
1. Thiocyanic (Thic): 0 - 9
a). Thiol alcohol
b). Ammonium thioglycolate
2. Hydrosulfic (Hyds): 0 - 9
a). Sulfuric acid
b). Hydrogen sulfide
c. Nitrogenoid (Nit): 0 - 9
1. Nitric (Nitr): 0 - 9
a). Nitrogen dioxide
b). Ammonia
c). Nitrous oxide
d). Nitric acid

C. Hydrocarbohalogend (Hy): 0 - 9
a. Halogenoid (Hal): 0 - 9
1. Chloric (Chlo): 0 - 9
a). Bromine
b). Chlorine
c). Fluorine
d). Iodine
e). Astatine
b. Oxyoid (Oxy): 0 - 9
1. Ozonic (Ozon): 0 - 9
c. Hydrocarboid (Hyc): 0 - 9
1. Methanic (Meth): 0 - 9
a). Ethane
b). Propane
c). Butane
2. Acetoic (Acet): 0 - 9
a). Methyl ethyl ketone
b). Acetone
c). Toluene

Chart of Proto-functional
Osmogenic Taxonomy:
Primes through Genera

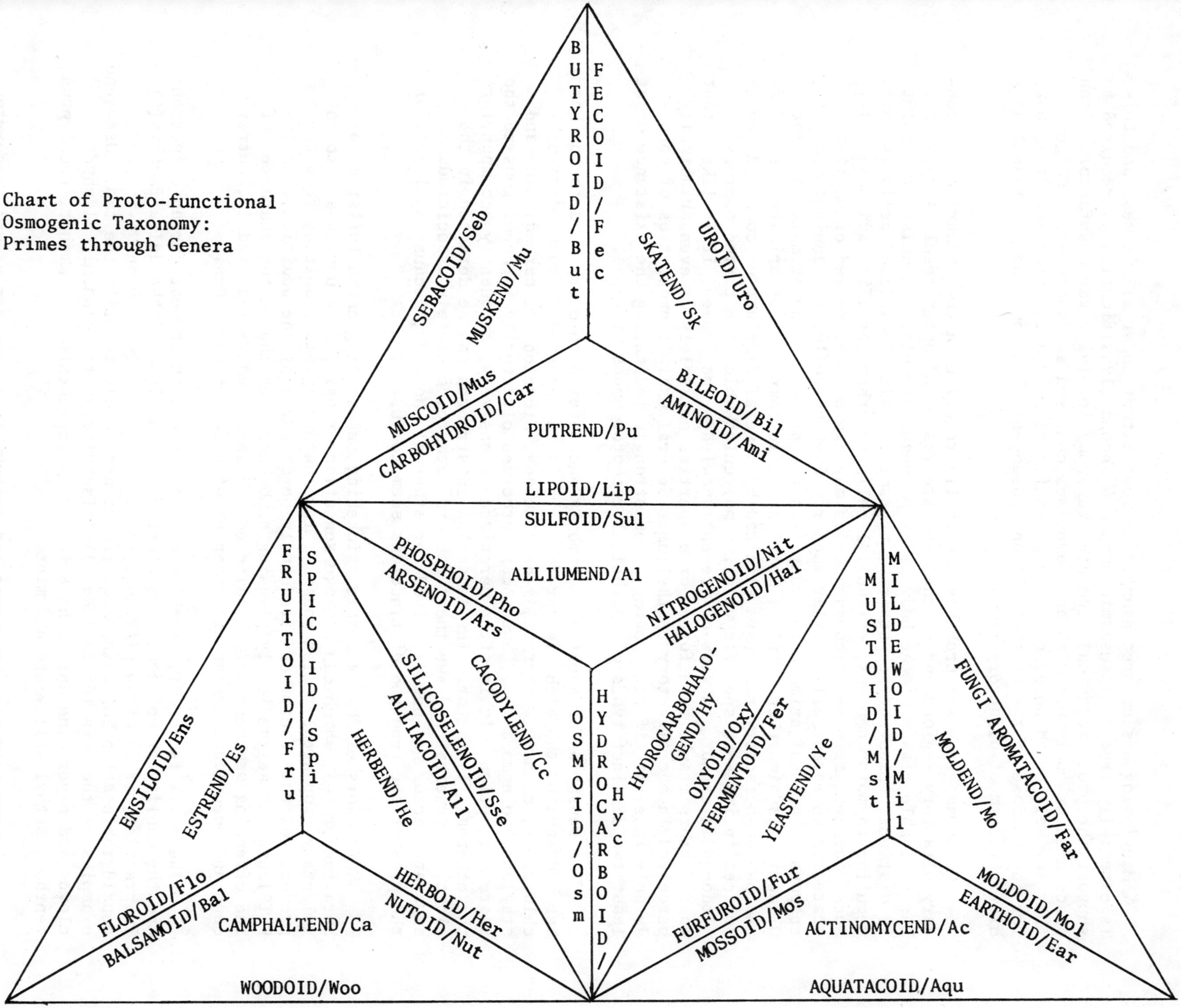

## Osmogenic Modifiers, Factors and Pseudosmogenes

Many osmogenes are represented to some extent under all primes, and this is especially true of casusosmic ones. A second classification is required to support the protobiological elemental taxonomy involving various factors often associated as modifiers with and sometimes confused as osmogenes. Osmogenic they may well be, depending on the classification or definition accepted, but for the purpose of the Proto-functional Osmogenic Taxonomy they represent a distinct form of olfactory responses.

Pseudosmogenes are probably chemically reactive in the primary and secondary olfactory regions and in the separate taste and upper respiratory areas. The excitable tissue of the body is by no means singularly modular or absolutely distinct. Bioelectric potential transmitted via specialized cells is not peculiar to motor neurons; epithelial cells or other specific excitable tissues, muscles, skin and secondary cells may exhibit the spread of excited states in an essentially similar manner. Even unicellular organisms exhibit responses to local stimulation that is not confined to the stimulated point. Olfaction is almost certainly a multi-specific composite of primary, secondary and pseudo-olfactory responses elicited by several distinct or combined energy sources intimate to specific volatile molecules which are termed odorous. Although it cannot, in view of present knowledge, be proven, it is likely that most factors result from forces or properties not solely or even principally perceived in the olfactory epithelium. Several exhibit properties of considerable interest, if not proving, then strongly indicating the existence of at least two distinct types of epithelial receptor modes or types.

The sensation of sweetness commonly encountered in odors as a factor has been designated the alpha factor ($\alpha$). It is represented in such odors as chloroform, cinnamyl butyrate, $\gamma$-decalactone, dicyclohexyl carbodiimide and ethylene, to name a few. Sweetness perceived olfactorily is homologous to the taste perception. It is often perceived extensively, frequently accompanying the ethereal ($\lambda$) factor. The sensation in strength can be detected in the glottis. Ethereal and sweetness factors seem to be closely associated. A separate factor has been reserved for ethereal, however, because at least for the present the reported distinctions seem to justify it.

Some odors exhibit a morbid, sickening, nauseating characteristic, or beta factor ($\beta$), which can provoke sensations ranging from unpleasant to involuntary esophageal reflex spasms. Involuntary spasms resulting from the presence of this factor can frequently be arrested by the addition of Prime P (Planta) or aesthetically pleasing osmogenes even though the character of the offending osmogene seems unaltered. Silane, cadaverine, indole, putrescene and phenylcarbylamine are examples of $\beta$-factor osmogenes.

The gamma factor ($\gamma$) is the sensation of warmth or heat during olfaction and the cooling or coldness characteristic is designated the delta factor ($\delta$). In practice, it is often difficult to distinguish between $\gamma$ and $\delta$-factors, considerable attention being required to accurately identify the two. Osmogene examples of the $\gamma$-factor include allyl isothiocyanate, cinnamic aldehyde, cloves and piperidine while the $\delta$-factor is represented by camphor, eucalyptus, menthol, methyl salicylate and mint.

Many osmogenes are irritants and lachrymators, properties well deserving of recognition as an osmogenic component. The lachrymator factor, epsilon ($\varepsilon$), may result solely from chemical destruction of mucosal tissues or be more generally destructive. It may or may not have a direct effect on the trigeminus. Acetic anhydride, allyl bromide, benzal chloride and methyl chloroformate are $\varepsilon$-factor osmogenes. Irritating and lachrymating sensations may ultimately require subdivision, but it is likely that they are related by cause and are merely degrees of activity or concentration.

Schizosmogenes, or theta factor ($\theta$) osmogenes, exhibit two distinct modalities of perception; they are not pseudosmogenes. When dilute, they often are aesthetically pleasing, but at greater concentrations become malaesthetic. This factor strongly supports the existence of two distinct receptor types (or the bimodality of olfactory receptors). The osmogene possesses two acceptable energy modes. One is perceptible at much lower concentrations representing the effect of resonance, and the other at much higher concentrations representing the effect of its chemically reactive nature. $\theta_1$ designates lower concentration modality; $\theta^2$ expresses the exhibition of the upper concentration modality. $\theta_1$ and $\theta^2$ are often very distinct, characteristic odors. In sufficient concentration, $\theta^2$ is overriding; nevertheless, $\theta^2$ is undoubtedly a composite of $\theta_1$ and $\theta^2$. Schizosmogenes represent a very interesting subject for research. The capacity to elicit two distinct and often entirely different perceptions is unique, and whatever the underlying phenomenon they must ultimately be anticipated by any theory. Examples of some known $\theta$-factor osmogenes are ambergris, civet, diphenyl oxide, indole, maltol and some musks. Schizosmogenes may be revealed by dilution, temperature alterations, or a result of other factors, but when a chemically unaltered osmogene displays two distinct, reversible modes, it is schizosmic.

The delicate, ethereal factor encountered commonly in the study of osmogenic vapors is the lambda factor ($\lambda$). Chloroform, ethyl chloride and many others are representative of this factor. The $\lambda$-factor is very likely a result of high lipid solubility and acts as a mucous solvent with otherwise relatively low characterizing reactivity.

Olfactory metallic sensations which may or may not result from reactions with but certainly affect the parotid glands are probably not uncommon. Heptyl salicylate, crude petroleum and petroleum products exhibit this mu factor ($\mu$).

The phenomenon of bitterness or astringency exhibited as an osmogenic factor is best exhibited by pyridine. Just how homologous with gustation reception this factor may be is at present unknown. Some examples are quinone, quinaldine and quinazoline. This factor is designated Nu ($\nu$).

Since all resonant receivers (receptors) within the specific harmonic range of the osmogene will react virtually simultaneously and to the same degree, the olfactory quality once perceived is not likely to display any great sensation of increasing intensity as the osmogene concentration is raised. There are examples of osmogenes exhibiting only the resonant modality without any display of concomitant shift in olfactory character. Vanilla is such a substance. The factor provided for this characteristic is xi ($\xi$). Such osmogenes would be expected to have vibration constants corresponding to resonant receptor lengths and diameters or harmonic multiples thereof. The capacity for the $\xi$-bearing (peaking) osmogene to elicit chemical response would be expected to be negligible, if at all. A study of $\xi$-factor osmogenes will undoubtedly yield significant results in understanding resonant olfaction. Vanilla is perceptible in extremely low concentrations, and it is likely that all $\xi$-factor osmogenes share this characteristic. As should be anticipated, an increase in concentration does not elicit a corresponding increase in the sensation of strength of intensity. Examples of $\xi$-factor osmogenes include 2,3-butanedione, cyclohexane and 1,1,4-trimethylcycloheptanone-3.

Some osmogenes bear a factor which causes the taste characteristics of other substances to change. This phenomenon may affect and alter the normal taste of cigar, cigarette or pipe smoke as well as foods. This factor is designated pi ($\pi$), taste change, and is not uncommon to high concentrations of chemicals such as some mercaptans and thiols, ammonium thioglycolate and pyridine being good examples. It is interesting to note that when copper sulfate dust is breathed the same results ensue, imparting a distinct sensation of sweetness on breathing or swallowing to the back of the throat and tongue which may be of some duration (1 to 2 days). With the nasal cavity completely blocked, pyridine can be detected on the tongue when inspired through the mouth.

The capacity of osmogenes to stimulate (in small or trace quantities) the olfactory sense for relatively extreme periods of time, i.e., from days to as long as 100 years, is termed persistence or tenacity. This factor is designated rho ($\rho$) and may be sufficiently related to the $\xi$ or $\theta$-factors to cause difficulty in determining the difference. This factor is not a pseudosmogene. The $\rho$-factor may prove to have a bearing on the fixative properties of some osmogenes, and as might be expected, there is a relationship with vapor pressure. Ambergris, cadaverine, civet, isatin and musk are examples.

When odorants are burned or oxidized or result from burning or oxidizing, they often exhibit an odor characteristic reminiscent of the pre-oxidized substance, coupled with a burned, empyreumatic or pyrotic character. Many osmogenes may be described as possessing this factor, designated the sigma factor ($\sigma$) and ozone is not unsurprisingly almost entirely an empyreumatic osmogene. Acrolein, p-cresol, furfural mercaptan, guaiacol, heptyl undecatate and l-tartaric acid are $\sigma$-factor osmogenes.

The capacity to anesthetize the olfactory sense, the tau factor ($\tau$), is widely known. The action has been proposed as entirely trigeminal. If it is not, the olfactory epithelium and receptor cells are depotentiated as well as the trigeminus. Formaldehyde and sulfur dioxide are known examples. This capacity is interesting for research since the physiological responses at some point must be interferred with. Pinpointing this specifically would go far toward explaining olfactory physiology and chemistry.

Many osmogenes exhibit the phi factor ($\phi$), a stifling, choking or suffocating characteristic. These osmogenes in concentration almost always are toxic vapors. Nitric acid, phosgene, propionaldehyde, sulfural chloride and sulfurous acid are examples.

Sour, sharp and pungent sensations are included in the psi factor ($\psi$) osmogenes and are frequently, if not always, a result of ionic reactions between osmogene and olfactorily excitable tissues. The presence of this characteristic can often be detected by the exposure of a sensitive pH meter probe atmospherically impregnated with the osmogene. Ammonia, acetic acid, iodine, heptafluoride, hypophosphorous acid, isopentaldehyde, mustard oil and oxeladin are examples.

Some osmogenes display a penetrating, permeating, diffusing characteristic, termed the omega factor (ω). The ω-factor sensation may result from the high solubility of the osmogene in the lipoids of the mucosa and unlike the λ-factor reacts with underlying excitable tissues. This factor, however, may also or alternatively be a composite of singular sensations resulting from cell permeability in the olfactory and upper respiratory region. In this it shares a similarity with the λ and ε-factors. The bronchus and upper alveola respond with a sense of expansion. Overall respiration, blood pressure and cardiac activity may initially be affected. Allyl isothiocyanate, amyl nitrate, bromal, isopentanoic acid, β-methyl allylchloride and l-octanol are examples of ω-factor osmogenes.

The use of appropriate symbols to connotate intensity of the character or factor is necessary for a more complete description. The presence of the factorial symbol means it is present and detectable. The symbol followed by "!" denotes strong, followed by "!!" very strong is denoted, and followed by "!!!" overpowering or ultimate is denoted.

Other potential factors or supporting factors which are at present too obscure in meaning and context to determine if they are factors in themselves include cacosmic, resosmic (insistence), polosmic (polar osmogene), fixative, sternutatory, hedonic, aesthetic, mood altering or pheromone, green, saline. The "green" associated with osmogenes is encountered frequently and is presently included as a characteristic variety in the Planta prime.

Use of the classifications and factors should permit a high degree of numerical and symbolic accuracy in describing an osmogene. It is likely that the characters and factors will be condensed or expanded and improved with experience. The rules for use of the classification are as follows:

## Rules of Classification

1. All primes end with "a" and may be assigned a value from zero to nine, depending on perceptual analysis of the extent of occurance in an osmogene.
2. The sequential order of primes is Animalia, Thallophyta, Planta, Elementa.
3. All classes end with "end" and may be assigned a value of zero to nine, depending on the perceptual analysis of the extent of occurance in an osmogene.
4. The sequential order of class is clockwise from apex opposite base.
5. All genuses end with "oid" and may be assigned a value from zero to nine, depending on the perceptual comparison of varietal types within the specie.
6. The sequential order of genus is clockwise to the apex opposite the base.
7. Species are included in the taxonomy, but not on the chart. They have a value of zero to nine. They represent select headings for comparative varieties or in some cases serve in themselves as comparative examples of the parent genus.
8. Varieties are included in the taxonomy but not on the chart. They have no specific value and are intended as comparative standards of specie.
9. When using the chart to express, appropriate symbols are employed. For a general description, the prime symbols which apply are noted down in order of (1) Animalia, (2) Thallophyta, (3) Planta, (4) Elementa, and the appropriate sub-numeral between one and nine written in. If any prime is

not represented in the broad class, a zero should be inserted in its place. Factors are suffixed after Elementa as necessary. If the factor can be identified with its prime, it can be suffixed following the prime.

Example: Wood smoke extract — Expression: $0\ 0\ P_9\ E_1\ \sigma!!\ \psi$

0: No Animalia component
0: No Thallophyta component
9: Planta component, full strength
1: Elementa component, very weak
σ: Pyrotic factor, very strong
ψ: Acrid factor

10. When expressing a more specific description, the sensory analysis of classes will be necessary. Each class has a two letter symbol, the first letter capitalized, i.e., Ca. The classes should be extracted from the primes in order as given in the rules: (1) Animalia, (2) Thallophyta, (3) Planta, (4) Elementa, then clockwise from the apex opposite the base chart triangle. The appropriate symbols are written in order. If the class is not represented in the odor, it may be omitted. No zero is required. If there are no classes in a prime, a zero should be inserted in its proper order. If more than one, each class of a prime should be enclosed parenthetically after the appropriate numerical designation of occurance is registered. A sub-value may be inserted at the end of the parenthesis when there is more than one class or variety in the prime. This value may be from one to nine and can total more or less than the values of the class, genus or variety entered. If no sub-number is given after the parenthesis, the value is the total of all values enclosed unless the enclosed values exceed nine, in which case the total value is nine.

Example: Wood smoke extract — Expression:

$0\ 0\ Ca_9\ Hy\ \sigma!!\ \psi$

11. For specific expressions, the genus will require comparative sensory analysis. A three letter symbol with the first letter capitalized, i.e., Woo, is assigned to each genus. The rules are otherwise the same for genus as class.

Example: Wood smoke extract — Expression:

$0\ 0\ Woo_9\ Hyc\ \sigma!!\ \psi$

12. A four letter designation with the first letter capitalized is assigned to each specie, i.e., Turp. All other rules for genus and class apply.

Example: Wood smoke extract — Expression:

$0\ 0\ Turp_9\ Meth\ \sigma!!\ \psi$

Summary: Wood smoke extract 0 0 $Turp_9$ Meth σ!! ψ

0: No Animalia component
0: No Thallophyta component
9: Planta component, full strength, Camphaltend class, Woodoid genus, Turpenic variety
1: Elementa component, very weak, Hydrocarbohalogend class, Hydrocarboid genus, Methanic variety
σ: Pyrotic factor, very strong
ψ: Acrid factor

Example of Analysis and Expression

Example: Aniseed (general description)

Prime Character: $A_2$ $T_1$ $P_9$ 0 α! γ σ ψ or 2 1 9 0 α! γ σ ψ

Expression: 2: Animalia component, weak
1: Thallophyta component, very weak
9: Planta component, full
0: No Elementa component
α: Sweet factor, strong
γ: Warm factor
σ: Burnt factor
ψ: Sour factor

Class Character: $Mu_2$ Ye ($He_5Ca_2Es_2$) 0 α! γ σ ψ

Expression: 2: Animalia component, weak, Muskend class
1: Thallophyta component, very weak, Yeastend class
9: Planta component, full strength, 5 parts Herbend class, 2 parts Campholtend class and 2 parts Estrend class
0: No Elementa component
α: Sweet factor, strong
γ: Warm factor
σ: Burnt factor
ψ: Sour factor

Specific Genus Description:

Expression: $But_2$ Fur ($SpiHer_4NutWooFloFru$) 0 α! γ σ ψ

Summary:

Anise has an Animalia character of two parts in nine, entirely like butyric acid. It has a slight Thallophyta odor similar to furfural of one in nine parts and a substantial Planta character of nine in nine parts. The Planta character is composed of one part in nine of Spicoid, four parts in nine of Herboid, one part in nine of Nutoid, one part in nine of Woodoid, one part in nine of floroid and one part in nine of fruitoid. No Elementa component is detectable. There is a strong sweet characteristic (α-factor) and a warm (γ-factor), burnt (σ-factor) and acrid (ψ-factor) characteristic present.

When necessary, primes, classes, genuses and varieties may be mixed. The following are examples:

Ammonium thioglycolate: $Ami_3$ 0 0 $Thic_9$ α β μ π σ!! or

3 0 0 9 α β μ π σ!!

Acetophenone: $A_5$ $Mst_5$ $(Spi_6FloNut_2)_7$ $(ChloMeth)_2$ α! γ σ! ψ! or

5 5 7 2 α! γ σ! ψ!

## Some Osmogene Taxonomy Classification Expressions

| | |
|---|---|
| Ammonia: | $Uro_2$ 0 0 $Nit_9$ δ ε!!! ϕ!!! ψ!!! ω!! or |
| | 2 0 0 9 δ ε!!! ϕ!!! ψ!!! ω!! |
| Amyl acetate: | $Lip_2$ 0 $Fru_6$ $Hyc_2$ α! γ λ σ ψ! ω! or |
| | 2 0 6 2 α! γ λ σ ψ! ω! |
| Benzaldehyde: | 0 0 $Nut_9$ 0 γ or |
| | 0 0 9 0 γ |
| Benzoin: | 0 0 $(Spi_4Her_3Woo_4)$ 0 α!! γ! λ ρ σ or |
| | 0 0 9 0 α!! γ! λ ρ σ |
| 2,3-Butanedione: | $\theta_1$: $Seb_9$ 0 0 0 ψ ω or 9 0 0 0 ψ ω |
| | $\theta^2$: $Seb_4$ 0 0 $(HycHal_5)_5$ μ ψ! ω! or 4 0 0 5 μ ψ! ω! |
| Camphor: | 0 $Mil_3$ $Woo_9$ 0 α δ! σ! ψ ω or |
| | 0 3 9 0 α δ! σ! ψ ω |
| Carbon tetrachloride: | 0 0 0 $(Hyc_5Hal_2)_6$ α! γ λ!! or |
| | 0 0 0 6 α! γ λ!! |
| Cedar fragrance: (Norda #714) | 0 0 $Woo_7$ 0 α ρ or |
| | 0 0 7 0 α ρ |
| Clove oil: | 0 0 $Spi_9$ 0 α γ!! σ or |
| | 0 0 9 0 α γ!! σ |
| Isopropyl alcohol: | 0 Fru Mst $Hyc_5$ α! γ λ σ! ψ |
| | 0 1 1 5 α! γ λ σ! ψ |
| Lemon fragrance (Norda #714) | $Mu_2$ 0 $(AllFru_7)_7$ Hyc δ ψ or 2 0 7 1 δ ψ |

2 0 7 1

2-Octanol: $(MusBut_9)_9$ 0 $Fru_2$ $Hyc_2$ α β! λ ψ! ω or

9 0 2 2 α β! λ ψ! ω

Pyridine: 0 0 0 $(Hyc_5Oxy_3)_8$ β! ν!!! σ!!! φ ψ! ω! or

0 0 0 8 β! ν!!! σ!!! φ ψ! ω!

Vanillin: 0 $Mst_2$ $Bal_9$ 0 α!! ξ!! σ or

0 2 9 0 α!! ξ!! σ

## ODOR CONTROL BACKGROUND

There are many practical reasons for the technological study of odor control. Reduction of malodorous pollution of the environment by industry, utilization of malodorous but otherwise usable goods, control or eradication of abnormal odors associated with disease and natural occurances such as fire with its attendent smoke odor damage to furniture and goods and water or flood damage with the attendent mildew and mold problem. The sickroom, the home, the office, the car, the food we eat, the air we breathe, the quality of our day to day lives can be deprecated and depressed by malodor. The osmic quality of the air we breathe is for most people one of the significant values of life. From this it follows that the ability to understand and control odors is one additional capability of enriching the personal domain.

An air borne malodor disseminated by one party to become a part of another's environment is an invasion of privacy and a theft of life quality. The laws of man have long recognized the rights of individuals to pursue their liberty within the confines of their own personal environment, but when that liberty encroaches another person's, the action is considered a trespass and is recognized by all civilized men as unlawful. With man pressing in on himself and the confines of his personal environment shrinking, his need for self expression and freedom become paramount. How, then, can his necessary requirements be met if his small domain is open to intrusion, trespass and deprecation?

The man of yesterday and his predecessors to the dawn of time could find ample solitude in which to exercise his needs. He could own hunting dogs, yell to the open spaces, dress as he pleased, keep his dwelling as he saw fit and exercise as a matter of choice a thousand or more freedoms, right down to the quality of the air he breathed. The man of today does not enjoy these prerogatives, and the small spaces of privacy left to him are more important than they have ever been. If man is to preserve his integrity and maintain his characteristics and values, then it is imperative that this living space be recognized and protected.

The roots of modern odor control technology basically rest on the esoteric perfume industry. It is here that identification, classification, extraction methods and considerable nomenclature and chemistry were born. To some extent an extension of the foundation of modern odor control would have to include the spice and aromatics trade. Medieval history is replete with references to the odoriferous nature of existence, perhaps nowhere more humorously expressed than in Mark Twain's novelette, 1600, describing the intimacies of Elizabethan court life. And, of course, everyone has read of Marco Polo's trip to Cathay in search of aromatics and spices for European commerce. Prior to the twentieth century wherever people congregated the olfactory evidence of lack of sanitary facilities was prevalent. Unquestionably the sensitive, intelligent people who gathered under such circumstances found the perfumer's art preferable to Nature's handiwork. Incenses and perfumes were an accepted way to come to terms with odor pollution. Spices were originally used as much for hedonic enjoyment as for the preservation of food. The modern custom of drinking red wines with red meat and white wines with white meat is undoubtedly derived from the days when merchants used wine to preserve meats. Red wines would, of course, discolor white meats whereas white wines would bleach red meats.

Perfumers found their market among royalty and in catering to this market considerable secrecy surrounded the arcane profession. The concoctions, brews and remedies supplied became evermore complex, the ingredients more bizarre. From the four corners of the earth came frankincense, myrrh, sandalwood oil, ylang ylang. Nothing was sacred to the perfumer's appointed task. He and his agents combed the plant world; lifted up the civet cat, probed its anus and harvested its glands; depressed the tongue of the great whales and finding yesterday's squid dinner, reeking of new promise, withdrew ambergris, scrounging it from the shores in great, gray bobbling chunks. The perfumer's procurer pounded the arctic tundra, capturing the fanged musk deer to strip him of his sex glands; fantastic prices were paid for these scarce commodities. Although he denied mankind the benefit of his knowledge, the perfumer's secrets slipped out, one by one. Exceedingly small amounts of ambergris added to a perfume resulted in ambrosial qualities of odor unreproducible with any other material; moreover, the perfume lasted on the wearer much longer. It became "fixed." The search for other materials proceeded, and fixatives became a standard tool of perfumery. Many things possess the fixing property. Add a little water to ammonia, and the ammonia will not dissipate nearly as fast as without it. Water is a fixative for ammonia; it retards its atmospheric dissipation. It is in reality an adsorbant, an odor vector, for ammonia.

Attempting to turn the perfumer's art into a useful technology is not an easy task. The profession has a record of haughtiness and contempt for the common element befitting its noble birthright. This contempt is well expressed in a statement by Messrs. Schimmel and Company in October of 1894. The statement was in response to speculation that since Schimmel and Company had synthesized ionone for the first time, the price would drop and common persons could enjoy its element in perfumes (E. J. Parry, 1908), quote:

> "The opinion, which is frequently expressed, that the price of ionone solution will probably be reduced before long is not justified. It is not the intention of the manufacturer to depreciate the article without reason or necessity, a policy which can only meet with the approval of the maker of highclass perfumes, for whose use ionone is intended, and who cannot gain by seeing violet odor, like so many other preparations, brought down to the level of a vulgar scent for common people."

In order to protect the commerce from adulterations, perfumers began noting and keeping track of characteristics of essential oils. These original crude chemical laboratories began experimenting and, one by one, uncovered synthetic analogs to natural products. Complex esters were synthesized; remarkable breakthroughs in fixatives and artificial perfumes and odors followed, aldehydes, ketones, anhydrides, ketals, lactones, amines, to name a few. The work, of course, was proprietary. The profession was filled with a self generated mystique which relegated the perfumer to the arts. Mistrusted by science and technology, perfumery has chosen to remain a mysterious and jaded profession, willingly contributing little or nothing to the great scientific surge of the twentieth century.

## MEASURING ODORS

The measurement of odor falls into three categories: (1) determination of the threshold concentration of odoriferous gases, (2) determination of the type (recognition) and intensity of atmospheric odors, and (3) hedonic reactions of normal persons to osmogenes.

Considerable research has been carried out on ways of measuring the odor threshold of various substances and characterizing the intensity of various odors. Most olfactometers are based on a vapor dilution method in which the amount of osmogenic substance added to purified air is gradually increased until an observer or "sniffer" can just barely detect the odor. Attempts have also been made to measure odor by chemical, physical and biological means. One of these is the Perdu Pendant Drop method (J. O. Kopplin, 1959) of surface tension measurement. Nevertheless, organoleptic methods (those based on sensory perception, in this case by smelling) are still the most reliable. Several investigators have prepared lists of the odor thresholds for various chemicals. The more important lists have been combined and published by the Manufacturing Chemists' Association.

The most important tool in detection today is the gas chromatograph. Much work has been attempted to date in point source identification and so-called "signatures" where ambient air samples are trapped and compared against suspect site source sample print-outs. In practice these methods have proven impractical. An example of procedures presently employed is the high speed collection of organic vapors method by Dravnieks, Krotoszynski, Whitfield, O'Donnell and Bingwald (1971). A typical procedure is for the investigator to take two site samples of a suspect odor source. One is taken for gas chromatograph analysis and the other for sensory evaluation by a panel, the Chromosorb 102 collection procedure being used. This procedure results in a two time enrichment of the sample, a factor which must be taken into account when the sample is eluted from the gas chromatograph. Samples collected for panel evaluation in 18-liter polyethylene bags are presented to a selected panel for evaluation. Each sample is diluted with air to establish the point at which 50% of the panel members cannot detect an odor. This establishes the $ED_{50}$ value. This value is the number of volumes an equal volume of the original odor sample must be diluted by before 50% of the panel members can detect no odor.

To establish if the ambient air samples contain components characteristic of specific source emissions, gas-chromatograms of various source emissions must be compared with the gas-chromatogram of the particular ambient air sample. Conclusions are based on groups of gas chromatograph patterns. The presence of emissions of a source in the ambient air sample may be presumed if: (a) a number of gas chromatograph peaks found in the emissions sample must also be found in the ambient air sample, (b) the relative sizes of the peaks common to both samples should follow a similar pattern, (c) the similarity of patterns should reach adequate statistical significance.

The gas-chromatogram of an ambient air sample is compared separately to each of the available source emissions gas-chromatograms. Those peaks which occur in both are marked off; their gas chromatograph areas are ranked separately for gas chromatographs in order of increasing size. Rank order correlation coefficient is calculated and the statistical probability of the correlation, if any, is established using appropriate tables (W. Volk, 1958).

In comparing the gas-chromatograms, two types of gas chromatograph peaks are disregarded: (1) peaks occurring at less than one minute retention time are present in almost all samples, and their retention times are sensitive to the sample injection (into gas chromatograph) variables; (2) peaks that are quite small are disregarded in the source emissions since they are too small if found in ambient air. Such small peaks are ignored also in the ambient samples, since they easily can arise from small contaminations, insignificant sources, etc. "Small" peak was defined somewhat arbitrarily as one less than 5,000 integrator units in size; this corresponds approximately to $6 \times 10^{-9}$ g/liter for emissions and $6 \times 10^{-10}$ g/liter for ambient air.

Complete tables of comparisons follow. Table I illustrates an examination of ambient air sample taken for the possible presence of components emitted by the suspect source, Sample 1. The latter, Sample 2, was taken at a different time. Ideally, it is desirable that emission samples be taken simultaneously from all possible emission sources and from the ambient air at the site of a complaint. However, this is usually impractical.

Column 1 lists all gas chromatograph peaks of the suspect source emission sample except those excluded on the basis of considerations in the method of comparison. The next column lists gas chromatograph areas of these peaks.

Next, gas chromatograph of the ambient air is inspected, entering retention times (5th column) of those which reasonably match the retention times of the emission source. A reasonable match is assumed when the retention time difference (6th column) between the peaks that are matched is of the order of a few seconds at short retention times (up to a few minutes) and up to 0.5 minutes at longer retention times. These values are based on experience of the repeatability of retention times for the same known chemical. In those cases where differences in the retention times reach somewhat questionable magnitude they are placed in parentheses.

Areas of gas chromatograph peaks of ambient air are entered in column 7. Column 3 is used to mark off those peaks that appear in both gas chromatographs and are considered for size pattern match.

Matching peaks are then ranked by size, from the smallest (rank 1) to the largest (rank 8, since 8 peaks were matched). This is done separately for the source emission, column 4, and ambient air, column 8.

Rank correlation coefficient r is then calculated as follows: differences between ranks for each matching peak are calculated, column 9, and the differences squared, column 10. The sum of the squares is obtained, bottom of column 10. This sum is used to calculate the rank correlation coefficient r:

$$r = 1 - \frac{6\ (\text{sum of squares})}{n^2\ (n - 1)}$$

where n is the number of samples. For the present case:

$$r = 1 - \frac{6 \times 10}{64 \times 7} = 0.86$$

Table I. Evaluation of Gas Chromatograph of Ambient Air for Possible Presence of Components of Emission from Suspect Source 2

| Retention Time, min. | Area, Integrator Units | Found in GC of Ambient | Rank Order | Ambient Retention Time | Ambient Retention Difference | Area, Integrator Units | Rank Order | Rank $\Delta$ | Rank $\Delta^2$ |
|---|---|---|---|---|---|---|---|---|---|
| 1.04 | 16000 | | | (1.12) | (0.08) | (9830) | | | |
| 1.25 | 15480 | X | 2 | 1.24 | 0.01 | 11730 | 1 | 1 | 1 |
| 1.44 | 26580 | X | 4 | 1.47 | 0.03 | 25050 | 5 | 1 | 1 |
| 1.73 | 84080 | X | 6 | 1.78 | 0.05 | 28840 | 6 | 0 | 0 |
| 2.63 | 150090 | X | 8 | 2.66 | 0.03 | 38660 | 7 | 1 | 1 |
| 3.12 | 114400 | X | 7 | 3.19 | 0.07 | 66160 | 8 | 1 | 1 |
| 3.49 | 45360 | X | 5 | 3.47 | 0.02 | 21290 | 4 | 1 | 1 |
| 3.94 | 25840 | X | 3 | 3.83 | 0.09 | 16030 | 2 | 1 | 1 |
| 4.23 | 14870 | | | | | | | | |
| 4.41 | 46990 | | | | | | | | |
| 6.90 | 13800 | X | 1 | 6.68 | 0.22 | 17220 | 3 | 2 | 4 |
| 24.70 | 49100 | | | | | | | | |
| 46.09 | 51490 | | | | | | Sum $\Delta^2$ | | 10 |

Number of Peaks Common to Both Gas Chromatographs 8

Rank Correlation Coefficient $= 1 - \frac{6 \times 10}{64 \times 7} = 0.86$

Probability of Correlation by Chance $p < 0.01$
(99 percent confidence level)

Correlation would not change materially if 1.04 min. peak of source were considered to correspond to 1.12 min. peak of ambient air and also included in correlation.

The following table reproduces the statistical levels of significance for various values of r for different numbers of sample pairs:

| Number of Sample Pairs | Probability Level | |
|---|---|---|
| | 0.05 | 0.01 |
| 5 | 0.900 | 1.000 |
| 6 | 0.829 | 0.943 |
| 7 | 0.714 | 0.893 |
| 8 | 0.643 | 0.833 |
| 9 | 0.600 | 0.783 |
| 10 | 0.564 | 0.746 |
| 12 | 0.506 | 0.712 |

For the present case, $r = 0.86$ (8 sample pairs) is larger than 0.833, in the third column of the table.

This indicates the $p < 0.01$, or that such correlation in the rank order of matched peak sizes could occur by mere chance in less than one case out of 100. In tests related to sensory and life-science problems, a correlation is assumed to have basis if $p < 0.05$ (can occur by chance in one case out of 20). Thus, strong indications exist that the suspect source, Sample 1, emissions such as observed were present in the ambient air sample obtained in suspect source, Sample 2.

Such procedures have not stood up well in the courts and are therefore of questionable value for correction or enforcement. A procedure presently being tested by the Northwest Air Pollution Authority may overcome these difficulties and make enforcement and engineering a much simpler problem.

## Procedure

Immediately upon receipt of a complaint, the authority should establish wind direction at the site of the complaint, and determine the pollution suspect by opinion of the complainant or by investigation. If less than two offenders are implicated, send two investigators: one to the complaint site and one to the suspected offender site. Upon arrival at the complaint site, the investigator should confirm wind direction, velocity and origin of offender. Upon arrival at the suspect site, the investigator should note the wind direction, velocity and examine the site for any obvious source. If malodor exists, the investigator should attempt to determine the exact location of evolution.

Locating as close as practicable to the source investigated, the investigator should trap a known volume of effluent in an adsorbant trap for gas chromatograph analysis, marking the sample "exhibit source, Sample 1." When the trap sample is completed, the investigator should release from as close as possible to the source an exact amount of selected odorant tracer over an exact period of time. During the release, the investigator should again take a sample trap, marked "exhibit source, Sample 2."

At the complaint site the investigator should take a known volume gas chromatograph adsorbant trap at the complaint site while the malodor is present, marked "exhibit site, Sample 1." The site investigator who has been familiarized with the selected odorant tracer used, notes down the exact time of arrival of the odorant tracer with any pertinent observations such as intensity. The investigator immediately should take a second adsorbant trap sample, marked "exhibit site, Sample 2." The taking of sample exhibit site, Sample 2 concludes the test.

Trap samples exhibit site, Sample 2 and exhibit source, Sample 2 are analyzed by gas chromatography. Peaks for odorant tracer and effluent gas exhibit source, Sample 2 are referenced. Ratios between strong peaks and reference peaks are established. Peaks in exhibit site, Sample 2 are analyzed and similar or correspondent ratios are used for positive identification. All samples, analysis and investigative reports are marked "exhibits."

Trap samples exhibit site, Sample 1 and exhibit source, Sample 1 are analyzed by an odor panel. The trap samples should be eluted to original volume and exposed to the panel. The panel should respond "pleasant," "indifferent," "objectionable" and note "fairly," "moderately," "strongly," or "overpoweringly" behind the selected term. Alternatively, a value established by tests and acceptable by the courts may be used for reference to determine objectionability of specific osmogenes.

A hedonic unit value of $HU_5^5 50 = 2.4 \times 10^{-4}$ means that in concentrations of 240 PPM the osmogene is overpoweringly strong and totally unpleasant to 50% of the people tested. By referencing exhibit source, Sample 2 against exhibit site, Sample 2, a very close approximation of PPM of tracer and malodorant peaks can be established and stated as a range to a court. The specific osmogene and tracer occurred in a PPM range of 17 to 50 PPM. The HU value established for the particular osmogene in this range is $HU_4^4 50 = 2.0 \times 10^{-6}$ which is objectionable to 50% of those tested and constitutes a violation.

If more than one source is suspected, the procedure varies only inasmuch as an additional investigator is sent to each suspected source and releases a different odorant tracer. The time of release must be coordinated.

Three odorant tracers have been initially selected which meet the ideal criteria (2,3-butanedione, vanillin, α-ionone):

1. Discernable in extreme dilution.
2. Preferably of a composition unlikely to occur in the natural or particular waste environment.
3. Non-toxic.
4. Highly characteristic.
5. Readily detectable by available equipment, i.e., gas chromatographs, mass spectrometers.
6. Pure.
7. Non-reactive with point source or ambient atmosphere contaminants.
8. Pleasant, rather than unpleasant, aesthetically.

A thermal fog can be used for dispersing the tracer, thereby providing visible tracing by observing the fog downwind.

This odor tracer technique accomplishes the following: it positively identifies the source, confirms downwind velocity, establishes a known reference for gas chromatograph peaks, permits identification and separation of distinct contributors to an odor nuisance problem, permits analysis of point source improvements. Additionally, it is probably substantiative in law. The ultimate judgement about what criteria establishes a nuisance must be left to the courts. However, physical identification and quantification are possible with this technique.

In England, radioactive tracers (J. R. Keane, E. M. R. Fisher, 1967) (L. Magos, 1966) have been employed in similar procedures, but present public opinion in the United States would not permit this technique as good practice. Sulfur hexafluoride ($SF_6$), a tracer developed by the United States Center for Air Pollution (Anonymous, 1968), has been used to detect one part per 100,000,000 parts of air (10 PPB). $SF_6$ does not occur naturally and is therefore an excellent choice; however, recent concern over fluorides may preclude this method from general use.

Aldehydes may be specifically detected by absorbing them on a carrier such as silica gel, paper, etc., which is impregnated with para-diphenylene diamine and hydrogen peroxide. The reaction is colorimetric, the intensity being proportional to the concentration of aldehydes. The sensitivity is from $10^{-8}$ mole % (E. E. Hughes, S. H. Lias, 1960). Alternatively, ambient source (A. P. Altshuller, L. J. Lang, 1963)(T. R. Hauser, R. L. Cummins, 1964) (B. E. Saltzman, A. F. Wartburg, 1965) can be aspirated through an aqueous solution of 3-methyl-2-benzothiazole hydrazone (MBTH). The technique is colorimetric and results in a proportional intensity of color to the aldehyde concentration. The sensitivity is about 2.68 $mg/m^3$ (2 PPB). Interference of the reaction can be caused by the presence of aromatic amines, hetercyclic imino compounds and carbazoles.

Ammonia is detected colorimetrically by aspirating ambient air through dilute sulfuric acid in a standard impinger. The ASTM reference distillation method adjusts the pH to 7.4 and distills the ammonia into a solution of boric acid. Nessler's reagent is reacted to produce a yellowish-brown color, the intensity of which is proportional to the ammonia concentration, 1 mg per volume of solution, sensitivity tested in a colorimeter (M. B. Jacobs, 1960).

Chlorine may be determined colorimetrically by passing ambient air through a sodium hydroxide solution in a standard impinger at 68°F and 104°F. The solution is neutralized with sulfuric acid, diluted and treated with ortho-tolidine in hydrochloric acid. The reaction produces a yellow color, the intensity being proportional to the chlorine concentration (M. B. Jacobs, 1960) 1 mg in volume, sensitivity analyzed colorimetrically.

Hydrogen sulfide reacts with para-aminodimethylaniline and ferric chloride, yielding methylene blue which is determined spectrophotometrically. 0.05 mg per ml is the sensitivity (M. B. Jacobs, 1960).

Ozone may be quantitatively determined by impinging ambient air samples into a solution containing potassium iodide in a buffer solution of potassium dihydrogen phosphate and disodium hydrogen phosphate, having a pH of 6.8. The adsorption is measured spectrophotometrically, being accurate to 0.01 PPM of oxidant (0.021 $mg/m^3$ expressed as ozone) using a 60 liter sample (B. E. Saltzman, A. F. Wartburg, 1965), or by liberation of iodine (C. W. Wadelin, 1957):

$$O_3 + 2KI + H_2O \rightarrow O_2 + 2KOH + I_2$$

and then reacting with sodium thiosulfate which reacts with iodine:

$$\underset{\text{sodium thiosulfate}}{2Na_2S_2O_3} + \underset{\text{iodine}}{I_2} \rightarrow \underset{\text{sodium iodide}}{2NaI} + \underset{\text{sodium tetrathionate}}{Na_2S_4O_6}$$

which is then titrated.

Phenols produce color in the presence of para-aminodimethylaniline sulfate when oxidized. The color is measured spectrophotometrically. Sensitivity is about 1.05 mg/m$^3$ (0.25 PPB) in a one cubic meter air sample (Braverman, Hochheiser, Jacobs, 1957). Air borne phenols may also be determined by photosensitors using para-nitraniline as reagent. Sensitivity is 1 X $10^{-5}$ mg/L (E. Lohmann, 1966).

Other phenomenon associated with odorous gases which may be of future importance in measurement are considerable and are summarized as follows:

The Perdu Pendant Drop technique (J. O. Kopplin, 1959) has indicated certain analogies between changes in surface potential and the olfactory stimulation produced by certain vapors. A thin film adsorber of zinc oxide has been used (T. Seiyama, S. Kagawa, 1966) as a semiconductor to detect various organic vapors. Sensitivity varies with the nature of the chemical substance in vapor. The lower limit being 10 to 100 PPB, the detector's sensitivity decreases as follows: amines > ethers > mercaptans > alcohols > ketones > aldehydes > carboxylic acids > cyanides.

To date, certain enzymes have been separated from vomeronasal organs of Anguis fragilis (reptile slowworm) from both sensory and non-sensory regions which may prove a physiological-enzymatic relationship with smell. The enzymes have been identified as acid phosphatase, alkaline phosphatase, cytochrome oxidase, succinic dehydrogenase, $ca^{++}$-ATPase and non-specific esterase (L. H. Bannister, A. Cuschieri, 1972).

H. G. De Jong and G. P. Saubert (1937) found that coacervates (fine droplets of emulsified oleates) are shrunk by vapors of some organic substances when the concentration is low, but swell when it is high. When the vapors pass out, the coacervates resume their original volume. Sometimes the reaction is dependent on homologous series; methyl, ethyl and propyl alcohol cause swelling while hexyl and heptyl cause shrinking.

H. Zwaardemaker and F. Hogewind (1920) discovered that the spray formed by water from a fine jet is not electrically charged, but if the water contains an odorant then the spray exhibits a strong positive charge.

G. Briegleb (1961) maintains that all chemically pure substances having an odor are capable of forming hydrogen bonds by means of electron donator-acceptor complexes with groups like aldehydes, ketones, esters, nitro, cyano, sulfhydryl, thioether, halogen, benzene, etc. He further suggests that the arrangement of these secondary valency forces is responsible for the generation and kind of odor.

At present, no theory has emerged to serve as the basis for instrumentation, and it is unlikely that anything surpassing the gas chromatograph will be forthcoming in the near future as the instrument of choice for determination of odorous volatiles.

Osmic hedonics describes the subjective likes or dislikes of odors: pleasant vs. unpleasantness. The whole of modern odor control really centers on this amorphous factor. It should be realized that the desire of pollution odor control is the elimination of odors, or an HU value of $HU^0_0$. The hedonic value is expressed by the term $HU^a_x y$, where HU is the hedonic unit, a is the numerical value of the odor strength measured on an arbitrary scale of zero to six, x is the aesthetic quality of the odor, also measured on a scale of zero to six, and y is the best physical description of the odor or the percentage of persons among those tested who found the odor objectionable.

| a: Odor Strength* | x: Aesthetic Quality* |
|---|---|
| 0: No odor | 0: No odor |
| 1: Very weak | 1: Very pleasant |
| 2: Moderate | 2: Pleasant |
| 3: Assertive | 3: Indifferent |
| 4: Very strong | 4: Unpleasant |
| 5: Overpowering | 5: Very unpleasant |
| 6: Painful | 6: Nauseating |

For example, $HU^4_5 50 = 2.4 \times 10^{-4}$ means that 50% of all persons tested found the osmogene very strong and very unpleasant in concentrations of $2.4 \times 10^{-4}$. Therefore, an $HU^1_2 50 = 2.4 \times 10^{-4}$ would be very weak and pleasant to 50% of the people tested in concentrations of $2.4 \times 10^{-4}$ (68°F). The HU value may be used by those totally unfamiliar with the confusing nomenclature of osmics. The use of this value permits the ready quantification of effects heretofore in questionable standing such as masking efficiency, reodorization, neutralization, odor vector mode, etc. The value $HU^4_4$vinegar, for example, is changed to $HU^0_0 0$ upon addition to test samples of equal parts of ammonia, obviously complete neutralization. As a matter of practical fact, it is often impossible to provide a control system yielding an $HU^0_0 0$, and it becomes less expensive and more productive to consider alteration of HU values to hedonically or aesthetically acceptable values. This is not to say that indiscriminate masking is a solution to the malaesthetic stench problem. It certainly is not. A mixture of unpleasant and independently acceptable odors can work synergistically toward the offensive as well as pleasant. But judicious selection of odor complaints can result in an HU value just as acceptable, if not more so, than $HU^0_0 0$.

Fortunately or not, the basis of malodorous pollution control will be based on hedonic values. No device or series of devices will ever supplant human aesthetic response to smell, and according to R. W. Moncrieff (1966), hedonic reactions will change not only with age but also with popular trend.

All legislation and enforcement must ultimately be founded on average responses to ambient levels of particular odors. Finally, the courts must decide what percentage of objectionable responses constitute a nuisance; it is likely, however, that this determination will not be as difficult as many believe. First of all, hedonic reactions to odors are far more universal than credited in the literature. As stated by A. Dravnieks (1974), "hedonic judgements are, of course, rather individualistic, but not as widely different as popularly believed," or by R. W. Moncrieff (1966) in Rule #9: "as even a little unpleasantness creeps in, agreement between observers improves sharply." With the advent of gas chromatographs and supporting techniques not only levels

* See Osmogene Index

and point source location are possible but specific identification as well.

To date, most efforts at odor quantification have been aimed at objective identification and quantification, and although this has been somewhat helpful, especially in dealing with thresholds, dilutions and such, it is an unrevealing method for the odor control expert.

Taste panels as used by the food industry are not encouraged to report objective reactions to food, but hedonic values instead. It is on the hedonic-organoleptic scale that virtually all foods are valued and judged fit for the marketplace. Objectification of food values would provide scant aid to marketing people in selling or to the public in buying. Subjective reactions, statistically averaged, can be considerably more revealing than all the objective reactions put together when it comes to solving a serious odor problem.

Objectification and quantification of odors when no comprehensive classification system or basic working theory of odor exists is probably impossible. The uncertainty of modern techniques in this regard is well appreciated by those who must draft, enforce, obey and judge malaesthetic stench pollution problems. Due to the inconsistency of odor control panels, courts have been reluctant to find against alleged offenders. The result has been the reduction of agencies and legislation to practical impotency with regard to correction of the problems. Even if these fundamental problems did not exist as practical impediments to the correction of the malaesthetic stench offender, the objectification quantification of odors would still not qualify a particular odor situation since merely determining within a reasonable degree of accuracy threshold levels of perception and odor descriptions reasonably analogous or exact does not imply or quantify an odor's social acceptability. Only statistical averaging of an odor's hedonic characteristics can result in this determination. The only odor acceptable to all people is no odor. In malaesthetic stench pollution control when a malodor cannot be neutralized or abated entirely, the least offensive in character and intensity within the limits of reasonable expense must be the goal.

## Malaesthetic Stench

The past decade has seen an almost hysterical reaction to environmental pollutants. It is no secret that technology by and large has been ill prepared to offer ready-made solutions. The public mandate, industrial lobby, political legislators and technology merge at an interface of general chaos. Nowhere has the misdirected intent of the public, the impotency of modern pollution technology and, as a result, confused political reaction been more evident than in those industries associated with malaesthetic stench (the term is here used to mean stench associated solely with non-toxic or non-toxic levels of various effluents and industrial environments).

By now, everyone who is interested must be aware that no viable science of osmics really exists. No one knows what a smell is or why it is smelly. All tests available are subjective, and they tend to fail even in basic agreement as to what is pleasant or unpleasant. There exists no practical system of classification of odors. Without these basic tools the technologists are reduced to the role of witch doctors, and enforcement agencies become tyrants.

There seems to be an intolerable factor on the part of many people sensitive to this type of sensory imperative which R. W. Moncrieff points out in his rule #97: "a small minority of people are very susceptible emotionally to odors and can be upset by their presence."[1] A rendering plant operator, for example, may well find himself at the mercy of this public mandate and futily attempt to exorcise the wicked imp of malodor from his establishment, calling upon every known appellation of pollution control. He may find legislation restrictive and unreasonable, lumping all polluters into general categories and catchalls.

There is absolutely no reason why an industry which is prone to malaesthetic stench should be classed with those who are by various means stinky or otherwise doing serious and perhaps irreparable injury to the environment. It is time that such industries coordinate their thinking and isolate the objective of their pollution enterprises.

Where malaesthetic stench is the only crime, it is principally a social impropriety. It is true that malaesthetic stench degrades the environment where it is perceived. It is equally true that it represents an invasion of privacy. It is, however, not an irreversible action. So long as certain industries are to continue, the cause cannot be eliminated; only the effects can be dealt with, and therefore the major objective should be to reverse or modify them.

What have been the palliative weapons in the arsenal of malaesthetic stench generating industries? The very same employed in other industries with non-related problems. It should be obvious from past experience that they are, for the most part, (1) too expensive and (2) ineffective, or, at best, effective at times and ineffective at others. Scrubbers, incinerators, stacks (dilution solutions), mechanical collectors, adsorption units, electrostatic precipitators, air filters, etc., all, alone and in combination, fail more often than not to solve the problem facing the malaesthetic stench polluter.

What can be done? First, an understanding of what the problem is, attaining a general knowledge of the phenomenology and psychology of odors and malodors, and the realization that it must, in most instances, be attacked as an effect. In any given process, certain characteristic odors will emanate and be associated with the raw materials and procedures. If it so happens that they stink, a problem in public relations and with ill equipped and uninformed enforcement officials will probably occur. In any procedure resulting in malaesthetic odor pollution it should be noted that the source of malodorant will be (1) volatile components of materials being processed, and (2) the particulates which have adsorbed the volatile components (odor vectors). If an aerosol or smoke vane configuration is studied, it will become apparent that except for the immediate plant vicinity the problem of odor vectors carrying and settling in concentrical or downwind geographical areas is a major problem.

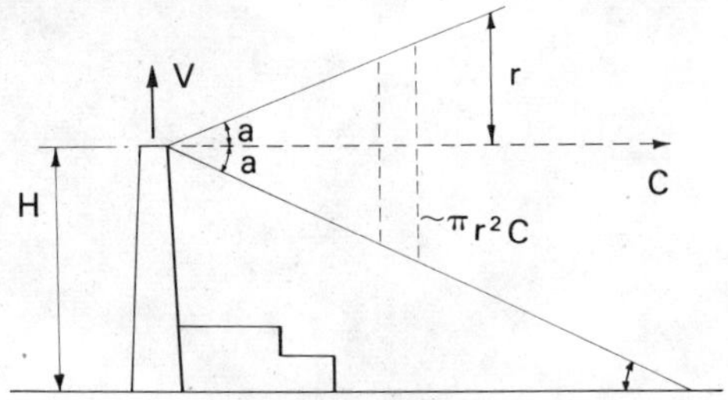


Plume shape and odor free area is dependent on stack height (H), exit velocity (V) and wind velocity (C).

[1] R. W. Moncrieff, Odour Preferences, John Wiley, New York: 1966, p. 320.

In the game of eliminating malaesthetic stench, the axiom "dilution is the solution to pollution" is fair play if it can be depended upon. In some jurisdictions, dilution is not legal. The methods required by the agency, however, are often really a form of dilution for many malodorants, i.e., 0.03 seconds of incineration at 1200°F. Actually, when malodor is the only problem, dilution may be a very practical and logical method of control. Many intensely malodorous materials are pleasing when sufficiently diluted, i.e., indole. A volatile by its nature (vapor pressure) will tend to rise to the upper atmosphere unless it is trapped on a heavier molecule or a particulate, both odor vectors, by adsorption or weak electrostatic forces. Therefore, an unadsorbed volatile is, to a great extent, self diluting. If a particulate from a stack is a fully laden malodor vector, then any excess volatiles may be adsorbed by atmospheric particulates which will add to the problem as malodor vector fallout.

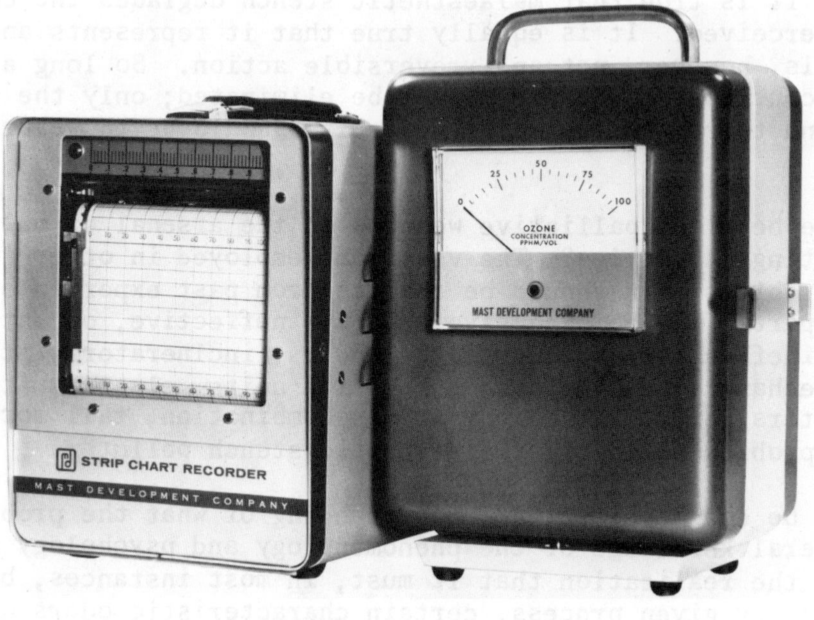


Ozone detector and recorder. Courtesy Mast Development Corporation.

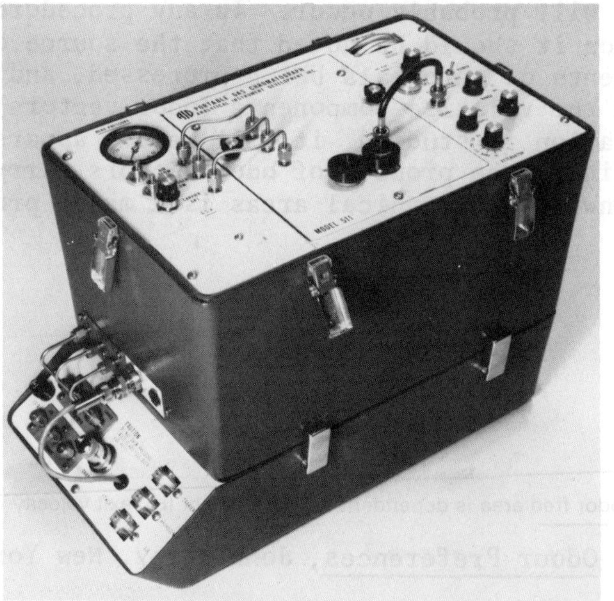


Field portable gas chromatograph. Model 511. Courtesy Analytical Instrument Development, Inc.

## MEANS AND METHODS OF ODOR CONTROL

The following are so far as is known the sole means of altering odors. All methods utilize one or more of these means.

### 1. Decomposition

Decomposition is also referred to as destruction, combustion, catalytic combustion, incineration, chemical oxidation, scrubbing (chemical) oxidation, ultraviolet, sonic disruption, etc. The approach to decomposition of the odorant molecules by whatever means is the dismemberment and simplification of the molecule until it no longer exhibits an odorous property. The decomposition of the molecule can be a result of loss of electrons or total destruction into elemental forms. Means presently employed in air pollution control using this principle include scrubbers with oxidizing chemicals, incineration, catalytic incineration, ultraviolet treatment, ozone generators and thermal harmonic disintegration. Listed in order of present widespread usage they are: (1) scrubbers with oxidizing chemicals, (2) incinerators, (3) catalytic incinerators, (4) Ozone generators, (5) ultraviolet treatment and (6) thermal harmonic disintegrators.

Thermal Decomposition:

Incineration is perhaps the oldest method of odor control. There are basically three types of incinerators used for odor pollution control per se.

Thermal oxidation: Under ideal conditions odors can, like all matter, be altered by oxidation (incineration). High temperatures and resident time of the odorant are the key factors. What is normally considered to be an incinerator for malodors is more often merely a method of adding velocity to the stack gases by heating them and thereby propelling them into the atmosphere. In many instances, the so-called incineration or combustion of odorants will result in partial oxidation which will in turn result in partially oxidized end products. These end products often are more highly malodorous than the initial gases. Many such cases have been reported (A. Turk, 1970).

In order for complete thermal oxidation to take place efficiently, nascent oxygen must be available. The temperature normally encountered in industrial furnaces does not produce nascent oxygen. As a matter of fact, over 10 times the amount of heat energy available in a furnace operating at 1200°F to 1500°F is required with residence times of 0.25 to 0.50 seconds. 15,000°F would be required at a minimum. A gram mole of oxygen at 116.4 kilocalories equals $487.25 \times 10^{10}$ ergs in required energy. A furnace operating at 2192°F yields infrared $\lambda$ 2898/2192°F at 2$\mu$; the amount required is $10^{-11}$ ergs. It should be obvious from the foregoing that thermal oxidation is seldom achieved, and on a cost basis seldom is justified as a means of dealing with malodors. The exception may in general be industries which evolve flammable stack gases as waste such as oil refineries.

Thermal incineration occurs at hot surfaces in the absence of fuels. In all other respects the basic principles of operation are the same as for direct flame afterburning.

The foregoing examples were selected from currently available units.

Direct fired afterburners are commonly used to control emissions of aerosols, vapors, gases and odors of industries using:

- Aluminum chip driers
- Animal blood driers
- Asphalt blowing stills
- Automotive brake shoe ovens
- Citrus pulp driers
- Coffee roasters
- Electric insulation burnoff ovens
- Flue fed incinerators
- Foundry core ovens
- Rendering cookers
- Varnish cookers

Components of afterburners: afterburner temperatures seldom exceed 2000°F. The combustion chamber must be designed to provide complete mixing of effluent airstream with the flames and burner combustion gases. Gas velocity in the afterburner throat in the range of 15 to 30 feet per second is normally adequate. A retention time of 0.3 to 0.5 seconds within the afterburner is usually considered sufficient. Operating ranges of between 850° to 1500°F are normally encountered and are satisfactory in most instances. Many arrangements are possible and the patent literature is replete with inventions claiming to provide more efficient results. The basic working factors remain the same: temperature, time of mixing (residence time), load ratio and effectiveness of mixing.

C. N. Sawyer and P. A. Kahn (1960), in studies of odor destruction in sludge digestion, found that a temperature of 1350°F in the combustion zone was a reasonably safe assurance of odor destruction. They indicated, however, that 1400°F was better and that 1500°F was optimum for total destruction of odors from sludge. J. F. Laboon (1961) states that 1425°F with a contact time of three seconds in the combustion zone would result in complete deodorization of sludge.

Malodorous gases can, under optimum conditions, be destroyed. Total oxidation, however, is a very expensive proposition and seldom is justified for a solely malaesthetic problem. In order to bring the costs of efficient combustion of malodorants into the realm of practicality, catalytic units have been designed.

Catalytic afterburning: catalytic afterburners have found use in most of the industries listed for direct fired afterburners. The basic components of a catalytic afterburner are the afterburner and a catalyst section. Catalysis (the term "catalyst" was coined in 1935 by J. J. Berzelius) is a phenomenon wherein the presence of a third material hastens dramatically events which otherwise would have proceeded slowly or causes reactions to occur which were only potentially able to happen. Catalytic combustion takes place without flames, is exothermic and normally requires very low temperatures, i.e., approximately 500°F. The catalyst is theoretically not involved in the actual event and is not altered. In practice, catalysts fatigue or become "poisoned" and lose their ability to promote if the poisons are not eliminated from the reaction.

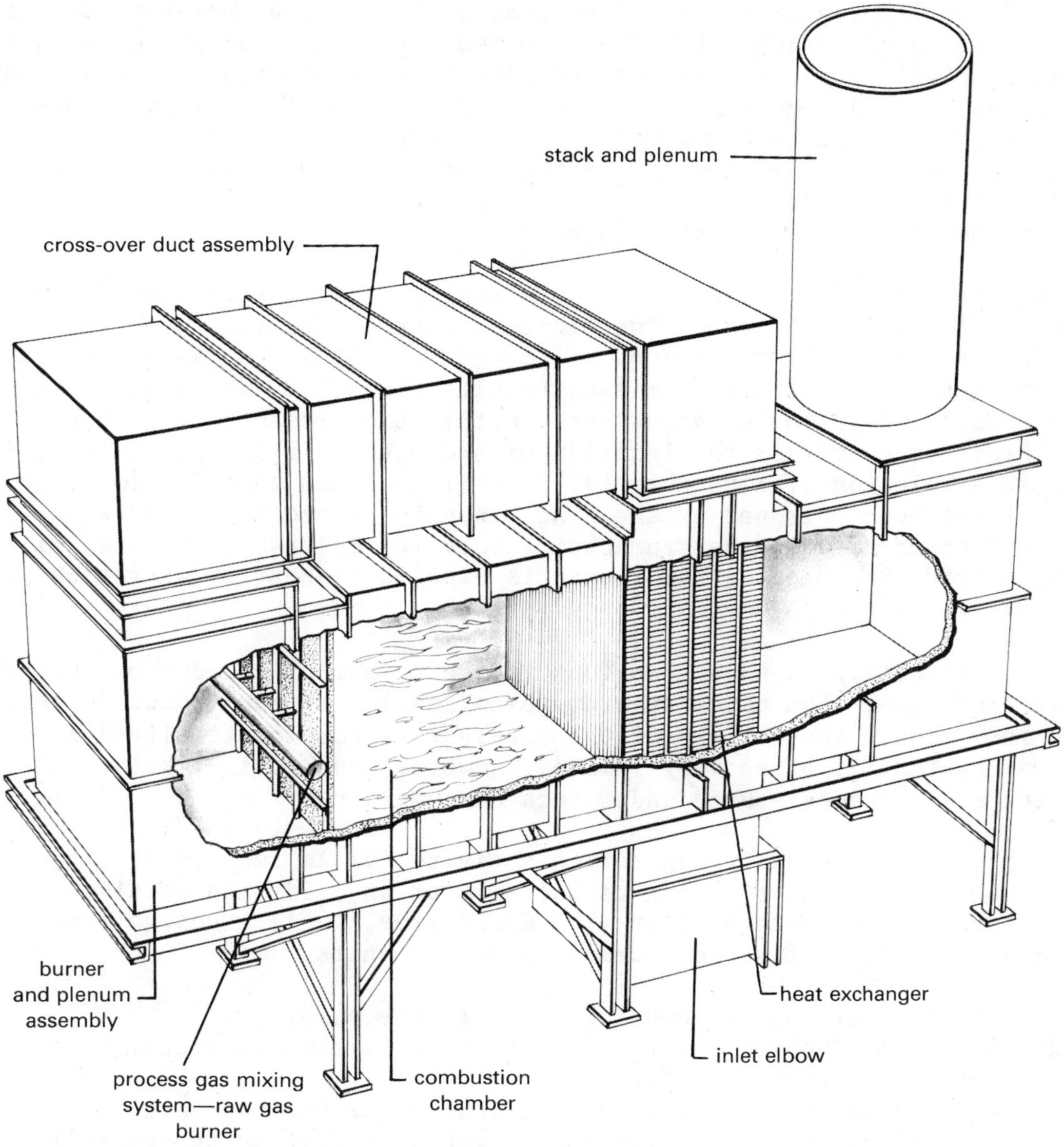


Fume incinerator system. Courtesy Air-Preheater Company, Inc.

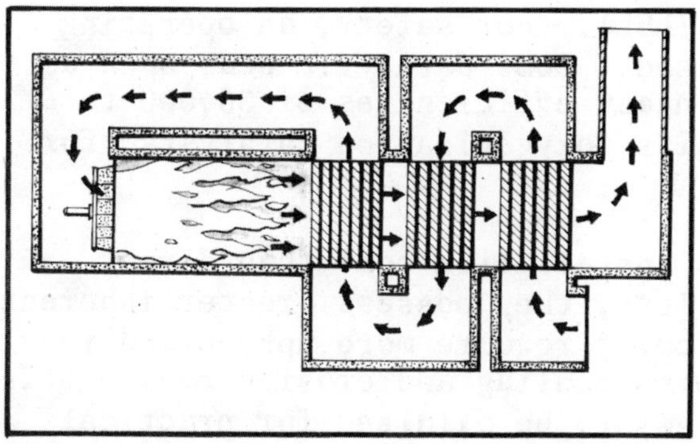

Integral three-pass heat exchanger arrangement. Courtesy Air-Preheater Company, Inc.

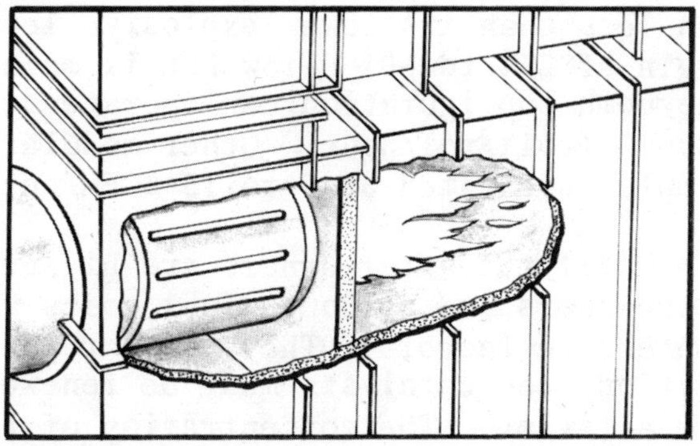

Process gas mixing system employing a nozzle-mix burner. Courtesy Air-Preheater Company, Inc.

A catalytic afterburner will incinerate most organic and solvent vapors at much lower temperatures than afterburning alone. The operating temperatures average 500° to 1000 °F. The selected catalyst is prepared in such a way that it is highly porous to permit the passing of preheated vapors and normally requires special conditions in order to be effective. Catalysts are generally required in comparatively small amounts relative to the reactants and tend to be extremely specific in the reactions they promote. Metals and metallic combinations such as silver, nickel, nichrome wire screen, platinum and platinum alloys are common catalysts.

If a jet of hydrogen and oxygen are impinged against each other, nothing happens. If a match is added, the flame acts as a catalyst to the reaction which ensues, violent combination. If oxygen and hydrogen gas are impinged in the presence of platinum, the same results occur. Hydrogen gas will not spontaneously ignite in the atmosphere, but in the presence of platinum it will. Platinum catalyzes the ignition of hydrogen. If the platinum is immersed in a solution of zinc chloride it will not then cause hydrogen to ignite. It has been poisoned by the zinc. Rennin, a protein found widely in nature but abundantly in the stomachs of suckling calves, coagulates milk. If sodium chloride is added or the rennin is exposed to heat or vibration, coagulation will not take place.

Specific catalysts have been found for a number of malodorous incineration applications. The catalyst promotes oxidation at much lower temperatures and in less time. The ability of the catalyst to accomodate alterations in stack gas content is often very limited, however, and it is likely that poisoning will be accelerated under such circumstances.

Catalysts occasionally can retain activity for as long as five to ten years. However, the most common useful life of an oxidation catalyst is about 15,000 hours or two to three years (F. R. Edwards, 1971). Design requirements are similar for catalytic and thermal oxidation units:

1. Thorough mixing of combustibles with the oxygen.
2. Sufficient heat input to raise the gas stream temperatures to catalytic oxidation temperatures.
3. Even temperatures and flow distribution within the unit.
4. Sufficient retention time and/or catalyst surface to accomplish oxidation.

Heat exchangers are used successfully on both catalytic and thermal oxidation units. The catalytic process requires a combustible pollutant at a concentration less than its lower explosive level (LEL). For safety, an operating margin of 25% to 50% below LEL is maintained. Some catalytic beds such as the honeycomb configuration can operate at contact efficiencies of 30,000 to 125,000 (vol)/vol/hour. Other modular units, oxygenization catalysts, for example, are rated at 5 to 15 SCFM/unit.

Catalytic afterburners are higher in installation cost than direct afterburners and although fuel costs are less, they possess greater inherent maintenance factors. They are more difficult, require more upkeep and in addition, the catalysts must be renewed when fouling and erosion reduce effective activity. The concentration of the gas to be oxidized for practical operation should be at least 1,000 to 1,500 mg/L, a factor which limits certain uses.

Thermal Incineration Applications for Odor Control

- Coffee roasters
- Core ovens
- Fat rendering
- Fiberglass curing
- Metal coating ovens
- Packing houses
- Paint baking ovens
- Smokehouses
- Varnish kettles

Afterburners: There are three main types of afterburners in current use: thermal oxidation as described in the foregoing, direct fired and catalytic.

Unquestionably due to lower capital cost, the direct fired afterburner is the most prevalent in use. Cost analysis indicates afterburning to be an inefficient and expensive means of odor control. Unfortunately, many installations are insufficient in design to cope with the effluent flow although under certain atmospheric conditions they seem to perform rather better than expected. This is a result of the super heating of the odorous emissions, causing them to rise much higher and faster in calm conditions, effectively resulting in substantial atmospheric dilution. There are numerous installations of note, however, where even this advantage is nullified by installation of scrubbers after the burner, causing a cooling effect and increasing visible emissions due to steam and heavy vapor formation.

Direct fired afterburners can cause a distinct increase in odorous emissions if incomplete combustion occurs. However, incineration at high temperatures (1200°F or more) with ample oxygen for complete combustion can be efficient in many instances. Cost of operation is normally prohibitive as an effective means of control for rendering plants, ranging from 65 to 90 cents per 1,000 CFM's per hour of effluent capacity. Heat exchangers can reduce the cost by as much as 50% at a capital investment increase of two or three times normal incineration. The following are examples of available incinerators: (W. Heilman, 1970)

Example I

| | | |
|---|---|---|
| Detention: | minimum 0.3 seconds at 1200°F | |
| Temperature range: | 1200°F+ | |
| Fuel consumption: | natural gas | CFM |
| | 1.0 MCF | 750 |
| | 2.8 MCF | 1,950 |

Example II

| | | |
|---|---|---|
| Detention: | minimum 0.3 seconds at 1200°F | |
| Operating temperature range: | 1200 to 1400°F | |
| Maximum: | 1600°F | |
| Fuel consumption: | natural gas | CFM |
| | 1.0 MCF | 1,000 |
| | 3.5 MCF | 3,500 |
| | 6.0 MCF | 6,000 |

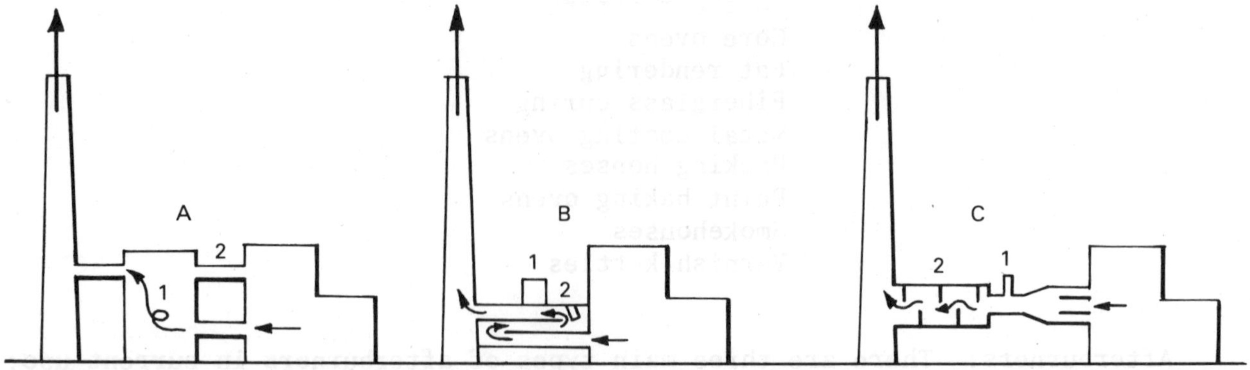


Various methods of incineration used in malasthetic stench control:
Direct Fired: Plant A has vented its waste through its main boilers: (1) main boiler furnace, (2) steam line to plant.
Catalytic: Plant B is catalyzing its stack gas: (1) burner, (2) catalyst.
Thermal Oxidation: Plant C is afterburning its stack gas: (1) burner, (2) baffles.

## Composition of Dry Atmospheric Air

| Component | Symbol | % (v/v) of Dry Air | % (w/w) of Dry Air |
|---|---|---|---|
| Argon | A | 0.934 | 1.27 |
| Carbon dioxide | CO | 0.033 | 0.05 |
| Helium | He | 0.000524 | 0.0007 |
| Hydrogen | H | 0.00005 | 0.00004 |
| Krypton | Kr | 0.000114 | 0.003 |
| Methane | CH | 0.0002 | N/C |
| Neon | Ne | 0.001818 | 0.0012 |
| Nitrogen | N | 78.084 | 75.54 |
| Oxygen | O | 20.946 | 23.14 |
| Ozone | O | 0.00005 | 0.0000017 |
| Xenon | Xe | 0.0000087 | 0.000036 |

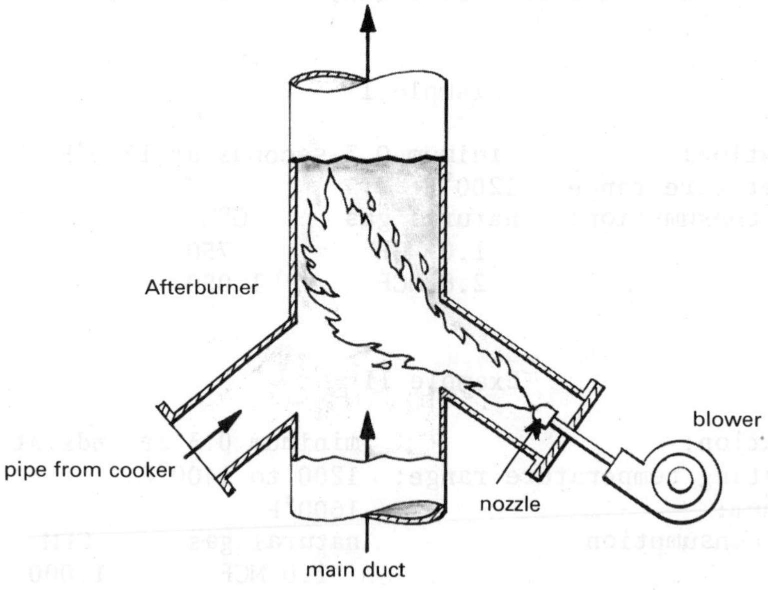


After burner installation. Pat. #3, 592,614 (Schmidt)

Chemical Decomposition:

Scrubbing with oxidant: decomposition of the odorant by chemical means can be effective in some circumstances. Many factors may interfere with the economy of their use, however. Potassium permanganate, for example, oxidizes:

$$2KMnO_4 + 3SO_2 + 4KOH = 2MnO_2 + 3K_2SO_4 + 2H_2O$$

Potassium permanganate is used in scrubbers in dilute solution, one to three percent, at slightly alkaline pH levels. If contaminating inodorous substances of any amount are encountered, the cost becomes rapidly excessive. Permanganate has been used in granular form as a surface deodorant in barnyards or cattle feedlots to oxidize feedlot odors.

Permanganate ($KMnO_4$) Effectiveness in Scrubbers

(1% Solution)

| | Odor Reduction |
|---|---|
| Acetaldehyde | 80 - 100% |
| Acetone | 0% |
| Acrolein | 100% |
| Allylisocyanate | 80 - 100% |
| Benzaldehyde | 100% |
| Benzene | 0% |
| Cadaverine | 30 - 60% |
| Carbon disulfide | 2 - 8% |
| Carbon monoxide | 0% |
| p-Chlorophenol | 100% |
| o-Cresol | 100% |
| Dimethylamine | 10 - 20% |
| Dipropylketone | 0% |
| Formaldehyde | 90% |
| Hydrogen sulfide | 100% |
| Indole | 30 - 50% |
| Monoethanolamine | 100% |
| Nitrobenzene | 0% |
| Phenol | 100% |
| Putrescine | 30 - 50% |
| Pyridine | 0% |
| Skatole | 10 - 30% |
| Sulfur dioxide | 100% |

(15,000 CFM low pressure scrubber)

Chlorination: Chlorine is often added to scrubbers, industrial waste streams and water supplies to decompose odors. It is added in the elemental form from pressurized bottles, as an hypochlorite solution made from calcium hypochlorite or as sodium hypochlorite solution. It is also sometimes used as chlorine dioxide. Chlorine fumes are toxic. Many instances of partial oxidation of pollutants resulting in intensified malodors have been reported. The control of chlorine to waste gas is critical. Experiments in a typical rendering operation with selected scrubbing solutions resulted in the conclusion

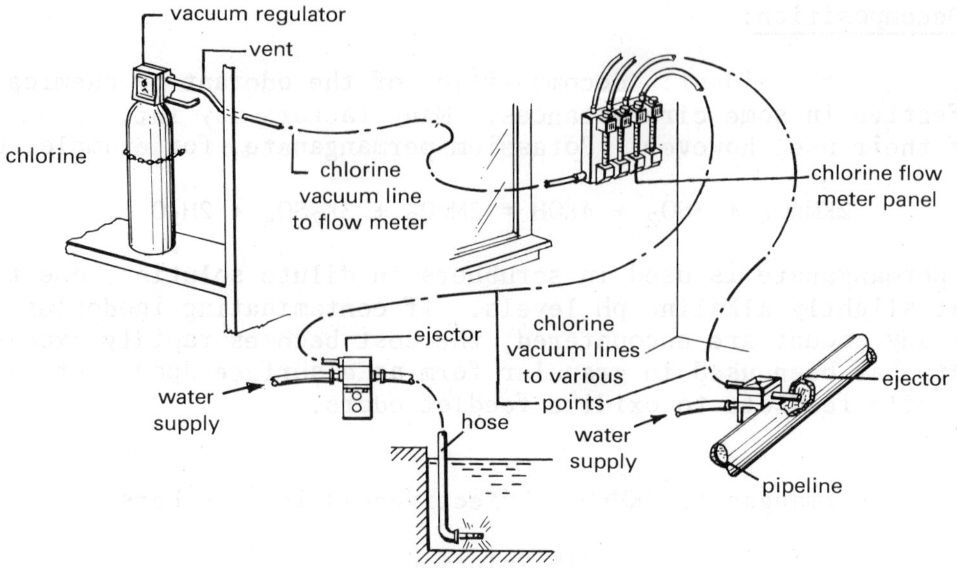


Multiple chlorine metering arrangement. Courtesy Capital Controls Company

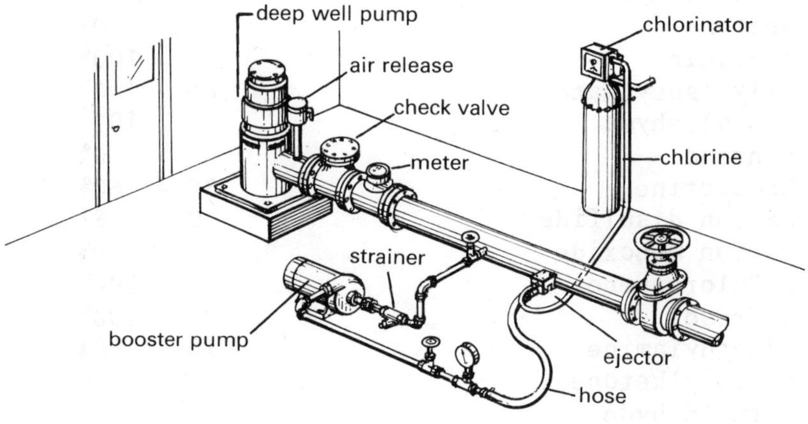


Typical chlorinator deep well installation. Courtesy Capital Controls Company

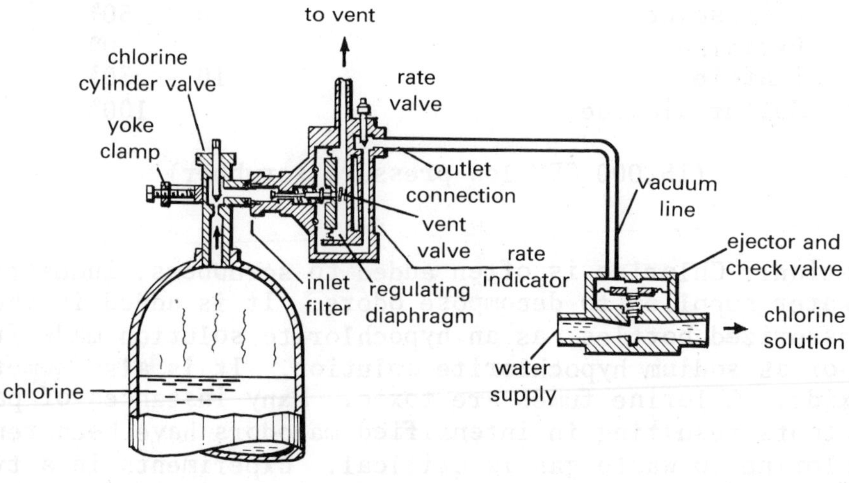


Flow diagram. Courtesy Capital Controls Company

that for reducing odors in plant ventillation air (low odor concentrations) chlorine solutions seemed to be very effective. Solutions tested and then subjected to odor panels were as shown in Tables I, II, III and IV.

Chlorination is one of the oldest methods of odor control, finding application for waste water control since about 1911. Chlorine is effective primarily because it is a strong oxidizing agent as well as an effective disinfectant. Among the more important reactions of chlorine are those with hydrogen sulfide and ammonia, both odorous gases. Chlorine reacts with hydrogen sulfide in the following manner:

$$H_2S + 4Cl_2 + 4H_2O \rightarrow H_2SO_4 + 8HCl$$

and with ammonia:

$$NH_3 + Cl_2 \rightarrow NH_2Cl + HCl$$

$$NH_2Cl + Cl_2 \rightarrow NHCl_2 + HCl$$

$$NHCl_2 + Cl_2 \rightarrow NCl_3 + HCl$$

In addition, chlorine reacts readily with some organic molecules:

$$\underset{\text{phenol}}{C_6H_5OH} + Cl_2 \rightarrow \underset{\text{chlorophenol}}{ClC_6H_4OH} + HCl$$

Chlorophenol is a malodorant with a detection threshold of 3.00 X $10^{-2}$ PPB.

Chlorine is an efficient bactericide and is effective in inhibiting microbial growth, especially of the sulfate reducing bacteria. Generalizations about quantities required for odor control are not possible since the amounts required will vary with the process differences. The oxidation of sulfide requires 8.87 mg's of chlorine per mg of sulfide. Solid hypochlorites of calcium and sodium are as effective as the gaseous form.

Ozonizing: Ozone is a slightly blue gas being triatomic oxygen ($O_3$). It smells of new mown hay or garlic, depending on the individual perceiving it. Ozone is a good disinfectant and is used to replace chlorine in certain water purification systems. Some experts maintain that in small controlled amounts ozone is beneficial and invigorating. Others, such as the United States Public Health service, maintain that no unnecessary exposure to ozone, regardless of how small an amount, should be permitted. The United States Public Health Department has taken the position that ozone is radiomimetic (a substance which produces effects similar to those produced by radiation). Ozone paralyzes the sense of smell in a fashion very similar to that of sulfur dioxide.

Although found naturally in the atmosphere as a by-product of ultraviolet radiation and lightning, in levels below 0.015 PPM in the atmosphere irritation of the respiratory or other mucous membranes is avoided. Ozone has a characteristic odor and when detectable it is present at a toxic and irritating level. The greatest density of ozone in the atmosphere is between 100,000 and 125,000 feet where it is formed by the interaction of ultraviolet rays and free oxygen atoms. Concentrations of natural ozone are low. Ozone is absorbed by water in inverse proportionality to the temperature. Between 32° and 68°F ozone is absorbed about 35 times as much as air. One PPM is normally sufficient to cause irritation, while 10 PPM is considered highly toxic, being

Table I
(Courtesy of Zurn Industries, Inc.)

Odor Concentrations from Specific Unit Operations

| Source Sampled | Time[1] | Sample Number | Cooker Number | Odor Levels* Air Dilution 1/10 | 1/100 | 1/1,000 |
|---|---|---|---|---|---|---|
| Hogger & Cooker Loading | | | | | | |
| Hogger | | | | | | |
| -1st floor | 1515 | H-1 | - | D | D | N |
| Cooker loading | | | | | | |
| -Bone & fat | 1545 | L-1 | 4 | D | N | N |
| -Grease | ---- | ---- | - | - | - | - |
| -Pork offal** | 1700 | L-3 | 2 | S | D | D |
| Cooker Exhaust Gases | | | | | | |
| Cooker Effluent | | | | | | |
| -Bone & fat | 1220 | C-1 | 1 | D | D | N |
| -Grease | 1415 | C-2 | 7 | S | S | D |
| -Pork offal** | 1427 | C-3 | 5 | S | S | S |
| Non-condensable | | | | | | |
| -Bone & fat | 1230 | N-1 | 1 | D | D | N |
| -Grease | 1355 | N-2 | 7 | D | D | D |
| -Pork offal** | 1450 | N-3 | 5 | S | D | D |
| -Combination | 1555 | N-4 | 1, 2, 5, 6, 7, 8 | D | D | N |
| Stack gases | | | | | | |
| -Bone & fat | 1240 | S-1 | 1 | N | N | N |
| -Grease | 1340 | S-2 | 7 | N | N | N |
| -Pork offal** | 1445 | S-3 | 5 | D | D | N |
| -Combination | 1535 | S-4 | 1, 2, 5, 6, 7, 8 | D | D | N |
| Cooker Dumping | | | | | | |
| -Bone & fat | 1305 | D-1 | 1 | D | D | N |
| -Grease | 1300 | D-2 | 8 | D | D | D |
| -Pork offal** | 1625 | D-3 | 5 | S | D | D |
| -Trap grease | 1710 | D-4 | 6 | D | D | D |

Table I (Continued)

| Source Sampled | Time[1] | Sample Number | Cooker Number | Odor Levels* Air Dilution 1/10 | 1/100 | 1/1,000 |
|---|---|---|---|---|---|---|
| Other Sources | | | | | | |
| -Grease processing | 1503 | T-1 | - | D | D | N |

* N: None D: Detectable S: Strong

** Decayed pork offal was obtained from another rendering plant and processed for purposes of this study; it was selected because the industry considers decayed pork offal as the most intensive odor producing raw material that could be used.

1 24-Hour system, with the day beginning at midnight and hours being consecutively numbered 0 through 23. Thus 8 a.m. is 0800, and 8:25 a.m. is 0825.

Table II
(Courtesy of Zurn Industries, Inc.)

Test Conditions for Comparison of Scrubber
Odor Removal Efficiencies

| Test Number | Absorbing Solution: Chemical | Absorbing Solution: Strength (Percent) | Pressure Drop (Inches of $H_2O$) | Flow Rate (SCFM) | Odorous Gas: Source | Odorous Gas: Strength (Odor Units) |
|---|---|---|---|---|---|---|
| 16 | Water | - | 5.7 | 4800 | #7 cooker | 10 - 100 |
| 17 | Water | - | 5.7 | 4800 | #8 cooker | 10 - 100 |
| 13 | Calcium hypochlorite | 0.2 | 5.8 | 4800 | #7 cooker | 10 - 100 |
| 14 | Calcium hypochlorite | 0.2 | 5.8 | 4800 | #8 cooker | 10 - 100 |
| 15 | Calcium hypochlorite | 0.2 | 5.6 | 4800 | Third floor | 1 - 10 |
| 25 | Chlorine gas | - | 5.8 | 4800 | #8 cooker | 1 - 10 |
| 18 | Hydrogen peroxide | 0.2 | 4.5 | 4000 | Third floor | 1 - 10 |
| 19 | Hydrogen peroxide | 0.2 | 5.7 | 4800 | #8 cooker | 10 - 100 |
| 8 | Lime | 1.0 | 5.7 | 4800 | #7 cooker | 10 - 100 |
| 9 | Lime | 1.0 | 5.7 | 4800 | Third floor | 1 - 10 |
| 3 | Politol "S" | 1.0 | 4.4 | 5100 | #8 cooker | 10 - 100 |
| 4 | Politol "S" | 1.0 | 4.8 | 5100 | #7 cooker | 10 - 100 |
| 5 | Potassium permanganate | 0.75 | 5.5 | 4800 | #7 cooker | 10 - 100 |
| 6 | Potassium permanganate | 0.75 | 5.5 | 4800 | #8 cooker | 10 - 100 |
| 7 | Potassium permanganate | 0.75 | 5.5 | 4800 | Third floor | 10 - 100 |
| 10 | Soda ash | 1.0 | 5.7 | 4800 | #7 cooker | 1 - 10 |
| 11 | Soda ash | 1.0 | 5.7 | 4800 | #8 cooker | 10 - 100 |
| 12 | Soda ash | 1.0 | 5.8 | 4800 | Third floor | 1 - 10 |
| 1 | Sodium bisulfite | 0.75 | 5.3 | 4800 | #7 cooker | 10 - 100 |
| 2 | Sodium bisulfite | 0.75 | 5.8 | 4800 | #8 cooker | 10 - 100 |
| 20 | Sodium metasilicate | 0.6 | 5.8 | 4700 | #7 cooker | 1 - 10 |
| 21 | Sodium metasilicate | 0.6 | 5.8 | 4700 | #8 cooker | 1 - 10 |
| 22 | Sodium metasilicate | 0.6 | 5.5 | 4200 | Third floor | 1 - 10 |
| 27 | Calcium hypochlorite | 0.2 | 5.3 | 4800 | #7 cooker | 1 - 10 |
| 28 | Calcium hypochlorite | - | 6.5 | 4800 | #7 cooker | 10 - 100 |
| 29 | Calcium hypochlorite | - | 6.0 | 4800 | #8 cooker | 1 - 10 |
| 30 | Calcium hypochlorite | 0.0 | 5.5 | 4800 | Third floor | 1 - 10 |

Table II (Continued)

| Test Number | Absorbing Solution: Chemical | Absorbing Solution: Strength (Percent) | Pressure Drop (Inches of $H_2O$) | Flow Rate (SCFM) | Odorous Gas: Source | Odorous Gas: Strength (Odor Units) |
|---|---|---|---|---|---|---|
| 23 | Calcium hypochlorite | 0.2 | 9.9 | 4000 | #8 cooker | 10 - 100 |
| 24 | Calcium hypochlorite | 0.2 | 8.6 | 4000 | Third floor | 1 - 10 |
| 26 | Chlorine gas | - | 8.3 | 4600 | #7 cooker | 1 - 10 |
| 36 | Chlorine gas | 0.3 PPM | 8.0 | 5100 | #8 cooker | 10 - 100 |
| 37 | Chlorine gas | 1.0 PPM | 8.0 | 5100 | #7 cooker | 10 - 100 |
| 38 | Chlorine gas | 0.5 PPM | 8.0 | 5100 | Third floor | 10 - 100 |
| 34 | Potassium permanganate | 1.0 | 8.0 | 5100 | #7 cooker | 100 - 1000 |
| 35 | Potassium permanganate | 1.0 | 8.0 | 5100 | Third floor | 1 - 10 |
| 31 | Sodium bisulfite | 1.0 | 7.0 | 4000 | #8 cooker | 100 - 1000 |
| 32 | Sodium bisulfite | 1.0 | 6.9 | 4000 | #7 cooker | 100 - 1000 |
| 33 | Sodium bisulfite | 1.0 | 6.8 | 4000 | Third floor | 10 - 100 |

Table III
(Courtesy of Zurn Industries, Inc.)

Odor Removal Efficiencies of Selected Absorbing Solutions
at 5 to 6 Inches of Water Pressure Drop

| Test Numbers | Scrubbing Solution | Full Strength Odorous Gas | 1:10 Dilution of Odorous Gas |
|---|---|---|---|
| 16, 17 | Water | No change[1] | Improved |
| 13, 14, 15 | Calcium hypochlorite | Improved[3] | Improved |
| 25 | Chlorine gas | Questionable[2] | - |
| 18, 19 | Hydrogen peroxide | Questionable | Improved |
| 8, 9 | Lime | Questionable | Questionable |
| 3, 4 | Politol "S" | No change | Questionable |
| 5, 6, 7 | Potassium permanganate | No change | No change |
| 10, 11, 12 | Soda ash | Questionable | Questionable |
| 1, 2 | Sodium bisulfite | No change | No change |
| 20, 21, 22 | Sodium metasilicate | Questionable | - |

1. No change was recorded when effluent odor concentrations equalled inlet concentrations.
2. Questionable was recorded when several odor tests showed conflicting results.
3. Improved was recorded when the majority of effluent odor concentrations were definitely less than inlet concentrations.

Table IV
(Courtesy of Zurn Industries, Inc.)

Odor Removal Efficiencies of Selected Absorbing Solutions at 7 to 10 Inches of Water Pressure Drop

| Test Numbers | Scrubbing Solution | Full Strength Odorous Gas | 1:10 Dilution of Odorous Gas |
|---|---|---|---|
| 23, 24 | Calcium hypochlorite | Greatly improved[1] | Improved |
| 26, 36, 37, 38 | Chlorine gas | Improved[2] | Improved |
| 34, 35 | Potassium permanganate | Questionable[3] | Improved |
| 31, 32, 33 | Sodium bisulfite | Questionable | Improved |

1. Greatly improved was recorded when effluent odor concentrations were reduced two intensity levels below inlet concentrations.
2. Improved was recorded when the majority of effluent odor concentrations were definitely less than inlet concentrations.
3. Questionable was recorded when several odor tests showed conflicting results.

lethal after 30 minutes of exposure. Ozone is formed by ultraviolet radiation when free oxygen is present by silent electric discharge and by electrochemical dissociation. It is an odorant decomposer without peer, but due to its inherent toxic properties must be considered carefully before becoming an addition to a malodor pollution control system.

The ultraviolet rays within the 1850 to 2500 Å range are optimum for odor decomposition. Natural ultraviolet radiates from the sun. Numerous devices for the production of ultraviolet within the aforementioned ranges have been developed and are available: the monokymatic mercury vapor discharge tube, the OZ4W bulb, quartz tubes, the Buvan ultraviolet air deodorizer, to name a few.

Both ozonization and ultraviolet are efficient means of oxidizing by molecular destruction of the odorant. For example, ultraviolet at $\lambda$ 2000 Å is $E = hf - 6.624 \times 10^{-27} \times 15 \times 10^{14} = 10^{11}$ ergs. This amount of ultraviolet creates two nascent oxygen atoms from each oxygen molecule.

Ozone
Applications for Odor Control

| | |
|---|---|
| Chemical plants | Rendering plants |
| Fermentation processes | Restaurants |
| Fish processing plants | Rubber plants |
| Food processing | Sewage plants |
| Morgues | Sludge storage |
| Phenol plants | Tanneries |

The range of ozone is 1 to 50 PPM, the average used being about 8 PPM. Nascent oxygen, chlorine, hypochlorites, chlorine dioxide, ultraviolet, potassium permanganate and hydrogen peroxide all are analogous to ozonization.

The geometry of placement and residence time are important factors in the decomposition of odorants by ultraviolet. The conditions of operation pose considerable problems with respect to application of ultraviolet as an effective pollution control means. For low volume CFM applications, irradiation chambers can be designed which will effectively deodorize the duct gases. Restaurants, small hospitals and industries where the CFM is less than 1400 CFM's on the average would represent such a market.

A multi-stage scrubber for the reduction of particulate emissions, opacity and odorous vapors from asphalt saturator fumes is described in United States patent number 3,724,173 (1973). Utilizing aqueous solutions in the pH range of 8.0 to 9.0, the method is claimed to result in substantially reduced particulate emission, opacity and odor to conform to air pollution ordinances APC 9.A(3) and APC 9.B for the state of Minnesota utilizing the ASTM D1391-57 Measurement of Odor and Atmospheres (Dilution Method). The contacting fluids used were comprised of water maintained at a pH of 8.0 to 9.0 by means of sodium hydroxide and alternately with a 1% solution of potassium permanganate buffered with sodium carbonate to a pH of 8.0 to 9.0.

Other oxidants used in odor control are chromates (M. K. Nelson, 1963), manganese dioxide (A. C. Bryan, 1956), chlorinated and brominated hydrocarbons

(R. Eliassen, 1949). A. C. Bryan (1956) found that 75 CFM/mg/L of sulfide per million gallons of wastewater flow (0.55 $M^3$/min/mg/l/1,000 $M^3$) was effective aeration for odor control of sulfides. J. E. Laughlin (1964) states that the addition of 0.1 to 0.3 cubic feet per gallon (0.74 to 2.2$M^3/M^3$) of wastewater is adequate.

## 2. Atmospheric Dilution

Stacks: concealing or reducing malodors to below threshold limits by dilution is the most common and oldest method of dealing with atmospheric odor pollution. Means presently employed for dilution, in order of predominance, are:

Stacks: sheer height
Stacks: booster fan
Stacks: afterburner
Stacks: venturi

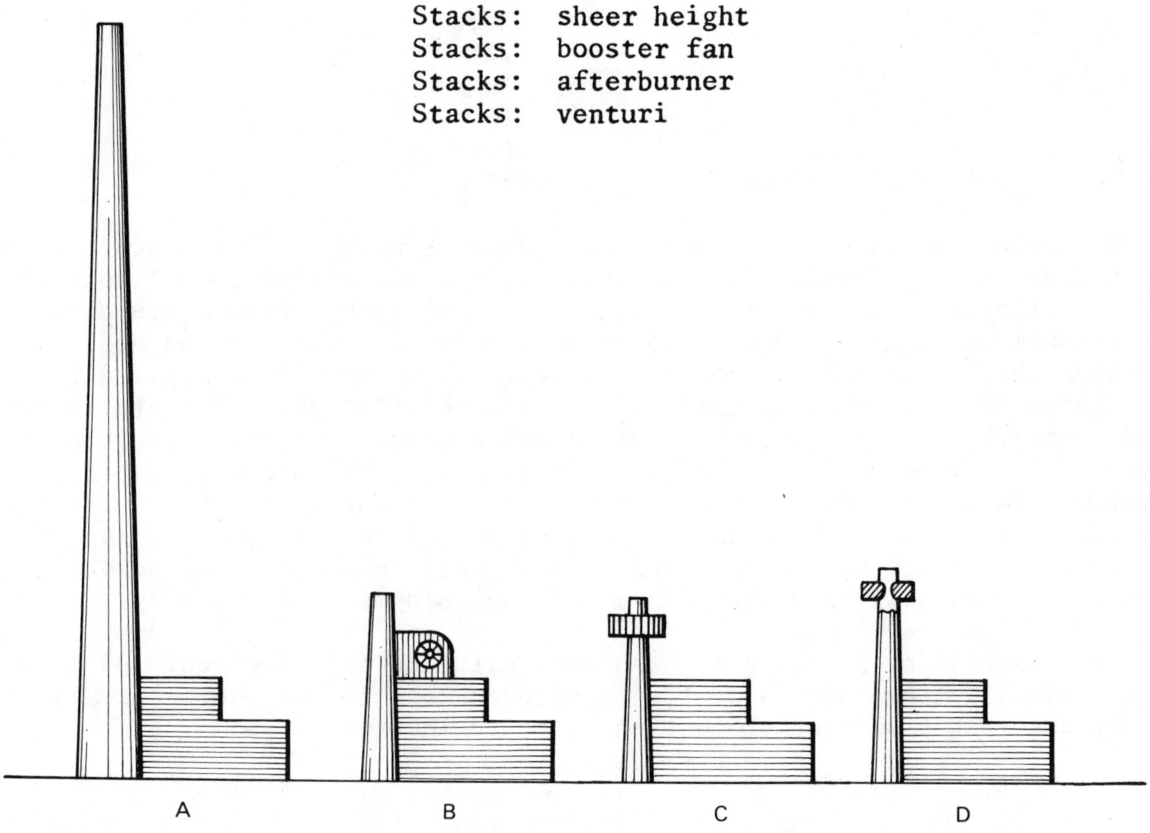


Atmospheric dilution
Dilution methods employed in malasthetic stench control: each stack is designed to release its effluent high into the atmosphere.
A Sheer height is relied upon,
B A booster fan causes greater velocity and predilutes,
C A so-called afterburner which is actually a super heater (hot stack gas rises higher),
D A venturi nozzle imparts considerable velocity to the stack gases.

### Maximum Floating Time of Airborne Particles

| Diameter (M) | Floating Time (Days) |
|---|---|
| 5 | 150 |
| 6 | 100 |
| 8 | 50 |
| 15 | 20 |
| 16 | 15 |
| 18 | 10 |
| 28 | 5 |

Rates of Fall of Spherical Particles

| Diameter (M) | Terminal Velocity (cm/sec) |
|---|---|
| 0.2 | 0.000225 |
| 0.3 | 0.00042 |
| 0.5 | 0.0010 |
| 1 | 0.0035 |
| 2 | 0.0128 |
| 3 | 0.0275 |
| 5 | 0.078 |
| 10 | 0.30 |
| 20 | 1.2 |
| 30 | 2.7 |
| 50 | 7.2 |
| 100 | 25 |
| 200 | 70 |
| 300 | 115 |
| 500 | 200 |
| 1000(=1 mm) | 385 |

Malodorous gases can be mixed with inodorous mixtures until sub-threshold levels have been achieved. Many devices have been designed in attempts to utilize dilution as the answer to malodorous pollution. Stacks are perhaps the oldest means of diluting odorous materials. Air can be collected and mixed in the stack which can be built to extreme heights. Heat can be applied to the stack gases to force them to rise higher into the atmosphere. Venturis can be added to stacks or high pressure fans to achieve the same effect. Dilution in itself obviously is not intended to alter or change the characteristics of the malodorous materials, but only to reduce their concentration, hopefully to below the threshold of perception. These means of resolving malodorous pollution seldom work all of the time and usually only reduce the degree of the problem, spreading it in diluted form for the enjoyment of the many.

In household or building maintenance, dilution is often achieved by airing and ventillating, but is of little value unless the malodor is transitory and not the result of deep or continuing contamination.

### 3. Construction

Polymerization of odorants results in a loss of their odorous qualities. Chemical reactions involving an odorant most often result in loss of odorous properties. Construction is among the more dramatic odor eliminating reactions. The following example is a simple but effective case of ionic reaction:

$$NH_3 + CH_3COOH \rightarrow CH_3COONH_4$$

Ammonia + Acetic Acid → Ammonium Acetate

or

$$NH_3 + HCl \rightarrow NH_4Cl$$

Ammonia + Hydrochloric Acid → Ammonium Chloride

In both of these examples, an acid is reacted with a base; in both cases all the reactants give rise to the olfactory sensation. It is not unusual to encounter ammonia or occasionally acetic acid as a significant component of a malodor problem. Nitrous gas can be reacted against hydrogen, yielding innocuous materials:

$$N_xO_y + 2yH \rightarrow yH_2O + N_x$$

Sulfur dioxide ($SO_2$) and sulfur trioxide ($SO_3$) can be removed by the addition of ammonia ($NH_3$), forming ammonia salts which are easily removed. This form of odor alteration requires adequate mixing of the reactants as well as sufficient reaction residence time. It is among this class that the most dramatic and immediate reactions approaching a value of $HU_0^0 0$ occur.

The principal cost in use is, of course, the reagent selected.

Certain metallic ions will combine with sulfide to reduce hydrogen sulfide odors. Other metallic ions are bacteriacidal and inhibit microbial growth, thereby suppressing odors. $Cu^+$ and $Cu^{2+}$, $Hg^{2+}$ and $Zn^{2+}$ were found by C. W. Beardsley (1949) to precipitate sulfide. W. H. Baumgartner (1934) used iron (ferric and ferrous) to precipitate sulfides. R. Pomeroy and F. D. Bowlus (1946) used iron, zinc and copper. They found that ferric iron ($Fe^{3+}$) was more effective than ferrous ($Fe^{2+}$) in precipitation of sulfide when the wastewater was devoid of oxygen. When a little oxygen was available, the ferrous iron became more effective. A mixture of ferrous and ferric was found to be more effective than either form alone. Iron is an effective means of treating anaerobic digester supernatants and sludges for odor control and in other instances where sulfide may be conveniently treated such as condensates from condensers.

Where nitrates ($NO_3^-$) or molecular oxygen ($O_2$) are available in sufficient quantities to wastewater, sulfate reduction will not occur (R. E. McKinney, 1956)(H. Henkelekian, 1943). One user reports that 10 pounds per pound of sulfide in the wastewater is the effective level for sulfide suppression.

Hydrogen sulfide and mercaptans can be removed from gases completely when they range in concentration from 0.001% to 20% (by volume) by contacting the gas with organic iodine solution such as in a tray column or a packed column. The hydrogen sulfide is oxidized to sulfur and mercaptans to disulfides. The iodine solution used in an organic solvent substantially increases the reaction velocity if small amounts of basic compounds are used. Aliphatic primary, secondary or tertiary monoamines (including cyclo-aliphatic amines), aromatic amines, pyrrolines, pyrrolidines, piperidines, n-alkyl pyrrolines, alkanolamines with primary, secondary or tertiary amine groups, aliphatic or aromatic diamines, aliphatic or aromatic triamines or tetramines are all considered efficacious (U. S. patent number 3,720,606). The amine solution preferred is from 0.1% to 1% (by weight); the solutions of iodine in the organic solvents may contain small amounts of water, the preferred range being 0.1% to 1% (by weight), with the iodine concentration preferably in the range of 0.005 to 1 molecule per liter. Water in small amounts increases the reaction velocity. Dimethyl sulfoxide is the preferred solvent. According to this process traces of hydrogen sulfide and/or mercaptans may be completely removed from a gas by washing, for example, at a pressure of 0.1 to 100 $kg/cm^2$ and a temperature of 10 to 80°C, without contaminating the gas with new impurities and without appreciable loss of iodine. The preferred temperature range is

20 to 40°C.

When a large part of the iodine has been transformed, it may be regenerated in the solution by any convenient oxidation process. For example, oxidizing agents such as hydrogen peroxide, sodium hypochlorite, ammonium perborate or potassium permanganate can be added or by bubbling oxygen, ozone, air, or ozonated air, by electrochemical oxidation, by catalytic oxidation. The regeneration with an oxidant of the sodium hypochlorite type is only economically practical when the iodine solvent is not miscible or only partially miscible with water.

### 4. Combining

When alcohols are added to acids, synthetic odorants (esters) are formed. They are not inodorous, in general representing pleasant bouquets reminiscent of floral or fruit odors. Occasionally organic acids and complex alcohols are encountered as components of malodorous pollution. It is possible by capitalizing on these components to formulate an additive compound which will use up the malodorant and yield a pleasant aromatic. Occasionally catalyst acids will be encountered among the malodor components, so all that is necessary to alter the malodorous exhaust is to add the necessary component for esterification. The results can be dramatic and replace troublesome malodorants with pleasant, mild odors of a generally acceptable level. The addition of an appropriate catalyst (or catalyst mixture) such as silver or iodine can in many instances bring about an odorously pleasant reaction between otherwise malodorous co-components of waste gas.

### 5. Interference

Zwaardemaker pairs of chemicals, when added, produced zero or close to zero odor. It is believed that certain odorants resonate at osmic frequencies, all of which are not mutually compatible but antagonistic. Two waves which cancel each other are said to interfere. Many pairs have been identified which neutralize each other. The phenomenon of neutralization of odor pairs was first noted by Zwaardemaker while introducing odors individually (monorhinically) and simultaneously (dirhinically) through each nostril. Zwaardemaker was able to identify numerous pairs which, when breathed together, interfered or neutralized the odor of both. Below are listed a number of antagonistic pairs, all of which result in a hedonic unit value of $HU_0^0 0$ upon addition:

| | |
|---|---|
| Beeswax | + Balsam of Tolu |
| Benzoin | + Rubber |
| Bitter almond | + Musk |
| Butyric acid | + Oil of juniper |
| Camphor | + Eau de Cologne |
| Ethyl mercaptan | + Eucalyptol |
| Ethyl mercaptan | + Caproic acid |
| Ionone | + Ammonia |
| Rubber | + Cedarwood |
| Skatole | + Cedarwood |
| Vanilla | + Chlorine |

In order for the pairs to neutralize each other completely, they must be balanced in the optimum ratio so that neither predominates. The search for Zwaardemaker pairs, triads or complexes is a fruitful endeavor in the modern odor laboratory. It is possible by judicious selection to substantially neutralize (interfere) a troublesome malodor component by addition to an otherwise efficacious formulation of appropriate Zwaardemaker components.

In a complex formulation such as for sewage odors, it may be necessary to rely upon many of the methods of odor control. For example:

Sewage Spray:
$HU_9^8$sewage

Malodorous Components in Order of Occurance:

Ammonia: $NH_2$
Trimethylamine: $(CH_3)_3N$
Hydrogen sulfide: $H_2S$
Skatole: $C_9H_9N$
Cadaverine: $NH_2(CH_2)_5NH_2$

The following formula will produce a value of $HU_4^2$fruit upon addition to the sewage in amounts of 90 to 100 PPM:

Amyl alcohol: $(CH_3)_2CHCH_2CH_2OH$
Coumarin: $C_9H_6O_2$
Ferric hydroxide: $Fe(OH)_3$
Glacial acetic acid: $CH_3COOH$
Glucose: $C_6H_{12}O_6$

The glacial acetic acid and amyl alcohol are catalyzed by hydrogen sulfide, yielding amyl acetate [$CH_3COOCH_2CH_2CH(CH_3)_2$], an ester reminiscent of bananas. Excess glacial acetic acid neutralizes the free ammonia completely. Glucose adsorbs the hydrogen sulfide where it is catalyzed by the ferric hydroxide to elemental sulfur. Skatole is neutralized by the trace coumarin. The amyl acetate and trimethylamine combined yield a fruity odor of low intensity. In this formula decomposition, construction, combining, catalysis, sorption and interference were all relied upon to achieve odor abatement.

Zwaardemaker was the first to maintain that selected pairs of osmogenes can diminish the effect of both. Many of his experiments were performed dirhinically, and he ultimately identified a number of antagonistic pairs. In spite of Zwaardemaker's contentions regarding the seemingly sound principle of osmogene neutralization by selective additions of antagonist osmogenes, the current popular belief remains fixed, at least in professional circles, that the addition of chemical perfumes only worsens the problem. It is true that in practice it is no easy matter to balance osmogenic antagonists to achieve a neutral odor. It is also true, however, that considerable benefit can be obtained by such additions if they are the result of careful experimentation. However, even under ideal conditions, disguising or neutralizing can be costly. In many field situations and under emergency conditions it may be the only practical solution. R. W. Moncrieff (1966) points out that the addition of perfumed oils to malodorous oils will result in deodorization after distilling away the perfumed oils.

Perhaps the most dramatic and convincing evidence to date supporting Zwaardemaker are various experiments done on insect olfaction. Recent experiments with the red banded leaf roller moth (Argyrotaenia velutinana) have proven that the addition of masks or perfumes to cis-11-tetradecenyl acetate destroy its appeal to the moth. This is startling support of Zwaardemaker since pheromones are virtually communication imperatives to insects (W. L. Roelofs and H. Arn, 1968). The addition of the mask to dodecyl acetate neutralizes the effect of the pheromone in Choristoneura rosaceana and enhances the effect in A. velutinana (W. L. Roelofs and J. P. Tette, 1970).

In more recent experiments many more inhibitors (masks) and synergists (enhancers) have been found. Certain properties are characteristic of inhibitors and synergists (W. L. Roelofs and A. Comeau, 1971):

1. The length of the straight chain moiety of the synergists is 11, 12, 14. The length of the straight chain moiety of the inhibitors is 10, 13, 14, 16.
2. When one starts from saturated compounds, the synergist effect is produced or increased by bromine, oxygen or sulfur within the chain in the 11 or 12 position. Different from that, the 5 cis- or 7 cis-dodecenyl acetates are strong synergists. The synergistic effect is lost when the acetate moiety is replaced by a hydroxy group.
3. Many of the inhibitory compounds are alcohols, formate or propionate. Nearly all inhibitors have a cis- or trans- double bond in the 9 or 11 position.

When over 15% of the cis isomer of the pheromone 10-propyl-trans-5,9-tridecadienyl acetate (propylure) is added to the pheromone, it is effectively masked to the pink bollworm moth (M. Jacobson, 1969). It has been found additionally that masking can be produced by chemically unrelated compounds. The Euglossinae bees which are attracted to orchid fragrances (1,8-cineole) can be inhibited by the addition of citronellal, benzyl acetate or methyl salicylate (Dodson, et al., 1969). Some insects produce masking substances which inhibit insect reactions. Female bark beetles (Dendroctonus pseudotsugae) exude a mask which inhibits the effects of the aggregating pheromone (J. A. Rudinsky, 1969).

These findings seem to support Zwaardemaker and extend his findings. If one osmogene can neutralize (mask, inhibit) another, then the addition of a different osmogene can also increase (synergize) the olfactory effect.

Disguising:

Terms commonly used synonomously with disguising are masking, deodorizing, counteracting and perfuming. In industry disguising agents are used as a last resort, normally because the cost is high, the applications are crude and uncertain, and the results questionable. The acceptability of odor disguising industrially is in question principally due to a lack of understanding. However, among the public it is generally accepted as the means of social odor control.

R. W. Moncrieff states in Rule #124: "Odour counteraction is an established phenomenon but for the most part it is only applicable to faint odours; a weak malodour can sometimes be removed by counteraction with a suitable odorant, e.g.

butyric acid can be compensated with juniper oil."[1] Restrooms invariably employ disguising agents as their sole means of odor control. Most commercial personal deodorants rely on disguising agents as the basis of their formulation and acceptance. The perfume industry in large measure owes its existence to the acceptability of the public of disguising or enhancing personal odors with strong perfumes and other personal odorizing agents. The food industry and specifically the spice and herb trade owe their existence to the addition to bland foods of exciting odors or the disguising of otherwise unpleasant odor-bearing foods. Odor disguising, when applied commercially, however, often falls far short of acceptable performance levels. This is due to the general lack of understanding of the potential of disguising as a sound means of odor control and the application of inappropriate formulations.

Indiscriminate additions of industrial deodorants could just as readily produce a more severe problem as solve one. The preparation and addition of effective industrial malodor masks or inhibitors is a highly specialized field and requires considerable experimentation to achieve results. Unfortunately, the terms "mask" and "deodorize" have come to represent the injudicious additions to malodor complexes of overwhelming amounts of perfume substances, often only replacing one malodor with two. This is unfortunate because in most cases the solution to the malodor problem can be resolved only by recourse to the selection of several appropriate means which will often include neutralizing chemicals.

A method for deodorizing aqueous solutions and reducing the biochemical demand when the solution contains at least one compound of hydrogen sulfide and compounds containing the -SH group is disclosed in United States patent number 3,459,852. The patent claims the discovery that α,β-aliphatically-unsaturated aldehydes and ketones are "sulfide-active." Acrolein and 3-buten-2-one when added to raw sewage leave it essentially odor free. The aldehydes and ketones are added at pumping stations "upstream" from the treatment plant and are admixed in transit. The additions do not interfere with other processing of sewage such as oxidation by aeration or bacterial action. The use of a stabilizer is recommended when acrolein is used, hydroquinone being preferred:

Example 1:

The following are tests illustrating the efficiency of acrolein and 3-buten-2-one for deactivating sewage odors, using a liter of water to which sufficient sodium sulfide ($Na_2S$) had been added to bring the $S^=$ concentration to 10 PPM. The acrolein had been diluted 1:10 in water and allowed to stand this way for several weeks. 30 drops of the diluted acrolein were used and three drops of pure 3-buten-2-one were used. The acrolein test gave the following results:

| Time (minutes) | Sulfide Ion Concentration, PPM |
|---|---|
| Control | 10 |
| 7 | 8 |
| 21 | 3 |
| 32 | 1.5 |

---

[1] R. W. Moncrieff, Odour Preferences, John Wiley, New York: 1966, p. 314.

The 3-buten-2-one test gave the following results:

| Time (minutes) | Sulfide Ion Concentration, PPM |
|---|---|
| Control | 10 |
| 7 | 8 |
| 21 | 2 |
| 30 | 1 |

These two tests are virtually identical. The acrolein had polymerized some and the size of the drops of the two chemicals may have been slightly different due to different viscosities.

Example 2:

Another series of tests were run with the same amounts of the sulfide-active compounds, except that 20 PPM of $S^{=}$ were present in the liter of water to which about 10 drops of 2.5 molar sodium hydroxide had been added. The second acrolein test produced the following results:

| Time | Sulfide Ion Concentration, PPM |
|---|---|
| Control | 20 |
| 18 minutes | 16 |
| 33 minutes | 13 |
| 100 minutes | 10 |
| 140 minutes | 9.5 |
| 175 minutes | 7.5 |
| 17 hours | 0 |

The 3-buten-2-one gave the following results:

| Time | Sulfide Ion Concentration, PPM |
|---|---|
| Control | 20 |
| 91 minutes | 10 |
| 154 minutes | 7.5 |
| 17 hours | 3.5 |

Following these tests, it was determined that 25 drops of 1:10 acrolein give approximately 1 cc liquid volume, as do about 50 drops of pure 3-buten-2-one. Therefore, three drops of pure acrolein equal 20 plus PPM of sulfide ion per liter and three drops (3/50th cc) pure 3-buten-2-one equal 16.5 PPM of sulfide ion per liter. This shows some superiority of acrolein, but only a slight difference. However, these two compounds are so close as to be in a class by themselves. Hence, these compounds are preferred for their high yield in treating sewage.

The following α,β-unsaturated ketones are among the suggested alternatives listed in the patent:

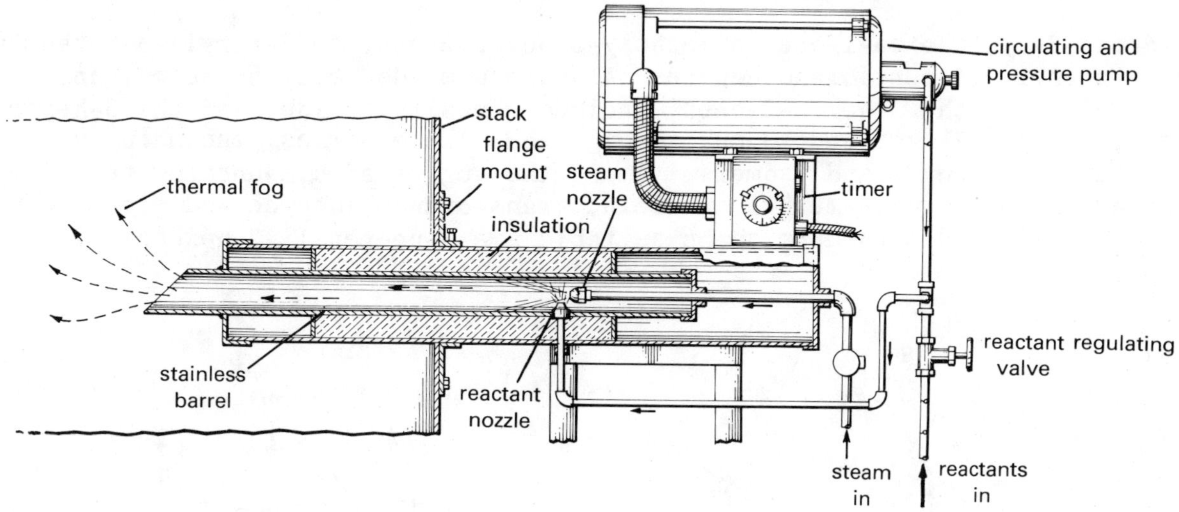


Thermal stack fogger. Ejects malodor reactants into stack (neutralizing and disguising). Courtesy Pace National Corporation

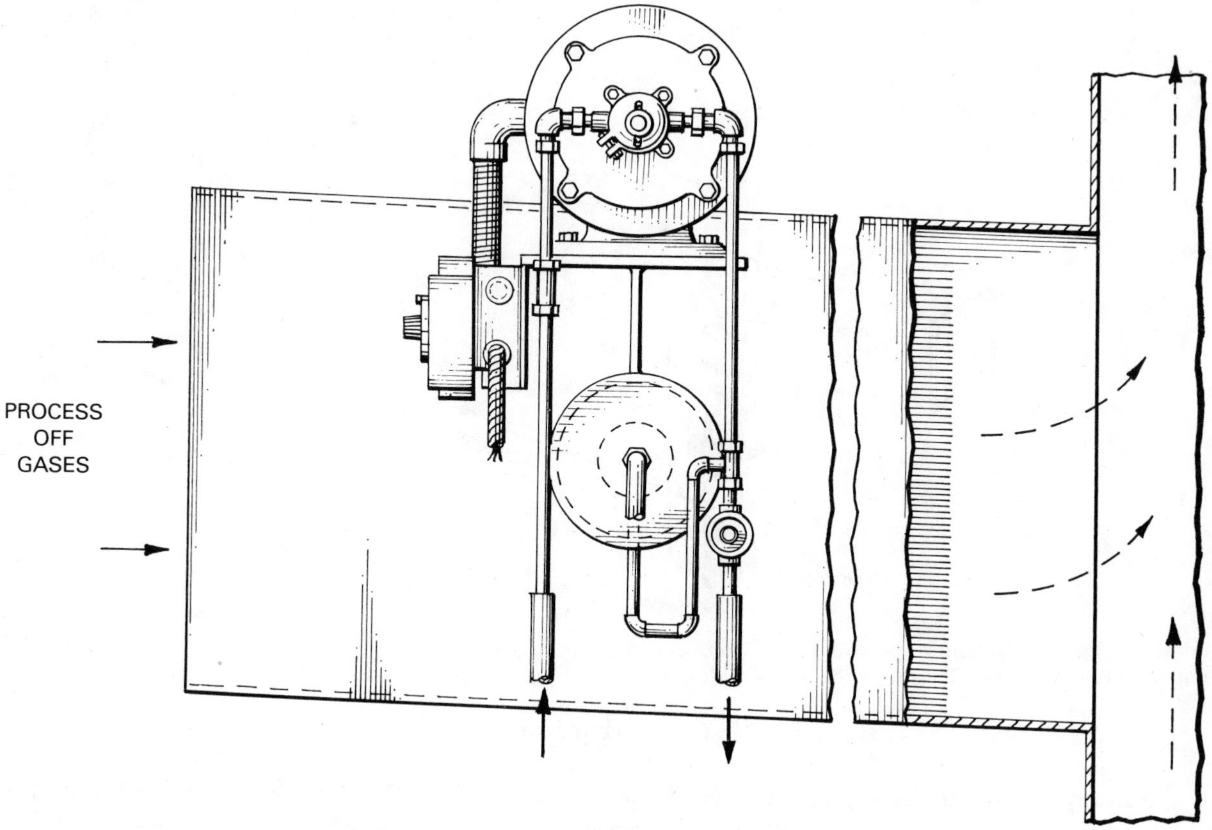


End view of thermal fogger installation. Courtesy Pace National Corporation

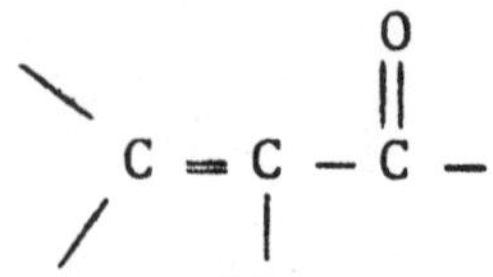

3-hydroxy-2-cyclohexen-1-one; 4-methoxy-3-buten-2-one; 4-(2-furyl)-3-buten-2-one; 5-phenyl-2,4-pentadienophenone. Also recommended are the normal and iso-3-penten-2-one, the 3-hexen-2-ones, including mesityl oxide, and the 3-hepten-2-ones, 3-octen-2-ones and so on, through the alkene series, including various substituted compounds and isomers. Among the suggested α,β-unsaturated aldehydes are acrolein, α,β-methyl acrolein, trans-cinnamaldehyde and tiglaldehyde. Additional aldehydes thought to be suitable are 2-pentenal, 2-hexenal, 2-heptenal, etc.

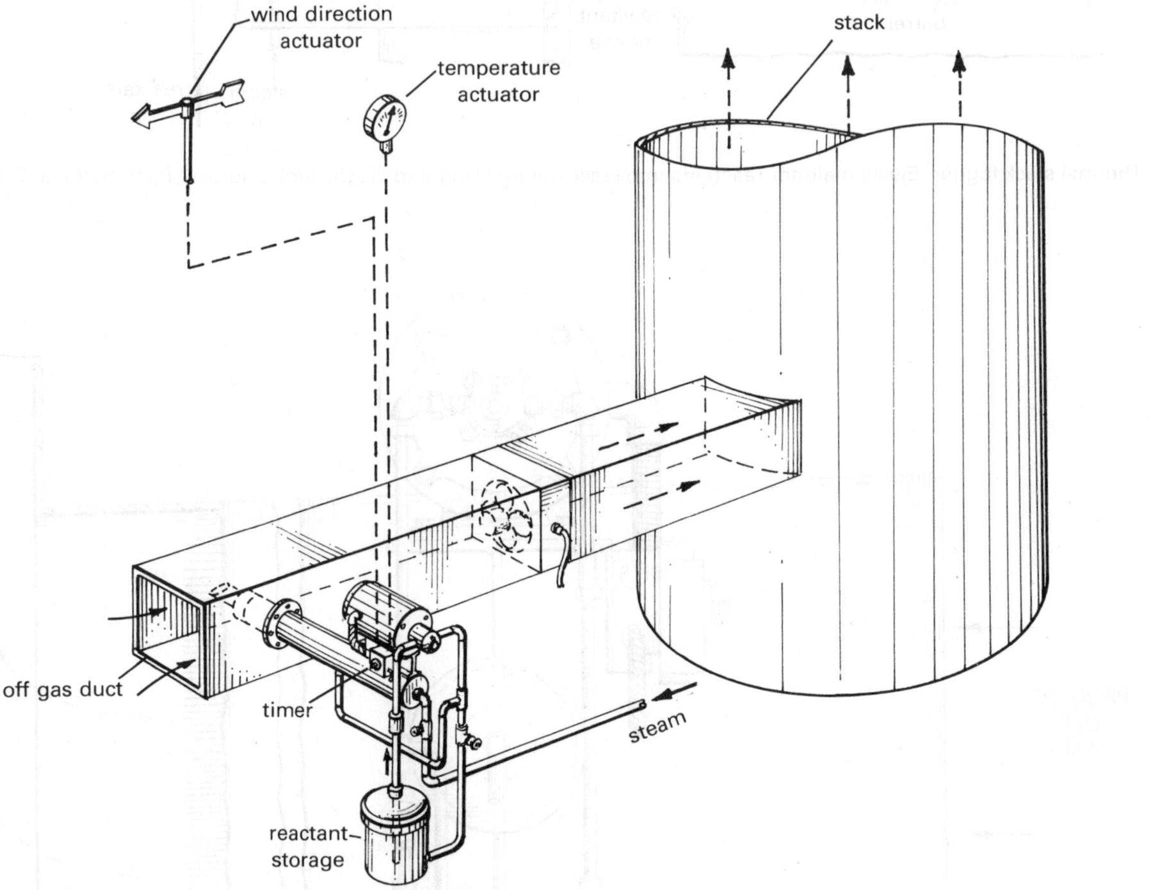


Thermal fogger application in rendering line. Unit activated during preset hours of operation when wind direction and temperature appropriate. Courtesy Pace National Corporation

## 6. Sorption

Adsorption and absorption are important means of odor control and can be utilized in many ways. Activated charcoal is normally considered the adsorbent par excellence. Due to its solid form, however, it is often not suitable for odor control applications. Activated charcoal also will not adsorb well at temperatures above 120°F. Many liquids, gases and solids are good adsorbents. Additionally, there are many fine specific adsorbents. Chlorophyll ($C_{55}H_{72}Mg$ $N_4O_5$) is a specific adsorbent for hydrogen sulfide ($H_2S$), being capable of adsorbing up to half its own weight in hydrogen sulfide. Actually, chlorophyll will adsorb specifically most all of the sulfhydryls including the thioalcohols methyl mercaptan ($CH_3SH$) and ethyl mercaptan ($C_2H_5SH$). When placed near silver, chlorophyll will prevent tarnishing, acting as a scavenger for any atmospheric sulfur compounds (Department of Scientific and Industrial Research, 1960). Moist earth is an excellent sorber and is capable of being used in lieu of other adsorbents. However, utilization of sorption techniques requires that gases be relatively free of particulates and oil droplets which will foul the adsorbent.

| Adsorption Applications for Odor Control | Major Adsorbents Used In Odor Pollution Control |
|---|---|
| Chemical plants | Activated alumina |
| Fermentation | Activated bauxite |
| Food processing | Aluminisilicate |
| Natural gas | Carbons |
| Rendering | Iron oxide |
| Sewage treatment | Silica gel |
| Textiles and leather | |

If the adsorbency capacity of the adsorbent is exceeded, vapors will pass through. The adsorbent then must be regenerated. Low pressure live steam is used in the regeneration process. The steam and solvent vapors are usually condensed to liquids and separated, but most often the vapors are incinerated. Many industrial adsorption systems have two or more beds so that one can be used while the other is regenerated.

The Reinluft process used in Germany utilizes charcoal formed from calcined coal to adsorb sulfur dioxide ($SO_2$). The charcoal is desorbed by heat and reactivated by treatment with sulfuric acid ($H_2SO_4$)(H. F. Lund, 1971).

One pound of activated carbon contains an internal surface area of approximately six million square feet (D. M. Larson, 1972). Presently available carbon adsorption systems are capable of handling capacities of over two tons per hour and air handling capacities in excess of 200,000 CFM's (Vick Manufacturing, 1973). The Federal Environmental Protection Agency has stated that carbon adsorption can reduce organic solvent emissions into the atmosphere by a minimum of 85% (Federal Register, 1971). Two limiting factors of present day processing, high fuel costs and water use limitations, will cause more careful consideration of alternatives such as adsorption beds where they may be efficaciously employed for odor control.

Sulfur dioxide ($SO_2$) is removed from gas streams by contacting the gas stream with a solid basic ion exchange resin in United States patent number 3,709,977. The gas stream is initially contacted with an alkali prior to contact with the resin to remove sulfur trioxide ($SO_3$) and prevent its contact with the resin. Fouling of the resin is thereby avoided which would result in a tightly bound chemical union, preventing resin regeneration by simple thermal means. A resulting gas stream free of sulfur oxides is claimed. Resins used are comprised of discrete solid particles of suitable basic ion exchange resins which preferably consist of cross-linked organic polymers containing amine or imine groups. Suggested resins are those produced by condensing an aldehyde, e.g., formaldehyde, acetaldehyde, propionaldehyde, butyraldehyde, cinnamyl aldehyde, furfural, etc., with one or more amino compounds such as urea, thiourea, dicyandiamide, etc., or with other active components such as phenol, aniline, phenylene diamine, quinoline, etc. After removal of sulfur trioxide by alkali treatment, the resulting hot tail gases are cooled to below 122°F and then contacted with the resin adsorption bed. Regeneration of the resin bed is accomplished by a desiccated heated air stream at between 176°F and 266°F.

United States patent number 3,723,308 teaches the use of a zeolite cation exchange of ammonium ions from aqueous solutions containing at least one alkali or alkaline earth cation, and the selective cation exchange of such solutions with a synthetic crystalline aluminosilicate to purify wastewaters containing ammonium cations in addition to other alkali or alkaline earth cations.

Cation exchange for ammonia removal, using a variety of cation-active zeolites has been studied extensively. The permutits (synthetic gel zeolites derived from sodium silicate and aluminum sulfate) and the hydrous gel-type amorphous minerals such as glauconite (green sand) (G. H. Gleason, 1933-1934) are effective, but suffer from hydrolytic instability. They have relatively low exchange capacities, often have unsatisfactory regeneration characteristics and may be difficult to form into useful shapes of acceptable physical properties. Organic zeolites, which are sulfonated or carboxylated high polymers, are not selective for the ammonium ion, and instead prefer other cations such as calcium (B. M. Mercer, 1960).

Since ion exchange is an equilibrium phenomenon, the selectivity of the zeolite for one ion in preference to another may be expressed in terms of a separation factor: $\alpha_B{}^A$. This factor, $\alpha_B{}^A$ is defined by the equation:

$$\alpha_B{}^A = (A_z \cdot B_s / A_s \cdot B_z)$$

for the ion exchange reaction, at equilibrium, of the system:

$$A_s + B_z = A_z + B_s$$

in the above equation:

$A_s$ Is equivalent fraction of exchanging ion A in solution,
$B_z$ Is equivalent fraction of ion B in the zeolite,
$A_z$ Is equivalent fraction of ion A in the zeolite,
$B_s$ Is equivalent fraction of ion B in solution.

Otherwise expressed, and with reference to the system where one is interested in the selectivity of a zeolite for the ammonium cation in solution together with other cations, the first equation above may be expressed as: Selectivity of zeolite for P' compared to $P_n$ = (equivalent fraction of P' in zeolite)/(equivalent fraction of P' in solution) × (equivalent fraction of $P_n$ in solution)/(equivalent fraction of $P_n$ in zeolite).

In the above equations, the separation factor $\alpha_B{}^A$ is a function of the ions, the zeolite and the solution composition. Thus, $\alpha_B{}^A$ implicitly refers to a specified temperature (isotherm), total ionic concentration and degree of exchange ($A_z$).

## 7. Catalysts

Odors can be rendered inodorous by passing them through a catalyst. Due to the "turn over" (TO) of catalysts, they represent very attractive means of odor control. In many instances where the catalyst cannot be easily applied in a matrix, it is possible to vaporize, or spray directly into the odor-laden gas stream. Frequently the mere addition to an operating scrubber of the appropriate catalyst can bring about odor reduction or elimination of the most profound type. Catalysts will alter odors in several ways:

1. With chemical additives cause reactions between additives and odor forming polymers or agglomerations that would otherwise not occur (construction),
2. With chemical additives cause a breakdown of the odor that would otherwise not occur or occur too slowly (decomposition),
3. With chemical additives cause combinations which are still odorous but hedonically more acceptable.

Catalysts are the matchmakers for otherwise timid reactants. Formaldehyde ($CH_2O$), acetaldehyde ($CH_3CHO$) and propionaldehyde ($C_2H_5CHO$) are all pungent lachrymatory odorants which can be decomposed by the addition of small amounts of iodine, acting as a catalyst:

$$CH_3CHO + I_2 \rightarrow CH_3I + HI + CO$$

Acetaldehyde + Iodine → Methyl iodide + Hydrogen Iodide + Carbon Monoxide

$$CH_3I + HI \rightarrow CH_4 + I_2$$

Methyl Iodide + Hydrogen Iodide → Methane + Iodine

Obviously, where aldehydes are a problem, the use of minute amounts of iodine as a catalyst will resolve the problem very satisfactorily, yielding methane ($CH_4$) and carbon monoxide (CO), both odorless. The addition of ferric hydroxide [$Fe(OH)_3$] to hydrogen sulfide ($H_2S$) will catalyze the hydrogen sulfide to elemental and odorless sulfur:

$$4Fe(OH)_3 + 6H_2S \rightarrow 2Fe_2S_3 + 12H_2O$$

Ferric Hydroxide + Hydrogen Sulfide → Iron sulfide + Water

$$2Fe_2S_3 + 3O_2 + 6H_2O \rightarrow 4Fe(OH)_3 + 3S_2$$

Iron Sulfide + Oxygen + Water → Ferric Hydroxide + Sulfur

The temperature requirement for the reaction is 86 to 104°F, and 30 molecules for each molecule of hydrogen sulfide are required.

Iron rust ($Fe_2O_3$ or $Fe_2O_4$), copper (Cu), iodine (I), silver (Ag), chromium (Cr), nickel (Ni), platinum (Pt), manganese (Mn) or manganese dioxide ($MnO_2$) are among the promising catalysts, both alone and in combination. The application of catalysts is in many cases restricted to matrixes since the accumulation in the environment of heavy metals is undesirable. It is possible for the purpose of ease of application to vaporize in aerosol the catalyst directly into a gas flow, then recapture the catalyst in a bath or by electrostatic precipitation.

United States patent number 3,709,660 discloses a method of catalytically treating thiosulfate solutions with hydrogen to produce sulfide in aqueous solutions of thiosulfate. Thiosulfate solutions are commonly produced as wastes or encountered in industrial processes such as chemical manufacture, petroleum refining, natural gas sweetening and paper and steel industries. In the petroleum industry, for example, an aqueous solution containing ammonium thiosulfate $[(NH_4)_2S_2O_3]$ is produced as a drag stream from sulfur recovery systems that employ an oxidation method to recover sulfur from ammonium hydrosulfide solutions. These solutions are commonly available as side streams from such typical refinery processes as hydrorefining, hydrocracking, catalytic cracking, etc. Ammonium thiosulfate is evolved in processes for gas sweetening, coal gas purification, town gas purification, etc. where hydrogen sulfide is scrubbed from a gaseous mixture and thereafter oxidized to elemental sulfur in a regeneration step.

The Thylox process utilized for coke-oven gas treating and the Perox process both yield thiosulfate by-product formation. The thiosulfate must be removed before safe discharge of wastes into sewers, streams or rivers can be made. The inorganic thiosulfate compounds present as a water soluble salt normally occur as various alkali metal thiosulfates such as sodium and potassium thiosulfate and alkaline earth metal thiosulfates such as calcium, magnesium, strontium and barium thiosulfate. The solutions typically contain thiosulfate ions. The thiosulfate compound may be present in the aqueous solution in any amount up to the solubility limit and will comprise from 0.1 to approximately 30% (by weight) of the solution. The method of treatment involves contacting an aqueous solution of the thiosulfate compound with hydrogen and a catalytically effective amount of cobalt sulfide with a porous carrier material at reduction conditions, including a temperature of about 212°to 662°F and a pressure at least sufficient to maintain a portion of the aqueous solution in the liquid phase. The catalytic action of cobalt sulfide is claimed to be unique and not shared by other iron group sulfides.

Hydrogen is used alone or in mixture with $C_1$ to $C_4$ hydrocarbons in an amount equivalent to or greater than the stoichiometric amount (4 moles of hydrogen per mole of thiosulfate) required for the reduction of thiosulfates to sulfides. 6 to 50 moles of hydrogen per mole of thiosulfate is preferred. The results of tests for thiosulfate catalysts are as follows:

| Catalyst Designation | Metallic Ingredient | Amount of Metal, % (by Weight) | Inlet Reactor Temperature, °F | Conversion to $S^=$ % |
|---|---|---|---|---|
| A | NiS | 4.8 | 169 | 7 |
| B | CoS | 2.3 | 171 | 77 |
| C | NiS | 20.5 | 169 | 21 |
| D | NiS | 38 | 168 | 10 |
| E | CoS | 4.6 | 170 | 100 |
| F | FeS | 20 | 168 | 27 |
| G | CoS | 9 | 171 | 99 |
| H | PdS | 1 | 169 | 28 |

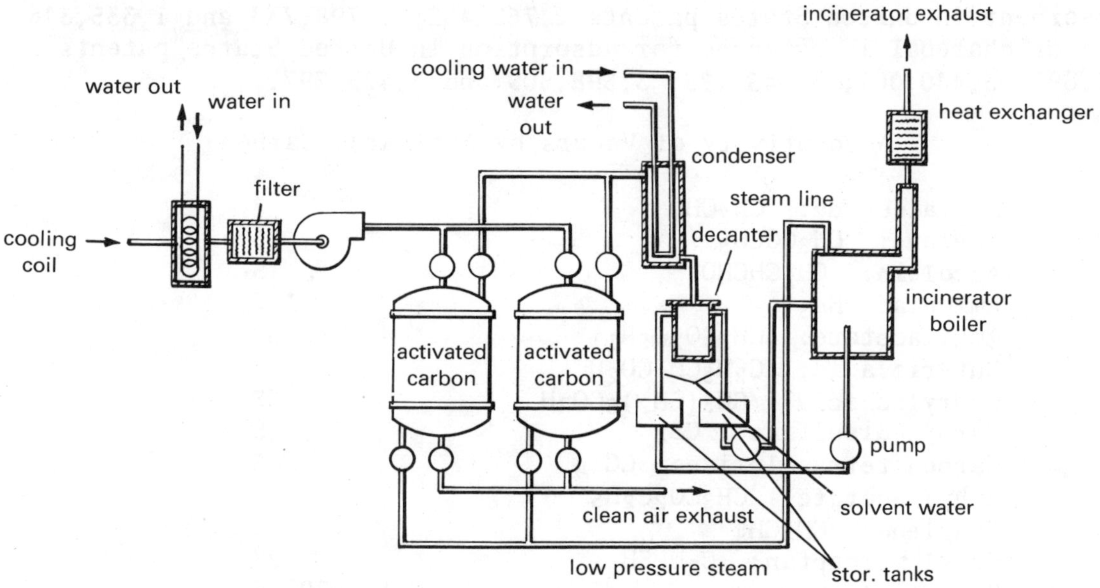


Combination installation, volatile adsorption, condensing, and incineration. (Recommended for metal finishing, bake ovens, paint spray booths). Courtesy Vic Manufacturing Inc.

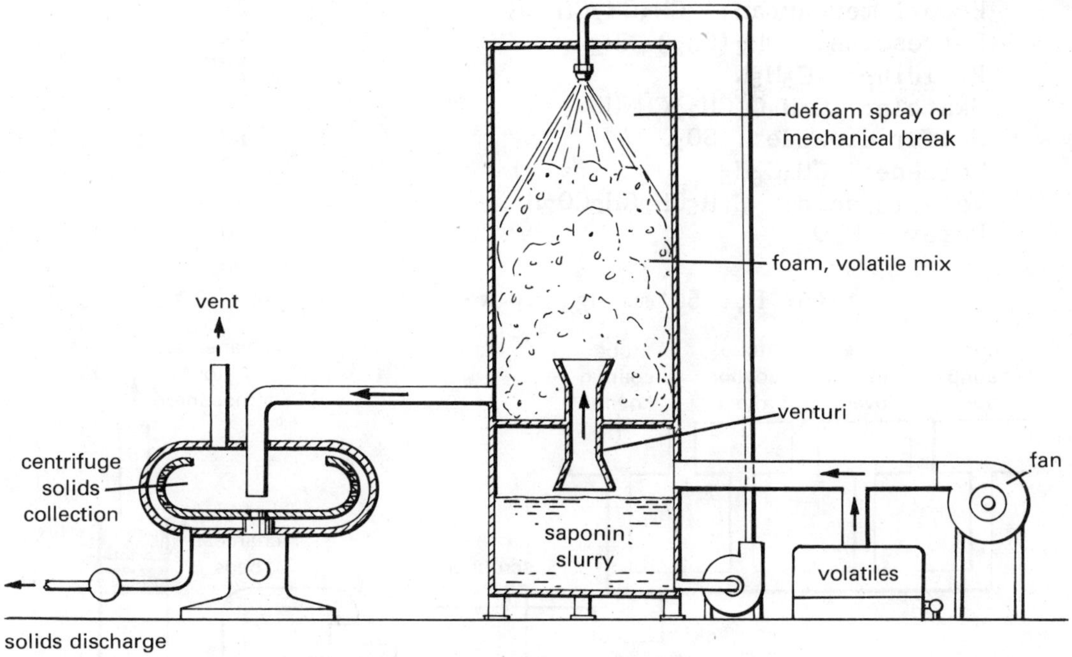


Laboratory apparatus for saponin sorption of volatiles

Patents pertinent to various resins include United States patents 3,330,621 and 2,285,750; British patent 805,853. Silica gel is proposed as an absorbent in United States patents 2,762,452; 1,798,733 and 1,335,348. Carbon or charcoal is patented for adsorption in United States patents 2,992,895; 3,440,007; 3,345,125; 3,398,509 and 3,473,297.

Adsorptivity of Vapors by Activated Carbon

| | % |
|---|---|
| Acetaldehyde: $CH_3CHO$ | 7 |
| Acetone: $CH_3COCH_3$ | 15 |
| Acrolein: $CH_2CHCHO$ | 15 |
| Ammonia: $NH_3$ | 1-2 |
| Amyl acetate: $CH_3CO_2C_5H_{11}$ | 34 |
| Butyric acid: $C_2H_5CH_2CO_2H$ | 35 |
| Caprylic acid: $CH_3(CH_2)_6CO_2H$ | 35 |
| Carbon disulfide: $CS_2$ | 15 |
| Carbon tetrachloride: $CCl_4$ | 45 |
| Ethyl acetate: $CH_3CO_2C_2H_5$ | 19 |
| Ethylene: $CH_2CH_4$ | 3 |
| Ethyl mercaptan: $C_2H_5SH$ | 23 |
| Essential oils | 20-35 |
| Eucalyptol: $C_{10}H_{18}O$ | 20 |
| Formaldehyde: $CH_2O$ | 3 |
| Hydrogen sulfide: $H_2S$ | 3 |
| Indole: $C_8H_7N$ | 25 |
| Methyl chloride: $CH_3Cl$ | 5 |
| Methyl mercaptan: $CH_3SH$ | 20 |
| Nitrogen dioxide: $NO_2$ | 10 |
| Ozone: $O_3$ | decomposes to oxygen |
| Propyl mercaptan: $CH_3CH_2CH_2SH$ | 25 |
| Putrescine: $NH_2(CH_2)_4NH_2$ | 25 |
| Pyridine: $C_5H_5N$ | 25 |
| Skatole: $C_6H_4C(CH_3)CHNH$ | 25 |
| Sulfur dioxide: $SO_2$ | 10 |
| Toluene: $CH_3C_6H_5$ | 29 |
| Valeric acid: $C_2H_5CH_2CH_2CO_2H$ | 35 |
| Water: $H_2O$ | 0 |

(68°F, 760 mm Hg, by weight)

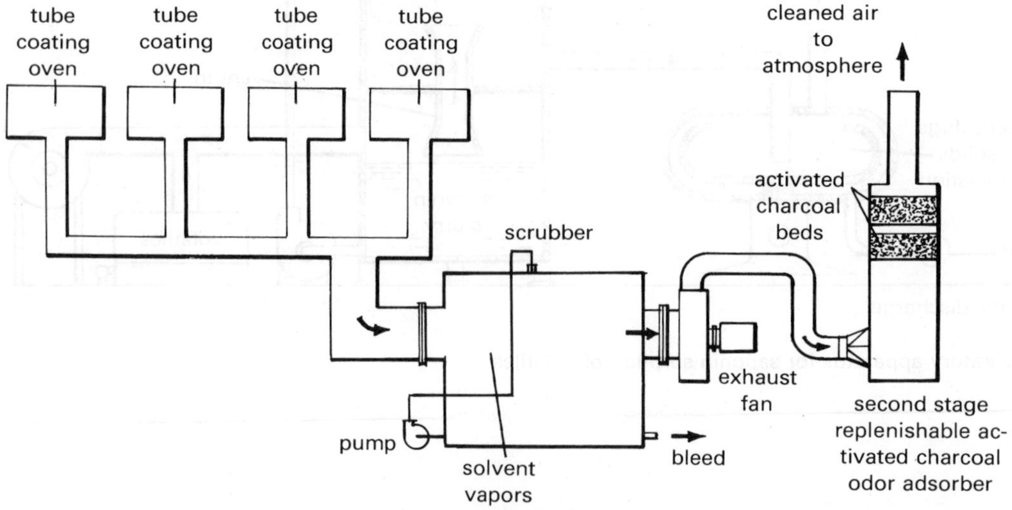


Combination installation, particle removal by scrubber and volatiles removed by charcoal adsorption beds. (Recommended for odor control of paint coating, paper coating, textile dyeing, wall paper painting, food processing, meat rendering and chemical process exhausts). Courtesy Air Pollution Industries, Inc.

Fuel Additives to Reduce Malodor:

It has been stated that efficient burning of a fuel depends on the cetane number, a cetane greater than 45 being best for good ignition. A number of chemical additives are available which improve combustion, causing greater efficiency and thereby fewer malodorants. The addition of 0.25 to 1% of isotane ($C_3H_7NO$), a derivative of isopropyl nitrate, is an example. A number of proprietary formulations are available including sulfur inhibitors and catalysts, and one investigator reports that the addition of 0.5 pounds of water to 1 pound of fuel injected into the intake manifold reduces nitric oxide emissions by 80 to 90%. Due to the catalytic reaction of iodine and aldehydes, an inexpensive additive to deodorize diesel buses can be formulated which will eliminate the malodorous and irritating aldehydes. Recent discoveries, however, have uncovered irritants with as much as 200 times the lachrymatory effect as formaldehyde such as peroxybenzol nitrate (PBzN).

Typical oxidation catalysts for auto exhaust systems are disclosed in United States patents 3,288,558; 3,295,918; 3,304,150; 3,322,491; 3,338,666; 3,455,843; 3,346,328; 3,470,150; 3,740,349, 3,741,725; 3,751,386 and 3,755,534. Monolithic structures made from α-alumina, mullite, spinel, zircon-mullite, cordierite, spodumene, etc. or conventional particulate beds are used to support the catalysts.

Typical Hydrocarbon, Nitrogen Oxides and Carbon Monoxide Catalysts

| Catalyst | |
|---|---|
| A: | 10% cupric oxide (CuO), 4% chromic oxide ($Cr_2O_3$), 0.02% palladium (Pd) |
| B: | 8% cupric oxide (CuO), 12% manganese dioxide ($MnO_2$), 0.02% palladium (Pd) |
| C: | 4% cupric oxide (CuO), 6% manganese dioxide ($MnO_2$), 4% chromic oxide ($Cr_2O_3$), 0.02% palladium (Pd) |
| D: | 0.02% to 0.5% platinum (Pt) |
| E: | 0.02% to 0.5% palladium (Pd) |
| F: | 2% cobaltic oxide ($Co_2O_3$), 8% nickel monoxide (NiO), 1% manganese dioxide ($MnO_2$) |
| G: | 7% nickel monoxide (NiO), 2% cobaltic oxide ($Co_2O_3$), 1% manganese dioxide ($MnO_2$) |
| H: | 30.4% chromic oxide ($Cr_2O_3$), 20% cupric oxide (CuO) |
| I: | 25% cupric oxide (CuO), 25% chromic oxide ($Cr_2O_3$), 10% nickel monoxide (NiO) |

## 8. Vector Capture

Most odor vectors can be readily removed from stack gases through the use of cyclones, electrostatic precipitators, scrubbers, venturis, rotoclones, baghouses, etc. Generally, the first step in odor control is the removal of odor vectors, especially those above the two micron size since they are odor pregnant and will cause the most serious immediate problems. They are usually easy to remove due to the abundance of equipment available for particle capture. An odorous gas stream may be charged with adsorbants in a particle form and then collected as a means of odor reduction.

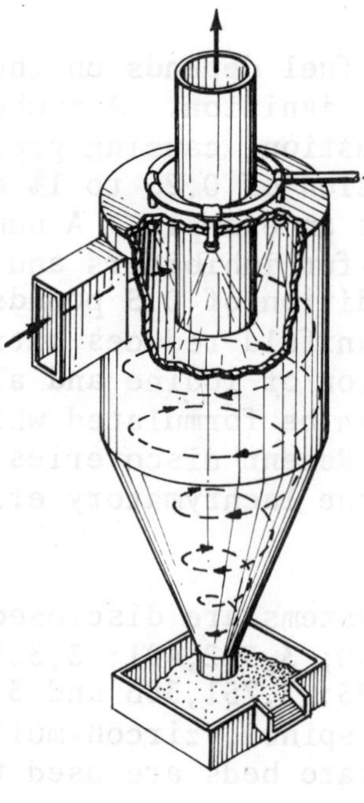

Conventional cyclone converted to a scrubber

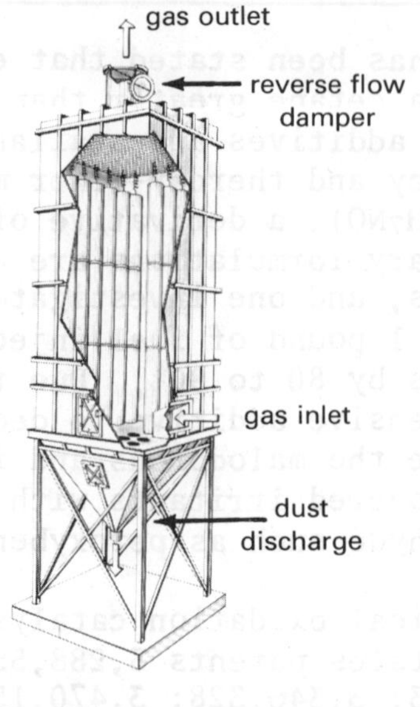


Bag house. (≈ 99% efficient for particle vector removal. Recommended for pulverized coal fired boilers, flour mills, stone crushers, feed mills, etc.). Courtesy Zurn Industries, Inc.

**Vector purge chemicals can be utilized in amounts ranging from one to five PPM. Many solvents, alcohols and essential oils are good vector purges. Precipitates from the stack can be exposed to atmospheres of the various vector purge chemicals, then sniffed. The replacement of malodorants with the preferred vector purge is positive.**

**Unites States patent number 3,736,727 describes an electrostatic system for the removal of particulates and chemical pollutant contents of a fluid stream.**

Stages of Collection

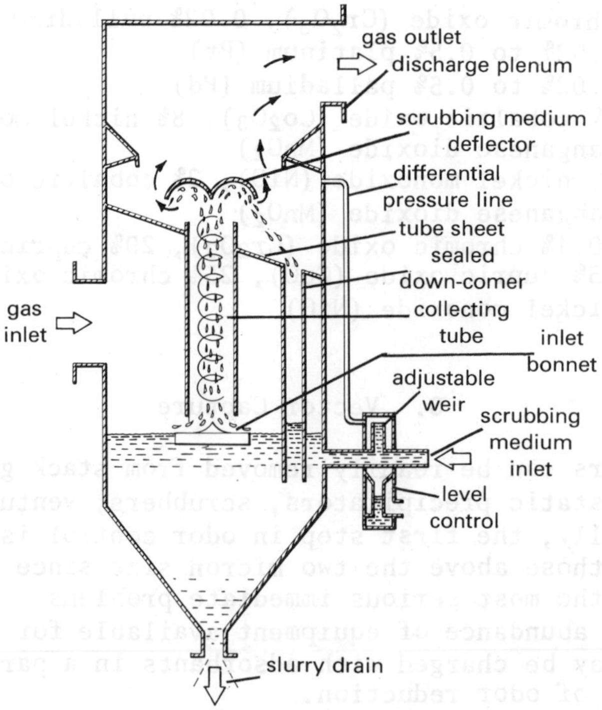


1. Impaction of the dust particles into the scrubbing medium as the high velocity gases pass through the slot between the inlet bonnets and the collecting tubes. 2. Cyclonic spinning and mixing of gas and liquid droplets within the collecting tube. 3. Impingement of gases and water upon the flooded surface of the scrubbing medium deflector. 4. Scrubbing of the gas as it passes through a curtain of liquid being discharged from the scrubbing medium deflector. Courtesy Zurn Industries, Inc.

Chemical Solutions Commonly Used in Scrubbers

| | Concentration | Estimated Results |
|---|---|---|
| "By-Pro-D" | 0.2% | 50% reduction |
| "Cairox" | 0.5% | 35% reduction |
| Calcium hypochlorite | 0.2% | 50% reduction |
| Chlorine | 600 PPM | 30% reduction |
| Hydrogen peroxide | ---- | 25% reduction |
| Lime | 1.0% | 0 |
| Politol "S" | 1.0% | 0 |
| Potassium permanganate | 0.75% | 0 |
| Soda ash | 1.0% | 0 |
| Sodium bisulfite | 0.75% | 0 |
| Water | Saturate | 20% reduction |

### 9. Condensation

Hot, moist, odor-bearing gases can be condensed as a means of reducing to some extent odorous gases. In general, this method of odor reduction will work well only where the gases condensed are water soluble, an unlikely circumstance where the malodorant is of any complexity. It would be the rare case where condensing in itself would be an adequate means of odor reduction. There are basically two types of condenser in use today: the contact condenser and the surface condenser. Condensers reduce the odor by removing condensible odorants from gas streams. The condensate cannot be reused and may pose a disposal problem. Contact condensers generally use more water than do surface condensers.

Condensers, like scrubbers and stacks, may be considered old art, and there are many available varieties.

Condensers
Applications for Odor Control

- Blood meal driers
- Chemical manufacturing
- Degreasers
- Esterification processes
- Petrochemical industry
- Refineries

### 10. Dehydration

"Drying is basically a matter of time and temperature. Heat must be properly applied to the material to vaporize and remove both surface, or external moisture and internal moisture from the product. The removal of surface moisture, even from heat-sensitive materials, usually can be done quickly and easily at a fairly high temperature, but the removal of internal moisture is a much more difficult problem and requires considerably more time. As soon as the material surface becomes dry, the temperature must be reduced to avoid scorching. With a low temperature, drying time must be lengthened to permit sufficient time for internal moisture to diffuse and migrate to the surface of the particle and be subsequently evaporated."[1]

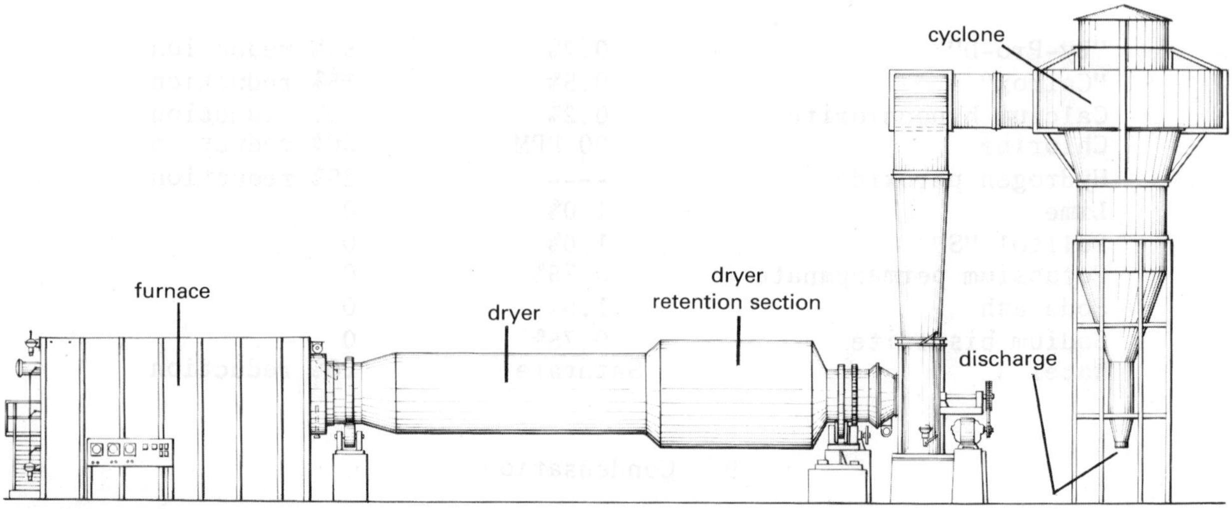


Enclosed rendering system for odor free operation: Dehydro-mat. Courtesy Edw. Renneburg & Sons Company

## 11. Source Control

In many instances proper handling and control of raw materials before processing can substantially reduce the odor control problem. Renderers often periodically pick up meat scraps and other wastes that must be accumulated several days before sufficient amounts are available to warrant collection. Numerous factors contribute to the degradation of such wastes resulting in a considerably amplified malodor problem. Bacteriological degradation and oxidative rancidity of fats are the most predominant. The temperature conditions where the materials are held contribute significantly to both factors. It is not always possible to hold such wastes under refrigeration or where permissible bactericides, bacteriostats, antioxidants or bactericidal ultraviolet installations could significantly reduce the problem. Unquestionably, an additional factor is the use of bare metal containers for handling. Metallic ions may considerably accelerate the oxidative rancidity of fats and oils, especially copper and iron ions. Citric acid will chelate these ions, and the containers can be rinsed with a citric acid solution prior to loading to reduce the problem. Antioxidants often contain citric acid as a synergist. After pickup the holding areas can be better controlled by the use of bactericidal ultraviolet placed at strategic locations.

Favorable improvements in odor quality in the treatment of sludge have been shown upon addition of lipases (N. S. Chamberlin, 1930) and trypsin (W. Rudolfs, 1932). The primary problem has been cost. Enzymes are not only finicky and ill-suited to the harsh environments encountered in sludge, but are expensive as well. The advent of enzymes bound in matrix may alter the economics of this application and result in a sludge of considerably improved quality.

United States patent number 3,708,421 describes a process for the removal of mercaptan sulfur from sour oils in the manufacture of petroleum products. Sour gasolines and other petroleum distillates in the range of 100 to 400°F are

---

[1] Courtesy of Edward Renneburg & Sons Company, Baltimore, Maryland 21224.

treated with a reagent formed by reacting a water soluble metal salt with a mixture of a glycinate derivative in an alkaline solution. The metal salt in alkaline solution combines with mercaptan sulfur compounds in a sour gasoline and distillate stream. The sour gasoline and distillates are prewashed with a caustic hydrogen sulfide solution, the first step of extracting the mercaptan sulfur compounds in the presence of the alkaline reagent. The second step involves oxidizing the mercaptan sulfur compounds in the spent alkaline reagent with a gas containing oxygen which regenerates the spent alkaline reagent for recycling. In the third step the disulfide sulfur is extracted from the regenerated reagent. This process is said to reduce the requirement for tetraethyl lead (TEL) and thereby reduce the amount of lead particles in automotive exhausts.

The iron glycinate reagent used in the invention is prepared by reacting one weight of ferric chloride $6H_2O$ and thirty weights of amino acetic acid-glycine with suitable mixed chelating agents in a known volume of water and by adding a calculated amount of this reagent to a known volume of caustic soda solution. Variations in ratios depend on the quality of the sour gasoline treated. An example of an average iron glycinate reagent contains 150 to 300 PPM of iron and 40 to 120 grams per liter of sodium hydroxide for the treatment of 50 to 2000 PPM of mercaptan sour gasolines. Cobalt diethanol glycinate is the reagent of preference followed by iron diethanol glycinate.

### 12. Paralysis

Finally, there have been and are still a number of marketed products which rely intentionally as well as unintentionally on the ability of certain materials to paralyze or anesthetize the ability to detect odors. It is obvious that there is no place for such materials in the methods of odor pollution control.

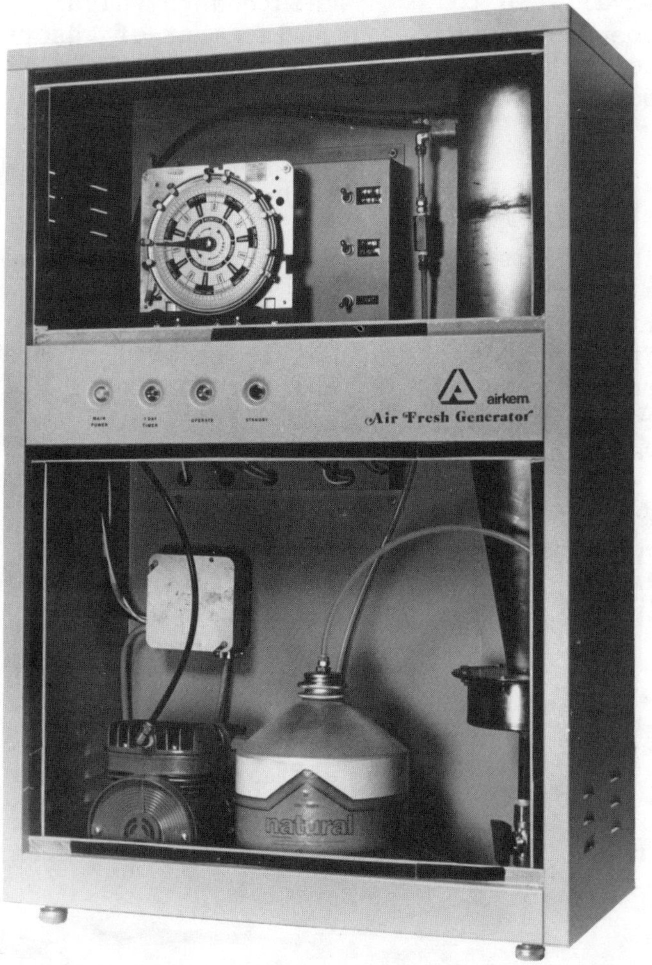


Controlled release unit for commercial industrial odor control, using disguising, neutralizing agents. Courtesy Air Kem, Inc.

## ECONOMICS FOR AIR POLLUTION ODOR CONTROL EQUIPMENT

### Generalized Averages

| Method | *Range of Efficiency | Average $/SCFM Installed Cost | Average $/Hr/SCFM Maintenance Operation | Average $/Yr/SCFM Total Cost |
|---|---|---|---|---|
| Adsorption | 80 - 100% | $7.00 | $3.75 | $4.65 |
| Absorption | 10 - 60 | 1.85 | .425 | .65 |
| Catalytic oxidation | 60 - 85 | 9.00 | 2.25 | 3.90 |
| Condensation | 30 - 75 | 6.50 | .625 | 1.55 |
| Chemical Neutralizer thru hot fogger | 65 - 95 | 1.00 | 2.60 | 3.00 |
| Thermal incineration | 40 - 85 | 10.00 | 2.25 | 3.90 |

*Averages from all users surveyed

### Advantages and Disadvantages of Odor Control Methods

| Method | Advantages | Disadvantages |
|---|---|---|
| Adsorption | Efficient process for odor removal. 80 to 100%, depending on gases; no fuel or water requirements. | Fouling of adsorbant; maintenance; high replacement of adsorbant. Sometimes unexpected reactions resulting in new contaminants of toxic value. |
| Absorption | Efficient for some specific odor problems; versatility for adding scrubbing compounds. Good particle remover. Good recovery potentials; waste easy to handle. | Use of water required can be high in operating and maintenance. Not in general complete malodor control. Wear and corrosion. |
| Catalytic oxidation | Increased efficiency over thermal with considerably reduced fuel costs. | Catalyst replacement lack of versatility. Catalyst poisoning; high maintenance necessary; fouling. |
| Condensation | Low cost. | Disposal problem; not efficient odor control and lacks versatility; space. Corrosion. |

| Method | Advantages | Disadvantages |
| --- | --- | --- |
| Chemical neutralizers and catalysts; stack fogger | Very low installation and upkeep cost. Specific formulation can result in high efficiency odor removal: 95%. Versatile; little space. | Cannot normally deal with toxic materials. Moderate to high CFM operating cost. |
| Thermal incineration | Ease of operation; low maintenance cost. Good efficiency in odor removal. | Operational costs; installation costs; space. |

## SOURCES OF MALODOR PROBLEMS

The so-called "offensive trades" whose common denominator is offensive or malodors were at one time generally recognized as a loosely identified group of industries which included abatoirs, blood boiling, tanning, rendering of all sorts, glue manufacturing, tankage reduction, garbage dehydration, privy cleaning, etc. Added to this archaic list in a modern context are food processing plants (especially fish), vegetable processing, fat frying, pet food manufacturing, breweries, coffee roasters, distilleries, soap works, grape press wastes, oil refineries, pulp mills, various chemical manufacturers, feed lots, sanitary land fills, rubber works, smelters, gas works, aeration ponds and lagoons, foundry operations, pharmaceutical plants, textile mills, asphalt plants, and sewage plants, to name a few.

Not only do many industries contribute to malodorous pollution, but in many cases the products produced are malodorous and must be treated before sale. Often a problem is encountered in some small workshop where local authorities have served notice, such as rubber hose cutting or small vulcanizing operations. In many cases malodor is an inherent part of the trade such as pest control operations whose trade chemicals are often in themselves foul smelling. Malathion is an example. Also, where the pest control operator finds his treatment successful, he often has serious malodor problems as a result, with dead rodents putrefying in difficult to get at ceiling, floor and wall spaces. Painters often receive considerable complaints regarding the paint smell which to some people can be overpowering. Mattress stuffers sometimes need to hold batting for months in inventory before it can be used due to the strong phenol odor. Motels, hotels, rest homes and hospitals deal with counteracting or eradicating specific odors that occur from day to day in their trades, urine, fecal odors, dead body odors, cancer and burn odors, to name but a few. Many products could find wider and more acceptable markets if an inherent malodor could be eliminated. Inexpensive printing inks, some textiles and plastics are good examples.

Various oils which were once a drudge on the market are now used for everyday cookery and a whole industry was born with the discovery of hydrogenation. Rapeseed, cottonseed and other by-product oils which tasted bitter and smelled distinctly malodorous were subjected to polymerization, a known way of eliminating malodor. The oils were placed under great pressure with catalytic nickel and in an atmosphere of hydrogen. The resulting product is a solid without taste or odor, and "Crisco" and dozens or other "shortenings" found their way to the market.

Methyl bromide is an excellent disinfectant and sterilant. It cannot be used by pest control operators, however, since a nauseating odor results upon any contact with foam rubber. Fortunately in this case a replacement was found in sulfuryl fluoride which is almost as effective and lacks the unpleasant malodor reaction.

## ANIMALS AS ODOR SOURCES

Waste production by America's domestic animals equals the waste from 1.9 billion humans. As a matter of fact, it has been estimated that if this manure was divided equally, every family would receive 25 cubic yards a year to assimilate and appreciate, enough to fill the average 9 foot by 15 foot living room to a depth of 5 feet, or chin level. A large poultry operation may produce as much as five tons of chicken droppings per day and a feed lot with 10,000 head of beef may produce 260 tons of waste. The feedlot problem equals the sewage problem of a city with a million people. Farmyard and feedlot runoff waters may be 10 to 100 times as high in BOD as untreated municipal sewage and is rich in the nutrients nitrogen and phosphorous which cause algal blooms and eutrophication. A 1966 study of the Potomac river area revealed the preponderance of pollution to be caused from animal wastes.

Some pollutants from animal wastes are air borne. About 90% of the ammonia in urine and manure volatizes into the air where it is easily trapped by plant and water surfaces. It has been calculated that a 35 foot deep lake a mile from a feed lot with 80,000 head of cattle absorbs enough ammonia each year to raise its entire volume to the eutrophic level (G. Soucie, 1972).

Odor is generally regarded as the toughest problem facing livestock and poultry producers. Unfortunately, many waste treatment processes intensify the odor problem instead of relieving it. In a recent report, the USDA has concluded that "perhaps the odor problem cannot be solved" (F. G. Viets, Jr., 1971). The energy evolved from a feedlot of 100,000 cattle could produce enough natural gas for a city of 30,000 people, and the by-product sludge would have twice the nutrient value (H. L. Bohn, 1970).

Presently the solutions which have been offered for this problem have been costly and empirical. The wastes are not deposited in a central area nor are they readily collectible economically.

Disguising chemicals have been sold in drum lots for spraying atmospherically across the feedlots. The results have been more than disappointing. None of the conventional devices or methods used by industry lend themselves to the solution to this problem. Several methods are being experimented with at present which may help or resolve the problem. Perhaps one of the more significant is to find a use for the waste which would make it economical to collect. Poultry do not represent the problem encountered in beef feedlots since it is already characteristic of the poultry industry to collect the fecal waste at central points where it can more easily be treated.

Degraded beef manure can result in excellent fertilizer but it is not generally economically feasible to ship for any distance. There are two reasons for this: low density and odor. At present a formulation which hastens the bacterial degradation of the manure is being tested. The basis of the formula is, in general, as follows:

Mnft-75

| | |
|---|---|
| Calcium chloride | Activated charcoal |
| Bacteria | Odor neutralizers |
| Enzymes | Buffers |

(Courtesy of Pace National Corp.)

This material is available in granular form and is spread directly on the feedlot surface at the rate of 400 pounds per acre, semiannually. The formula is relatively inexpensive and works in the following manner:

The calcium chloride is hygroscopic, which means that it draws and holds moisture from the atmosphere. This moisture is requisite for the bacteria and enzymes to break down the manure. The activated charcoal adsorbs many of the odorants, and the specific odor neutralizers interfere and cancel others. The buffers hold the pH at optimum. The topsoil layer is thereby turned into a surface septic layer with concomitant odor control. The residual charcoal and calcium enhance or sweeten the manure while the bacteria and enzymes degrade it to a composted, enriched manure with little or no odor level.

The addition to feedlot wastes of sulfa drugs and sulfaguanidine applied as a solid mixture with inert diluents in acid solution is a recommended method for feedlot odor control in United States patent 3,706,663 (1972).

United States patent 3,816,577 suggests the use of water soluble constituents of cherry pits, especially the water soluble proteins, as an effective animal waste deodorizer (1974).

United States patent 3,720,606 (1973) claims the use of a mixed culture of Bacillus, including Bacillus megaterium and/or Bacillus subtilis, and an odor suppressing agent such as amyl acetate. A mixture of 200 ml's of pecan oil, 200 ml's of amyl acetate and 8 ml's of bacterial liquid concentrate diluted with water to a volume of one gallon is claimed to suppress undesirable odors from holding pits used in connection with livestock and poultry housing.

A perimeter ducting around predominate downwind areas of feedlots, sanitary landfills and lagoons is offered by several suppliers in the United States. Chemical masks are dispersed in either aerosol or thermal hot fog from a central location and forced through spaced apertures in the ducting. This creates a perfumed atmosphere which is drawn off and intermixed into the ambient air downwind.

Gas Chromatographic Identification
Of Feedlot Volatiles

| | |
|---|---|
| Ammonia | Isobutylamine |
| n-Amylamine | Isopropylamine |
| n-Butylamine | Methylamine |
| sec-Butylamine | n-Methylamine |
| ter-Butylamine | n-Methylbutylamine |
| Diethylamine | n-Methyldiethylamine |
| Dimethylamine | n-Propylamine |
| Ethylamine | Triethylamine |
| Iso-Amylamine | Trimethylamine |

## INDUSTRIAL LAGOONS AS MALODOR SOURCE

Many industrial plants utilize lagoons to reduce the BOD of fluid wastes. The average time for waste to stabilize is between 90 and 120 days. There are basically two types of lagoons: aerobic and anaerobic. Aerobic lagoons rely on natural conditions such as shallow depths or sunlight as well as mechanical agitators and aerators for reoxygenization. Anaerobic lagoons are often called storage lagoons. Waste loading is, for the most part, a seasonal factor. Food processors, farms, poultry producers, renderers and sewage treatment facilities are but a few of the industries who use lagoon systems.

Odor control, especially in anaerobic lagoons, can become a considerable problem. Aerobic lagoons are a little easier to control since it has been shown that by judicious metering into the lagoon of sodium nitrate, odors can be controlled. The function of the nitrate is to supply oxygen to the aerobic bacteria to stimulate their decomposition of the waste and to stimulate growth of algae and other organisms which through photosynthesis will produce additional ogygen. The nitrate also assists in maintaining an alkaline reaction, necessary for overall production of oxygen. The addition of sodium nitrate, therefore, supplies oxygen directly and indirectly.

In the biochemical oxidation of organic matter the microorganisms remove hydrogen atoms from the organic molecule and in the process gain energy (R. E. McKinney, 1956). The process is sometimes called dehydrogenation. Through a series of biochemical reactions the hydrogen atoms are transferred to what is commonly called a hydrogen acceptor. The molecule gaining hydrogen is reduced. The possible hydrogen acceptors and the products of hydrogen addition are shown by the following series of equations:

| | Hydrogen Acceptor | | Hydrogen Atoms added | | Reduced Product |
|---|---|---|---|---|---|
| 1. | $O_2$ | + | $4H^+$ | = | $2H_2O$ |
| 2. | $2NO_3^-$ | + | $12H^+$ | = | $N_2 + 6H_2O$ |
| 3. | $SO_4$ | + | $10H^+$ | = | $H_2S + 4H_2O$ |
| 4. | Oxidized organics | + | $xH^+$ | = | Reduced organics |
| 5. | $CO_2$ | + | $8H^+$ | = | $CH_4 + 2H_2O$ |

Reactions one, two and five result in odorless products. Reaction three results in hydrogen sulfide, and reaction four often results in malodorants.

R. R. Dague (1972) concludes that:

1. The most common cause of odors in wastewater systems is hydrogen sulfide.
2. The conditions that lead to hydrogen sulfide production also favor the production of odorous organic compounds.
3. The reduction of the sulfate ion ($SO_4^{2-}$) is the most significant mechanism of hydrogen sulfide production in wastewaters.
4. The population of sulfate reducing organisms is low in fresh domestic wastewater and higher in sludge.
5. Sulfate reducing bacteria thrive at a low oxidation reduction potential (ORP) of -200 to -300 mv, a pH in the range of 6 to 9, and at warm temperature (86°F).
6. Sludge deposits and slime growths are the major cause of prolific hydrogen sulfide production in sewers.

Among the many methods that have been tried to control malodors are aeration of wastewater, addition of nitrate, precipitation of sulfide with metallic salts, increasing pH, addition of chromates, adsorption on activated charcoal, adsorption on soil, dilution, combustion of gases, counteraction, chlorination, masking and alkaline scrubbing.

Lagoons act as equalization and stabilization ponds for a wide variety of wastes. The anaerobic lagoon often creates a considerable downwind malodor problem. As with feedlots, the open lagoon is a difficult odor problem since the malodors cannot readily be collected for conventional treatment. There have been recent attempts to resolve this problem by physically covering entire lagoons with custom-made tarpaulins, collecting the offeed malodors and treating them by incineration. The coverings reported to date have not withstood the weather well and have lasted for only short periods of time in practice, losing their integrity.

Zinc sulfate monohydrate and citric acid is claimed to neutralize fecal odors and reduce bacterial contamination. The suggested use ratio of zinc sulfate to citric acid is one to four and added to fecal material in a concentration of from 50 to 100 PPM (United States patent 3,509,254, 1970).

Actinomycetes have been implicated as a principal contributor to lagoon malodors as early as 1929. In 1967 Gerber and Lechevalier succeeded in isolating the earthy smelling substances from cultures of numerous actinomycetes. The odorous compound produced by all organisms was identical (most were Streptomyces), and was named geosmin. Geosmin is converted by hydrochloric acid to an inodorous substance called argosmin. Rosen and coworkers (1968) showed that argosmin is a group of related compounds and thus cannot readily elucidate the structure of the parent, geosmin. Gerber showed that geosmin has the molecular formula $C_{12}H_{22}O$ and argosmin has the formula $C_{12}H_{22}$.

Morris and coworkers (1961) in studies of musty smelling substances produced by actinomycetes discovered volatile metabolites which consisted overwhelmingly of a single substance with an intense, musty odor. Named mucidone, the substance differed slightly from geosmin in molecular formula, $C_{12}H_{18}O$, and in some optical properties. Subsequent tests by the American Water Works Association established the two compounds to be distinct. Observers were also able to distinguish the two odors (American Water Works Association Committee Report, 1968).

United States patent 3,376,219 (1968) claims that an addition of Bacillus cereus in combination with an essentially nitrogen free starch medium to malodorous wastewater will produce emissions free of both geosmin and mucidone.

Small balls ranging from 0.75 to six inches in diameter have been proposed for lagoon coverings and are offered for sale to retard malodors (Author unknown, 1974). The manufacturer claims that the procedure of covering lagoons entirely in floating balls "repels smells" and that several large applications have proven efficacious as a means of odor control. The underlying mode of action of the spheres may be a physical reduction in the liquid surface area of the emitting source. The overriding constraints which may preclude use of this system are (a) cost constraints and (b) physical and operational constraints. A 100 acre application of 1.75 inch in diameter balls at the best manufacturer's price would cost between 17 and 20 million dollars. In terms of physical and operational constraints, the balls clog pumps by induction through suction lines, and wind and wave action may cause considerable loss (C. Lue-Hing, 1975). For very small applications, i.e., under 4,000 square feet, this procedure may be of some benefit.

A recent invention outlines the use of high melting point paraffin as an impervious covering for lagoons. The paraffin is melted and spread on the surface of the lagoon to form an island from 0.20 to 0.5 inch in thickness. The outer peripheral edge of the island is separated from the lagoon shore by three to five feet, depending upon the lagoon dimensions. The floating island of paraffin is affixed to the shore by a flexible apron which acts to secure the island and as a collection apron for off gases. The gases may be incinerated or stored and used as an energy source (R. Duclos, 1975). The average analysis of the gases collected showed a composition of 64% methane, 28% carbon dioxide, 3.4% hydrogen, 4.3% nitrogen and a heat value of 640 BTU's per cubic foot (A. M. Bushwell, 1939). The cost of the paraffin is stated to range between 14 and 18 cents per square foot of lagoon surface.

Other methods of lagoon odor control include the addition to lagoon surfaces of chemical agents which disguise or neutralize malodors. Drip systems from 55 gallon drums, spraying through nozzles over the lagoon and pouring chemicals in containers with wicks bordering lagoons have all been and are presently being used for odor control. In general, the results have not been considered promising.

A relatively new system used for many exposed emitting sources is the installation around the predominant peripheral downwind edge of the site ductwork which exhausts at strategic points of an atomized or thermal fog of selected chemicals which act as a disguising and neutralizing curtain. The system may be manually operated or activated by wind vanes, pre-set to operate when conditions for malodor emission are within an optimum range.

An interesting application for lagoon odor control is the floating body concept which is shaped as shown. The floating body incorporates malodor neutralizers in a volatile, biodegradable base which is buoyant. Cetyl alcohol is also contained in the formulation and forms a monomolecular layer on the surface of the lagoon, acting as a flexible covering and preventing odors that normally occur at the atmosphere lagoon interface through oxidation. The core material of the floating body is impregnated with enzymes and bacteria in a nutrient base with trace elements to promote good anaerobic activity. The floating body additionally carries optimum pH buffers for the specific lagoon. Several features are favorable for proper malodor control. The volatiles in the floating body increasingly volatize as the temperature gradient goes up, being stable at approximately 77°F and increasing upon direct exposure to forced air. In other words, as the malodor problem increases due to wind and temperature conditions, the floating body disseminates at a proportionally increasing rate. Since the floating body is free to "random walk" the lagoon, bacterial, enzymatic and grooming materials will be released over the entire surface.

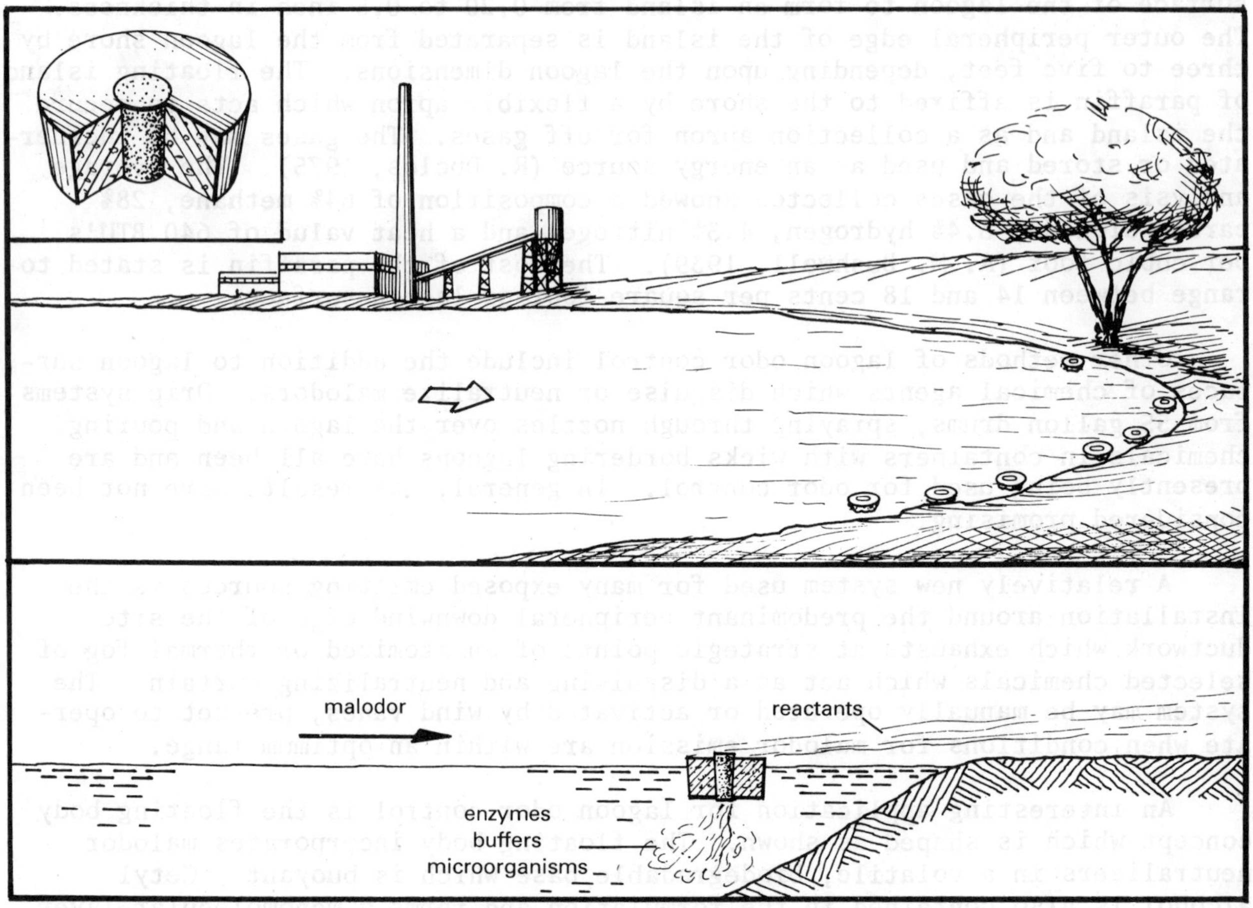


Solid floating body for lagoon odor control. Courtesy Pace National Corporation

# REGULATIONS FOR THE CONTROL OF MALODORS

At the present time the most informative statement regarding the state of odor control regulation is the absence of any federal regulations regarding odorous pollution. With an estimated 50% of all citizen complaints directed at odors, state and local authorities have desperately tried to find a workable basis for regulation. The 52 state agencies rely on regulations which may be classified into nine general types:

1. No specific regulations.
2. Air pollution/nuisance regulations.
3. Use of specified criteria to determine objectionability of an odor in ambient air.
4. Scentometer measurements by control officers in the ambient air by measuring dilutions to threshold (D/T). Violations are deemed to have occurred if stated D/T values are exceeded, usually within specified time periods.
5. The use of the highest and best practicable or reasonable and suitable control system is required at the source.
6. Source emission standards specifying the concentrations (as odor units per cubic feet or odor concentration units) of odor that are not to be exceeded. These are based on the syringe dilution technique.
7. Regulations based on instrumental analysis at the source or in the ambient air.
8. Control regulations that serve as statements of policy for handling odor problems.
9. Both source and ambient standards specified.

(Journal of the Air Pollution Control Association, May 1974)

What constitutes a complaint, or confirmed complaint, varies substantially from authority to authority. In some locales a telephone call is considered a complaint. In others, only a signed complaint with an agreement to testify in court against the polluter is considered a complaint. The majority of the agencies rely on the public nuisance concept to establish enforcement. It is obvious at the present time that no community has written objective odor criteria into their air pollution control ordinances nor could they, for no technical basis has existed as foundation for such a need.

Due to the general chaos wrought by lack of objective enforcement procedures, the courts have begun to look beyond the immediate problem and several important rulings which look to the overall economic impact of the malodor bearing industry have been handed down. In an important decision by the Illinois Supreme Court in the Illinois Environmental Protection Agency vs. Mystik Tape, it was decided in effect that whether odor emissions in fact constitute air pollution or not is a matter the Illinois Pollution Control Board may determine on a case-by-case basis within the limits imposed by law (60 Ill.2d 330):

(No. 46543.--Affirmed in part & reversed in part & remanded).
MYSTIK TAPE, Division of Borden, Inc., Appellee, v.
THE POLLUTION CONTROL BOARD et al.--
(Environmental Protection Agency, Appellant).

Opinion filed March 24, 1975

Section 9(a) of the Environmental Protection Act provides:

"No person shall:

(a) Cause or threaten or allow the discharge or emission of any contaminant into the evvironment in any state so as to cause or tend to cause air pollution in Illinois, either alone or in combination with contaminants from other sources, or so as to violate regulations or standards adopted by the Board under this Act." Ill. Rev. Stat. 1971, ch. 111 1/2, par. 1009 (a).

Section 3(b) of the Act defines air pollution as follows:

"Air Pollution is the presence in the atmosphere of one or more contaminants in sufficient quantities and of such characteristics and duration as to be injurious to human, plant, or animal life, to health, or to property, or to unreasonably interfere with the enjoyment of life or property." Ill. Rev. Stat. 1971, ch. 111 1/2, par. 1003(b).

Section 33(c) states:

"In making its orders and determinations, the Board shall take into consideration all the facts and circumstances bearing upon the reasonableness of the emissions, discharges, or deposits involved including, but not limited to:

(i) the character and degree of injury to, or interference with the protection of the health, general welfare and physical property of the people;

(ii) the social and economic value of the pollution source;

(iii) the suitability or unsuitability of the pollution source to the area in which it is located, including the question of priority of location in the area involved; and

(iv) the technical practicability and economic reasonableness of reducing or eliminating the emissions, discharges or deposits resulting from such pollution source."

Ill. Rev. Stat. 1971, ch. 111 1/2, par. 1033(c)(i), (ii), (iii), (iv).

The Supreme Court concluded that Mystik had not violated section 9(a). This decision is of sufficient importance to include the exact reasoning of the court:

"The appellate court additionally noted the Board did not appear to require that the emission of contaminants must unreasonably interfere with the enjoyment of life or property for there to be a violation of section 9(a). (16 Ill. App. 3d 778, 795, 796, 797-804). We concur with the conclusion of the appellate court in this regard, and we agree that this failure on the part of the Board constitutes error. The Board reviewed the testimony of various witnesses insofar as they described the nature of the odor and concluded: "The odor did not appear to cause any property damage or to force people to seek medical treatment. However, there is no question that the odors interfered with the comfort and enjoyment of life of the nearby residents, and constituted a nuisance and violated section 9(a) of the Act prohibiting the causing of air pollution."

"The opinion of the Board does not indicate that it took into consideration the various factors, bearing upon 'reasonableness,' as set forth in section 33(c). Rather, it appears that the Board viewed the question of reasonableness in light of its interpretation in Moody v. Flintkote Co. (1971), 2 Ill.

P.C.B. Op. 341. In Moody the Board stated:

> 'All of this testimony conclusively proves that the emissions from the Flintkote plant interfere with the enjoyment of life or property of the neighbors and those who come near the plant. The sole question remaining, then, is to determine whether such interference is unreasonable as required by the Act. It is the position of this Board that air contaminant emissions are unreasonable within the meaning of the Act when there is proof that there is an interference with life and property and that economically reasonable technology is available to control the contaminant emissions.' 2 Ill. P.C.B. Op. 341,350."

"The Moody test has been used by the Board in later cases involving section 9 (a) violations. See Employees of Holmes Bros. v. Merlan, Inc. (1971), 2 Ill. P.C.B. Op. 405; Environmental Protection Agency v. Incinerator, Inc. (1971), 2 Ill. P.C.B. Op. 505; Environmental Protection Agency v. Chicago Housing Authority (1972), 4 Ill. P.C.B. Op. 145; Environmental Protection Agency v. American Generator and Armature Co. (1972), 3 Ill. P.C.B. Op. 373."

"The interpretation given by the Board to the questions of 'unreasonable' and 'reasonableness' clearly is not that dictated by the statute. (Incinerator, Inc. v. Pollution Control Board (1974), 59 Ill.2d 290,296.) There is neither the detailed recitation of facts and reasons justifying the conclusion reached by the Board which the Act required (see Maywood Park Trotting Association, Inc. v. Illinois Harness Racing Com. (1959), 15 Ill.2d 559,563; Environmental Defense Fund, Inc. v. Ruckelshaus (D.C. Cir. 1971), 439 F.2d 584, 597-598; 2 K. Davis, Administrative Law Treatise secs. 16.01, 16.05 (1958)) nor such recitation as to indicate that the Board considered the factors set forth in the Act."

"We conclude that the determination of the Board that Mystik violated section 9(a) of the Act requires reversal. Unlike the appellate court, however, we believe the cause should be remanded to the Board for the taking of additional evidence, if either party deems it advisable, and for a determination then to be made based upon the evidence before the Board and the legal principles herein set forth. See Ill. Rev. Stat. 1971, ch. 110, par. 275(f), (g)."

"We conclude that the finding by the Board of the violation of section 9(a) of the Act was improper and that the finding of violations of section 9(b) and Rule 3-2.110 and the imposition of a $3,500 fine were proper. In the latter regard the order of the Board should be affirmed. As to the first issue, this matter is to be remanded to the Board for further proceedings, not inconsistent herewith."

"The judgement of the appellate court accordingly is affirmed in part and reversed in part, and the cause is remanded to the Board."

## Who Complains?

Practical experience has shown that with odor there are certain generalities about complaints:

The more notariety, the more the complaints.

Any association with morbid or "unclean" materials of process, the more vigorous and greater the complaints.
Any visible emissions will evoke complaints about malodor where it is anticipated.
Where there is any possibility of financial gain through forcing the malodor prone processor to buy real estate at inflated prices, there will be regular and vigorous complaints.
The more casual the means acceptable to the authorities for receiving complaints, the more complaints there will be.
The more warm and humid the weather, the more complaints there will be.

These are but a few generalities anyone familiar with odor complaints will recognize, but what about who complains? There are three categories of complainants familiar to odor plagued industry and authorities:

1. The genuine, normal complainant.
2. The psychological complainant.
3. The vested interest complainant.

Among the genuine complainants there are the hyposmics, normally about .5% of the population. The hyposmic often senses malodors imperceptible to others; his sensitivity to odors may be as high as 10,000 times normal. Menopausal women, menstruating women or persons with tumors, Addison's disease, metabolic disorders and other debilities may give rise to temporary or permanent hyposmia.

Among the psychological complainants encountered are those whose deep sensibilities are offended by the nature of the process materials involved. Sludge, sewage, garbage, renderers and crematoriums have all shared their proportion of this type of complainant. They are often identifiable by their extreme agitation and unreasonable attitudes. Another of the common psychological complainants are those who seek notoriety, often leading local citizen groups and seeking redress through publicized confrontation. Actually, in some small communities the opportunity to be involved in an important issue of controversy often polarizes otherwise indifferent citizens into pros or cons.

It is difficult to know how prevalent the vested interest complainant is as a factor in overall pollution complaints, but there is no question that they are encountered. When a local situation develops as a result of the vested interest complainant, it is often a malignant problem. The malodor prone processor may try all forms of redress and work to the limit of the state of the art, even going so far as to try ridiculous remedies which only fail and sometimes backfire, causing a worsening of the problem. As attendant notoriety builds over the situation, complaints become more frequent and the authorities more troubled. All too often the malodor prone processor, after repeated attempts to solve the problem and placate the complainants, takes on the attitude that the complainants are not sincere and becomes himself antagonistic to the authorities and complainants. Such an attitude can hardly help, but in view of the futile exercise often rigorously gone through by the processor, is not unexpected.

At present, there is no qualification for a complainant. He may complain and the processor must answer, guilty or not. Case after case can be cited where processors have been virtually driven to the wall by an aggressive complainant group. Analysis indicates that far from being typical, complaint groups are often representative of only the smallest fraction of the immediate population. Records of a large sludge processing operation are given as an example:

Odor Complaints, 1974

| | |
|---|---|
| January: | 1 |
| February: | 0 |
| March: | 5 |
| April: | 6 |
| May: | 15 |
| June: | 21 |
| July: | 45 |
| August: | 33 |
| September: | 15 |
| October: | 20 |
| November: | 0 |
| December: | 0 |
| Total | 162 |

Of 162 complaints received by phone, 83 were from four people representing 51% of the total calls received. Two of the four are known to have offered for sale their premises at prices 40% to 50% higher than appraised values to the processor. These calls received from a community of approximately 60,000 people represent $6.3^{-4}$% of the population. The processor has been plagued, and the operation brought to a standstill on numerous occasions in spite of the essential nature of the processor's service and, at least in this case, application of every known procedure to eliminate or reduce odor by the processor.

The motives of the four persons representing 51% of the complaints have not been called to question, nor are they likely to be. Undoubtedly many complainants who called were sincere, but there is every evidence that they all were not. In addition, the project deals with sludge, a case where abnormal complaints are anticipated, and has been attended by considerable publicity. All are factors which experienced odor control technicians recognize as danger signs for complaints. Of the 162 complaints received, only 27 were confirmed by investigators and only two were verified. In order to complain in this jurisdiction, all that is required is a telephone call. No provision has been made to protect the processor's rights or the general public's rights, for the processor more than likely serves the best interest of the general public, contrary to the outcry from the abnormal or vested interest complainant. No test is required to determine if a complainant is hyposmic, and if he is are his interests unilateral with the public welfare when he can detect otherwise indetectable odors or reacts in sensitivity as much as 10,000 times above normal? If among any group of complainants there are not hyposmics, why are they absent?

If an investigator judges that a complainant is psychologically disturbed, why isn't this taken into consideration? Why should agencies support methods and techniques which actually are known to amplify a problem such as "hot lines," etc., when a more sensible approach would be a signed complaint, stating willingness to testify?

It is desirable that more thoughtful and fair treatment of the malodor prone processor be given consideration in future ordinances, for all too often the malodor prone industry is essential to the common welfare and when they are subjected to arbitrary and capricious treatment, it is to the disadvantage of the general public. One major question faces those concerned with malodor prone processors, and before more costly mistakes are made it should be answered. Does dissemination of air borne malodor constitute air pollution?

## Sample Odor Complaint Form

Time of Complaint: __________ Location: __________

Name of Complainant: __________

Address: __________

Can you describe the odor? __________

Do you feel you know from where it emanates? __________

If yes, what is the basis for this belief? __________

Are you sensitive average not sensitive to odors (circle one)?

Do you think that odors cause illness? __________

Have you filed prior complaints? How many? Dates? __________

__________

Have you read or heard about this source from others? __________

Do you or have you recently suffered any illness? __________

I affirm that this complaint constitutes my objective response to the problem as stated, that I in no way expect to gain financially or materially from this complaint, that I believe the odor is injurious to human health or welfare and/or unreasonably interferes with my enjoyment of life and property, and I am willing to testify, if the matter should be brought before a board or court of law for determination.

__________
Signed

__________
Date

Observer verified: Yes No

Time:

Date: __________
Officer

Summary of Odor Control Regulations of 52 Agencies
(States, District of Columbia and Bay Area)

(Journal of the Air Pollution Control Association, May 1974)

ALABAMA: Air pollution is defined as presence of air contaminant (includes odor) in quantities and duration to injure human health and welfare.

ALASKA: Air pollution prohibited: No emission ... unreasonably interfere with enjoyment of life and property.

ARIZONA: No regulations.

ARKANSAS: Section 10. Emission of Air Contaminants such as to Constitute Air Pollution -- odors mentioned.

CALIFORNIA: No discharge of air contaminants which cause injury, detriment, nuisance or annoyance to any considerable number of persons or to the public (agricultural odors exempt).

COLORADO: No person shall cause ... the emission of odorous air contaminants ... such as to result in detectable odors which are measured in excess of specified limits as determined by Scentometer or equivalent (Regulation 2).

CONNECTICUT: No person ... shall emit ... into the outdoor air any substance which creates an objectionable odor beyond his property line. Three methods for determining objectionable odor specified (Sec. 19.508-23).

DELAWARE: No person shall cause ... the emission of an odorous air contaminant such as to cause air pollution. The purpose is to control odorous air contaminants which significantly affect the citizens of the state outside the source boundaries. Methods for determining air pollution condition suggested include Scentometer tests, air quality monitoring and affidavits from citizens and investigators (Proposed Regulation XX).

DISTRICT OF COLUMBIA: The emission of an odor shall be deemed a violation, after three separate complaints when odor is detected at Number 1 odor strength (1 part odorous air to 1 part odor-free air) using a Scentometer or equivalent (Section 8-2:715).

FLORIDA: Objectionable odor defined as any odor ... may be harmful or injurious to human health and welfare, which unreasonably interferes with the comfortable use and enjoyment of life and property or which creates a nuisance. Affidavits obtained from affected persons. Objectionable odor prohibited (Ch. 17.2).

GEORGIA: No specific odor regulation.

HAWAII: No specific odor regulation (nuisance laws can apply).

IDAHO: No person shall allow ... the emission of odorous gases ... into the atmosphere as to cause air pollution. No person shall allow ... any plant engaged in processing ... to be operated without employing reasonable measures (as approved) for the control of odorous emissions (Reg. K). TRS (Total

Reduced Sulfides) emission standards for kraft pulp mills (Reg. O). Inedible rendering plants -- condensation and incineration (1200°F, 0.3 sec.) required (Reg. Q).

ILLINOIS: Inedible Rendering Process Only. (a) Exemption of human food processing and food service. (b) No person shall operate or use any device ... for the inedible rendering of animal or marine matter unless all gases ... shall be controlled ... to effectively abate any objectionable odor nuisance. If more than one company, abatement effective if not more than 120 odor units/cubic foot. Provision is made for the existence and determination of an objectionable odor nuisance by use of Scentometer at specified dilutions depending on type of land use (3 indicated) (Part VIII Rules 801, 802). Other odor cases in Illinois are prosecuted on a nuisance basis rather than on odor regulation per se.

IOWA: No regulation.

KANSAS: No specific odor regulation. For serious nuisance situation, regulation 28-19-13, Interference with Enjoyment of Life and Property, applies. Public hearing to determine this.

KENTUCKY: Ambient standard for odor. At any time, odor is not to equal or exceed 7 dilutions by use of a Scentometer.

MAINE: No specific regulation.

MARYLAND: No person shall cause ... any discharge of gases, vapors or odors in such a manner that a nuisance or air pollution is created. No person shall cause ... the use of any installation primarily engaged in the reduction of offal or vegetable oil unless all gases, vapors and gas-entrained matter from said installation are: (a) cooled to temperature of not greater than 160°F and then (b) non-condensible fraction is incinerated at a temperature of not less than 1400°F for not less than 0.4 sec. (c) alternate methods may be used if equally or more effective. Additional provisions for odor control from these sources are listed (Reg. F).

MASSACHUSETTS: No person having control of any dust or odor generating operations such as, but not limited to (several operations listed) shall permit emissions therefrom to the extent that such cause or contribute to a condition of air pollution.

MICHIGAN: No person shall cause ... the emission of an air contaminant (odor included by implication) ... which causes or will cause detriment to the health, safety, welfare and comfort of any person ... (R 336.46). The rule (336.47) prohibiting the dilution and concealment of emissions does not apply to the control of odors.

MINNESOTA: Chapter 9 (APC 9 Control of Odors in the Ambient Air) specifies odorous source emission standards, a source odor emission rate limitation of 1,000,000 odor units/minute, as well as ambient limits in 3 land use areas that are not to be exceeded. Chapter 10 (APC 10) requires odors from the Processing of Animal Matter to be controlled by incineration (1500°F, 0.3 seconds) or equivalent.

MISSISSIPPI: Miscellaneous Chemical Emissions. No person shall cause the emission of toxic, noxious or deleterious substances, in addition to those considered in these regulations, into the ambient air in concentrations sufficient to affect human health and well-being, or unreasonably interfere with the enjoyment of property or unreasonably and adversely affect plant or animal life beyond the boundaries of the property containing the air pollution source (Sec. 5.2).

MISSOURI: Regulations S-IX on Restriction of Emission of Odors applies throughout the state except for St. Louis City and 11 counties. No person may cause ... the emission of odorous matter in such concentrations and frequencies or for such durations that such odor can be perceived when 1 volume of odorous air is diluted with 7 volumes of odor-free air for 2 separate trials not less than 15 minutes apart within the period of one hour. Scentometer or equivalent is specified technique. One industry is exempted.

MONTANA: No person shall cause ... any emissions of gases, vapors or odors beyond the property line in such manner as to create a public nuisance. Legal proceedings may be instituted for abatement. Additional provisions require use of control devices on any odor creating process. Reduction of animal matter requires incineration or equivalent.

NEBRASKA: No regulation.

NEVADA: No person shall discharge any contaminant that ... is offensive to the senses ... An odor is deemed objectionable if 30% or more of a sample of at least 20 people deem it so, or 75% if less than 20. A violation is deemed to occur if odor is detectable in the ambient air after dilution with 8 or more volumes of odor-free air on 2 measurements within one hour, at least 15 minutes apart. (Article 10.1).

NEW HAMPSHIRE: Air pollution means one or more contaminant in sufficient quantities to among others, create a disagreeable or unnatural odor.

NEW JERSEY: No person shall cause ... to be emitted into the outdoor atmosphere substances in quantities which shall result in air pollution (Ch.6, Sec. 2.1).

NEW MEXICO: No regulation.

NEW YORK: Air pollution prohibited. Air pollution is the presence of an air contaminant, including odor, "which unreasonably interferes with the comfortable enjoyment of life and property."

NORTH CAROLINA: No person shall cause ... any plant engaged in the processing of animal, vegetable or mineral matter to be operated without employing suitable measures for the control of odorous emissions including wet scrubbers, incinerators or such other devices as may be approved by the Board. Applies to all operations that produce odorous emissions (Reg. 5).

NORTH DAKOTA: Air pollution control regulations do not cover odor control.

OHIO: AP-2-07. Air Pollution Nuisances prohibited. The emission or escape into the open air from any source ... of odors, ... or is unreasonably offensive and objectionable to the public.

OKLAHOMA: No regulation specific to odor other than public nuisance law.

OREGON: The highest and best practicable treatment and control of air contaminant emissions shall in every case be provided so as to maintain overall air quality at the highest possible levels and to maintain contaminant concentrations, visibility reduction, odors, soiling and other deleterious effects at the lowest possible levels (20 - 001). Registration and air-contaminant discharge permits required. Emissions from animal rendering (by incineration 1200°F for 0.3 sec. or equivalent) and hardboard tempering ovens (incineration 1500°F for 0.3 sec.) must be treated. Additional odor control rules apply to the area covered by the former (Columbia-Williamette Authority).

PENNSYLVANIA: No person shall cause ... at any time any emissions from the following processes (16 listed) unless the emissions have been incinerated at a minimum temperature of 1200°F for at least 0.3 sec. prior to their emission into the outdoor atmosphere (equivalent techniques -- if shown -- may be used). No person shall cause ... the emission into the outdoor atmosphere of any malodorous air contaminants from any source whatsoever, including those in compliance with the above, in such a manner that the malodors are detectable beyond the person's property (123.31).

RHODE ISLAND: "Create a disagreeable or unnatural odor." (Reg. 7).

SOUTH CAROLINA: No specific regulation.

SOUTH DAKOTA: "When as many as five complaints of an objectionable odor situation are registered ... the Commission is to interview the complainants and/or other occupants of the area to determine if violation has occurred and to determine the source or sources and circumstances of emission." If violation has occurred, that person shall take all steps required by the Commission to control the objectionable odor (Part II).

TENNESSEE: No specific regulation.

TEXAS: No person shall discharge from any source whatsoever one or more air contaminants or combinations thereof, in such concentration and of such duration as are or may tend to be injurious to or to adversely affect human health or welfare, animal life, vegetation or property, or as to interfere with the normal use and enjoyment of animal life, vegetation or property (Rule 5--Nuisance).

UTAH: No specific regulation

VERMONT: A person shall not discharge ... any emissions of objectionable odors beyond the property line of a premises. An objectionable odor shall mean those odors deemed objectionable by 15% or more of a sample of people (at least 20) exposed in a particular situation or 75% if panel of between 4 - 19 persons. Panel to be selected from those occupying or frequenting places closest to, but beyond the source property line (Section 2 of 5-241). No persons shall operate ... any device ... or other contrivance for the industrial processes which as determined by the A.P.C. officer is an odoriferous process per se, unless all gases ... are incinerated at 1600°F for not less than 0.5 seconds or by equally or more effective technique. (Section 3 of 5-241).

VIRGINIA: No person shall cause ... any source to discharge air contaminants (all operations that produce odorous emissions) which cause an odor objectionable to individuals of ordinary sensibility. The determination of an objectionable odor is to be made after review of all data and evidence gained by staff investigation and by public hearing to hear complaints. If in violation, control measures as approved shall be employed. Section IV, Rule 6, 4.06.00.

WASHINGTON: No specific regulations (see the nine local A.P.C. authorities which have regulations).

WEST VIRGINIA: Regulation IV -- To prevent and control the discharge of air pollutants into the open air which causes or contributes to an objectionable odor or odors. An odor is objectionable based on opinion based on investigation, in addition to odors generally recognized as objectionable. No person shall cause ... the discharge of air pollutants which cause or contribute to an objectionable odor at any location occupied by the public.

WISCONSIN: No person shall cause ... emission into the ambient air of any substance ... in such quantities that an objectionable odor is determined to result unless preventive measures satisfactory to the department are taken to abate or control such emission. An odor shall be deemed objectionable when either or both of the following are met: (1) Upon a decision from investigation by the agency based upon nature, intensity, frequency and duration of the odor as well as the type of area involved and other factors. (2) Or when 60% of a random sample (at least 9 persons) exposed to the odor in their place of residence or employment claim it to be objectionable and the nature, intensity, frequency and duration of the odor are considered (NR 154.18-1 malodorous emissions). TRS Limitations for kraft pulp mills (NR 154.18-2).

WYOMING: Section 16 Odors. (a) The ambient air standard for odors from any source shall be limited to: (1) an odor emission at the property line from which such emissions occur of sufficient strength to be equal to but not greater than that detectable after seven dilutions with odor-free air as determined by a Scentometer or equivalent techniques. The occurrence of odors shall be measured so that at least two measurements can be made within a period of one hour, these determinations being separated by at least 15 minutes. (b) Control of odors from animal reduction (incineration 1200°F for 0.3 seconds or equivalent).

BAY AREA POLLUTION CONTROL DISTRICT (CALIFORNIA): No person shall cause ... the emission of any of the substances listed in Column 1 of Table A in excess of the concentrations shown in Column 2 of Table A for that substance.

Table A: Maximum Allowable Emission of Odorous Substances

| Substance | Maximum Allowable Emission (PPM) Type A Emission Point | Type B Emission Point |
|---|---|---|
| Trimethylamine $(CH_3)_3N$ | 0.02 | 0.01 |
| Phenolic compounds calculated as phenol $C_6H_5OH$ | 5.0 | 2.5 |
| Mercaptans calculated as methyl mercaptan $CH_3SH$ | 0.2 | 0.1 |
| Ammonia $NH_3$ | 5000.0 | 2500.0 |
| Dimethylsulfide $(CH_3)_2S$ | 0.1 | 0.05 |

BAY AREA POLLUTION CONTROL DISTRICT: All sampling and analysis of exhaust gases for odorous substances listed in Column 1 of Table A shall follow the techniques prescribed in Chapter 2, Division 15. Tests for determining compliance with this regulation shall be for not less than 15 consecutive minutes or 90% of the time of the actual source operation, whichever is less (Division 15: Odorous Substances, 15101, 15103).

## LIST OF NATURAL PLANT AND ANIMAL ODORANTS

To illustrate the complexity of a natural essential oil, the following table is a breakdown of bergamot oil (Kirk-Othmer Encyclopedia of Chemical Technology, 1967):

Bergamot Oil Constituent Breakdown

| Constituent | Average % |
|---|---|
| Aldehyde $C_9$ | 0.180 |
| Aldehyde $C_{10}$ | 0.542 |
| Bergamottene | 0.077 |
| Bisabolene | 0.173 |
| Bisabolene isomer | 0.649 |
| Camphene | 0.054 |
| $\Delta^3$-Carene | 0.167 |
| Caryophyllene | 0.286 |
| Citronellal | 0.075 |
| Citronellol | 0.341 |
| p-Cymene | 0.765 |
| Decyl acetate | 0.097 |
| Dehydrolinalool | 0.174 |
| Ethyl glycollate | 0.238 |
| Geranial | 0.595 |
| Geranyl acetate | 0.525 |
| Humulene | 0.239 |
| d-Limonene | 28.323 |
| Linalool | 16.457 |
| Linalyl acetate | 29.626 |
| Methyl glycollate | 0.108 |
| Myrcene (alloocimene) | 0.933 |
| Neral | 0.532 |
| Neryl acetate | 0.718 |
| Octyl acetate | 0.074 |
| α-Phellandrene | 0.062 |
| α-Pinene | 1.387 |
| β-Pinene + sabinene 4:1 | 7.697 |
| Terpenyl acetate | 0.384 |
| γ-Terpinene | 7.651 |
| Terpinene-4-ol | 0.068 |
| α-Terpineol | 0.309 |
| Terpinolene | 0.494 |
| | 100.000% |

The following table of Natural Plant and Animal Odorants consists mainly of essential oils. These oils compose a class of odoriferous, volatile liquids, insoluble in water, which are obtained from the plants they impart their odors and other characteristic properties to. They are of various organic types such as aldehydes, esters, ethers, etc. or mixtures of the same. Some contain dissolved resin, known as oleoresins, and are sometimes called volatile oils in distinction from fixed oils.

All essential oils may be considered as agents used in odor control. Many merely mask while some show true chemical reactivity with malodorants, and still others show a specific capacity to neutralize (Zwaardemaker paris).

Natural Plant and Animal Odorants

| Name (Synonyms) | Odor Description | Use |
|---|---|---|
| Abies siberica (Siberian fir needle oil) | aromatic, balsamic | insecticides, soaps, bath salts, perfumes, inhalents, cosmetics, room sprays, medicinal and technical preparations |
| Absinthium oil (absinthe, wormwood) | | alcoholic beverages and cordials, pharmaceuticals |
| Allspice oil (pimenta, pimenta berry) | clove-like | pharmaceuticals, flavoring, bay rum manufacture, perfumery, soaps, cosmetics |
| Aloe oil | saffron-like | medicinals |
| Althea root (marshmallow) | | medicinals, emollients |
| Ambergris | characteristic, peculiar | medicinals, perfumery, perfume fixative |
| Amber, rectified | strong, penetrating | medicinals |
| Ambrette seed oil | fatty odor but upon aging a flowery-musk odor develops | perfume fixative |
| Angelica root oil | musky | insect attractant, liqueurs |
| Angelica seed oil | musky | liqueurs, medicinals |
| Angostura bark | unpleasant, musty | medicinals, alcoholic beverage flavoring |
| Anise oil | characteristic | condiments, flavoring |
| Anise oil, Japanese star | characteristic | insecticides, expectorants, medicinal flavoring |
| Asafetida | foul, garlic-like | medicinals, Eastern condiments |
| Asarum canadense oil (Canada snakeroot, Indian ginger) | strong, agreeable, aromatic | perfumery |
| Balm (Melissa) | aromatic, lemon-like | medicinals |

| Name (and Synonyms) | Odor Description | Use |
|---|---|---|
| Balsam tolu oil | aromatic, vanillin-hyacinth | medicinals, perfumery, fumigants, confectionery |
| Basil oil | aromatic, penetrating, estragon-like | flavoring, cosmetics, perfumery, medicinals |
| Bay oil (myrcia) | pleasant, sweet, deep odor with lemon-like top note | antiseptics, pharmaceuticals, flavoring, bay rum, hair tonics, aftershave lotions, perfumery |
| Benzoin, Siam resin | balsamic, vanilla-like | medicinals, cosmetics, perfumery, preservatives |
| Bergamot oil | agreeable | insecticides, pharmaceuticals, lotions, perfumery, toiletries, soaps, disinfectants |
| Birch oil (betula, sweet birch oil) | wintergreen odor | flavoring |
| Bitter almond oil | characteristic, benzaldehyde odor | pharmaceuticals |
| Bois de rose oil, Brazilian (rosewood) | fragrant | perfumery, preparation of linalool |
| Cabreuva oil | | source of nerolidol isolate |
| Cade oil (juniper tar) | smokey | medicinals, medicinal soaps |
| Cajeput oil | agreeable, pleasant, camphor-like | medicinals |
| Calamus oil | aromatic | medicinals, perfumery, liqueurs |
| Camphor oil, rectified | characteristic, camphor odor | medicinals, pharmaceuticals |
| Cananga oil | floral, ylang ylang odor | soaps, cosmetics, perfumery |
| Capsicum oil (cayenne pepper) | pungent | condiments |
| Caraway oil (carui) | characteristic | flavoring, liqueurs, medicinals, soaps, perfumery |
| Cardamon oil | agreeable, characteristic, strongly aromatic, camphoraceous | flavoring, medicinals |
| Carrot oil | spicy | liqueurs, flavoring, perfumery |

| Name (and Synonyms) | Odor Description | Use |
|---|---|---|
| Carrot seed oil | | perfumery |
| Cascarilla oil | faintly aromatic | flavoring, medicinals |
| Cashew nut shell oil | | insulating varnishes, typewriter rolls, brake linings |
| Cassia oil (Chinese cinnamon) | cinnamon-like | fungicide, local stimulent, medicinals, pharmaceuticals, soaps, flavoring, toothpastes, mouthwashes |
| Cassie flower oil | fragrant, orange-violet | perfumery |
| Catechu black oil | | tanning, dyeing, staining wood |
| Catechu pale (gambir) | | tanning, dyeing, astringents |
| Catnip oil | aromatic | medicinals, mild aromatic |
| Cedar leaf oil | | medicinals, commercial polishes |
| Cedar wood oil | mild, agreeable, persistent | soaps, perfumery fixative, insect repellent |
| Celery oil | celery odor | flavoring, medicinals |
| Celery seed oil | characteristic, peculiar and aromatic | flavoring, perfumery |
| Chamomile oil, English (Roman chamomile oil) | pleasant, strong, aromatic | perfumery, medicinals |
| Chamomile oil, German (Hungarian chamomile oil) | characteristic, agreeable | medicinals |
| Chenopodium oil (American wormseed oil, goosefoot oil) | characteristic, disagreeable | medicinals, anthelmintic |
| Cherry bark oil, wild | aromatic | beverages, medicinals |
| Cherry laurel oil | bitter almond odor | (very poisonous) |
| Cinnamon oil (cinnamon bark oil, cinnamon leaf oil) | cinnamon odor | pharmaceuticals, toothpastes, mouthwashes, flavoring, soaps, perfumery |
| Cinnamon oil, Ceylon | cinnamon odor | medicinals, flavoring, perfumery |
| Citronella oil, Ceylon | pleasant, pungent, citrus type | soaps, technical preparations, insecticides, perfumery |

| Name (and Synonyms) | Odor Description | Use |
|---|---|---|
| Citronella oil, Java | pleasant, pungent, citrus type | manufacture of isolates and synthetics, insecticides, technical preparations, soaps, perfumery |
| Civet | obnoxious, nauseating, becoming pleasing when greatly diluted | perfume fixative |
| Clove oil (Caryophyllus) | strong, aromatic, pungent, spicy | germicide, medicinals, soaps, flavoring, perfumery, pharmaceuticals, disinfectants |
| Cocoa | chocolate-like | flavoring |
| Coffee extract | characteristic of green coffee beans | flavoring |
| Cognac oil (ethyl enanthate) | pleasant, wine-like | flavoring, odorants |
| Copaiba oil | peculiar, pepper-like | perfume fixative, soaps, perfumery |
| Coriander oil | aromatic | flavoring, alcoholic beverages, medicinals |
| Costus oil | sweet, persistent, reminiscent of old wood and wet dog | perfumery |
| Cubeb oil | characteristic, strong, spicy | medicinals |
| Cumin oil | characteristic, cumin | flavoring, medicinals |
| Cypress oil | characteristic | perfume fixative, perfumery, medicinals |
| Dillseed oil, European | penetrating, caraway-like | flavoring, perfumery |
| Dillseed oil, Indian (Indian dill oil) | harsh, penetrating, caraway-like | flavoring, perfumery |
| Dillweed oil, American (dill herb oil, dill oil, anethum oil) | characteristic, penetrating | flavoring, perfumery |
| Dwarf pine needle oil | pleasant, aromatic | medicinals |
| Elder flower oil | honey-like | toiletries |
| Elecampane | heavy, woody | medicinals |

| Name (and Synonyms) | Odor Description | Use |
|---|---|---|
| Elemi oil | agreeable, aromatic | perfume fixative |
| Estragon oil (tarragon) | peculiar, anise-like | perfumery, flavoring |
| Eucalyptus oil | aromatic, characteristic, camphoraceous | disinfectants, chemical synthesis, perfumery |
| Fennel oil (fennel seed oil) | fennel odor | pharmaceuticals, flavoring, soaps |
| Fenugreek | pungent, aromatic | flavoring |
| Fir needle oil, Canadian (Canada fir oil) | pleasant, balsam-like | medicinals |
| Fleabane oil (erigeron) | peculiar, aromatic, fresh, spicy, herbaceous, persistent | perfumery, medicinals |
| Frankincense oil (olibanum) | agreeable, faintly lemon-like, balsamic | odorant |
| Galangal | rich, spicy | flavoring |
| Galbanum resin | aromatic (adds a greenish top note to perfumes) | perfumery, medicinals, incense |
| Garlic oil | strong, characteristic, exceedingly penetrating garlic odor; objectionable when concentrated but pleasant upon dilution | flavoring, therapeutic (reduces high blood pressure) |
| Geranium oil | exceedingly agreeable, pleasant rose-like | soaps, perfumery |
| Geranium oil, East Indian (palmarosa, Turkish geranium) | pleasant, rose-like | soaps, cosmetics, perfumery |
| Ginger oil | characteristic | flavoring, liqueurs |
| Grapefruit oil (shaddock) | citrus type odor | flavoring, lotions, colognes |
| Guaic wood oil | very agreeable, violet-tea odor | perfume fixative, perfumery |
| Hawthorne (aubepine) | | medicinals |

| Name (and Synonyms) | Odor Description | Use |
|---|---|---|
| Hemlock oil (spruce) | characteristic, pleasant, agreeable, balsam-like | medicinals |
| Hop oil | powerful, strong, penetrating | medicinals, flavoring |
| Horehound | aromatic | medicinals, flavoring |
| Horseradish | pungent | condiment flavoring |
| Hyacinth oil | sharp, penetrating, assuming a hyacinth odor on dilution | perfumery |
| Hyssop oil | aromatic | medicinals, liqueur flavoring, perfumery |
| Jasmine oil | characteristic, fragrant | perfumery |
| Juniper berry oil (jupiter oil) | characteristic, turpentine-like | medicinals, liqueurs, gin flavoring, pharmaceuticals |
| Juniper wood oil | weak juniper odor | veterinary medicine |
| Labdanum | sweet, balsam, amber-like | perfume fixative, perfumery |
| Laurel oil (sweet bay, laurel leaf) | aromatic | flavoring |
| Lavandin oil, abrial | slight camphoraceous, lavender | soap, perfumery |
| Lavender oil (lavender flower oil) | characteristic, lavender | cosmetics, lotions, medicinals, toiletries, soaps |
| Lemon oil (limonis) | fragrant, lemon-like | medicinal flavoring, food flavoring, perfumery, lotions, soaps |
| Lemongrass oil (Indian verbena) | fragrant, pronounced, heavy lemon-like | soaps. sprays, toiletries, technical preparations |
| Levant wormseed | | anthelmintic |
| Licorice extract | | medicinals, flavoring, foam producer |
| Lilac oil | fragrant | perfumery |
| Lily-of-the-valley oil | fragrant | perfumery |

| Name (and Synonyms) | Odor Description | Use |
|---|---|---|
| Lime oil | intense, lemon | flavoring, colognes, lotions |
| Linaloe wood oil (lignaloe oil) | pleasant, soft, sweet | preparation of linalool, perfumery |
| Lovage oil (levisticum) | sweet, aromatic, reminiscent of cardamon and celery | flavoring, perfumery |
| Macassar oil | pleasant | hair oil formulations |
| Mace oil (nutmeg oil, expressed) | agreeable, aromatic, nutmeg | flavoring, perfumery |
| Male fern resin | | medicinals, cosmetics, perfume fixative |
| Mandarin oil | pleasant, orange-like | flavoring |
| Mandarin petitgrain | | perfumery, flavoring |
| Marjoram oil, sweet (calamintha oil) | strong, penetrating | medicinals, perfumery, soaps, flavoring |
| Marjoram oil, Spanish | strong, penetrating | flavoring |
| Mastic resin | balsamic | perfume fixative, flavoring, medicinals, incense |
| Matico oil | powerful, aromatic | medicinals, perfumery |
| Mignonette oil | powerful, fragrant odor of violet leaves | perfumery |
| Mimosa oil | | perfumery |
| Monarda oil (wild bergamot) | balsamic, sweet, lavender-like | medicinals, source of thymol |
| Musk tonquin | strong musk | perfume fixative |
| Mustard oil (sinapis) | sharply pungent | medicinals |
| Myristica oil (nutmeg oil, volatile) | strong nutmeg | medicinals, flavoring, perfumery, cosmetics, soaps |
| Myrrh resin | aromatic | medicinals, perfume fixative, incense |
| Myrtle oil | strong, fragrant | medicinals |
| Neroli oil (orange flower oil) | very intense, pleasant orange blossom | perfumery, flavoring |

| Name (and Synonyms) | Odor Description | Use |
|---|---|---|
| Niaouli oil | aromatic | medicinals, mouthwashes, toothpaste |
| Oak moss oil | mossy | perfumery, perfume fixative |
| Ocotea oil | aromatic | soaps, technical preparations, sprays |
| Onion oil | penetrating | flavoring |
| Opopanax oil | similar to myrrh and galbanum but fruitier | perfumery, cosmetics |
| Orange oil (sweet orange peel oil, sweet orange oil) | mild, aromatic, characteristic orange | medicinals, flavoring, soaps, cosmetics, toiletries, perfumery |
| Orange oil, bitter (bitter orange peel oil) | orange odor | flavoring, cosmetics, toiletries, perfumery |
| Origanum oil (wild marjoram, Cyprian thyme) | thyme-like | antiseptics, flavoring, soaps, pharmaceuticals |
| Orris root oil | fine, fragrant | flavoring, soaps, cosmetics, floral perfumery, fixative in cheaper perfumes |
| Paprika oleo resin | | flavoring |
| Parsley oil (parsley seed oil) | strong, parsley | flavoring |
| Parsnip oil | | perfumery, cosmetics, soaps |
| Patchouli oil | strong, penetrating, powerful, persistent, intense, fragrant, camphoraceous | soaps, perfumery, perfume fixative |
| Peach kernel oil, expressed (persic oil, apricot kernel oil) | bland | substitute for oil of bitter almonds |
| Pennyroyal oil, American (hedeoma) | characteristic, pungent, mint-like, aromatic | insect repellents, medicinals |
| Pennyroyal oil, European | aromatic, mint-like | medicinals, soaps, insect repellents |
| Pepper oil | characteristic, pepper | flavoring, medicinals |

| Name (and Synonyms) | Odor Description | Use |
|---|---|---|
| Peppermint oil | penetrating, aromatic, minty | pharmaceuticals, flavoring |
| Perilla oil | peculiar, hay-like | perfumery, substitute for linseed oil |
| Peru balsam (Indian balsam oil, China oil, black balsam oil) | pleasant, aromatic, vanilla-like | medicinals, perfumery, confectionery |
| Petitgrain, Paraguey | similar to neroli | odorants, perfumery, flavoring, skin creams |
| Petitgrain bigarade | | soaps, cosmetics, lotions, perfumes |
| Pimenta leaf oil | spicy | pharmaceuticals, flavoring, soaps, cosmetics, perfumes |
| Pine oil | characteristic, pinaceous | germicides, disinfectants, soaps, insecticides, deodorants, polishes |
| Pine needle oil, Scotch | aromatic, turpentine-like, balsamic | medicinals, perfumery |
| Pipsissewa extract | | medicinals |
| Rose oil | strong, highly fragrant | perfumery, cosmetics, flavoring, medicinals |
| Rosemary oil | characteristic, pungent rosemary odor | medicinals, pharmaceuticals, soaps, technical preparations, perfumery |
| Rue oil | characteristic, sharp, fatty; unpleasant, becoming pleasant on dilution | medicinals |
| Safflower | | paints, varnishes, linoleum, medicinals, foods |
| Saffron oil (crocus) | intense odor of saffron | perfumery, flavoring |
| Sage oil, Clary (sage muscatel) | warm, sage, reminiscent of ambergris | flavoring, soaps, cosmetics, perfume fixative, toiletries |
| Sage oil, Dalmation (salvia) | warm, camphoraceous-sage odor | flavoring |
| Sage oil, Spanish | camphoraceous-sage | flavoring |

| Name (and Synonyms) | Odor Description | Use |
|---|---|---|
| Sandalwood oil, East Indian (sandol, santal) | faint, aromatic, persistent odor of sandalwood | medicinals, pharmaceuticals, cosmetics, perfumery, soaps, incense |
| Sandalwood oil, West Indian (amyris) | faint, somewhat unpleasant | medicinals, pharmaceuticals, cosmetics, perfumery, soaps, incense |
| Sassafras oil | characteristic, pungent, aromatic | antiseptic, disinfectant, soaps, technical preparations, flavoring, perfumery, medicinals |
| Savin oil | unpleasant | special perfumes, medicinals |
| Savory oil | aromatic, thyme-like | flavoring, perfumery |
| Serpolet oil (wild thyme) | | flavoring, soaps, lotions |
| Sesame (benne, teel) | almost odorless | margarine, cosmetics |
| Spearmint oil (mint) | characteristic spearmint odor | pharmaceuticals, flavoring |
| Spike oil (Spanish lavender oil; lavender spike oil) | camphoraceous, lavender-eucalyptol | soaps, cosmetics, veterinary medecine |
| Stillingia oil (tallowseed) | peculiar, linseed oil-like odor | medicinals |
| Styrax (storax) | balsamic | perfumery |
| Sweet almond oil (expressed almond oil) | almost odorless | perfumery, cosmetics, fine lubricants, pharmaceuticals |
| Tamarind oil | | medicinals |
| Tansy oil | strong odor | medicinals (poisonous) |
| Tea oil (teaseed oil) | | foods, soap, lubricant, substitute for olive oil |
| Thyme oil | pleasant thymol odor | germicide, antiseptic, dental preparations, flavoring, soaps |
| Tiglium oil (croton oil) | | medicinals (poisonous) |
| Tolu balsam (tolu) | aromatic, vanillin-hyacinth odor | medicinals, perfumery, confectionery, fumigants |

| Name (and Synonyms) | Odor Description | Use |
|---|---|---|
| Tuberose oil | fragrant | perfumery, flavoring |
| Turmeric oil (curcuma) | slight turmeric odor | medicinals, condiments, cosmetics |
| Turpentine | characteristic odor becoming more agreeable and less pronounced upon aging | paint solvents, chemical synthesis, varnishes, lacquers |
| Valerian oil | characteristic, penetrating | perfumery, flavoring |
| Vanilla extract | pleasant, vanilla aroma | perfumery, flavoring |
| Verbena oil | pleasant, lemon-like | perfumery |
| Vetivert oil (cuscus) | suggestive of myrrh, violet-like | perfumery, cosmetics, soaps, perfume fixative |
| Violet leaf oil | | perfumery |
| White cedar oil (thuja oil) | agreeable, camphor-sage odor | perfumery |
| Wintergreen oil (methyl salicylate, sweet birch, birch bark) | characteristic, wintergreen odor | pharmaceuticals, flavors |
| Yerba santa extract (eriodictyon) | slight aromatic | medicinals |
| Ylang Ylang oil (mosoi, anona) | fragrant | soaps, fine perfumes, medicinals |

## OSMOGENE INDEX: INTRODUCTION

The Osmogene Index is extracted from numerous sources. The reported characteristics are incomplete, many are inaccurate and some represent contradictory views. Where possible, each individual chemical has been cross referenced as many times as possible. The source can be determined by the alphabetical letters following the reported characteristics. The reported characteristics included in the Index are a composite of the listed sources. In many more cases than expected there is agreement between all references. It is likely that in a number of such cases the original reference was reported subsequently by many, if not all, other sources. It is not an infrequent occurrence, and absolute assumptions regarding actual characteristics should remain guarded even when many references seem to agree.

The classification expression is in most cases assigned solely on the basis of the reported reference characteristics. In a few cases more detailed results of a sensory analysis of the chemical are included. These entries can be identified by the considerable detail of the expression.

HU values are always preceded by a recognition threshold value or if not known the HU value is established between threshold to 10 times threshold. The HU value will change appreciably in most cases once 10 times threshold is exceeded. The HU value is established by panel for a known concentration of odorant and averaged. Where a range is stated, $HU^{2-5}_{4-5}$, for example, the range is based on evaluation of the odor sample between recognition threshold and 10 times recognition threshold, and between 10 times and 100 times recognition threshold. To expand these average values into terms of hedonic acceptability, recognition threshold to recognition threshold times 10 are added and then multiplied:

$$HU^{2-5}_{4-5} = 2 + 4 = 6 \times 6 = 36$$

and recognition threshold times 10 to recognition times 100 are added and then multiplied:

$$5 + 5 = 10, \quad 10 \times 10 = 100$$

The HU value range is therefore 36 to 100. This value states that the osmogene is hedonically acceptable in ranges of recognition threshold to 10 times recognition threshold, but decidedly unpleasant in ranges of recognition threshold times 10 or greater.

| | |
|---|---|
| 4, 16, 25, 36 | Pleasant |
| 49, 64 | Neutral |
| 81, 100, 121, 144 | *Unpleasant |

* 'Unpleasant' ranges from hedonically unpleasant to physiologically painful odors.

## Toxicity

Toxicity is not taken into consideration by an HU value. The toxicological properties of an osmogene should be referenced from standard sources.

It is hoped that contributions from workers in the field will assist in improving, extending and perfecting the accuracy of these data.

## Osmogene Index
### Key

Chemical Formula: Chemical formulas given are arranged alphabetically, and not according to structure.

Reference Sources:

- A: Amoore, J.
- C: Crocker, E. C. and Henderson, L. F.
- D: Dyson, G. M.
- F: Handbook of Food Additives, T. E. Furia, Ed., CRC, 1972.
- J: Journal of the Air Pollution Control Association, Hellman, T. M. and Small, H. F., 1974.
- M: Moncrieff, R. W.
- P: Dangerous Properties of Industrial Materials, N. I. Sax, Ed., Reinhold Publishing Corp., 1957.
- S: Compilation of Odor and Taste Threshold Values Data, W. H. Stahl, Ed., ASTM, 1973.
- X: Condensed Chemical Dictionary, A. and E. Rose, Reinhold Book Corp., 1966.
- Y: Merck Index, P. G. Stecher, Ed., Merck and Co., Inc., 1968.

Specific Gravity: Unless otherwise noted, specific gravity is given at 4/4°C.

Vapor Pressure: Unless otherwise noted, vapor pressure is given at 100 mm Hg.

Thresholds: All thresholds are given in parts per million (PPM).

Note: Where reported characteristics are in disagreement, references are placed in parentheses behind each description.

| Factors | Sensation | Examples |
|---|---|---|
| α Alpha | Sweet | Cinnamyl butyrate |
| β Beta | Morbid, sickening, nauseating | Skatole |
| γ Gamma | Warmth, heat | Cloves |
| δ Delta | Cool, cold | Menthol |
| ε Epsilon | Lachrymator, irritating | Allyl bromide, benzaldehyde |
| θ Theta | Schizosmic | Indole |
| λ Lambda | Ethereal | Carbon tetrachloride, chloroform |
| μ Mu | Metallic | Heptyl salicylate |
| ν Nu | Bitter, astringent | Isobutylquinoline, pyridine |

| Factors | Sensation | Example |
|---|---|---|
| ξ Xi | Peaking | Vanilla |
| π Pi | Taste change | Methyl mercaptan |
| σ Sigma | Empyreumatic, burnt, pyrotic | Acrolein, formaldehyde, petroleum |
| τ Tau | Anesthetize | Sulfur dioxide |
| ϕ Phi | Stifling, choking, suffocating | Nitric acid, phosgene |
| ψ Psi | Sour, sharp, pungent | Ammonia, mustard oil |
| ω Omega | Penetrating, diffusing | Bromol, pyridine |

Intensity: Strong = ! Very strong = !! Overpowering or ultimate = !!!

@: Osmogenes toward which genetic anosmia is displayed

†: Trademark

# OSMOGENE INDEX

| Chemical | Reported Characteristics | Specific Gravity | Vapor Pressure | Detection Threshold | Recognition Threshold | Classification Expression, Factors, HU Value |
|---|---|---|---|---|---|---|
| Acetal $C_6H_{14}O_2$ | agreeable: PX | .8254 (20/4°C) | 50.1 | | | |
| Acetaldehyde $C_2H_4O$ | characteristic, fruity, pungent, sharp: FPXY | .788 (16/4°C) | -22.6 | | .21 | $Fru_n$ $\psi$! $HU^{3-6}_{3-5}$ 36-121 |
| Acetamide $C_2H_5NO$ | mousy but odorless when pure: PXY | 1.159 (20/4°C) | 158.0 | | | $Uro_nBut_nMus_n$ |
| Acetanisole $C_9H_{10}O_2$ | sweet, musty, floral: C | | | | | $(MusBut_3)_4Mst_3Flo_60$ $\alpha$!! $\sigma$ $\psi$ |
| Acetic acid $C_2H_4O_2$ | very sharp, pungent: FPXY | 1.0492 (25/25°C) | 63 | | 1.0 | $\alpha$ $\varepsilon$ $\phi$!! $\psi$!! $HU^{4-6}_{4-5}$ 64-121 |
| Acetic anhydride $C_4H_6O_3$ | very strong, sour, acetic, pungent, lachrymator: AJMP XY | 1.08 (15/4°C) | 82.2 | | 0.36 | $\varepsilon$!!! $\psi$!! $HU^{4-6}_{3-5}$ 49-121 |
| Acetoin $C_4H_8O_2$ | pleasant, buttery: FY | .9972 (17/4°C) | | | | $Seb_n$ |
| Acetone $C_3H_6O$ | pleasant, fruity, fragrant, sweet, mint-like: JMPXY | .792 | 7.7 | | 140 | $He_n$ $\delta$ $\gamma$ $HU^{2-3}_{2-4}$ 16-49 |
| Acetonitrile $C_2H_3N$ | ether-like: Y | .78745 (15/4°C) | 27.0 | | | $Hyc_n$ $\alpha$ $\lambda$! $\psi$ |

| | | | | | | |
|---|---|---|---|---|---|---|
| Acetophenone $C_8H_8O$ | sweet, pungent, nutty, almond resembling chloral hydrate, burning, orange blossom, aromatic ketone: JXY | | 133.6 | | .60 | $A_5Mst_5$ $(Spi_6Flo$ $Nut_2)_7$ $(ChloMeth)_2$ α! γ σ ψ! $HU^{2-3}_{2-5}$ 16-25 |
| Acetoxime $C_3H_7NO$ | chloral-like: X | 97 (20/20°C) | | | | ε! ψ! |
| Acetylacetone $C_5H_8O_2$ | sour, rancid, unpleasant: JXY | .9753 | 7.0 (20°C) | | .024 | $But_n$ ψ! $HU^{3-5}_{4-5}$ 49-100 |
| Acetylallylamine $C_5H_{10}NO$ | garlic: A | | | | | $All_n$ |
| Acetyl bromide $BrC_2H_3O$ | irritating: X | 1.663 | | .89 | | ε |
| α-Acetylbutyrolactone $C_6H_8O_3$ | ester-like: XY | 1.18-1.19 | | | | $Es_n$ |
| Acetyl chloride $C_2ClH_3O$ | strong, pungent: AXY | 1.1051 | 3.2 | | | ψ!! $HU^{3-6}_{4-5}$ 49-121 |
| Acetylene $C_2H_2$ | ethereal: A | .91 (air=1) | 107.9 | | | λ! |
| Acetyl-1,1-dimethylcyclohexanol-3 $C_{10}H_{18}O_2$ | camphor: A | | | | | $Woo_n$ |
| Acetylene dichloride $C_2Cl_2H_2$ | pleasant, slight acrid, ethereal: XY | 1.282 | | | | λ! ψ |
| Acetylene tetrabromide $Br_4C_2H_2$ | camphor, ethereal, iodoform-like: AY | 2.98-3.00 | 170 | | | $Woo_nHal_n$ λ! |

| Chemical | Reported Characteristics | Specific Gravity | Vapor Pressure | Detection Threshold | Recognition Threshold | Classification Expression, Factors, HU Value |
|---|---|---|---|---|---|---|
| Acetyliodide $C_2H_3IO$ | pungent, suffocating: AY | 2.0674 (20/4°C) | | | | φ!!! ψ! $HU^{3-6}_{4-5}$ 49-121 |
| Acetylisoeugenol $C_{12}H_{14}O_3$ | spicy, clove-like: CFX | | | | | $But_2$ 0 $Spi_7$ 0 σ ψ! |
| Acridine $C_{13}H_9N$ | sternutatory: X | | 256 | | | ε! $HU^{3-6}_{4-5}$ 49-121 |
| Acrolein $C_3H_4O$ | unbearably irritating, disagreeable, pungent, choking: AMPXY | .8447 (15°C) | 2.5 | | .21 | ε!!! φ!! ψ! ω! $HU^{3-6}_{4-5}$ 49-121 |
| Acrylic acid $C_3H_4O_2$ | rancid, sweet, more pungent than acetic acid, acrid: JMXY | 1.0621 (16/4°C) | 86.1 | | 1.04 | $But_n$ α ψ!!! $HU^{3-5}_{4-5}$ 49-100 |
| Acrylonitrile $C_3H_3N$ | pungent: A | .8060 (20/4°C) | 22.8 | | | ψ! $HU^{3-6}_{4-5}$ 49-121 |
| Allicin $C_6H_{10}OS_2$ | sharp, true garlic, onion: AFPXY @ | 1.112 (20/4°C) | | | 21.4 | $Alin$ ψ! $HU^{3-5}_{3-6}$ 36-121 |
| Allopregnan-3α-ol $C_{21}H_{36}$ | musky: A | | | | | $Mus_n$ |
| $\Delta^{17,20}$-Allopregnan-3-one $C_{21}H_{34}O_2$ | cedar: A | | | | | $Mus_n$ |
| Allyl alcohol $C_3H_6O$ | pungent, mustard-like: APXY | .8540 (20/4°C) | 50.0 | 7.1 | | $Alin_n$ ψ! $HU^{3-6}_{4-6}$ 49-144 |
| Allylamine $C_3H_7N$ | strong ammonia, lachrymator, sternutatory: XY | .760 (20/20°C) | | 28.689 | | $Uro_nNit_n$ ε!!! $HU^{3-6}_{4-5}$ 49-121 |

| | | | | | | |
|---|---|---|---|---|---|---|
| Allylanthranilate $C_{10}H_{11}NO$ | spicy, slightly grape-like: F | | | | | $Mst_nSpi_nFru_n$ |
| Allyl bromide $BrC_3H_5$ | unpleasant, leek-like, pungent, irritating, lachrymator: MXY | 1.398 (20/4°C) | | | | $Ali_n$ ε!!! ψ!!! |
| Allyl butyrate $C_7H_{12}O_2$ | ethereal: F | | | | | λ |
| Allyl caproate $C_9H_{16}O_2$ | fruity, pineapple: CFX | .885-.888 | | | | $(MusBut_2)_3$ 0 $Fru_8$ 0 α σ ψ!!! |
| Allyl caprylate $C_{11}H_{20}O_2$ | pineapple: F | | | | | $Fru_n$ |
| Allyl chloride $C_3ClH_5$ | pungent, leek-like, unpleasant: MXY | .938 (20/4°C) | -4.5 | | .47 | $Ali_n$ ψ!! $HU^{3-6}_{4-6}$ 49-144 |
| Allyl chlorocarbonate $C_4ClH_5O_2$ | pungent, irritating: X | | | | | ψ!! $HU^{3-6}_{4-5}$ 49-121 |
| Allyl cinnamate $C_{12}H_{12}O_2$ | fruity: F | | | | | $Fru_n$ |
| Allyl cyanide $C_4H_5N$ | agreeable, onion-like: XY | .8341 (20/4°C) | | | | $Ali_n$ |
| Allyl disulfide $C_6H_{10}S_2$ | sharp, garlic: F | | | .0012 | | $Ali_n$ ψ! $HU^{3-5}_{3-5}$ 36-100 |
| Allyl ether $C_6H_{10}O$ | radish-like: X | .805 (18/0°C) | | | | $Ali_n$ |
| Allyl heptylate $C_{10}H_{18}O_2$ | pear, pineapple: F | | | | | $Fru_n$ |

| Chemical | Reported Characteristics | Specific Gravity | Vapor Pressure | Detection Threshold | Recognition Threshold | Classification Expression, Factors, HU Value |
|---|---|---|---|---|---|---|
| Allyl iodide $C_3H_5I$ | pungent, unpleasant, leek-like: MY | 1.848 (12°C) | | .018 | | $Hal_n$ ψ! |
| Allyl α-ionone $C_{16}H_{24}O$ | fruity, raspberry, violet: FX | .928-.935 (25/25°C) | | | | $Fru_n$ |
| Allyl isothiocyanate $C_4H_5NS$ | strong, pungent, irritating, biting, mustard, penetrating: AFM PXY @ | 1.013-1.020 | 89.5 | | .192 | $Ali_n$ γ ψ!!! ω $HU^{3-6}_{4-6}$ 49-144 |
| Allyl isovalerate $C_4H_9$ | ethereal: F | | | | | λ |
| Allyl mercaptan $C_3H_6S$ | strong garlic, coffee: FX | .925 (23/4°C) | | .016 | | $Ali_n$ σ $HU^{3-5}_{4-6}$ 49-121 |
| Allyl pelargonate $C_{12}H_{22}O_2$ | fruity, ethereal: FX | | | | | $Fru_n$ λ |
| Allyl phenoxyacetate $C_{11}H_{14}O_3$ | ester-like: F | | | | | $Es_n$ |
| Allyl phenylacetate $C_{11}H_{14}O_2$ | rosey: F | | | | | $Flo_n$ |
| Allyl propionate $C_6H_{10}O_2$ | fruity: F | | | | | $Fru_n$ |
| Allyl sulfide $C_6H_{10}S$ | garlic: AMPXY | .888 (27/4°C) | 75.8 | .0107 | | $All_nSul_n$ $HU^{3-5}_{2-5}$ 25-100 |
| Allyl thiourea $C_4H_8N_2S$ | slight garlic: PXY | 1.22 | | | | $All_nSul_n$ |

| | | | | | |
|---|---|---|---|---|---|
| Allyl tiglate $C_8H_{12}O_2$ | fruity: F | | | | $Fru_n$ |
| Allyl trichloro-silane $C_4Cl_3H_5Si$ | pungent, irritating: X | 1.217 (27°C) | 59.3 | | ψ! $HU^{3-6}_{4-5}$ 49-121 |
| Althein $C_4H_8N_2O_3$ | sweet marshmallow: F | | | | $Bal_n$ α! |
| ALUMINUM Al | no reported odor | 2.708 | 1749 | | |
| Aluminum phenol-sulfonate $Al_2C_{36}H_{25}O_{24}S$ | slight phenol: X | | | | $Mol_n$ |
| Aluminum subacetate solution $AlC_4H_7O_5$ | acetic acid: Y | 1.045 | | | α ε ϕ ψ<br>α |
| Aluminum sulfide $Al_2S_3$ | hydrogen sulfide: PXY | 2.02 | | | $Sul_n$ $HU^{3-6}_{3-6}$ 36-144 |
| Ambrettolide $C_{16}H_{28}O_2$ | powerful, strong, musky: AFY | | | | $Mus_n$ ψ $HU^{3-5}_{1-5}$ 16-100 |
| Aminophylline $C_{16}H_{24}N_{10}O$ | slight ammoniacal: X | | | | $Uro_nNit_n$ ψ |
| 2-Aminopropanol $C_3H_9NO$ | fishy: XY | | | | $Ami_n$ μ |
| 4-Aminosalicylic acid $C_7H_7NO_3$ | slight acetous: X | | | | ψ |
| Ammonia $H_3N$ | very pungent, resembling drying urine: XY | .7710 (0°C) | -68.4 | 46.8 | $Uro_nNit_n$ ψ!! $HU^{3-6}_{4-6}$ 49-144 |

| Chemical | Reported Characteristics | Specific Gravity | Vapor Pressure | Detection Threshold | Recognition Threshold | Classification Expression, Factors, HU Value |
|---|---|---|---|---|---|---|
| Ammonium acetate $C_2H_7NO_2$ | slight acetous: Y | 1.07 | | | | ψ |
| Ammonium benzoate $C_7H_9NO_2$ | faint benzoic acid: Y | 1.260 | | | | |
| Ammonium carbamate $CH_6N_2O_2$ | ammonia: Y | | 26.7 | | | $Uro_nNit_n$ ψ!! |
| Ammonium carbonate $H_3N \cdot CO_2$ | strong ammonia: XY | | | | | $Uro_nNit_n$ ψ!!! |
| Ammonium embalate $C_{17}H_{32}N_2O_4$ | sternutatory: Y | | | | | ϕ |
| Ammonium hydroxide $H_5NO$ | strong, characteristic: X | | | | | |
| Ammonium linoleate $C_{18}H_{35}NO_2$ | ammoniacal: X | 1.1 | | | | $Uro_nNit_n$ ψ! |
| Ammonium polysulfide $H_8N_2S$ | hydrogen sulfide: X | | | | | $Sul_n$ |
| Ammonium sulfide solution, yellow $H_8N_2S$ | ammonia and hydrogen sulfide: Y | | | | | $Uro_nNit_nSul_n$ ψ $HU^{3-6}_{3-6}$ 36-144 |
| Ammonium tetrathiotungstate $H_8N_2S_4W$ | hydrogen sulfide: X | | | | | $Sul_n$ α β! τ ϕ |
| Ammonium thioglycolate $C_2H_7NO_2S$ | strong, skunk-like: P | | | | | $Ami_3$ 0 0 $Thic_9$ α β π σ!! $HU^{3-5}_{4-6}$ 49-121 |

| | | | | | | |
|---|---|---|---|---|---|---|
| Ammonium valerate $C_5H_{13}NO_2$ | pungent, unpleasant: X | | | | | ψ! |
| Amphetamine $C_9H_{13}NO_2$ | strong, characteristic, amine: XY | .913 (25/4°C) | | | | $Ami_n$ |
| Amyl acetate $C_7H_{14}O_2$ | sweet ester, pear oil, banana oil: FJPXY | .876 (15/4°C) | | | .21 | $Lip_2$ 0 $Fru_6$ $Hyc_2$ α! γ λ ψ!! ω! $HU^{2-3}_{1-3}$ 9-36 |
| p-Amyl acetate $C_7H_{14}O_2$ | | | | .112 | | |
| n-Amyl alcohol $C_5H_{12}O$ | sweet, fruity, mild, characteristic ester-like: FJXY | .812-.819 (20/20°C) | 85.8 | | .31 | $Fru_n$ σ! ψ ω!! $HU^{2-3}_{2-3}$ 16-36 |
| sec-Amyl alcohol $C_5H_{12}O$ | characteristic: Y | .811 (20/20°C) | 70.7 | | | σ ψ ω!! |
| tert-Amyl alcohol $C_5H_{12}O$ | characteristic, camphoraceous, sour, sharp: AJXY | .81 (20/20°C) | 55.3 | | .23 | $Woo_n$ σ ψ ω!! $HU^{2-3}_{2-4}$ 16-49 |
| Amyl butyrate $C_9H_{18}O$ | apricot-like, pear-like, ester-like: FY | .8713 (15/4°C) | 113.1 | | | $A_3$ 0 $Fru_5$ Hyc α λ ψ! |
| γ-Amyl-γ-butyrolactone $C_9H_{16}O_2$ | cocoa with trace of aniseed: M | | | | | $Woo_nHer_n$ σ ψ |
| Amyl caproate $C_{11}H_{22}O_2$ | ester-like, pear-like: F | | | | | $Fru_nHyc_n$ |
| Amyl caprylate $C_{13}H_{26}O_2$ | plum: F | | | | | $Fru_n$ |
| tert-Amyl carbamate $C_6H_{13}NO_2$ | camphor: PX | | | | | $Woo_n$ |

| Chemical | Reported Characteristics | Specific Gravity | Vapor Pressure | Detection Threshold | Recognition Threshold | Classification Expression, Factors, HU Value |
|---|---|---|---|---|---|---|
| Amylcinnamaldehyde dimethyl acetal $C_9H_{18}O_2$ | floral: F | | | | | $A_4$ 0 $Flo_7$ 0 σ ψ!! |
| α-Amylcinnamic alcohol $C_7H_6:C_7H_{14}O$ | floral: FX | .954-.962 (25/25°C) | | | | $Flo_n$ |
| α-Amylcinnamic aldehyde $C_7H_6:C_7H_{12}O$ | floral, jasmine-like: ACFX | .962-.968 | | | | $(MusBut_2)_3$ 0 $Flo_8$ 0 σ ψ!!! |
| Amyl cinnamyl acetate $C_{11}H_{20}O_3$ | spicy, cinnamon: F | | | | | $Spi_n$ |
| Amyl crotonyl acetate $C_{11}H_{20}O_3$ | fruity, jasmine-like: C | | | | | $(MusBut_2)_3$ 0 $(Fru_6\ Flo_5)_7$ 0 α σ ψ!! |
| Amylene $C_5H_{10}$ | disagreeable: Y | .66 (15/4°C) | | 2.3 | | |
| Amyl formate $C_6H_{12}O_2$ | plum-like, sharp, fruity: CFX | .880-.885 | | | | $Mus_2$ 0 $Fru_7$ Hyc σ ψ!! |
| Amyl heptanoate $C_{12}H_{24}O_2$ | apple, pear: F | | | | | $Fru_n$ |
| tert-Amylisothiocyanate $C_6H_{11}NS$ | aromatic: A | | | | | |
| tert-Amyl isovalerate $C_{10}H_{20}O_2$ | valerian, odor of apples when diluted with alcohol: XY | .8729 (0/4°C) | | | | $\theta^2$: $Fru_n$ |

| | | | | | |
|---|---|---|---|---|---|
| n-Amyl mercaptan $C_5H_{12}S$ | penetrating, unpleasant, putrid, offensive, powerful: AMXY | .857 (20/4°C) | | | β!!! π ω!! $HU^{3-5}_{4-6}$ 49-121 |
| Amyl methyl ketone $C_7H_{14}O$ | pear: F | | | | $Fru_n$ |
| Amyl nitrite $C_5H_{11}NO_2$ | peculiar, fragrant, ethereal, somewhat fruity, penetrating: PXY | .865-.875 (25°C) | | | $Fru_n$ λ ω!! |
| p-tert-Amylphenyl acetate $C_{13}H_{18}O_2$ | fruity: CX | .996 (20°C) | | | $Mus_5$ 0 $Fru_5$ 0 σ ψ!! |
| α-Amylpyridine $C_{10}H_{16}N$ | flowery, floral: AM | | | | $Flo_n$ |
| Androstan-3α-ol $C_{19}H_{30}O_2$ | strong musk: A | | | | $Mus_n$ |
| Androstan-3β-ol $C_{19}H_{30}O_2$ | very weak musk: A | | | | $Mus_n$ |
| $\Delta^{16}$-Androsten-3-ol $C_{19}H_{28}O_2$ | musk: A | | | | $Mus_n$ |
| Anethole $C_{10}H_{12}O$ | licorice or oil of anise: CFX | .983-.987 | 164.2 | | $(Mus_3But_2)$ Mst $(Her_5Fru_2Flo_3)$ 0 α! σ ψ! |
| Angelic acid $C_5H_8O_2$ | spicy: XY | .9539 (76/4°C) | | | $Spi_n$ |
| Aniline $C_6H_7N$ | characteristic, gas-lime: MXY | | 119.9 | 1 | |

| Chemical | Reported Characteristics | Specific Gravity | Vapor Pressure | Detection Threshold | Recognition Threshold | Classification Expression, Factors, HU Value |
|---|---|---|---|---|---|---|
| o-Anisaldehyde $C_8H_8O_2$ | burnt, slightly phenolic: X | 1.1274 (25/25°C) | | | | $Mol_n$ σ! |
| p-Anisaldehyde $C_8H_8O_2$ | floral, hawthorne, resembling coumarin but aldehyde must be mixed with other odorous substances to yield an agreeable odor, soft: AFMXY @ | 1.119 (15/4°C) | 176.7 | | | $(MusBut_2)_3$ 0 $Flo_5$ 0 α! σ! ψ! |
| p-Anisic acid $C_8H_8O_3$ | sweet, slight rosy: C | 1.385 (4°C) | | | | $(MusBut_2)_2$0 $Flo_3$ 0 α σ ψ |
| Anisic alcohol $C_8H_{10}O_2$ | floral, suggesting hawthorne, sweet peach: CFX | 1.111-1.114 | | | | $(MusBut_2)$ 0 $Flo_4$ 0 α σ ψ |
| Anisole $C_7H_8O$ | agreeable, floral, aromatic, anise: AFXY @ | .9956 (18/4°C) | 93.0 | | | $Flo_nHer_n$ |
| Anisyl acetate $C_{10}H_{12}O_3$ | vermouth, lilac-type: CFX | 1.104-1.107 | | | | $(MusBut_2)_3$ $Fer_2$ $Flo_4$ 0 |
| Anisyl butyrate $C_{14}H_{19}O_3$ | fruity, ester-like: F | | | | | $Fru_n$ |
| Anisyl formate $C_9H_{10}O_3$ | floral, lilac, strawberry: CFX | 1.139-1.141 | | | | $(MusBut_2)_2$ 0 $(Flo_3Fru)_3$ 0 α σ ψ |
| Anisyl phenylacetate $C_{11}H_{14}O_3$ | fruity, floral: F | | | | | $Fru_nFlo_n$ |

| | | | | |
|---|---|---|---|---|
| Anisyl propionate $C_{11}H_{14}O_3$ | fruity, ester-like, floral: CF | | | $(MusBut_2)_3$ 0 $(Fru_3 Flo_2)_4$ 0 α σ ψ! |
| p-Anol $C_9H_{10}O$ | weak clove, resembling eugenol: Y | | | $Spi_n$ |
| ANTIMONY Sb | no reported odor | 6.68 | 1223 | |
| Antimony pentachloride $C_{15}Sb$ | offensive: PX | 2.358 (16/4°C) | 114.1 | $Hal_n$ β!! |
| Antimony sodium thioglycolate $C_4H_4NaO_4S_2Sb$ | faint mercaptan odor develops on standing: XY | | | $Mus_nSul_n$ |
| Apiol $C_{12}H_{14}O_4$ | faint parsley, herb-like: FXY | | 218 | $Her_n$ |
| Apocynin $C_9H_{10}O_3$ | faint vanilla: Y | | | $Bal_n$ |
| ARSENIC $As_2$ | odor of garlic when burned: Y | 5.727 | 518 | $Ars_nAll_n$ |
| Arsine $AsH_3$ | mild, disagreeable, garlic: PY | | -98.0 | $Ars_nAll_n$ |
| ASTATINE $At_2$ | halogenic: X | | | $Hal_n$ |
| Aurothioglucose $AuC_6H_{11}O_5S$ | slight mercaptan-like: Y | | | $Mus_n$ |
| Bacitracin methylenedisalicylic acid | slight, unpleasant, disagreeable: XY | | | |
| BARIUM Ba | no reported odor | 3.5 | 1301 | |

| Chemical | Reported Characteristics | Specific Gravity | Vapor Pressure | Detection Threshold | Recognition Threshold | Classification Expression, Factors, HU Value |
|---|---|---|---|---|---|---|
| Barium bromate $BaBr_2O_6$ | slight odor of bromine on standing: Y | 3.99 | | | | $Hal_n$ |
| Bendroflumethiazide $C_{15}F_3H_{14}N_3O_4S_2$ | faint, rose-like: X | | | | | $Flo_n$ ξ |
| Benzal chloride $C_7Cl_2H_6$ | faint, aromatic, pungent, lachrymator: XY | 1.26 | 138.3 | | | ε!!! ψ!! |
| Benzaldehyde $C_7H_6O$ | odor of almonds or oil of bitter almonds: AXY | 1.050 (15/4°C) | 112.5 | .042 | | $Nut_n$ ν |
| Benzaldehyde dimethyl acetal $C_9H_{12}O$ | nutty: F | | | | | 0 0 $Nut_9$ 0 γ σ! ψ |
| Benzene $C_6H_6$ | characteristic: XY @ | .8787 (15/4°C) | 26.1 | | 4.68 | $Hyc_n$ $HU^{1-2}_{2-3}$ 6-25 |
| Benzofuran $C_8H_6O$ | aromatic: XY | 1.0913 (22.7/4°C) | | | | |
| Benzonitrile $C_7H_5N$ | almond, oil of almond: APXY | 1.010 (15°C) | 123.5 | | | $Nut_n$ |
| Benzophenone $C_{13}H_{10}O$ | sweet, persistent, rose-like, floral, geranium-like, peach, apricot: AFPXY | 1.1108 (18/4°C) | 224.4 | | | ($Mus_4But$) 0 ($Flo_2$ $Fru_2$) 0 α! ρ σ ψ |
| Benzothiazole $C_7H_5NS$ | quinoline: M | 1.246 (20/4°C) | | | | |

| | | | | |
|---|---|---|---|---|
| Benzotrichloride $C_7Cl_3H_5$ | highly irritant, stupifying: MX | 1.3756 | 144.3 | ε!!! |
| Benzoxazole $C_7H_5NO$ | tobacco: M | | | $He_n$ |
| Benzoyl chloride $C_7ClH_5O$ | pungent, penetrating, lachrymator: PXY | 1.2070 (25/4°C) | 128.0 | $Hal_nHyc_nOxy_n$ ε!!! ψ!! ω $HU^{3-4}_{4-6}$ 49-144 |
| Benzoyl peroxide $C_{14}H_{10}O_4$ | faint, benazldehyde: X | 1.3340 (25°C) | | $Nut_n$ |
| Benzyl acetate $C_9H_{10}O_2$ | pleasant, floral, pear-like: AFXY | 1.050 (25/4°C) | 144 | A 0 $(Fru_2Flo)_2$ 0 α σ ψ! |
| Benzyl acetoacetate $C_{11}H_{12}O_3$ | pungent, cherry-like: F | | | $Fru_n$ ψ |
| Benzyl alcohol $C_7H_8O$ | faint aromatic, slight benzaldehyde odor after exposure to air, fragrant, slight orange: AFXY @ | 1.0454 (25/4°C) | 141.7 | A 0 $(NutFru_2)$ Hyc α γ λ σ |
| Benzyl benzoate $C_{14}H_{12}O_2$ | faint, aromatic, pleasant, chemical: CFXY | 1.118 (25/4°C) | | 0 0 0 $Hyc_n$ λ |
| Benzyl bromide $BrC_7H_7$ | faint, pleasant, lachrymator: PXY | 1.4380 (22/0°C) | 129.8 | $Hal_nHyc_n$ ε! |
| β-Benzylbutane $C_{11}H_{17}$ | aromatic: A | | | |
| Benzyl butyrate $C_{11}H_{14}O_2$ | heavy, fruity, sweet, pear: FX | 1.016 (17.5°C) | | $A_2$ 0 $(Fru_5Flo_2)_8$ Hyc α σ ψ! |

| Chemical | Reported Characteristics | Specific Gravity | Vapor Pressure | Detection Threshold | Recognition Threshold | Classification Expression, Factors, HU Value |
|---|---|---|---|---|---|---|
| α-Benzyl-γ-butyrolactone $C_9H_{16}O_2$ | floral, tolu balsam: AM | | | | | $Flo_nBal_n$ |
| Benzyl chloride $C_7ClH_7$ | highly irritating, pungent, aromatic, unpleasant, stupifying, lachrymator: MPXY | 1.100 (20/20°C) | 114.2 | | .047 | $Hal_n$ ε!!! ψ $HU^{4-6}_{4-6}$ 64-144 |
| Benzyl cinnamate $C_{16}H_{14}O_2$ | aromatic, woody, spicy, sweet balsam: FPXY | | 281.5 | | | $Mst_nWoo_nSpi_nBal_n$ α ψ |
| Benzyl cyanide $C_8H_7N$ | aromatic: PXY | 1.0214 (15/15°C) | | | | |
| Benzyl ethoxyacetate $C_{11}H_{16}O_3$ | floral: A | | | | | $Flo_n$ |
| Benzyl ethyl ether $C_9H_{12}O$ | aromatic: XY | .949 | 118.9 | | | |
| Benzyl formate $C_8H_8O_2$ | fruity, spicy, pleasant, apricot, pineapple: FXY | 1.081 | | | | $Fru_nSpi_n$ |
| Benzylideneacetone $C_{10}H_{10}O$ | heavy, pungent, floral, coumarin: CXY | 1.0377 (15/15°C) | | | | $A_4$ 0 ($Flo_3Bal_2Ens_2$) 0 α ρ ψ! |
| Benzyl iodide $C_7H_7I$ | lachrymator: X | 1.7335 | | | | $Hal_n$ ε! $HU^{3-6}_{4-6}$ 49-144 |
| Benzyl isobutyrate $C_{11}H_{13}O_2$ | strawberry: F | | | | | $Fru_n$ |

| | | | | |
|---|---|---|---|---|
| Benzyl isoeugenol<br>$C_{17}H_{18}O_2$ | light floral, carnation type: X | | | $A_2$ 0 $Flo_6$ 0<br>α ψ |
| Benzyl isovalerate<br>$C_{12}H_{17}O_2$ | apple: F | | | $Fru_n$ |
| Benzyl mercaptan<br>$C_7H_8S$ | strong: PX | | | |
| p-Benzyloxyphenole<br>$C_{13}H_{12}O_2$ | faint, pleasant: X | 1.26 | | |
| Benzyl pelargonate<br>$C_{16}H_{24}O_2$ | mild, pleasant: X | .962<br>(15.5/15.5°C) | | |
| Benzyl phenylacetate<br>$C_{15}H_{14}O_2$ | sweet, honey-like: FX | 1.097-<br>1.099 | | $Car_n$ α! |
| Benzyl propionate<br>$C_{10}H_{12}O_2$ | sweeter than acetate: CX | 1.036 | | A 0 $(Fru_2Flo)_2$ 0<br>α!! σ ψ! |
| Benzyl salicylate<br>$C_{14}H_{12}O_3$ | very faint, sweet, slight, pleasant, raspberry: CFPXY<br>@ | 1.176-<br>1.179 | | (MusBut) Mst $(Fru_4$<br>Bal) 0 α σ ψ |
| Benzyl sulfide<br>$C_{14}H_{14}S$ | | 1.0712 | .006 | |
| BERYLLIUM<br>Be | no reported odor | 1.85 | | |
| BERYLLIUM COMPOUNDS | no reported odors | | | |
| Betaine salicylate<br>$C_{12}ClH_{17}N_2O_2$ | salicylate odor: Y | | | $He_n$ δ |
| Bethanechol chloride<br>$C_7ClH_{17}N_2O_2$ | slight, amine-like: XY | | | $Ami_n$ |

| Chemical | Reported Characteristics | Specific Gravity | Vapor Pressure | Detection Threshold | Recognition Threshold | Classification Expression, Factors, HU Value |
|---|---|---|---|---|---|---|
| Biphenyl $C_{12}H_{10}$ | pleasant, peculiar: PXY | | 180.7 | | | |
| 2-Biphenyl benzyl ether $C_{19}H_{19}O$ | nut-like (at 212° F), pleasant: D | | | | | $\theta^2$: $Nut_n$ |
| 2-Biphenyl ethyl ether $C_{14}H_{15}O$ | weak, sweet, floral: AD | | | | | $Flo_n$ $\alpha$ |
| 2-Biphenyl methyl ether $C_{13}H_{13}O$ | fruity, aromatic: D | | | | | $Fru_n$ |
| 2-Biphenyl propyl ether $C_{15}H_{17}O$ | faint, aromatic: D | | | | | |
| Bis(2,6-diethyl-phenyl)carbodiimide $C_{21}H_{26}N_2$ | faintly acrid: X | 1.007 (20/20°C) | | | | $\psi$ |
| Bisethylxanthogen $C_6H_{10}O_2S_4$ | onion-like: XY | | | | | $All_n$ |
| Bishydroxycoumarin $C_{19}H_{12}O_6$ | faint, pleasant: XY | | | | | |
| Bismethylselenide $C_2H_6Se$ | garlic: M | | | | | $All_n$ |
| BISMUTH Bi | no reported odor | 9.78 (20/4°C) | 1271 | | | |
| Bismuth bromide $BiBr_3$ | hydrogen bromide: Y | 5.72 | | | | $\psi$! |

| | | | | | |
|---|---|---|---|---|---|
| Bismuth chloride $BiCl_3$ | hydrochloric: Y | 4.56 | | | $\phi$ $\psi$! |
| Bismuth ethyl camphorate $BiC_{36}H_{57}O_{12}$ | faint, aromatic: XY | | | | |
| Bismuth nitrate $BiN_3O_9$ | nitric acid: Y | 2.83 | | | $Nit_n$ $\phi$! $\psi$! |
| Bismuth subacetate $BiC_2H_3O_{12}$ | slight acetic: Y | | | | $\psi$ |
| Bismuthtrimethyl $BiC_3H_9$ | garlic: M | | | | $All_n$ $\psi$ |
| Bismuth valerate monohydrate $BiC_5H_9O_3 \cdot H_2O$ | valeric acid: Y | | | | |
| Bisphenol A $C_{15}H_{16}O_2$ | mild phenolic: X | 1.195 (25/25°C) | | | $Mol_nHyc_n$ $\sigma$ |
| Borneol $C_{10}H_{18}O$ | peculiar, woody, medicinal, camphor-like, peppery: AFXY | 1.011 | | | $A_3$ 0 ($Woo_4$Spi) 0 $\delta$! $\sigma$ $\psi$ |
| Bornyl acetate $C_{12}H_{20}O_2$ | piney, woody, camphoraceous: FX | .980-.984 | 149.8 | | $A_2$ 0 $Woo_6$ Hyc $\delta$! $\sigma$! $\psi$ |
| Bornyl chloride $C_{10}ClH_{17}$ | turpentine, camphoraceous: AXY | | | | $Woo_nHyc_n$ |
| Bornyl formate $C_{11}H_{18}O_2$ | piney, woody: X | 1.007-1.009 | 145.8 | | $Woo_n$ |
| Bornylisocyanate | pungent: A | | | | $\psi$! |
| Bornyl isovalerate $C_{15}H_{26}O_2$ | aromatic, fruity, valerian, camphor, woody: FXY | .955 | | | $Fru_nWoo_n$ |

| Chemical | Reported Characteristics | Specific Gravity | Vapor Pressure | Detection Threshold | Recognition Threshold | Classification Expression, Factors, HU Value |
|---|---|---|---|---|---|---|
| BORON B | no reported odor | 2.34 | | | | |
| Boron trifluoride $BF_3$ | pungent, suffocating: X | 2.33 (air=1) | -123 | | | $Hal_n$ ε φ!!! ψ!! |
| Bromal $Br_3C_2HO$ | | 2.66 | | | | ω!! |
| Bromal hydrate $Br_3C_2H_3O_2$ | chloral: Y | 1.49 | | | | $Hal_n$ ψ! |
| BROMINE $Br_2$ | halogenic, suffocating, irritating: XY | 3.1193 (20/4°C) | 9.3 | | .047 | $Hal_n$ ε φ!! ψ!! $HU^{4-6}_{4-6}$ 64-144 |
| n-Bromoacetamide $BrC_2H_4NO$ | bromine-like: PX | | | | | $Hal_n$ ε! φ!! ψ!! |
| Bromoacetone $BrC_3H_5O$ | powerful irritant, pungent, lachrymator, chemical war gas: PXY | | | | | $Hal_nHyc_n$ ε!! ψ!!! |
| ω-Bromoacetophenone $BrC_8H_7O$ | lachrymator: Y | | | | | $Hal_n$ ε! |
| Bromoacetonitrile $BrC_2H_3N$ | pungent: A | | | | | $Hal_n$ ψ! |
| Bromobenzene $BrC_6H_5$ | pleasant, aromatic, characteristic: XY | 1.49519 (20/4°C) | 90.8 | | | |
| α-Bromobenzyl cyanide $BrC_8H_6N$ | sour fruit, pungent, lachrymator, war gas: PXY | 1.5939 (29/4°C) | | | | $Nit_nHal_nFru_n$ ε!! ψ!! $HU^{5-6}_{5-6}$ 100-144 |

| | | | | |
|---|---|---|---|---|
| 2-Bromo-4-tert-butyl-5-methoxytoluene $BrC_{12}H_{18}O$ | weak musk: A | | | $Mus_n$ |
| 3-Bromo-d-camphor $BrC_{10}H_{15}O$ | camphor-like: Y | 1.449 | | $Woo_n$ |
| sym-Bromochloroethane $BrC_2ClH_4$ | sweet, chloroform-like: PX | 1.70 | 28.0 | α! λ! |
| Bromochloromethane $BrCClH_2$ | chloroform-like: X | 1.93 (25°C) | | α! λ! |
| n-Bromodimethylamine $BrC_2H_8N$ | pungent: A | | | ψ! |
| 3-Bromo-1,1-dimethylcyclohexane $BrC_8H_{17}$ | camphor: A | | | $Woo_n$ |
| 3-Bromo-1,1-dimethylcyclohexen (3)-one(5) $BrC_9H_{15}O$ | minty: A | | | $He_n$ δ! |
| Bromoform $Br_3CH$ | ethereal, chloroform: AXY | 2.8887 | | λ! |
| Bromol $Br_3C_6H_3O$ | disagreeable, penetrating, bromine: X | 2.55 (20/20°C) | | $Hal_n$ β ϕ! ψ! $HU^{3-6}_{4-6}$ 49-100 |
| Bromomethyl acetate $BrC_3H_5O_2$ | pungent: A | | | λ! ψ! |
| 6-Bromo-1-methyl-3-isopropylbenzene $BrC_{10}H_{14}$ | floral: A | | | $Flo_n$ |

| Chemical | Reported Characteristics | Specific Gravity | Vapor Pressure | Detection Threshold | Recognition Threshold | Classification Expression, Factors, HU Value |
|---|---|---|---|---|---|---|
| Bromonitroacetic acid, methyl ester $BrC_3H_6NO_4$ | pungent, weak: A | | | | | ψ |
| α-Bromonitroethane $BrC_2H_4NO_2$ | pungent: A | | | | | ψ! |
| 2-Bromo-2-nitropropane $BrC_3H_7NO_2$ | pungent: A | | | | | ψ! |
| 3-Bromo-3-nitroso-2,2-dimethylbutane $BrC_6H_{13}NO$ | pungent, camphor: A | | | | | $Woo_n$ ψ! |
| 2-Bromopentane $BrC_5H_{11}$ | strong: | 1.1850 (25/25°C) | | | | |
| o-Bromophenol $BrC_6H_5O$ | unpleasant: XY | 1.5 | | | | |
| o-Bromophenylisothiocyanate $BrC_6H_5NS$ | pungent: D | | | | | ψ! |
| p-Bromophenylisothiocyanate $BrC_6H_5NS$ | aniseed: AD | | | | | $Her_n$ |
| Bromophosgene $Br_2CO$ | strong: X | | | | | |
| Bromopicrin $Br_3CNO_2$ | very irritant, strong, pungent, military poison gas: AX | | | | | $Nit_nHal_n$ ε!!! ψ!!! $HU^{5-6}_{5-6}$ 100-144 |
| β-Bromostyrene $BrC_8H_7$ | strong, floral, pungent, hyacinth: CX | 1.395-1.424 | | | | $Flo_n$ ψ!! |

| | | | | | | |
|---|---|---|---|---|---|---|
| Bromotrichloro-methane $BrCCl_3$ | chloroform-like: X | | | | | α λ! |
| 3-Bromo-2,2,3-trimethylbutane $BrC_{17}H_{16}$ | camphoraceous: A | | | | | $Woo_n$ |
| 1,3-Butadiene $C_4H_6$ | mild, aromatic, undefined: JX | | -46.8 | | 1.3 | $HU^{2-3}_{3-4}$ 25-49 |
| Butane $C_4H_{10}$ | characteristic, natural gas: X | .6012 (0/4°C) | -44.2 | | | $Hyc_n$ |
| 2,3-Butanedione $C_4H_6O_2$ | strong, quinone, in extreme dilution distinct butter odor, cream: PXY | .990 (15/15°C) | 127.8 | | | $\theta^2$: $Seb_4$ 0 0 $(HycHal_5)_5$ μ ψ! ω!<br>$\theta_1$: $Seb_9$ 0 0 0 ψ ω |
| 1-Butene $C_4H_8$ | | .5951 (20/4°C) | -48.9 | 1.3 | | |
| cis-2-Butene $C_4H_8$ | | .6213 (20/4°C) | 39.8 | 2.1 | | |
| trans-2-Butene $C_4H_8$ | | .6042 (20/4°C) | 42.7 | | | |
| Butopyronoxyl $C_{12}H_{18}O_4$ | aromatic: XY | 1.052-1.060 (25/25°C) | | | | |
| n-Butyl acetate $C_6H_{12}O_2$ | sweet, ester, fruity, pineapple: FJX | .8826 (20/20°C) | 8.7 mm hg (20°C) | | .037 | $Fru_n$<br>$HU^{2-3}_{1-3}$ 0-36 |
| sec-Butyl acetate $C_3H_9O_2$ | mild: P | .870 (20/4°C) | 59.7 | | | |

| Chemical | Reported Characteristics | Specific Gravity | Vapor Pressure | Detection Threshold | Recognition Threshold | Classification Expression, Factors, HU Value |
|---|---|---|---|---|---|---|
| Butyl acetyl ricinoleate $C_{24}H_{44}O_4$ | mild: X | .940 (20/20°C) | | | | |
| n-Butyl alcohol $C_4H_{10}O$ | rancid, sweet, vinous, slightly fusel, slightly bananas, vapors irritate and cause cough: FJXY | .8098 (20/4°C) | 70.1 | | 2.0 | $Ami_nBut_nMst_nFru_n$ $\alpha$ $\psi$! $HU^2_{3-4}$ |
| sec-Butyl alcohol $C_4H_{10}O$ | sweet, strong, pleasant: JX | .8080 (20/4°C) | 54.1 | | .56 | $HU^{2-5}_{2-3}$ 16-64 |
| tert-Butyl alcohol $C_4H_{10}O$ | camphor-like: AXY | .78581 (20/4°C) | 39.8 | | | $Woo_n$ |
| Butylamine $C_4H_{11}N$ | sour, ammonia-like, amine: JPXY | .7327 (25/4°C) | | | .24 | $Ami_nUro_nNit_n$ $\psi$ $HU^{3-5}_{2-4}$ 25-81 |
| sec-Butylamine $C_4H_{11}N$ | aniline: X | .724 (20/4°C) | | | | |
| N-n-Butylaniline $C_{10}H_{15}N$ | aniline: X | .932 (20°C) | | | | |
| Butyl anthranilate $C_{11}H_{15}NO_2$ | grape: F | | | | | $(But_2Lip_2)Mst$ $Fru_3$ 0 $\psi$ |
| Butylbenzenesulfonamide $C_{10}H_{15}NO_2S$ | pleasant: X | 1.48 (25/25°C) | | | | |
| sec-Butyl bromide $BrC_4H_9$ | pleasant: XY | 1.2530 (25/4°C) | | | | |
| p-tert-Butylbenzaldehyde $C_{11}H_{15}O$ | almond: A | | | | | $Nut_n$ |

| | | | | | |
|---|---|---|---|---|---|
| n-Butyl n-butyrate $C_8H_{16}O_2$ | fruity, pineapple, irritating in high concentrations: FY | .8692 (20/4°C) | | | $Fru_n$ |
| Butyl chloral $C_4Cl_3H_5O$ | pungent, disagree-able: XY | 1.3956 (20/4°C) | | | β ψ! |
| n-Butyl chloride $C_4ClH_9$ | pungent: J | .88648 (20/4°C) | 24.0 | 16.7 | ψ!! $HU^{3-6}_{4-5}$ 49-121 |
| sec-Butyl chloride $C_4ClH_9$ | pleasant, ethereal: Y | .871 (20/4°C) | 14.2 | | λ |
| Butyl crotonate $C_8H_{14}O_2$ | pleasant, persis-tent: X | .9037 (20/20°C) | | | ρ! |
| Butyl cyclohexane carboxylate $C_{11}H_{21}O_2$ | fruity, green, anise-like, sweet: W | | | | $Fru_n Her_n Ens_n$ α |
| n-Butyldichloro-arsine $AsC_4Cl_2Hg$ | somewhat agreeable, very irritating: X | | | | ψ!! |
| n-Butyl diethanol-amine $C_8H_{17}NO_2$ | faint amine: X | .97 (20°C) | | | $Ami_n$ |
| 1,2-Butylene oxide $C_4H_8O$ | sweet, alcohol: J | .8312 (20/20°C) | | .71 | $HU^{2-3}_{2-3}$ 16-36 |
| Butyl epoxystearate $C_{22}H_{42}O_3$ | slightly fatty, slightly fruity: X | .910 (20°C) | | | $Lip_n Fru_n$ |
| n-Butylethanolamine $C_6H_{15}NO$ | very faint amine: X | .892 (20°C) | | | $Ami_n$ |
| Butyl ether $C_8H_{18}O$ | mild, ethereal, fruity, sweet: JX | .769 (20/20°C) | 4.8 mm Hg (20°C) | .47 | $Fru_n$ α λ $HU^{2-3}_{2-3}$ 16-36 |

| Chemical | Reported Characteristics | Specific Gravity | Vapor Pressure | Detection Threshold | Recognition Threshold | Classification Expression, Factors, HU Value |
|---|---|---|---|---|---|---|
| Butyl ethyl ketone $C_8H_{14}O$ | pungent, extremely irritating: X | .8266 (20/4°C) | | | | ψ!!! |
| n-Butyl formate $C_5H_{10}O_2$ | plum, sweet: F | .885-.9108 | 51.0 | | | $Fru_n$ α |
| Butyl hexyl ketone $C_{11}H_{22}O$ | fruity, rue: M | | | | | $Fru_n$ |
| tert-Butyl hypochlorite $C_4ClH_9O$ | irritating: Y | .910 (20/20°C) | | | | $Hal_n$ ε ψ! |
| tert-Butyliso-cyanate $C_5H_9NO$ | aromatic, pungent: A | | | | | ψ! |
| tert-Butylisothio-cyanate $C_5H_9NS$ | aromatic: A | | | | | |
| n-Butyl mercaptan $C_4H_{10}S$ | heavy, skunk-like: PXY | .8337 (20/4°C) | | .379 | | $Mus_nHal_n$ β!! π σ!! ψ $HU^{3-5}_{4-6}$ 49-121 |
| sec-Butyl mercaptan $C_4H_{10}S$ | heavy, skunk-like: PY | .8288 (20/4°C) | | | | $Mus_nHal_n$ β!! π σ!! ψ |
| tert-Butyl mercaptan $C_4H_{10}S$ | strong, heavy, skunk: PXY | .79-.82 (60/60°F) | | | | $Mus_nHal_n$ β!! π σ!! ψ |
| tert-Butyl methyl carbinol $C_6H_{15}O$ | camphoraceous: A | | | | | $Nut_n$ δ |
| tert-Butyl methyl ether $C_8H_{18}O$ | camphoraceous: A | | | | | $Nut_n$ δ |

| | | | | |
|---|---|---|---|---|
| p-tert-Butyl-α-methylhydrocinnamaldehyde $C_{14}H_{20}O$ | strong, floral: X | .942<br>.949<br>(25/25°C) | | $Flo_n$ |
| n-Butyl nitrate $C_4H_9NO_3$ | ethereal: X | 1.03<br>(20°C) | | λ! |
| tert-Butyl nitrite $C_4H_9NO_3$ | agreeable: Y | .8671<br>(20/4°C) | | |
| n-Butyl pelargonate $C_{14}H_{26}O_2$ | fruity: X | .865<br>(15.5/15.5°C) | | $Fru_n$ |
| tert-Butyl peroxybenzoate $C_{11}H_{15}O_3$ | mild, aromatic: X | 1.04<br>(25/25°C) | .33<br>mm hg<br>(50°C) | |
| p-tert-Butylphenol $C_{10}H_{14}O$ | distinctive: X | .9081<br>(114/4°C) | 170.2 | |
| n-Butyl phenyl-acetate $C_{12}H_{16}O_2$ | rose, honey, slightly floral: FX | .991-<br>.994<br>(25/25°C) | | $Flo_nCar_n$ α |
| n-Butyl phenylether $C_{10}H_{14}O$ | aromatic: X | .929<br>(20°C) | | |
| 4-tert-Butylphenyl salicylate $C_{17}H_{18}O_3$ | slight, salol-type odor or odorless: XY | | 305.8 | ξ |
| n-Butylphthlate $C_{16}H_{22}O_4$ | sweetish, caprylic: C | 1.0459-<br>1.0465<br>(20°C) | | $But_n$ α |
| n-Butyl propionate $C_7H_{14}O_2$ | apple-like: XP | .8754<br>(20/4°C) | | $Fru_n$ |
| Butyl stearamide $C_{22}H_{45}NO$ | amide: X | .869<br>(20/20°C) | | $Ami_n$ |

| Chemical | Reported Characteristics | Specific Gravity | Vapor Pressure | Detection Threshold | Recognition Threshold | Classification Expression, Factors, HU Value |
|---|---|---|---|---|---|---|
| Butyl stearate $C_{22}H_{44}O_2$ | faint fatty or odorless: X | .855-.875 (25/25°C) | | | | $Lip_n$ ξ |
| Butyl sulfide $C_8H_{18}S$ | mild, non-mercaptan: X | .852 (0/4°C) | 118.6 | .015 | | $Sul_n$ |
| 7-tert-Butyl-α-tetralone $C_{13}H_{19}O$ | musk, sandalwood: A | | | | | $Mus_nWoo_n$ |
| Butylthiamine $BrC_{15}H_{23}N_4OS\cdot BrH$ | slight thiazole: Y | | | | | $Hyc_nOxy_n$ β σ ϕ |
| 4-tert-Butylthiophenol $C_{10}H_{14}S$ | mild, non-mercaptan: X | .986 (25°C) | | | | $Sul_n$ |
| tert-Butyltrimethyl acetate | aromatic: A | | | | | |
| Butyraldehyde $C_4H_8O$ | characteristic, sweet, rancid, pungent, aldehyde, suffocating: JMX | | | .99 | .039 | α ϕ! ψ! $HU^{3-6}_{4-6}$ 49-144 |
| Butyric acid $C_4H_8O_2$ | unpleasant, rancid butter: FXY | .959 (20/4°C) | 108.0 | .0007 | .001 | $Lip_nBut_nSeb_n$ β ψ $HU^{4-5}_{4-6}$ 121 |
| Butyric anhydride $C_8H_{14}O_3$ | disagreeable, pungent, lachrymator: M | .9668 (20/4°C) | .3 mm Hg (20°C) | | | $But_n$ β ε!! ψ! |
| Butyrolactone $C_4H_6O$ | pleasant, faintly aromatic: AMX | 1.1441 (0/0°C) | | | | ξ |
| Butyronitrile $C_4H_7N$ | bitter almonds: AM | .7954 (15/4°C) | 59.0 | | | $Nut_n$ ν |

| | | | | |
|---|---|---|---|---|
| Butyroyl chloride $C_4ClH_7O$ | characteristic, pungent, acid-chloride: X | 1.0263 (20/4°C) | | $Hal_n$ ψ!! |
| Cacodyl $As_2C_4H_{12}$ | almost intolerable, garlicky, putrid, repulsive: AMY | 1.447 (15°C) | | $All_n$ β!!! |
| Cacodyl hydroxide $As_2C_4H_{13}O$ | putrid: A | | | β! |
| Cacodyl oxide $As_2C_4H_{12}O$ | putrid, objectionable: AM | | | β!! |
| Cacodyl sulfide $As_2C_4H_{12}S$ | putrid: A | | | β! |
| Cadaverine $C_5H_{14}N_2$ | characteristic, putrid, decaying flesh: AMPX | | | $Ami_n$ α!! β!!! ρ |
| Cadinene $C_{15}H_{24}$ | slight, woody, pleasant, spicy: FY | .9239 (20/4°C) | | $Woo_nSpi_n$ |
| CADMIUM Cd | no reported odor | 8.65 (20°C) | 611 | |
| Cadmium ricinoleate $C_{36}CdH_{66}O_6$ | nearly odorless: X | 1.11 (20°C) | | |
| Caffeine acetate $C_8H_{10}N_4O_2 \cdot C_4H_8O_4$ | acetic acid: Y | | | φ! ψ! |
| CALCIUM Ca | no reported odor | 1.54 (20/4°C) | 1207 | |
| Calcium acetate $C_4CaH_6O_4$ | acetic acid: X | 1.50 | | φ! ψ! |
| Calcium alginate | slight characteristic: X | | | |

| Chemical | Reported Characteristics | Specific Gravity | Vapor Pressure | Detection Threshold | Recognition Threshold | Classification Expression, Factors, HU Value |
|---|---|---|---|---|---|---|
| Calcium bisulfite solution $CaH_2O_6S_2$ | strong sulfur dioxide: PXY | 1.06 | | | | $Sul_n$ β τ φ ψ! |
| Calcium formate $C_2CaH_2O_4$ | slight acetic acid-like: Y | 2.015 | | | | φ ψ |
| Calcium iodobehen-ate $C_{44}CaH_{84}I_2O_4$ | slight fatty or odorless: XY | | | | | $Lip_n$ ξ |
| Calcium levulinate $C_{10}CaH_{14}O_6$ | faint burnt sugar: X | | | | | $Car_n$ σ |
| Calcium ricinoleate $C_{36}CaH_{66}O_6$ | slight fatty acid: X | 1.04 | | | | $Lip_n$ |
| Calcium sulfide CaS | hydrogen sulfide odor in moist air: XY | 2.5 | | | | $Sul_n$ β π τ φ! ψ!! |
| Camphene $C_{10}H_{16}$ | insipid, camphor, woody: FXY @ | .8422 (54/4°C) | 97.9 | | | $Nut_nWoo_n$ |
| Campholylamine $C_{10}H_{19}NO_2$ | garlic, ammoniacal: A | | | | | $All_nUro_nNit_n$ ψ! |
| Camphor $C_{10}H_{16}O$ | characteristic, familiar, fragrant, penetrating, cam-phor: AFPXY @ | .992 (25/4°C) | 138 | | | $Woo_n$ δ! ψ ω! |
| Camphotamide $C_{21}H_{32}N_2O_5S$ | slight camphor-like: Y | | | | | $Woo_n$ |
| Capric acid $C_{10}H_{20}O_2$ | unpleasant, rancid, buttery, oily, sweet: AFXY | .8782 (50/4°C) | 200 | | | $Lip_nBut_nSeb_n$ α! $HU^{4-5}_{4-6}$ 64-121 |

| | | | | |
|---|---|---|---|---|
| Caproic acid $C_6H_{12}O_2$ | characteristic, goat-like, rancid, limberger cheese, oily, sweet, slightly brandy-like: AFPXY @ | .9265 (20/4°C) | 144 | $Mus_n Lip_n But_n Hyc_n$ α β λ σ!! ω $HU^{4-5}_{4-6}$ 64-121 |
| Caprylic acid $C_8H_{16}O_2$ | slight, unpleasant: XY | .910 (20/4°C) | 172.2 | $But_n$ |
| Capsaicin $C_{18}H_{27}NO_3$ | pungent, slight ginger: F | | | $Spi_n$ ψ! |
| Captan $C_9Cl_3H_8NO_2S$ | pungent(X), odorless (Y) | 1.74 | | ψ |
| Carbachol $C_6ClH_{15}N_2O_2$ | faint amine odor develops on standing resembling aliphatic amines: XY | | | $Ami_n$ |
| Carbamyl chloride $CClH_2NO$ | acrid, offensive: PY | | | β ψ! |
| Carbazole $C_{12}H_9N$ | characteristic: X | 1.10 (18/4°C) | 265.0 | |
| 2-Carbethoxycyclo-hexanone $C_9H_{14}O_3$ | characteristic, ester-like: X | 1.074 (25°C) | | $Es_n$ |
| 2-Carbethoxycyclo-pentanone $C_8H_{12}O_2$ | characteristic, ester-like: X | 1.0976 (0°C) | | $Es_n$ |
| Carbobenzoxy chloride $C_8ClH_7O_2$ | lachrymator, acrid, phosgene: PXY | | | $Ens_n Hal_n$ ε! ψ! $HU^{4-6}_{4-6}$ 64-144 |
| CARBON C | no reported odor | 2.26 (20°C) | 4373 | |

| Chemical | Reported Characteristics | Specific Gravity | Vapor Pressure | Detection Threshold | Recognition Threshold | Classification Expression, Factors, HU Value |
|---|---|---|---|---|---|---|
| Carbondiselenide $CSe_2$ | rotten radishes: Y | 2.6626 (25/4°C) | | | | $Mol_nSse_n$ σ! ψ $HU^{3-5}_{4-6}$ 49-121 |
| Carbon disulfide $CS_2$ | pure: sweet, almost odorless, ethereal; impure: disagreeable, foul, strong: AXY | 1.2632 (20/4°C) | -5.1 | | .21 | α! β! λ! $HU^{4-6}_{4-6}$ 64-144 |
| Carbonic acid, ethyl ester dimethylamide | minty: A | | | | | $He_n$ δ! |
| Carbonic acid, methyl ester dimethylamide | minty: A | | | | | $He_n$ δ! |
| Carbon monoxide CO | exceedingly faint metallic odor (X), odorless (Y) | .814 (-195/4°C) (liq.) | -205.7 | | | μ |
| Carbon suboxide $C_3O_2$ | acrolein and mustard oil in small amounts, lachrymator in large amounts, suffocating, pungent: AY | 1.114 (0/4°C) (liq.) | -36.9 | | | $Oxy_n$ ε!! σ!!! ϕ!! ψ!! $HU^{4-6}_{4-6}$ 64-144 |
| Carbon tetrachloride $CCl_4$ | peculiar, heavy, ethereal, characteristic: APXY | 1.589 (25/25°C) | 23 | | 21.4 | 0 0 0 ($Hyc_nHal_n$) α Y λ!! $HU^{2-3}_{3-4}$ 25-49 |
| Carbon tetraiodide $CI_4$ | iodine: Y | 4.32 (20/4°C) | | | | $Hal_n$ |
| Carbonyl fluoride $CF_2O$ | pungent: Y | 1.139 (-114°C) (liq.) | | | | ψ |

| | | | | |
|---|---|---|---|---|
| Carbonyl sulfide $COS$ | typical sulfide: X | 2.1 (air=1) | -85.9 | $Sul_n$ |
| $\Delta^3$-Carene $C_{10}H_{16}$ | sweet, pungent, more agreeable than turpentine: Y | .8668 (15/15°C) | | $Woo_nHyc_n$ $\alpha$ $\psi$ |
| Carone $C_{10}H_{16}O$ | camphor, mint: A | | | $Nut_nHe_n$ $\delta$ |
| Carotol $C_{15}H_{26}O$ | spicy: F | .9624 (20°C) | | $Spi_n$ |
| Carvacrol $C_{10}H_{14}O$ | thymol, burnt, camphor-like, medicinal: FXY | .976 (20/4°C) | 169.7 | $Mst_nHer_nWoo_n$ $\delta$! $\sigma$!! |
| 4-Carvomenthenol $C_{11}H_{19}O$ | fruity: F | | | $Fru_n$ |
| Carvone $C_{10}H_{14}O$ | caraway, strong, characteristic: XY | .960 (20°C) | 157.3 | $He_n$ |
| d-Carvone $C_{10}H_{14}O$ | dill, caraway: FXY | 965 (20/4°C) | | $He_n$ |
| 1-Carvone $C_{10}H_{14}O$ | spearmint: FXY | .9652 (15/15°C) | | $He_n$ $\delta$! |
| Caryophyllene $C_{15}H_{24}$ | midway between clove and turpentine, turpene, balsamic: FY | .9052 (17/4°C) | | $Spi_nWoo_nBal_n$ $\delta$! |
| Castoreum | powerful, resinous, animal-like: M @ | | | $A_5Mst$ $\psi$! |
| Catechol diisopropylketol $C_{13}H_{20}O_4$ | floral: A | | | $Flo_n$ |

| Chemical | Reported Characteristics | Specific Gravity | Vapor Pressure | Detection Threshold | Recognition Threshold | Classification Expression, Factors, HU Value |
|---|---|---|---|---|---|---|
| Cedrol $C_{15}H_{26}O$ | cedarwood: FXY | | | | | $Woo_n$ σ |
| Cedryl acetate $C_{17}H_{28}O_2$ | light cedar: X @ | .975-.995 | | | | $Woo_n$ |
| CERIUM Ce | no reported odor | 6.75 | | | | |
| CERIUM COMPOUNDS | no reported odors | | | | | |
| CESIUM Cs | no reported odor | 1.873 | 509 | | | |
| CESIUM COMPOUNDS | no reported odors | | | | | |
| Cetyl alcohol $C_{16}H_{34}O$ | faint: X | .8176 (49.5°C) | 251.7 | | | |
| Chimaphilin $C_{12}H_{10}O_2$ | minty, green: F | | | | | $He_nEns_n$ δ! |
| Chloral $C_2Cl_3HO$ | pungent, irritating: PXY | 1.510 (20/4°C) | 40.2 | | .047 | ε! ψ! $HU^{2-5}_{4-5}$ 36-100 |
| Chloral hydrate $C_2Cl_3H_3O_2$ | aromatic, penetrating, slightly acrid, peculiar, pungent: PXY | 1.91 | 55.0 | | | ψ ω |
| Chlorbenside $C_{13}Cl_2H_{10}S$ | almond-like: XY | 1.4210 (25/4°C) | | | | $Nut_nHal_nSul_n$ |
| Chlorethiazol $C_6ClH_8NS$ | characteristic, disagreeable, thiazol-like: Y | 1.233 (25/4°C) | | | | $Hyc_nOxy_n$ β! σ! φ $HU^{3-5}_{4-5}$ 49-100 |
| Chlorinated lime | strong chlorine: XY | | | | | $Hal_n$ φ! ψ! |

| | | | | | | |
|---|---|---|---|---|---|---|
| CHLORINE $Cl_2$ | pungent, halogenic, irritating, suffocating: XY | 3.214 (gas) (air=1) | -71.7 | .01 | .314 | $Hal_n$ ε! ϕ! ψ! $HU^{3-6}_{3-6}$ 36-144 |
| Chlorine dioxide $ClO_2$ | unpleasant, similar to chlorine and nitric acid: Y | 3.09 g/l (gas) (air=1) | -29.4 | | | $Hal_n$ β ϕ! ψ! |
| Chlorine monoxide $Cl_2O$ | disagreeable, penetrating: Y | 3.89 g/l (gas) (air=1 | -39.4 | | | $Hal_n$ σ!! ω! |
| Chlorine trifluoride $ClF_3$ | somewhat sweet, suffocating: Y | 2.026 (-78°C) (liq.) | -34.7 | | | $Hal_n$ α! ϕ!! |
| Chloroacetaldehyde $C_2ClH_3O$ | pungent, very corrosive to mucous membranes, acrid, penetrating: PXY | | | | | $Hal_n$ α ρ! ψ! |
| Chloroacetamide $C_2ClH_4NO$ | characteristic: X | | | | | |
| Chloroacetic anhydride $C_2Cl_2H_4O_3$ | pungent: X | 1.5494 (20/4°C) | 159.8 | | | ψ! |
| Chloroacetone $C_3ClH_5O$ | pungent, irritating, lachrymator: PXY | 1.123 (25/4°C) | | | | ε! ψ! |
| Chloroacetonitrile $C_2ClH_2N$ | pungent: AX | 1.2020-1.2035 (25/25°C) | | | | ψ! |
| 2-Chloroacetophenone $C_8ClH_7O$ | floral, pungent, fragrant, nonpersistent, powerful lachrymator, war gas: APXY | 1.324 (15°C) | | 1.34 | | $Flo_n$ ε!! ψ! |

| Chemical | Reported Characteristics | Specific Gravity | Vapor Pressure | Detection Threshold | Recognition Threshold | Classification Expression, Factors, HU Value |
|---|---|---|---|---|---|---|
| Chloroacetyl chloride $C_2Cl_2H_2O$ | very pungent: XY | 1.4202 (20/4°C) | | | | ψ!! |
| β-Chloroallyliso-thiocyanate $C_4ClH_5NS$ | pungent, aromatic: A | | | | | ψ! |
| p-Chloro-tert-amylbenzene $C_{11}ClH_{16}$ | aromatic: A | | | | | $Hal_nHyc_nOxy_n$ |
| 2-Chloro-4-tert-amylphenol $C_{11}ClH_{15}O$ | aromatic: X | 1.11 (20°C) | | | | $Hal_nHyc_nOxy_n$ |
| o-Chloroaniline $C_6ClH_6N$ | amine: X | 1.2114 (22/4°C) | 139.5 | | | $Ami_nHal_n$ |
| Chloroazodin $C_2Cl_2H_4N_6$ | faint chlorine: XY | | | | | $Hal_n$ φ ψ |
| p-Chlorobenzalde-hyde $C_7ClH_5O$ | almond: A | | | | | $Nut_nHal_n$ |
| Chlorobenzene $C_6ClH_5$ | faint, aromatic, not unpleasant, mild, almond-like: AMXY | 1.107 (20/4°C) | 70.7 | | .21 | $Nut_nHal_nHyc_n$ $HU^{2-3}_{2-4}$ 16-49 |
| Chlorobromodi-nitrocarbon $BrCClN_2O_4$ | pungent: A | | | | | $Hal_n$ ψ! |
| Chlorobutanol $C_4Cl_3H_7O$ | characteristic, strong, camphor: APXY | | | | | $Woo_nHal_nHyc_n$ δ! |

| | | | | |
|---|---|---|---|---|
| n-Chlorobutylamine $C_4ClH_{11}N$ | pungent: A | | | $Hal_nNit_n$ ψ! |
| 4-Chloro-1-tert-butylbenzene $C_{10}ClH_{13}$ | aromatic: A | | | |
| 4-Chloro-m-cresol $C_7ClH_7O$ | impure-phenolic; pure-odorless: XY | | | $Mol_nHyc_n$ |
| Chlorocyanohydrin $C_3Cl_3H_2NO$ | hydrocyanic acid, chloral: PY | | | $Nut_nHal_nNit_n$ |
| n-Chlorodiethyl-amine $C_4ClH_{12}N$ | pungent: A | | | $Hal_nNit_n$ ψ!! |
| Chlorodifluoro-acetic acid $C_2ClFHO_2$ | pungent: X | | | ψ! |
| n-Chlorodimethyl-amine $C_2ClH_8N$ | pungent: A | | | ψ! |
| 1-Chloro-2,4-dinitrobenzene $C_6ClH_3N_2O_4$ | almond: X | 1.69 | | $Nut_nHal_nNit_nHyc_n$ |
| n-Chloro-n-ethylacetamide $C_5ClH_{10}NO_3$ | pungent, camphor-like: A | | | $Woo_nHal_n$ ψ! |
| n-Chloroethylamine $C_2ClH_7N$ | pungent: A | | | ψ! |
| Chloroform $CCl_3H$ | heavy, ethereal: APXY | 1.484 (20/20°C) | 10.4 | $Hal_nHyc_n$ α!! λ!!! π |
| Chloroformic acid ethylamide $C_4ClH_6NO_2$ | pungent: A | | | ψ! |

| Chemical | Reported Characteristics | Specific Gravity | Vapor Pressure | Detection Threshold | Recognition Threshold | Classification Expression, Factors, HU Value |
|---|---|---|---|---|---|---|
| Chloroformoxime $CClH_2NO$ | hydrocyanic acid-like: PX | | | | | $Nut_nHal_n$ ψ! |
| n-Chloro-n-isoamylacetamide $C_8ClH_{16}NO_3$ | pungent: A | | | | | ψ! |
| Chloromethyl acetate $C_3ClH_5O_2$ | sweet, pungent: AX | 1.238 (20/20°C) | 73.5 | | | α! ψ! |
| Chloromethyl chloroformate $C_2Cl_2H_2O_2$ | penetrating, irritating: PX | 1.465 (15°C) | | | | ψ! ω! |
| 1-Chlormethyl-naphthalene $C_{11}ClH_9$ | sharp, pungent: X | 1.182 (25/25°C) | | | | ψ! |
| 2-Chloro-2-nitrospropane $C_3ClH_6NO_2$ | pungent: A | | | | | $Hyc_nHal_nNit_n$ ψ! |
| m-Chlorophenol $C_6ClH_5O$ | phenol-like: X | 1.245 (45/4°C) | 143 | .034 | | $Mol_nHal_nHyc_n$ σ!! ψ $HU^{2-3}_{3-4}$ 25-49 |
| o-Chlorophenol $C_6ClH_5O$ | unpleasant, penetrating: X | 1.2573 (25/4°C) | 106.0 | | | $Hal_nHyc_n$ σ!! ω! |
| p-Chlorophenol $C_6ClH_5O$ | characteristic, phenolic, penetrating, unpleasant: Y | 1.2238 (78/4°C) | 150.0 | | | $Mol_nHal_nHyc_n$ σ! ψ ω! |
| m-Chlorophenyl-isothiocyanate $C_7ClH_5NS$ | strong, pungent: D | | | | | $Hal_nSul_n$ ψ!!! |

| | | | | | |
|---|---|---|---|---|---|
| o-Chlorophenyl-isothiocyanate $C_7ClH_5NS$ | pungent: D | | | | $Hal_nSul_nNit_n$ ψ!! |
| P-Chlorophenyl-isothiocyanate $C_7ClH_5NS$ | sweet, anise, aniseed: AD | | | | $Her_n$ α! |
| p-Chlorophenyl phenyl sulfone $C_{12}ClH_9O_2S$ | slight, aromatic: XY | | | | |
| Chloropicrin $CCl_3NO_2$ | very irritating, pungent, intense, lachrymator: XY | 1.6558 (20/4°C) | 53.8 | 1.08 | $Hal_nNit_n$ ε!!! ψ!! $HU^{4-6}_{4-6}$ 36-144 |
| β-Chloropropionitrile $C_3ClH_4N$ | acrid, characteristic: Y | 1.1363 (25/4°C) | | | $Hal_nHyc_n$ ψ! |
| N-Chloropropylamine $C_3ClH_9N$ | pungent: A | | | | $Hal_nNit_n$ ψ! |
| Chloropyramine $C_{16}ClH_{20}N_3$ | pungent: Y | | | | $Ami_nHyc_n$ ψ!! |
| n-Chlorosuccinimide $C_4ClH_4N$ | mild, chlorine: PY | | | | $Hal_n$ ψ |
| Chlorosulfonic acid $ClHO_3S$ | pungent, sharp: PXY | 1.753 (20/4°C) | 105.3 | | $Hal_nSul_n$ ψ!! |
| Chlorothiolphenol $C_6ClH_5S$ | pungent, burning, sweetish: M | | | | α! γ ψ! |
| Chlorothymol $C_{10}ClH_{13}O$ | characteristic: X | | | | |

| Chemical | Reported Characteristics | Specific Gravity | Vapor Pressure | Detection Threshold | Recognition Threshold | Classification Expression, Factors, HU Value |
|---|---|---|---|---|---|---|
| Chlorotrifluoro-ethylene $C_2ClF_3$ | faint, ethereal: X | 1.305 (20°C) (liq.) | -66.7 | | | λ ξ |
| Chlorotrifluoro-methane $CClF_3$ | ethereal: PX | | -111.7 | | | λ! |
| Chlorotrimethoxy-silane $C_3ClH_{13}O_3Si$ | ethereal: A | | | | | λ! |
| 3-Chloro-2,2,3-trimethylbutane $C_7ClH_{19}$ | camphor: A | | | | | $Woo_nHal_n$ δ σ! |
| β-Chlorovinyldi-chloroarsine $AsC_2Cl_3H_2$ | faint, geranium-like, war gas: PXY | 1.8855 (20°C) | | | | $Flo_n$ |
| 4-Chloro-3,5-xylenol $C_8ClH_9O$ | phenolic: XY | | | | | $Mol_nHyc_n$ σ!! |
| Chlorpromazine $C_{17}ClH_{19}N_2S$ | amine-like: XY | | | | | $Ami_n$ σ! |
| Chlorprothixene $C_{18}ClH_{18}NS$ | amine-like: X | | | | | $Ami_nHal_n$ σ ψ! |
| Chlorquinaldol $C_{10}Cl_2H_7NO$ | pleasant, medici-nal: XY | | | | | |
| Choline $C_5H_{15}NO_2$ | strong, amine: X | | | | | $Ami_n$ σ ψ! |
| Choline bicarbonate $C_6H_{15}NO_4$ | strong, fishy, amine-like: Y | 1.0965 (25/4°C) | | | | $Ami_n$ β μ ψ!! |

| | | | | |
|---|---|---|---|---|
| Choline bitartrate $C_9H_{19}NO_2$ | faint, trimethyl-amine-like: X | | | $Ami_n$ μ ψ |
| Choline chloride $C_5ClH_{14}N$ | fishy: X | | | $Ami_n$ μ ψ! |
| Choline gluconate $C_{11}H_{25}NO_8$ | amine-like: XY | | | $Ami_n$ ψ |
| CHROMIUM Cr | no reported odor | 7.14 | 2139 | |
| Chromium oxy-chloride $Cl_2CrO_2$ | musty, burning: P | 1.91 (25/4°C) | 58 | $Mst_n$ γ |
| Chrysanthemummono-carboxylic acid, ethyl ester $C_{12}H_{20}O_2$ | pleasant, ester: X | .924-.927 (25/25°C) | | $Hyc_n$ |
| Cinchophen $C_{16}H_{11}NO_2$ | faint, benzoic acid: X | | | |
| Cineole $C_{10}H_{18}O$ | camphor-like: AFXY | .921-.923 (25/25°C) | 108.2 | $Woo_n$ |
| Cinnamic acid $C_9H_8O_2$ | apricot: F | | | $Bal_nFru_n$ |
| Cinnamic alcohol $C_9H_{10}O$ | hyacinth, slightly cassia, warm: FXY | 1.0397 (35/35°C) | 177.8 | $Flo_n$ γ ψ |
| Cinnamic aldehyde $C_9H_8O$ | strong, cinnamon: FXY @ | 1.048-1.052 (25/25°C) | 177.7 | $Spi_n$ γ σ ψ |
| Cinnamyl acetate $C_{11}H_{12}O_2$ | floral, spicy, pineapple: FX | 1.048-1.052 | | $Flo_nSpi_nFru_n$ α! ψ |

| Chemical | Reported Characteristics | Specific Gravity | Vapor Pressure | Detection Threshold | Recognition Threshold | Classification Expression, Factors, HU Value |
|---|---|---|---|---|---|---|
| Cinnamyl anthranilate $C_{16}H_{14}NO_3$ | fruity, grape: F | | | | | $Fru_n$ |
| Cinnamyl butyrate $C_{16}H_{16}NO_2$ | honey: F | | | | | $Car_n$ $\alpha$ |
| Cinnamyl cinnamate $C_{18}H_{16}O_2$ | cinnamon, spicy: F | | | | | $Spi_n Bal_n$ $\alpha!$ |
| Cinnamyl phenylacetate $C_{17}H_{16}O_2$ | rosy, cinnamon: F | | | | | |
| Cinnamyl propionate $C_{12}H_{14}O_2$ | slightly spicy, sharp: F | | | | | $A_n Mst_n Spi_n$ $\psi!$ |
| Cinnoline $C_8H_6N_2$ | geranium-like: Y | | | | | $Flo_n$ $\alpha$ |
| Citraconic acid $C_5H_6O_4$ | characteristic: Y | 1.62 | | | | |
| Citral $C_{10}H_{16}O$ | strong, citrus, lemon: FXY @ | .891-.897 (15°C) | 160 | .00004 | | $Fru_n$ $\psi!$ |
| d-Citronellal $C_{10}H_{18}O$ | pleasant, intense, lemon, rose: X | .847-.850 | 140.1 | | | $Mus_n Mst_n Fru_n Flo_n$ $\sigma!$ $\psi$ |
| Citronellol $C_{10}H_{20}O$ | rose: FX | .849-.859 | 159.8 | | | $Flo_n$ $\alpha!$ |
| Citronellyl acetate $C_{12}H_{22}O_2$ | bergamot-like, sweet, fruity: FX | .884-.891 | 161.0 | | | $Her_n Fru_n$ $\alpha$ $\psi$ |
| Citronellyl butyrate $C_{14}H_{26}O_2$ | plum-like: F | | | | | $Fru_n Flo_n$ $\sigma$ $\psi$ |

| | | | | |
|---|---|---|---|---|
| α-Citronellyl-γ-butyrolactone $C_{14}H_{24}O_2$ | musky, pear, peach: A | | | $Mus_nFru_n$ |
| Citronellyl formate $C_{11}H_{20}O_2$ | fruity, floral plum-like: FX | .890 .903 (25/25°C) | | $Fru_nFlo_nEns_n$ $\sigma$ $\psi$!! |
| Citronellyl phenylacetate $C_{18}H_{26}O_2$ | fruity, floral, woody: C | | | $Woo_nFru_nFlo_n$ $\sigma$ $\psi$ |
| Citronellyl propionate $C_{11}H_{24}O_2$ | plum: F | | | $Fru_nFlo_n$ $\sigma$ $\psi$! |
| Civetone $C_{17}H_{30}O$ | disgustingly obnoxious, becoming pleasant in extreme dilution, musky, fecal: AFY | .917 (33/4°C) | | $\theta^2$: $Mus_nFec_n$ $\theta_1$: $Fec_nMus_n$ $\beta$!!! |
| COBALT Co | no reported odor | 8.92 | | |
| COBALT COMPOUNDS | no reported odors | | | |
| γ-Coniceine $C_8H_{15}N$ | mousy: Y | .8753 | | $Uro_nBut_nMus_n$ |
| Coniferyl alcohol $C_{10}H_{12}O_3$ | chocolate: F | | | $Woo_n$ $\nu$ $\sigma$ $\psi$ |
| Coniine $C_8H_{17}N$ | mousy, stupifying: MPXY | .844-.848 (20/4°C) | | $Uro_nBut_nMus_n$ |
| COPPER Cu | no reported odor | 8.94 | 2207 | |

| Chemical | Reported Characteristics | Specific Gravity | Vapor Pressure | Detection Threshold | Recognition Threshold | Classification Expression, Factors, HU Value |
|---|---|---|---|---|---|---|
| Coumarin $C_9H_6O_2$ | pleasant, floral, fragrant, vanilla, new mown hay: AMPXY | | 216.5 | | | $Flo_nBal_nEns_n$ |
| Creosol $C_7H_8O$ | aromatic: Y | 1.092 (25/4°C) | | | | |
| m-Cresol $C_7H_8O$ | phenolic: Y | 1.034 (20/4°C) | 138.0 | | | $Mol_nHyc_n$ σ!! ω |
| o-Cresol $C_7H_8O$ | phenolic: Y | 1.047 (20/4°C) | 127.4 | | | $Mol_nHyc_n$ σ!! ω |
| p-Cresol $C_7H_8O$ | phenolic, burnt: FY | 1.0341 (20/4°C) | 140 | | .001 | $Mol_nHyc_n$ σ!!! ω |
| m-Cresyl acetate $C_9H_{10}O_2$ | characteristic, phenolic, acetone-like: XY | 1.048 (26/4°C) | | | | $Mol_nHyc_n$ σ!! ω |
| p-Cresyl acetate $C_9H_{10}O_2$ | floral, narcissus: X | 1.0532 (15°C) | | | | $Flo_n$ |
| Crotamiton $C_{13}H_{17}NO$ | faint fish: X | | | | | $Ami_n$ |
| Crotonaldehyde $C_4H_6O$ | pungent, extremely irritating, war gas, lachrymator: PXY | .853 (20/20°C) | | 7.32 | | ε!!! φ!!! ψ!!! $HU^{5-6}_{5-6}$ 100-144 |
| Crotonic acid $C_4H_6O_2$ | acrid, butyric: M | 1.018 (15/4°C) | | | | $But_n$ ψ! $HU^{4-5}_{4-6}$ 64-121 |
| Crotyl mercaptan $C_4H_8S$ | @ (undetectable by 1 in 1,000 persons) | | | .0077 | | |

| | | | | | | |
|---|---|---|---|---|---|---|
| Cumene $C_9H_{12}$ | musty, floral, sharp: CJ | .864 (20/4°C) | 88.1 | | .047 | $Mus_nSpi_nFlo_n$ σ ψ! $HU^{3-4}_{4-5}$ 49-64 |
| Cuminaldehyde $C_{10}H_{12}O$ | strong, pungent, persistent, cumin, sweaty: FXY | .978 (20°C) | 160 | | 1.2 | $A_nSpi_nFlo_n$ σ ψ! |
| Cuminic alcohol $C_{10}H_{14}O$ | intense, strawberry, persistent, caraway-like: FXY | .981 (15°C) | 176.2 | | | $Fru_nHer_n$ ρ!! |
| Cumyl phenol $C_{15}H_{16}O$ | characteristic, phenol: X | 1.115 (25°C) g/ml | | | | $Mol_n$ |
| Cupric butyrate $C_8CuH_{18}O_6$ | butyric acid: P | | | | | $But_n$ |
| Cyanogen $C_2N_2$ | pungent, almond-like, penetrating, acrid and pungent when in lethal concentrations, war gas: APXY | .9537 (-21.17/4°C) | -51.8 | | | $Nut_n$ ψ! ω |
| Cyanogen bromide BrCN | penetrating, highly irritant: XY | 2.015 (20/4°C) | 22.6 | | | ψ!! ω! |
| Cyanogen chloride CClN | pungent, highly irritating, very poisonous, lachrymator, war gas: APXY | 1.186 | -24.9 | .99 | | ε! ψ!! |
| Cyanogen iodide CIN | very pungent: PXY | 2.84 | 97.6 | | | ψ!! |
| Cyclamen alcohol $C_{12}H_{17}O$ | floral: C | | | | | $Flo_n$ ψ |
| Cyclamen aldehyde $C_{13}H_{18}O$ | heavy, floral, violet: FX | .949-.959 | | | | $Flo_n$ ψ |

| Chemical | Reported Characteristics | Specific Gravity | Vapor Pressure | Detection Threshold | Recognition Threshold | Classification Expression, Factors, HU Value |
|---|---|---|---|---|---|---|
| Cyclamen butyrate $C_{16}H_{26}$ | fruity: C | | | | | $Fru_n\ \psi$ |
| Cyclamen propionate $C_{15}H_{23}O_2$ | floral, fruity: C | | | | | $Fru_nFlo_n\ \psi$ |
| Cyclobutylamine | pungent: A | | | | | $\psi$! |
| Cyclobutyl dimethyl carbinol | minty: A | | | | | $He_n\ \delta$! |
| Cyclobutyl ethyl ketone $C_7H_{12}O$ | minty: A | | | | | $He_n\ \delta$! |
| Cyclobutyl methyl carbinol $C_7H_{13}O$ | minty: A | | | | | $He_n\ \delta$! |
| β-Cyclobutylpropyl alcohol $C_7H_{15}O$ | minty: A | | | | | $He_n\ \delta$! |
| Cyclodecanone $C_{10}H_{18}O$ | camphor: A | | | | | $Woo_n$ |
| Cyclododecanone $C_{12}H_{24}O$ | camphor: A | | | | | $Woo_n$ |
| Cyclogeraniol $C_{10}H_{16}O$ | floral: C | | | | | $Flo_n\ \sigma\ \psi$! |
| Cycloheptanone $C_7H_{12}O$ | peppermint, minty: AX | .9490 (20/4°C) | | | | $He_n\ \delta$! |
| Cycloheptylformaldehyde $C_8H_{14}O$ | almond: A | | | | | $Nut_n$ |

| | | | | | | |
|---|---|---|---|---|---|---|
| Cyclohexadecanone $C_{16}H_{32}O$ | musky: A | | | | | $Mus_n$ |
| Cyclohexane $C_6H_{12}$ | pure-solvent-like; impure-pungent: PXY | .7781 (20/4°C) | 25.5 | | | $\theta^2$: $Hyc_n$ $\psi$<br>$\theta_1$: $Hyc_n$ |
| Cyclohexane-carboxylic acid $C_7H_{12}O_2$ | when in liquid or solution form valerian-like: Y | 1.0480 (15/4°C) | | | | |
| Cyclohexanol acetate $C_8H_{14}O_2$ | amyl acetate-like: X | .966 | | | | $Fru_nHyc_n$ $\sigma$ $\psi$ |
| Cyclohexanone $C_6H_{10}O$ | sweet, sharp, peppermint, acetone, almond: AJPXY | .9478 (20/4°C) | 90.4 | .003 | .24 | $He_nHyc_nNut_n$ $\alpha$ $\delta$! $\psi$<br>$HU^3_{2-3}$ 10-16 |
| Cyclohexanone diallyl acetal $C_{14}H_{22}O_3$ | mild, minty: A | | | | | $He_n$ $\delta$ |
| Cyclohexanone diethyl acetal $C_{13}H_{23}O_3$ | minty: A | | | | | $He_n$ $\delta$! |
| Cyclohexanone dimethyl acetal $C_{11}H_{19}O_3$ | minty: A | | | | | $He_n$ $\delta$! |
| 2-Cyclohexene-1-hexanoic acid, 2-chloroethyl ester | strong fruity: W | | | | | $Fru_n$ |
| Cyclohexene oxide $C_6H_{10}O$ | strong: X | .967 (25/4°C) | | | | |
| Cyclohexen-3-one $C_7H_{10}O$ | stale urine: S | | | | | $Uro_n$ |

| Chemical | Reported Characteristics | Specific Gravity | Vapor Pressure | Detection Threshold | Recognition Threshold | Classification Expression, Factors, HU Value |
|---|---|---|---|---|---|---|
| Cyclohexylacetal-dehyde $C_{14}H_{23}O$ | pungent, almond: A | | | | | $Nut_n$ ψ! |
| Cyclohexylamine $C_6H_{13}N$ | strong, fishy, amine: PXY | .8647 (25/25°C) | | | | $Ami_n$ β ψ! |
| Cyclohexyl bromide $BrC_6H_{11}$ | penetrating: XY | 1.329 (15/15°C) | | | | ω!! |
| Cyclohexyl butyrate $C_{10}H_{18}O_2$ | floral, jasmine: C | | | | | $Spi_nFlo_n$ ψ! |
| Cyclohexylcarbinol $C_7H_{14}O$ | slight, camphor: Y | .9215 (25/4°C) | | | | $Woo_n$ |
| Cyclohexylchloride $C_6ClH_{11}$ | slight, pungent, suffocating: AY | 1.000 (20/4°C) | | | | ϕ!! ψ |
| Cyclohexyl cinnamate $C_{15}H_{18}O_2$ | mild, balsamic: C | | | | | $Bal_n$ |
| β-Cyclohexylethyl alcohol $C_8H_{13}O$ | floral: A | | | | | $Flo_n$ |
| Cyclononanone $C_9H_{18}$ | camphor: A | .769 | | | | $Woo_n$ |
| Cyclo-octadecanone | weak musk: A | | | | | $Mus_n$ |
| Cyclo-octane $C_8H_{16}$ | strong camphor: A | .835 | | | | $Woo_n$ |
| Cyclopentanol $C_5H_{10}O$ | pleasant, amyl alcohol: XY | .946 (20/4°C) | | | | $Flo_n$ ψ ω |

| | | | | |
|---|---|---|---|---|
| Cyclopentanone $C_5H_8O$ | agreeable, minty, peppermint-like, mild, distinctive, ethereal, almond: AMXY | .9509 (18/4°C) | | $He_nNut_n$ δ! λ |
| Cyclopentenyl acetone $C_8H_{12}O$ | characteristic, ketone: X | | | |
| $\Delta^{11}$-Cyclopentenyl formaldehyde $C_6H_{11}O$ | almond: A | | | $Nut_n$ |
| Cyclopentyl bromide $BrC_5H_9$ | sweet, aromatic: X | 1.3866 (20/4°C) | | $Hal_nHyc_n$ α! |
| Cyclopropane $C_3H_6$ | characteristic, solvent, naphtha-like: Y | .72-.79 | -70 | $Hyc_n$ ψ |
| Cyclopropyl methyl ether $C_4H_8O$ | cyclopropane: Y | | | $Hyc_n$ |
| Cyclotetradecanone | musky: A | | | $Mus_n$ |
| Cyclotridecanone | weak musk, cedar: A | | | $Mus_nWoo_n$ |
| Cycloundecanone | camphor, moldy: A | | | $Woo_nMol_n$ |
| Cymene (s) $C_{10}H_{14}$ | aromatic, herbal: FX | m: .862<br>o: .8748<br>p: .8551 | 110.8 | $Her_n$ |
| Cysteamine $C_2H_7NS$ | disagreeable, unpleasant: XY | | | |

| Chemical | Reported Characteristics | Specific Gravity | Vapor Pressure | Detection Threshold | Recognition Threshold | Classification Expression, Factors, HU Value |
|---|---|---|---|---|---|---|
| cis-Decahydro-naphthalene $C_{10}H_{18}$ | aromatic: X | .8927 (20/4°C) | 123.2 | | | |
| trans-Decahydro-naphthalene $C_{10}H_{18}$ | aromatic: X | .8700 (20/4°C) | 114.6 | | | |
| γ-Decalactone $C_{11}H_{18}O$ | sweet, flowery: D | | | | | $Flo_n$ α |
| Decamethylene carbonate | faint, floral, camphor, cedar: A | | | | | $Flo_nWoo_n$ δ |
| Decamethylene malonate | faint, musky: AM | | | | | $Mus_n$ |
| Decamethylene oxalate $C_{12}H_{20}O_4$ | fresh, musky: AM | | | | | $Mus_n$ δ ψ |
| n-Decanal $C_{10}H_{20}O$ | pronounced floral-fatty, orange: FX | .831-.838 (15°C) | | | | $Mus_nFlo_nLip_nFru_n$ σ ψ |
| Decane $C_{10}H_{22}$ | powerful, petrol: M | .7298 | 108.6 | | | $Hyc_n$ μ |
| 1-Decanol $C_{10}H_{22}O$ | musty, alcohol, fat-like, sharp, orange, sweet: FJX | .8297 (20/4°C) | | | .042 | $Mus_nLip_nMil_nFru_n$ α λ ψ! $HU^{3-4}_{2-4}$ 25-49 |
| 2-(9-decenyl)-4,5-dimethyl-1,3-dioxolane | powerful, floral, fruity: W | | | | | $Flo_nFru_n$ |

| | | | | |
|---|---|---|---|---|
| Decyl acetate $C_{12}H_{24}O_2$ | floral, fatty, orange-rose: CX | .862-.864 | | $Lip_nFlo_nFru_n$ ψ |
| n-Decylamine $C_{19}H_{23}N$ | amine: X | .797 (20/20°C) | | $Ami_n$ |
| Deoxyanisoin $C_{17}H_{16}O_3$ | sweet, faint, cinnamon: X | | | $Spi_n$ α |
| Diacetonamine $C_6H_{13}NO$ | amine: Y | | | $Ami_n$ |
| Diacetone alcohol $C_6H_{12}O_2$ | pleasant, sweet, sharp: JPXY | .9306 (25/4°C) | 1.7 | α ψ $HU^{3-2}_{2-4}$ 25-36 |
| Diacetylperoxide $C_4H_6O_4$ | pungent: A | 1.18 (20°C) | | ψ! |
| Diallyl isophthalate (monomer) $C_{14}H_{14}O_4$ | mild, characteristic: X | 1.124 (20°C) | | |
| 1,3-Diaminobutane $C_4H_{12}N_2$ | amine: X | .858 (20/20°C) | | $Ami_n$ |
| Diaminodiethyl sulfide $C_2H_{12}N_2S$ | amine: X | 1.054 (25°C) | | $Ami_n$ |
| 1,2-Diaminopropane $C_3H_{10}N_2$ | ammoniacal, sharp amine: JX | .8732 (20/20°C) | .067 | $Uro_nNit_n$ ψ $HU^{3-6}_{4-5}$ 49-121 |
| 1,3-Diaminopropane $C_3H_{10}N_2$ | amine: X | .8881 (20/20°C) | | $Ami_n$ |
| N,N-Diamylaniline $C_{16}H_{27}N$ | faint, aniline: X | .898 (20°C) | | |
| Diamyl ketone $C_{11}H_{22}O$ | fruity: M | | | $Fru_n$ |

| Chemical | Reported Characteristics | Specific Gravity | Vapor Pressure | Detection Threshold | Recognition Threshold | Classification Expression, Factors, HU Value |
|---|---|---|---|---|---|---|
| Diamyl maleate $C_{14}H_{24}O_4$ | faintly alcoholic: X | .981 (20°C) | | | | $Hyc_n$ |
| Diamyl phenol $C_{16}H_{25}O$ | mild, phenolic: X | .930 (20°C) | | | | $Mol_nHyc_n$ σ! |
| Diazoacetic ester $C_4H_6N_2O_2$ | pungent: PY | 1.0852 (17.6/4°C) | | | | ψ! |
| p-Diazodiphenyl-amine sulfate $C_{24}H_{20}N_6O_4S$ | unpleasant: X | | | | | |
| Dibenzyl $C_{14}H_{14}$ | pungent: A | .9782 | 202.8 | | | ψ! |
| Dibenzylamine $C_{14}H_{15}N$ | ammoniacal: Y | 1.017 (20°C) | 227.3 | | | $Uro_nNit_n$ ψ! |
| Dibenzyl disulfide $C_{14}H_{14}S_2$ | benzaldehyde-like: X | | | | | $Nut_n$ |
| Dibenzyl ether $C_{14}H_{14}O$ | faint almond, nutty: FX | 1.035 | | | | $Nut_n$ |
| Diborane $B_2H_6$ | repulsive, sickly, sweet: PXY | .210 (15°C) | | | | α!!! β!! |
| Dibromoacetoni-trile $Br_2C_2H_3N$ | pungent: A | | | | | $Hal_n$ ψ! |
| Dibromoacetylene $Br_2C_2$ | disagreeable: X | | | | | |
| 1,3-Dibromoadaman-tane | camphor: A | | | | | $Woo_n$ |

| | | | |
|---|---|---|---|
| o-Dibromobenzene $Br_2C_6H_4$ | pleasant, aromatic: X | 1.9767 (25/4°C) | $Hyc_n$ λ! |
| 1,3-Dibromo-2,2-dimethylpropane | strong, ethereal: A | | λ!! |
| N,N-Dibromomethyl-amine | pungent: A | | ψ! |
| β,γ-Dibromo-β-phenylpentane | pungent, peppery: A | | $Spi_n$ ψ! |
| 1,2-Dibromo-1,1,2-trifluoroethane | ethereal: A | | $Hal_nHyc_n$ λ! |
| Dibutoxyethyl adipate $C_{18}H_{34}O_6$ | mild, butyl-type: X | .997 (20/20°C) | |
| Dibutoxytetraglycol $C_{16}H_{30}O_5$ | characteristic: X | .9436 (20/20°C) | |
| Di-n-butylamine $C_8H_{19}N$ | amine: X | .7601 (20/4°C) | $Ami_n$ |
| Di-sec-butylamine $C_8H_{19}N$ | amine: X | .754 (20/20°C) | $Ami_n$ |
| N,N-Di-n-butyl-aminoethanol $C_{10}H_{23}NO$ | faint, amine-like: X | .859 (20°C) | $Ami_n$ |
| Dibutyl butylphosphonate $C_{12}H_{27}O_2P$ | mild: PX | .948 (20/4°C) | |
| Dibutyl oxalate $C_{10}H_{18}O_4$ | mild: PX | | |

| Chemical | Reported Characteristics | Specific Gravity | Vapor Pressure | Detection Threshold | Recognition Threshold | Classification Expression, Factors, HU Value |
|---|---|---|---|---|---|---|
| Dibutyl selenide $C_8H_{18}Se$ | putrid: A | | | | | $Sse_n$ $\beta$! $HU^{3-6}_{4-6}$ 49-144 |
| Dichloramine-T $C_7Cl_2H_7NO_2S$ | strong, chlorine: XY | | | | | $Hal_nSul_n$ $\phi$!! $\sigma$! $\psi$!! |
| Dichloroacetal-dehyde $C_2Cl_2H_2O$ | penetrating, pungent: X | 12.1 (lbs/gal) (25°C) | | | | $Hal_nHyc_n$ $\psi$! $\omega$! |
| Dichloroacetic acid $C_2Cl_2H_2O_2$ | pungent: PY | 1.563 (20/4°C) | 134 | | | $\psi$! |
| 2,2-Dichloroacetyl chloride $C_2Cl_3HO$ | acrid, pungent, penetrating: AY | 1.5315 (16/4°C) | | | | $Hal_nHyc_n$ $\psi$! $\omega$! |
| 2,4-Dichlorobenz-aldehyde | almond: A | | | | | $Nut_nHal_n$ |
| 3,4-Dichlorobenz-aldehyde | almond: A | | | | | $Nut_nHal_n$ |
| o-Dichlorobenzene $C_6Cl_2H_4$ | pleasant, aromatic: X | 1.3059 (20/4°C) | 112.9 | | | |
| p-Dichlorobenzene $C_6Cl_2H_4$ | penetrating, characteristic, camphor, naphthalene: AXY @ | 1.458 | 108.4 | | | $Woo_nHal_nHyc_n$ $\mu$ $\sigma$ $\psi$ $\omega$! |
| 1,4-Dichlorobutane $C_4Cl_2H_8$ | mild, pleasant: PX | 1.141 (20/4°C) | | | | |

| | | | | | | |
|---|---|---|---|---|---|---|
| 1,1-Dichloro-1,2-dibromofluoroethane | camphor: A | | | | | $Woo_nHal_n$ δ |
| Dichlorodiethyl sulfide $C_4Cl_2H_8S$ | pungent, weak, sweet, agreeable, horseradish: DXY | 1.2741 (20/4°C) (liq.) | .115 mm Hg (20°C) | .199 | | $All_nHal_nSul_n$ α ψ! |
| 2,2-Dichloro-1,1-difluoroethyl methyl ether $C_3Cl_2F_2H_4O$ | characteristic, fruity: X | 1.4223 (25°C) | | | | $Fru_n$ |
| 1,3-Dichloro-5,5-dimethylhydantoin $C_5Cl_2H_6O_2$ | mild, chlorine: X | 1.5 (20/20°C) | | | | $Hal_n$ ϕ ψ |
| N,N'-Dichloro-N,N'-dimethylurea | pungent: A | | | | | $Hal_nNit_n$ ψ! |
| 1,2-Dichloroethane $C_2Cl_2H_4$ | sweet, pleasant, chloroform-like, ethereal: AJPXY @ | 1.2554 (20/4°C) | 29.4 | 1.06 | 40.0 | α λ $HU^{2-3}_{3-4}$ 25-49 |
| Dichloroethyl ether $C_4Cl_2H_8O$ | pungent, 1,2-dichloroethane-like: XY | 1.22 (20/20°C) | | | | α λ |
| Dichloroformoxime $C_2Cl_2HNO$ | disagreeable, penetrating, powerful irritant: X | | | | | $Hal_n$ β ε!!! σ ω! |
| α-Dichlorohydrin $C_3Cl_2H_6O$ | faint, ethereal, chloroform-like: APXY | 1.36-1.39 | | | | $Hal_nHyc_n$ α λ! |
| sym-Dichloromethyl ether $C_2Cl_2H_4O$ | suffocating: Y | 1.315 (20/4°C) | | | | $Hal_nHyc_n$ ϕ!!! |
| Dichlorophene $C_{13}Cl_2H_{10}O_2$ | weakly phenolic: X | | | | | $Mol_nHyc_nHal_n$ σ! |

| Chemical | Reported Characteristics | Specific Gravity | Vapor Pressure | Detection Threshold | Recognition Threshold | Classification Expression, Factors, HU Value |
|---|---|---|---|---|---|---|
| 2,4-Dichlorophenyl-isothiocyanate $C_7Cl_2H_5NS$ | aniseed, sweet anise: AD | | | | | $Her_n$ α |
| 2,5-Dichlorophenyl-isothiocyanate $C_7Cl_2H_5NS$ | pungent: D | | | | | $Sul_nNit_nHal_n$ ψ! |
| 3,4-Dichlorophenyl-isothiocyanate $C_7Cl_2H_5NS$ | pungent, strong anise: D | | | | | $Her_n$ ψ! |
| 3,5-Dichlorophenyl-isothiocyanate $C_7Cl_2H_5NS$ | pungent: D | | | | | $Sul_nNit_nHal_n$ ψ! |
| 1,3-Dichloropropene $C_3Cl_2H_4$ | chloroform: Y | 1.225 (20/4°C) | | | | $Hal_nHyc_n$ α γ λ! |
| Dicyclohexyl $C_{12}H_{22}$ | pleasant: PX | .883 (25/16°C) | | | | |
| Dicyclohexylamine $C_{12}H_{23}N$ | faint, fishy, amine: PXY | .9104 (25/25°C) | | | | $Ami_n$ |
| Dicyclohexyl carbodiimide $C_{13}H_{22}N_2$ | heavy, sweet: X | | | | | α!! |
| Dicyclohexyl phthalate $C_{20}H_{26}O_4$ | mildly aromatic: X | 1.20 (25/25°C) | | | | |
| Dicyclopentadiene $C_{10}H_{12}$ | sweet, sharp: J | | | | .02 | α! ψ! $HU^{2-3}_{2-4}$ 16-49 |

| | | | | | |
|---|---|---|---|---|---|
| Didecylamine $C_{38}H_{25}N$ | faint amine: X | .840 (20/20°C) | | | $Ami_n$ |
| Diethanolamine $C_4H_{11}NO_2$ | mild, ammoniacal: Y | 1.0881 (30/4°C) | | | $Uro_n Nit_n$ ψ |
| Diethylacetic acid $C_6H_{12}O_2$ | resembling caproic acid somewhat, resembling butyric acid but less pronounced: XY | .9225 (20/20°C) | .08 mm Hg (20°C) | | $But_n$ |
| Diethyl acetic acid diethylamide | weak, minty: A | | | | $He_n$ δ |
| Diethyl adipate $C_{10}H_{18}O_4$ | fruity: M | 1.002 (25°C) | 179 | | $Fru_n$ |
| Diethylamine $C_4H_{11}N$ | ammoniacal, musty, fishy, amine: JPX | .7074 (20/4°C) | 6 | .06 | $Ami_n Mil_n Nit_n$ ψ $HU^{3-5}_{4-6}$ 49-121 |
| 5-Diethylamino-2-aminopentane $C_9H_{22}N$ | amine: X | .82 | | | $Ami_n$ |
| Diethylaminoethanol $C_6H_{15}NO$ | amine: J | .88-.89 | 21 mm Hg (20°C) | .04 | $HU^{3-5}_{4-6}$ 49-121 |
| 3-Diethylaminopropylamine $C_7H_{18}N_2$ | amine: X | .82 (20/20°C) | | | $Ami_n$ |
| Diethylbromoacetamide $BrC_6H_{12}NO$ | camphor: XY | | | | $Woo_n$ δ |
| Diethyl carbonate $C_5H_{10}O_3$ | mild, pleasant, ethereal: XY | .9764 (20/4°C) | 69.7 | | λ |

| Chemical | Reported Characteristics | Specific Gravity | Vapor Pressure | Detection Threshold | Recognition Threshold | Classification Expression, Factors, HU Value |
|---|---|---|---|---|---|---|
| Diethyl diethylmalonate $C_{11}H_{20}O_4$ | sweet: X | .984 (25/25°C) | | | | α! |
| sym-Diethyldi-phenylurea $C_{17}H_{20}N_2O$ | peppery: X | 1.12 (20°C) | | | | $Spi_n$ |
| Diethyldiselenide $C_4H_{10}Se_2$ | putrid: A | | | | | $Sse_n$ β! |
| Diethyl disulfide $C_4H_{10}S_2$ | garlic: A | | | | | $All_nSul_n$ |
| Diethyl dithioliso-phthalate $C_{12}H_{14}O_2S_2$ | garlic: Y | | | | | $All_nSul_n$ |
| Diethylene glycol dibutyl ether $C_{12}H_{26}O_3$ | characteristic: X | .8853 (20/20°C) | 159.8 | | | |
| Diethylene glycol dimethyl ether $C_6H_{14}O_3$ | mild: X | .9451 (20/20°C) | | | | |
| Diethylene glycol monobutyl ether $C_8H_{18}O_3$ | characteristic, butyl: X | .9536 (20/20°C) | | | | |
| Diethylene glycol monoethyl ether $C_6H_{14}O_3$ | mild, pleasant, sweet, musty: JX | 1.0273 (20/20°C) | | | 1.10 | $HU^2_{2-4}$16-36 |
| Diethylene glycol monoethyl ether acetate $C_8H_{16}O_4$ | sweet: J | | | | .263 | $HU^2_{2-4}$16-36 |

| | | | | |
|---|---|---|---|---|
| Diethylenetriamine $C_4H_{13}N_3$ | ammoniacal: X | .9542 (20/20°C) | .37 mm Hg (20°C) | $Uro_nNit_n$ ψ! |
| Diethyl ethyl-malanate $C_9H_{16}O_4$ | ester: X | .9994 (25/25°C) | | $Es_n$ |
| Diethyl ethyl-phosphonate $C_6H_{15}O_3P$ | mild, sweet: PX | 1.025 (20/4°C) | | $Pho_nHyc_n$ α |
| Di(2-ethylhexyl)-amine $C_{16}H_{35}N$ | slightly ammoniacal: PX | .8062 (20/20°C) | | $Uro_nNit_n$ ψ |
| Di(2-ethylhexyl) ether $C_{16}H_{34}O$ | mild, characteris-tic: X | .8121 (20/20°C) | | |
| Di(2-ethylhexyl) 2-ethylhexyl-phosphonate $C_{24}H_{51}O_3P$ | mild: X | .908 (20/4°C) | | |
| Di(2-ethylhexyl) phosphite $C_{16}H_{35}O_3P$ | mild: X | .937 (20/4°C) | | |
| Diethyl isoamyl-ethylmalonate $C_{14}H_{26}O_4$ | sweet: X | .950 (25/25°C) | | α! |
| Diethyl ketone $C_5H_{10}O$ | acetone-like: PXY | .816 (19/4°C) | 56.2 | $Hyc_n$ |
| Diethyl mercury $C_4H_{10}Hg$ | hazel-like: P | | | $Nut_n$ |
| Diethylmethyl ar-sine $AsC_5H_{12}$ | putrid: A | | | β! $HU^{3-5}_{4-6}$ 49-121 |

| Chemical | Reported Characteristics | Specific Gravity | Vapor Pressure | Detection Threshold | Recognition Threshold | Classification Expression, Factors, HU Value |
|---|---|---|---|---|---|---|
| Diethyl phthalate $C_{12}H_{14}O_4$ | odorless or almost odorless: XY | 1.232 (14/4°C) | 219.5 | | | $\lambda$ $\psi$ |
| Diethylpyrocarbonate $C_6H_{10}O_5$ | sweet, ester-like: X | | | | | $Es_n$ $\alpha$! |
| Diethyl selenide $C_4H_{10}Se$ | | 1.23 (20/4°C) | 51.8 | | | |
| Diethyl succinate $C_8H_{14}O_4$ | faint, pleasant: PXY | 1.040 (20/4°C) | 151.1 | | | |
| Diethyl sulfate $C_4H_{10}O_4S$ | minty, peppermint, faint, ethereal, sweet, heavy: AMPXY | 1.172 (25/4°C) | 142.5 | | | $He_n$ $\alpha$!! $\delta$ $\lambda$ |
| Diethyltelluride $C_4H_{10}Te$ | putrid: A | | | | | $\beta$! |
| N,N-Diethyl-m-toluamide $C_{12}H_{17}O$ | mild, bland, weak, pungent, fruity: WX | .996 (20/4°C) | | | | $Fru_n$ $\psi$ |
| p-Difluorobenzene $C_6F_2H_4$ | pungent, aromatic: Y | 1.17006 (20°C) | | | | $\psi$! |
| 4,4-Difluoro-diphenyl $C_{12}F_2H_8$ | aromatic: XY | 1.04 | | | | |
| Difluorodiphenyl-trichloroethane $C_{14}Cl_3F_2H_9$ | faint, ripe apple: X | | | | | $Fru_n$ |
| Diglycol oleate $C_{22}H_{42}O_4$ | fatty: X | .93 | | | | $Lip_n$ |

| | | | |
|---|---|---|---|
| Diglycol stearate $C_{40}H_{78}O_5$ | faint, fatty: X | .9333 (20/4°C) | $Lip_n$ |
| Dihydrocoumarin $C_9H_8O_2$ | feeble, new mown hay, sweet: MX | | $Ens_n$ α! ξ |
| Dihydropyran $C_5H_8O$ | ethereal: P | | λ! |
| 2,3-Dihydro-4H-pyran $C_5H_8O$ | ethereal: X | .927 (20/4°C) | λ! |
| Dihydroxyacetone $C_3H_6O_3$ | characteristic: XY | | |
| α,β-Dihydroxybutane phenylacetal $C_4H_{10}O_2$ | floral, hyacinth: AM | | $Flo_n$ |
| α,γ-Dihydroxybutane phenylacetal $C_4H_9O_2$ | floral, hyacinth: AM | | $Flo_n$ |
| 2,4-Dihydroxy-4-methylpentane phenylacetal $C_6H_{14}O_2$ | floral, mignonette: AM | | $Flo_n$ |
| α,β-Dihydroxypropane phenylacetal $C_3H_8O_2$ | floral, roses: AM | | $Flo_n$ |
| Diiodoacetylene $C_2I_2$ | unpleasant: PX | | |
| Diisoamylarsine $AsC_{10}H_{22}$ | putrid: A | | β! |
| Diisoamyltrisulfide $C_{10}H_{22}S_3$ | putrid: A | | β! |

| Chemical | Reported Characteristics | Specific Gravity | Vapor Pressure | Detection Threshold | Recognition Threshold | Classification Expression, Factors, HU Value |
|---|---|---|---|---|---|---|
| Diisobutylamine $C_8H_{19}N$ | amine: PX | .745 (20°C) | 79.2 | | | $Ami_n$ |
| Diisobutyl ketone $C_{10}H_{18}O$ | mild, sweet, ester: JX | .8089 (20/20°C) | 1.7 mm Hg (20°C) | | .31 | $Es_n$ $\alpha$ $HU^{2-3}_{2-3}$ 16-36 |
| Diisocetyl adipate $C_{22}H_{42}O_4$ | mild: X | | | | | |
| Diisodecyl adipate $C_{26}H_{40}O_4$ | mild: X | .918 (20/20°C) | | | | |
| Diisodecyl phthalate $C_{28}H_{46}O_4$ | mild, characteristic: PX | .966 (20/20°C) | | | | |
| Diisopropylamine $C_6H_{15}N$ | amine-like, fishy, characteristic, ammoniacal: JPXY | .7178 (20/20°C) | | | .85 | $Ami_nNit_n$ $\psi$ $HU^{2-4}_{4-5}$ 36-81 |
| Diisopropylcarbamic acid, methyl ester | minty: A | | | | | $He_n$ $\delta$! |
| Diketene $C_4H_4O_2$ | pungent: PX | 1.096 (20/20°C) | | | | $\psi$! |
| Dilauryl thiodipropionate $C_{28}H_{56}O_4S$ | sweetish, ester-like: X | .975 (25°C) (solid) | | | | $\alpha$! |
| 2,3-Dimercaptopropanol $C_3H_8OS_2$ | pungent, strong, offensive, mercaptan: XY | 1.2385 (25/4°C) | | | | $Mus_n$ $\psi$! |

| | | | | | | |
|---|---|---|---|---|---|---|
| Dimethoxane $C_8H_{14}O_4$ | mustard-like: Y | 1.068-1.076 (25/25°C) | | | | $All_n$ ψ |
| 1,2-Dimethoxy-ethane $C_4H_{10}O_2$ | mild, sharp, ethereal: PXY | .86258 (20/4°C) | 31.8 | | | λ ψ! |
| Di(2-methoxyethyl) phthalate $C_{14}H_{18}O_6$ | mild, aromatic: PX | 1.172 (20/20°C) | | | | |
| Dimethylacetal $C_4H_{10}O_2$ | strong, aromatic: PX | .8516 (20/4°C) | | | | |
| Dimethylacetamide $C_4H_9NO$ | | .9429 (20/4°C) | | 46.8 | | |
| Dimethylamine $C_2H_7N$ | characteristic, putrid, strong, ammoniacal: AXY | .680 (0/4°C) (liq.) | -32.6 | | .047 | $Ami_nUro_nNit_n$ β! ψ! $HU^{3-5}_{4-6}$ 49-121 |
| 2-Dimethylamino-ethanol $C_4H_{11}NO$ | amine: J | .8879 (20/20°C) | | | .045 | $HU^{3-5}_{4-6}$ 49-121 |
| Dimethylamino-methanol $C_3H_9NO$ | pungent: A | | | | | ψ! |
| o-Dimethylamino-methyl-p-butyl phenol $C_{13}H_{21}NO$ | phenolic: X | .960 (25/25°C) | | | | $Mol_n$ |
| 1-Dimethylamino-2-propanol $C_5H_{13}NO$ | amine: X | .850 (20/20°C) | | | | $Ami_n$ |

| Chemical | Reported Characteristics | Specific Gravity | Vapor Pressure | Detection Threshold | Recognition Threshold | Classification Expression, Factors, HU Value |
|---|---|---|---|---|---|---|
| Dimethyl anthranilate $C_9H_{11}NO_2$ | grape-like, orange blossom: FX | 1.132-1.138 (15°C) | | | | $A_nFru_nFlo_n$ σ |
| 2,4-Dimethylbenzaldehyde | almond: A | | | | | $Nut_n$ |
| 2,5-Dimethylbenzaldehyde | almond: A | | | | | $Nut_n$ |
| p-α-Dimethylbenzyl alcohol $C_9H_{12}O$ | somewhat like menthol: Y | .9668 (15.5/4°C) | | | | $Woo_n$ δ |
| Dimethylbenzyl carbinol $C_{10}H_{14}O$ | hyacinth, lilac: X | .979 | | | | $A_nFlo_nEns_n$ σ ψ! |
| Dimethylbenzylcarbinyl acetate $C_{12}H_{16}O_2$ | woody, hyacinth, floral, fruity: CX | | | | | $Woo_nFlo_nFru_n$ σ! ψ! |
| 2,5-Dimethylbenzylchloride $C_9ClH_{11}$ | lachrymator, sharp, pungent: X | 1.035-1.045 (25/25°C) | | | | $Hal_n$ ε! ψ! |
| 2,2-Dimethyl-3-bromopropane | ethereal: A | | | | | $Hal_nHyc_n$ λ! |
| Dimethylcadmium $C_2CdH_6$ | disagreeable: Y | 1.9846 (17.9/4°C) | | | | |
| 3,3-Dimethylcamphor | camphor, minty: A | | | | | $Woo_nHe_n$ δ! |

| | | | | |
|---|---|---|---|---|
| Dimethyl chloro-acetal $C_4ClH_7O_2$ | pleasant: X | 1.082-1.092 (25/4°C) | | |
| Dimethylcyclo-hexane $C_8H_{16}$ | mild: X | .776 (15/15°C) | | |
| 1,1-Dimethylcyclo-hexane $C_8H_{16}$ | floral: A | | 57.9 | $Flo_n$ |
| 1,1-Dimethylcyclo-hexanol-3 $C_8H_{16}O$ | camphor, mint: A | | | $Woo_nHe_n$ δ! |
| 1,1-Dimethylcyclo-hexanone-3 $C_9H_{16}O$ | camphor, mint: AM | | | $Woo_nHe_n$ δ! |
| $1^{cis}3^{cis}$-Dimethyl-cyclohexanone-5 $C_9H_{16}O$ | camphor, minty: A | | | $Woc_nHe_n$δ! |
| 1,3-Dimethylcyclo-hexene(3)-one(5) $C_9H_{16}O$ | camphor: A | | | $Woo_n$ |
| 1,3-Dimethylcyclo-hexen(3)-one(6) $C_9H_{16}O$ | coumarin, almond, minty: A | | | $Spi_nNut_nHe_n$ δ! |
| Dimethyl cyclohexyl carbinol $C_9H_{20}O$ | camphor, mint: A | | | $Woo_nHe_n$ δ! |
| Dimethylcyclopenta-methylenesilicon | camphor: A | | | $Woo_n$ |
| 1,1-Dimethylcyclo-pentanone-2 | camphor, strong, mint: A | | | $Woo_nHe_n$ δ!! |

| Chemical | Reported Characteristics | Specific Gravity | Vapor Pressure | Detection Threshold | Recognition Threshold | Classification Expression, Factors, HU Value |
|---|---|---|---|---|---|---|
| 1,1-Dimethylcyclopentanone-3 | camphor, mint, almonds: A | | | | | $Woo_n He_n Nut_n$ δ! |
| Dimethylcyclopropyl carbinol $C_6H_{13}O$ | camphor: A | | | | | $Woo_n$ |
| 2,2-Dimethyl-3,3-dibromopropane | strong, ethereal: A | | | | | $Hal_n Hyc_n$ λ!! ω |
| 1,1-Dimethyl-1,2-dinitropropane | camphor: A | | | | | $Woo_n$ |
| Dimethyldiselenide $C_2H_6Se_2$ | putrid: A | | | | | β! |
| Dimethyldisulfide $C_2H_6S_2$ | sharp, garlic: F | | | | | $All_n$ ψ! |
| Dimethyl ether $C_2H_6O$ | ethereal: A | .661 | 62.7 | | | λ! |
| Dimethylethylarsine $AsC_2H_7$ | putrid: A | | | | | β! |
| N,N-Dimethylformamide $C_3H_7NO$ | faint, amine: Y | .9445 | | | | $Ami_n$ |
| 2,6-Dimethylheptanal | mellony, fatty, citrus, green: W | | | | | $Fru_n Lip_n Ens_n$ |
| 2,4-Dimethylheptanol-6 | floral: A | | | | | $Flo_n$ |

| | | | | | |
|---|---|---|---|---|---|
| 2,6-Dimethyl-4-heptanol | sweet, alcohol: J | .8121 (20°C) | | .160 | $Hyc_n$ α! $HU^{2-3}_{2-4}$ 16-49 |
| 2,6-Dimethylhepten (2)-nitrile(7) | minty: A | | | | $He_n$ δ! |
| 2,5-Dimethylhexa-diene-1,5 $C_8H_{14}$ | pleasant, hydro-carbon: X | .740-.760 (25/25°C) | | | $Hyc_n$ |
| 2,5-Dimethylhexa-diene-2,4 $C_9H_{14}$ | pleasant, hydro-carbon: X | .764-.772 (25/25°C) | | | $Hyc_n$ |
| N,1-Dimethylhexyl-amine $C_8H_{19}N$ | slight, amine: XY | | | | $Ami_n$ |
| Dimethyl hexynol $C_8H_{14}$ | camphor-like: PX | .8545 (20/20°C) | | | $Woo_n$ |
| 1,1-Dimethylhydra-zine $C_2H_8N_2$ | characteristic, ammoniacal, like aliphatic hydra-zines: XY | .791 (22/4°C) | | | $Uro_nNit_n$ ψ |
| 1,2-Dimethylhydra-zine $C_2H_8N_2$ | characteristic, ammoniacal, like aliphatic hydra-zines: Y | .8274 (20/4°C) | | | $Uro_nNit_n$ ψ |
| Dimethyl isopropyl carbinol $C_6H_{16}O$ | camphor: A | | | | $Woo_n$ |
| Dimethyl itaconate $C_6H_{10}O_4$ | slight odor: X | 1.27 (24°C) | 153.7 | | |

| Chemical | Reported Characteristics | Specific Gravity | Vapor Pressure | Detection Threshold | Recognition Threshold | Classification Expression, Factors, HU Value |
|---|---|---|---|---|---|---|
| N,N-Dimethyl-1-naphthylamine $C_{12}H_{13}N$ | aromatic: Y | 1.0522 (4/4°C) | | | | |
| 4,8-Dimethyl nonanol $C_{11}H_{24}O$ | geranium: M | | | | | $Flo_n$ |
| Dimethyl octanol $C_{10}H_{20}O$ | bittersweet lemon, slightly floral: F | | | | | $Fru_nFlo_n$ α ν |
| 3,6-Dimethyl-3-octanol $C_{10}H_{22}O$ | sweet, rosey: X | .8366 (20/20°C) | | | | $Flo_n$ α! |
| 3,7-Dimethyl-1-octanol $C_9H_{22}O$ | sweet, rose-like: X | .826-.842 (25°C) | | | | $Flo_n$ α! |
| Dimethyl phosphite $C_2H_7O_2P$ | mild: X | 1.200 (20/4°C) | | | | |
| cis-2,5-Dimethyl piperazine $C_6H_{14}N_2$ | typical amine: P | | | | | $Ami_n$ |
| 2,5-Dimethylpyrazine $C_6H_8N_2$ | pyridine: P | | | | | $Hyc_nOxy_n$ β! φ σ!! |
| Dimethylselenide $C_4H_{10}Se$ | putrid: A | | | .011 | | β! |
| Dimethyl sulfate $C_2H_6O_4S$ | pungent: A | 1.3322 (20/4°C) | | | | ψ! |
| Dimethyl sulfide $C_2H_6S$ | disagreeable, putrid: AXY | .846 (21/4°C) | -12.0 | | .001 | β! $HU^{3-6}_{4-6}$ 49-144 |

| | | | | |
|---|---|---|---|---|
| Dimethyltelluride $C_2H_6Te$ | putrid: A | | | β! |
| 1,1-Dimethyl-Δ$^3$-tetrahydrobenzene | camphor: A | | | $Woo_n$ |
| 2,4-Dimethylthiazole $C_5H_7NS$ | penetrating: Y | 1.0601 (15/4°C) | | ω! |
| Dimethyltrisulfide $C_2H_6S_3$ | putrid: A | | | β! |
| Dimethyl trithiocarbonate $C_3H_6S_3$ | | | .0058 | |
| 1,3-Dimethylurea $C_3H_8N_2O$ | slight formaldehyde: X | 1.142 | | φ ψ |
| Dimethylzinc $C_2H_6Zn$ | peculiar, garlic-like (in flame): Y | 1.386 (10.5/4°C) | | $All_n$ ψ |
| 4,6-Dinitro-2-azido-1,3-dimethyl-5-tert-butylbenzene | strong, musky: A | | | $Mus_n$ |
| 3,3-Dinitro-2,2-dimethylbutane $C_6H_{12}N_2O_4$ | strong, camphor: A | | | $Woo_n$ |
| 3,5-Dinitro-2,4-dimethyl-6-tert-butylacetophenone $C_{14}H_{18}N_2O_5$ | musky: A | | | $Mus_n$ |
| 3,5-Dinitro-2,4-dimethyl-6-tert-butylbenzaldehyde $C_{13}H_{16}N_2O_5$ | musky: A | | | $Mus_n$ |

| Chemical | Reported Characteristics | Specific Gravity | Vapor Pressure | Detection Threshold | Recognition Threshold | Classification Expression, Factors, HU Value |
|---|---|---|---|---|---|---|
| 2,2-Dinitro-3-ethyl pentane $C_4H_{14}N_2O_4$ | camphor: A | | | | | $Woo_n$ |
| 3,5-Dinitro-2-methyl-4-methoxy-acetophenone $C_{10}H_{10}N_2O_6$ | musky: A | | | | | $Mus_n$ |
| 2,2-Dinitropentane $C_5H_{10}N_2O_4$ | camphor: A | | | | | $Woo_n$ |
| 3,3-Dinitropentane $C_5H_{10}N_2O_4$ | camphor: A | | | | | $Woo_n$ |
| 2,2-Dinitropropane $C_3H_6N_2O_4$ | camphor: A | 1.30 (25°C) | | | | $Woo_n$ |
| 4,6-Dinitro-2,3,5-trimethyl-tert-butylbenzene $C_{13}H_{19}N_2O_4$ | musky: A | | | | | $Mus_n$ |
| Dioctyl sodium sulfosuccinate $C_{20}H_{37}NaO_7S$ | characteristic: Y | | | | | |
| Dioxane $C_4H_8O_2$ | faint, pleasant, ethereal, sweet, musty: AJMXY | 1.0329 (20/4°C) | 45.1 | | 5.7 | $Mst_n Hyc_n Oxy_n$ α λ $HU^{2-3}_{2-3}$ 16-36 |
| Dioxolane $C_3H_6O_2$ | sweet, musty: J | 1.065 | 70 mm Hg (20°C) | | 128.0 | $HU^{2-3}_{3-4}$ 25-49 |
| Dipentene $C_{10}H_{16}$ | pleasant, lemon-like: PXY | .847 (15.5/15.5°C) | 108.3 | | | $Fru_n$ ψ |

| | | | | | |
|---|---|---|---|---|---|
| Diphemanil methyl sulfate $C_{21}H_{27}NO_4S$ | faint, characteristic: X | | | | |
| Diphenylamine $C_{12}H_{11}N$ | floral: AMY | 1.159 | 222.8 | | $Flo_n$ |
| Diphenylamine-chloroarsine As $C_{12}ClH_9N$ | irritant, causes severe nose pain: PXY | 1.65 | | | ε! ψ!!! |
| Diphenylcyanoarsine $AsC_{13}H_{10}N$ | characteristic, resembling bitter almonds and garlic: PX | 1.45 (20°C) | | | $Nut_nAll_n$ ψ |
| 1,1-Diphenyl ethane $C_{14}H_{14}$ | aromatic: P | 1.004 (20°C) | | | |
| Diphenyl ether $C_{12}H_{10}O$ | floral, musty, characteristic, geranium on dilution: AMPXY | 1.072-1.075 | 178.8 | .1 | $\theta^2$: $Mst_n$ σ ψ<br>$\theta_1$: $Flo_n$ σ ψ<br>$HU_{1-2}^{2-3}$ 9-25 |
| Diphenylmethane $C_{13}H_{12}$ | floral, oranges: AXY | | 186.3 | | $A_nFlo_nFru_n$ σ ψ |
| Diphenyl sulfide $C_{12}H_{10}S$ | almost odorless: Y | 1.118 (15/15°C) | | .0021 | $HU_3^{1-2}$ 16-25 |
| Diphosgene $C_2Cl_4O_2$ | phosgene, new mown hay: PX | 1.65 (15°C) | | | $Ens_nMol_n$ |
| Dipropargyl $C_6H_6$ | pungent: A | .805 | | | ψ! |
| Di-n-propylamine $C_6H_{15}N$ | amine, ammonia: JPXY | .738 (20/4°C) | | .10 | $Uro_nNit_nAmi_n$ ψ<br>$HU_{3-5}^{3-4}$ 36-81 |

| Chemical | Reported Characteristics | Specific Gravity | Vapor Pressure | Detection Threshold | Recognition Threshold | Classification Expression, Factors, HU Value |
|---|---|---|---|---|---|---|
| 1,1-Dipropylcyclo-pentanone-2 $C_{12}H_{20}O$ | camphor, mint: A | | | | | $Woo_nHe_n$ |
| Dipropylene glycol monosalicylate $C_{13}H_{18}O_5$ | characteristic, fragrant: X | 1.16 (40°C) | 193.4 | | | |
| Dipropyl ketone $C_7H_{14}O$ | pleasant, fruity, penetrating, green: MWXY | .821 (15/4°C) | | | | $Fru_nEns_n$ ω! |
| Dipropylselenide $C_6H_{14}Se$ | putrid: A | | | | | β! |
| Disilane $H_6Si_2$ | repulsive: PY | .686 (-15/4°C) | -57.5 | | | β! |
| Dithioacetic acid $C_2H_4S_2$ | pungent, hydrogen sulfide: A | | | | | $Sul_n$ ψ! |
| Di-o-tolyl carbodiimide $C_{15}H_{14}O_2$ | slight, acrid: X | 1.063 (25/4°C) | | | | ψ |
| Di-o-tolylthiourea $C_{15}H_{16}NS$ | pungent: X | | | | | ψ! |
| Divinyl sulfide $C_4H_6S$ | characteristic: PX | .9174 (15°C) | | | | |
| γ-Dodecalactone $C_9H_{17}O_2$ | peach: F | | | | | $Fru_n$ |
| Dodecamethylene carbonate $C_{13}H_{24}O_3$ | musky: A | | | | | $Mus_n$ |

| | | | |
|---|---|---|---|
| Dodecanedicarboxylic acid anhydride | musky: A | | $Mus_n$ |
| Dodecyl acetate $C_{14}H_{28}O_2$ | light fruity, musty: CX | .860-.862 | $Mst_nFru_n$ σ ψ! |
| Dodecylaniline $C_{18}H_{31}N$ | aromatic, amine: X | .907-.912 (25/25°C) | $Ami_n$ |
| α-Dodecyl-γ-butyrolactone $C_{16}H_{30}O_2$ | musky, coconut: M | | $Mus_nNut_n$ |
| Dodecylphenol $C_{18}H_{30}O$ | phenolic: PX | .94 (20/20°C) | $Mol_nHyc_n$ σ!! ω |
| Doxylamine succinate $C_{21}H_{28}N_2O_5$ | characteristic: X | | |
| Durene $C_{10}H_{14}$ | camphor-like: AXY | .84 (81/4°C) | $Woo_n$ |
| DYSPROSIUM Dy | no reported odor | | |
| DYSPROSIUM COMPOUNDS | no reported odors | | |
| Echothiophate iodide $C_9H_{23}INO_3PS$ | slight, mercaptan-like: X | | $Mus_nMst_nHal_nSul_n$ β σ! |
| Emylcamate $C_7H_{15}NO_2$ | slight, camphor: Y | | $Woo_n$ |
| Epiandrosterone (dl-form) $C_{19}H_{30}O_2$ | musk-like when hot: Y | | $Mus_n$ |

| Chemical | Reported Characteristics | Specific Gravity | Vapor Pressure | Detection Threshold | Recognition Threshold | Classification Expression, Factors, HU Value |
|---|---|---|---|---|---|---|
| Epichlorohydrin $C_3ClH_5O$ | chloroform-like, irritating: PX | 1.1812 (20/4°C) | 62 | | | $Hal_nHyc_n$ α ε! λ |
| EPN $C_{14}H_{14}NO_4PS$ | aromatic: Y | 1.268 (25°C) | | | | |
| ERBIUM Er | no reported odor | | | | | |
| ERBIUM COMPOUNDS | no reported odors | | | | | |
| Erythromycin stearate $C_{53}H_{103}NO_{15}$ | almost odorless or slight musty odor: X | | | | | $Mst_nLip_n$ |
| Estradiol valerate $C_{23}H_{32}O_3$ | faint, fatty: X | | | | | $Lip_n$ |
| Estragole $C_{10}H_{12}O$ | characteristic, anise, sweet anise: FX | .9645 (21/4°C) | 148.5 | | | $Her_n$ α |
| 1,2-Ethanedithiol $C_2H_6S_2$ | may cause severe headache and nausea: Y | 1.123 (23.5°C) | | .415 | | $Sul_nHyc_n$ β!!! π ω |
| Ethanolamine $C_{20}H_7$ | ammoniacal: PXY | 1.0117 (25/4°C) | | | | $Uro_nNit_n$ ψ! |
| Ethchlorvynol $C_7ClH_9O$ | pungent, aromatic: XY | 1.065-1.070 (25/4°C) | | | | $Hal_nHyc_n$ ψ! |
| Ethosuximide $C_7H_{11}NO_2$ | characteristic: X | | | | | |

| | | | | | |
|---|---|---|---|---|---|
| 2-Ethoxy-3,4-dihydro-2H-pyran $C_7H_{12}O_2$ | sweet, fruity: J | .970 (20/20°C) | | .60 | $HU^{2-3}_{2-3}$ 16-36 |
| 2-Ethoxyethyl acetate $C_6H_{12}O_3$ | pleasant, sweet, musty, mild, ester-like: JXY | .975 (20/20°C) | | | $Mst_nEs_n$ $\alpha$ |
| Ethylacetanilide $C_{10}H_{13}NO$ | faint: PX | .994 | | | |
| Ethyl acetate $C_4H_8O_2$ | sweet, ester, characteristic, fruity, fragrant, musty: CFJPXY | .902 (20/4°C) | 27 | 13.2 | $Mst_nFru_n$ $\alpha$ $\sigma$ $\psi$!! $HU^{2-3}_{2-3}$ 16-36 |
| Ethyl acetoacetate $C_6H_{10}O_3$ | agreeable, fruity: PXY | 1.0213 (25/4°C) | 118.5 | | $Fru_n$ |
| Ethyl acrylate $C_5H_8O_2$ | acrid, penetrating, sour, pungent: JY | .9405 (20/4°C) | 44.5 | .00036 | $\psi$! $\omega$! $HU^{4-6}_{4-6}$ 64-144 |
| Ethyl alcohol $C_2H_6O$ | pleasant, vinous, fragrant, ethereal: PXY | .816 (15.56°C) | 34.9 | 10 | $Ens_nMst_n$ $\lambda$ $HU^{1-2}_{2-3}$ 9-25 |
| Ethylallylisopropenylmethane $C_9H_{16}$ | strong, minty, lemon: A | | | | $He_nFru_n$ $\delta$! |
| Ethylamine $C_2H_7N$ | sharp, strong, ammoniacal: JPXY | .689 (15/15°C) | -25.1 | .83 | $Uro_nNit_n$ $\psi$! $HU^{3-6}_{4-5}$ 49-121 |
| Ethyl amyl ketone $C_8H_{16}O$ | mild, fruity, pungent: XY | .820-.824 (20/20°C) | | | $A_nFru_n$ $\psi$! $\sigma$ |
| Ethylaniline $C_8H_{11}N$ | aniline-like: Y | .958 (25/25°C) | 137.3 | | |

| Chemical | Reported Characteristics | Specific Gravity | Vapor Pressure | Detection Threshold | Recognition Threshold | Classification Expression, Factors, HU Value |
|---|---|---|---|---|---|---|
| Ethyl anthranilate $C_9H_{11}NO_2$ | orange flower, grape-type: FX | 1.117 | | | | $A_nMst_nFru_nFlo_n$ σ |
| Ethylarsenious oxide $AsC_2H_5O$ | nauseating, garlic-like: PX | 1.802 (11°C) | | | | $All_nPho_n$ β!! ψ |
| Ethylbenzene $C_8H_{10}$ | aromatic: PX | .866 (25/25°C) | 74.1 | | | |
| Ethyl benzoate $C_9H_{10}O_2$ | aromatic, musty, sharp: CPXY | 1.050 (25/4°C) | 143.2 | | | $Mst_n$ ψ! |
| Ethyl benzoylacetate $C_{11}H_{12}O_3$ | pleasant: Y | 1.122 (15°C) | 205 | | | |
| α-Ethylbenzyl alcohol (dl-form) $C_9H_{12}O$ | weak, ester-like: Y | .9915 (25/4°C) | | | | $Es_n$ |
| Ethylbenzyl chlorides $C_9ClH_{11}$ | lachrymator: X | 1.0460-1.0475 (25/25°C) | | | | $Hal_nHyc_n$ ε!! |
| Ethyl borate $BC_6H_{15}O_3$ | mild, ethyl alcohol: PX | .863-.864 (20/20°C) | | | | $Mus_n$ λ |
| Ethyl bromide $BrC_2H_5$ | ethereal: AY | 1.4508 (20/4°C) | -10.0 | | | λ! |
| Ethyl-α-bromopropionate $BrC_5H_9O_2$ | sharp, pungent: Y | 1.447 (20/20°C) | | | | ψ! |
| Ethyl-β-bromopropionate $BrC_5H_9O_2$ | pungent: Y | 1.4123 (18/4°C) | | | | ψ! |

| | | | | | | |
|---|---|---|---|---|---|---|
| 2-Ethylbutyl alcohol $C_6H_{14}O$ | musty, sweet: J | .8328 (20/20°C) | .9 mm Hg (20°C) | | .77 | $Mst_n$ α! $HU^2_{2-3}$ 16-25 |
| N-Ethylbutylamine $C_6H_{15}N$ | amine: X | .8328 (20/20°C) | | | | $Ami_n$ |
| Ethyl butyrate $C_6H_{12}O_2$ | pineapple, fruity, musty: CFPXY | .879 (20/4°C) | 62 | | | $Mst_nFru_n$ |
| 2-Ethylbutyric acid $C_6H_{12}O_2$ | less pronounced than butyric acid: X | .9225 (20/20°C) | .08 mm Hg (20°C) | | | $Lip_nSeb_n$ |
| Ethyl caffeate $C_{11}H_{12}O_4$ | characteristic, aromatic: X | | | | | |
| Ethyl caprate $C_{12}H_{24}O_2$ | fragrant: PX | .862 (20°C) | | .00042 | | |
| Ethyl caproate $C_8H_{16}O_2$ | pleasant: FXY | .873 (20°C) | | .000013 | | |
| Ethyl caprylate $C_{10}H_{20}O_2$ | pleasant, pine-apple: XY | .878 (17°C) | | .00037 | | $Lip_nFru_n$ |
| Ethyl carbylamine $C_3H_5N$ | offensive, putrid, nauseating: AM | | | | | $Ami_n$ β! |
| Ethyl chaulmoog-rate $C_{20}H_{36}O_2$ | slight, fruity: Y | | | | | $Fru_n$ |
| Ethyl chloride $C_2ClH_5$ | characteristic, ethereal, sweet: AMPXY | .9214 (0/4°C) | -32.0 | | | $Hal_nHyc_n$ α! λ! |
| Ethyl chloroacetal $C_6ClH_{13}O_2$ | pleasant: PX | 1.022 (20°C) | | | | |

| Chemical | Reported Characteristics | Specific Gravity | Vapor Pressure | Detection Threshold | Recognition Threshold | Classification Expression, Factors, HU Value |
|---|---|---|---|---|---|---|
| Ethyl chloroacetate $C_4ClH_7O_2$ | pungent, fruity: PXY | 1.159 (20/4°C) | 86.0 | | | $Fru_n$ ψ! |
| Ethyl chloro-carbonate $C_3ClH_5O_2$ | irritating, lach-rymator: PXY | 1.1403 (20/4°C) | | | | ε!! |
| Ethyl-α-chloro-isovalerate $C_6ClH_{12}$ | minty: A | | | | | $He_n$ δ! |
| Ethyl-2-chloro-2-methylbutyrate $C_7ClH_{14}O$ | minty: A | | | | | $He_n$ δ! |
| Ethyl-α-chloro-propionate $C_5ClH_9O_2$ | pleasant: Y | 1.087 (20/4°C) | 89.3 | | | |
| Ethylchloro-sulfonate $C_2ClH_5O_3S$ | pungent, very irritant: PX | 1.379 (0°C) | | | | ε!! ψ! |
| Ethyl-α-chloro-valerate $C_6ClH_{12}$ | minty: A | | | | | $He_n$ δ! |
| Ethyl cinnamate $C_{11}H_{12}O_2$ | faint, cinnamon, honey, sweet, slightly spicy, strawberry-like, penetrating: CFXY | 1.049 (20/4°C) | | | | $Mus_nSpi_nCar_nFru_n$ α ψ ω! |
| Ethyl cocoinate | russet apples: X | .855 | | | | $Fru_n$ |
| Ethyl crotonate $C_6H_{10}O_2$ | characteristic, pun-gent, persistent: PX | .9207 (20/20°C) | | | | ρ! ψ! |

| | | | | | |
|---|---|---|---|---|---|
| Ethyl cyanoacetate $C_5H_7NO_2$ | slight, pleasant: Y | 1.0560 (25/4°C) | 152.8 | | |
| Ethylcyclohexane $C_8H_{16}$ | floral: A | .787 | 69 | | $Flo_n$ |
| 1-Ethylcyclohexen (1)-one(3) $C_9H_{11}O$ | minty: A | | | | $He_n$ δ! |
| 1-Ethylcyclohexen (1)-one(6) $C_9H_{11}O$ | minty: A | | | | $He_n$ δ! |
| 1-Ethylcyclopen-tanol-1 $C_7H_{13}O$ | camphor: A | | | | $Woo_n$ |
| Ethyldichloroarsine $AsC_2Cl_2H_5$ | fruit-like in high concentrations, biting, irritating: PX | 1.742 (14°C) | 2.29 mm Hg (21.5°C) | | $\theta^2$: $Fru_n$ ε! ψ! <br> $\theta_1$: ε! ψ! |
| Ethyldiethanol-amine $C_6H_{15}NO_2$ | amine-like: X | 1.015 (20°C) | | | $Ami_n$ |
| Ethyl diiodoace-tate $C_4H_8I_2O_2$ | pungent: A | | | | ψ! |
| Ethyl diphenyl ether $C_{14}H_{14}O$ | aromatic: P | | | | |
| Ethylene $C_2H_4$ | characteristic, sweet, ethereal, olefinic: AJPX | .30342 (6.5/4°C) (liq.) | -131.8 | 700 | $Hyc_nLip_n$ α! λ! <br> $HU^{1-2}_{2-3}$ 9-25 |

| Chemical | Reported Characteristics | Specific Gravity | Vapor Pressure | Detection Threshold | Recognition Threshold | Classification Expression, Factors, HU Value |
|---|---|---|---|---|---|---|
| Ethylene chlorohyd-rin $C_2ClH_5O$ | faint, ethereal: | 1.2045 (20/20°C) | 75 | | | $Hal_nHyc_n$ λ |
| Ethylenediamine $C_2H_8N_2$ | ammonia-like, musty: JPXY | .8995 (20/20°C) | 62.5 | | 11.2 | $Uro_nMst_nNit_n$ ψ $HU^{2-5}_{3-5}$ 25-100 |
| Ethylene dibromide $Br_2C_2H_4$ | chloroform, sweetish: PXY | 2.172 (25/25°C) | 70.4 | | | α! λ! |
| Ethylene glycol $C_2H_6O_2$ | | 1.1132 (20/4°C) | 141.8 | | | |
| Ethylene glycol n-butyl ether $C_6H_{14}O_2$ | pleasant: P | | | | | |
| Ethylene glycol diacetate $C_6H_{12}O_4$ | faint, fruity, acid: JX | 1.1063 (20/20°C) | | | .312 | $Fru_n$ ψ $HU^{1-2}_{2-3}$ 9-25 |
| Ethylene glycol dibutyl ether $C_{10}H_{22}O_2$ | characteristic: X | .8374 (20/20°C) | .09 mm Hg (20°C) | | | |
| Ethylene glycol diethyl ether $C_6H_{14}O_2$ | slight, ethereal: X | .8417 (20/20°C) | 51.8 | | | λ |
| Ethylene glycol ethyl ether $C_4H_{10}O_2$ | mild, pleasant: P | | | | | |
| Ethylene glycol monobenzyl ether $C_9H_{12}O_2$ | faint, rose-like: X | 1.070 (20/20°C) | .02 mm Hg (20°C) | | | $Flo_n$ |

| | | | | | |
|---|---|---|---|---|---|
| Ethylene glycol monobutyl ether $C_6H_{14}O_2$ | mild, sweet, ester: JX | .9019 (20/20°C) | .76 mm Hg (20°C) | .48 | $Es_n$ α $HU^{1-2}_{2-3}$ 9-25 |
| Ethylene glycol monobutyl ether acetate $C_8H_{16}O_3$ | sweet, ester, fruity: JX | .9424 (20/20°C) | | .20 | $Es_nFru_n$ α! $HU^{1-2}_{2-3}$ 9-25 |
| Ethylene glycol monoethyl ether $C_4H_{10}O_2$ | practically odorless (X); sweet, musty (J) | .9311 (20/20°C) | | 1.3 | $Mst_n$ α $HU^{1-2}_{2-3}$ 9-25 |
| Ethylene glycol monoisopropyl ether $C_5H_{12}O_2$ | mild, agreeable: P | | | | |
| Ethylene glycol monomethyl ether $C_3H_8O_2$ | mild, agreeable, sweet, alcohol: JPX | .9663 (20/20°C) | 68 | .40 | $Mst_nHyc_n$ α $HU^{2}_{2-3}$ 16-25 |
| Ethylene glycol monomethyl ether acetate $C_5H_{10}O_3$ | pleasant, sweet, characteristic, ester-like: JX | 1.0067 (20/20°C) | | .64 | $Es_n$ α! $HU^{2}_{2-3}$ 16-25 |
| Ethylene glycol monophenyl ether $C_8H_{10}O_2$ | faint, aromatic: XY XY | 1.1094 (20/20°C) | | | |
| Ethylene glycol monoricinoleate $C_{22}H_{38}O_4$ | mild: X | .965 (25/25°C) | | | |
| Ethylene oxide $C_2H_4O$ | ethereal, sweet, olefinic: AJM | .8711 (20/20°C) | -32.1 | 500 | $Lip_n$ α! λ! $HU^{1-2}_{2-3}$ 16-25 |
| Ethylene sebacate $C_{12}H_{20}O_4$ | musky: AM | | | | $Mus_n$ |

| Chemical | Reported Characteristics | Specific Gravity | Vapor Pressure | Detection Threshold | Recognition Threshold | Classification Expression, Factors, HU Value |
|---|---|---|---|---|---|---|
| Ethylene thiourea $C_3H_6N_2S$ | faint, amine: X | | | | | $Ami_n$ |
| Ethylene undecane-dioate $C_{13}H_{22}O_4$ | musk-like: M | | | | | $Mus_n$ |
| Ethylenimine $C_2H_5N$ | intense, pungent, ammoniacal: MPXY | .8321 (24/4°C) | | | | $Uro_nNit_n$ ψ!!! ω! |
| N-Ethylethanol-amine $C_4H_{11}NO$ | amine, pungent: AX | .914 (20°C) | | | | $Ami_n$ ψ! |
| Ethyl ether $C_4H_{10}O$ | pleasant, aromatic, ethereal, characteristic, sweetish, pungent, more agreeable than chloroform: AXY | .7134 (20/4°C) | -11.5 | | | $Hyc_n$ α! λ! ψ! |
| Ethylfluorosul-fonate $C_2FH_5OS$ | ethereal: PX | | | | | λ! |
| Ethyl formate $C_3H_6O_2$ | pleasant, aromatic, rum-like, pungent: FPX | .917 (20/4°C) | 5.4 | | | $A_nFru_n$ ψ! |
| α-Ethyl β-furyl-acrolein $C_9H_{11}O_2$ | sharp, musty, fatty: C | | | | | $Mst_nLip_n$ ψ! |
| Ethyl heptylate $C_9H_{18}O_2$ | wine-like: F | | | | | $Hyc_nFru_n$ |
| 2-Ethylhexaldehyde $C_8H_{15}O$ | characteristic, mild: X | .8205 (20°C) | | | | |

| | | | | | |
|---|---|---|---|---|---|
| 2-Ethylhexanol $C_8H_{18}O$ | musty: J | .8344 (20/20°C) | .36 mm Hg (20°C) | .138 | $Mst_n$ $HU^{2-4}_{3-4}$ 25-64 |
| 2-Ethylhexoic acid $C_8H_{15}O_2$ | mild: PX | .9077 (20/20°C) | | | |
| 2-Ethylhexyl acrylate $C_{11}H_{20}O_2$ | pleasant, musty, sharp: JX | .8869 | 147.9 | .18 | $HU^{2-4}_{2-4}$ 16-64 |
| N-2-Ethylhexyl-aniline $C_{14}H_{23}N$ | mild: PX | .9119 (20/20°C) | | | |
| Ethyl hydrogen adipate $C_{10}H_{18}O_4$ | floral: A | | | | $Flo_n$ |
| α-Ethyl-1-hydroxy-cyclohexaneacetic acid $C_{10}H_{18}O_3$ | butyric acid: Y | 1.0010 (18.8/4°C) | | | $Lip_nSeb_n$ |
| Ethylidene chlor-ide $C_2Cl_2H_4$ | aromatic, ethereal, chloroform: PXY | 1.175 (20/4°C) | 7.2 | | $Hal_nHyc_n$ α λ! |
| Ethylidene diace-tate $C_6H_{10}O_4$ | sharp, fruity: Y | 1.061 (12/4°C) | | | $Fru_n$ ψ! |
| Ethylidene norbor-nene | sweet, aromatic: J | | | .073 | $HU^{3-4}_{2-3}$ 25-49 |
| Ethyl iodide $C_2H_5I$ | ethereal, sweet: MY | 1.950 (20/20°C) | 18.0 | | $Hal_nHyc_n$ α! λ! |
| Ethylisoamylnitros-amine $C_7H_{13}N_2O$ | minty: A | | | | $He_n$ δ! |

| Chemical | Reported Characteristics | Specific Gravity | Vapor Pressure | Detection Threshold | Recognition Threshold | Classification Expression, Factors, HU Value |
|---|---|---|---|---|---|---|
| Ethyl isobutyrate $C_6H_{12}O_2$ | aromatic, fruity: Y | .870 (20/20°C) | 53.5 | | | $Fru_n$ |
| Ethyl isocyanide dichloride | strong, pungent: A | | | | | ψ! |
| Ethyl isothiocyanide dichloride $C_3Cl_2H_3NS$ | strong, pungent: A | | | | | ψ! |
| Ethyl isothiocyanate $C_3H_5NS$ | pungent, strong, mustard: AMPXY | 1.003 (18/4°C) | 71.9 | | | $All_n$ ψ! |
| Ethyl isovalerate $C_7H_{14}O_2$ | pleasant, fruity, apple, ester-like: FXY | .868 (20/20°C) | 75.9 | | | $Fru_n$ |
| Ethyl lactate $C_5H_{10}O_3$ | characteristic, mild: PXY | 1.042 (14/4°C) | | | | |
| N-Ethylmaleimide $C_6H_7NO_2$ | pungent, lachrymator liquid: AY | | | | | ε ψ! |
| Ethyl malonate $C_7H_{12}O_4$ | aromatic, typical sweet ester, pleasant: PXY | 1.055 (25/25°C) | | | | α! |
| 2-Ethylmenthene $C_{12}H_{22}$ | camphor, moldy: A | | | | | $Woo_nMol_n$ |
| Ethyl mercaptan $C_2H_6S$ | penetrating, garlic-like, leek-like, putrid: APXY | .83147 (25/4°C) | -13.0 | .00026 | .001 | $All_nSul_n$ β! γ ψ ω! $HU^{3-5}_{4-6}$ 49-121 |
| Ethyl mercuric phosphate $C_6H_{15}Hg_3O_4P$ | garlic-like: X | | | | | $All_nPho_n$ ψ |

| | | | | |
|---|---|---|---|---|
| p-Ethylmercurithio-benzenesulfonate, sodium salt $C_8H_9HgNaO_3S$ | characteristic: X | | | |
| N-(Ethylmercuri)-p-toluenesulfonanilide $C_{15}H_{17}HgNO_2S$ | pungent, garlic-like: XY | | | $All_n$ ψ! |
| Ethyl methyl-phenylglycidate $C_{12}H_{14}O_3$ | strong, strawberry, fruity, floral: CX | 1.104-1.123 | | $(MusBut_2)_2$ 0 $(Fru_5Flo_2)_5$ 0 α σ ψ |
| Ethylmethylselenide $C_3H_5Se$ | putrid: A | | | β! |
| Ethylmethylsulfide $C_3H_5S$ | putrid: A | | | β! |
| N-Ethylmorpholine $C_6H_{13}NO$ | ammoniacal: JX | .916 (20/20°C) | .25 | $Uro_nNit_n$ ψ! $HU^{2-5}_{3-5}$ 25-100 |
| Ethyl nitrate $C_2H_5NO_3$ | pleasant: MPX | 1.116 | | |
| Ethyl nitrite $C_2H_5NO_2$ | characteristic, highly aromatic, ethereal: PXY | .900 | | λ! |
| Ethyl octine carbonate $C_{16}H_{18}O_2$ | green: F | | | $Ens_n$ |
| Ethyl Octyl ketone $C_{11}H_{22}O$ | rue-like: M | | | |
| Ethyl oenanthate $C_9H_{18}O_2$ | fruity, musty, wine-like: XY | .8630 (25/4°C) | | $Mus_nMst_nFru_n$ σ ψ! |

| Chemical | Reported Characteristics | Specific Gravity | Vapor Pressure | Detection Threshold | Recognition Threshold | Classification Expression, Factors, HU Value |
|---|---|---|---|---|---|---|
| Ethyl orthoformate $C_7H_{16}O_3$ | sweetish, pungent, pine needle-like: XY | .897 (20/4°C) | | | | $Woo_n$ α! ψ! |
| Ethyl oxalate $C_6H_{10}O_4$ | aromatic: PX | 1.09 (20/20°C) | | | | |
| Ethyl pelargonate $C_{11}H_{22}O_2$ | fruity, wine, ether, brandy: FXY | .866 (18/4°C) | | | | $Fru_n$ λ |
| Ethyl phenylacetate $C_{10}H_{12}O_2$ | honey-like, sweet, pleasant, sharp: CFXY | 1.0333 (20/4°C) | | | | $Car_n$ α ψ! |
| Ethyl phosphorochloridite $C_4ClH_{10}O_2P$ | characteristic of acid chlorides: Y | 1.0816 (20/4°C) | | | | $Pho_nHal_n$ σ! ψ! |
| 3-Ethyl-4-picoline $C_8H_{11}N$ | aromatic: Y | .9286 (17/4°C) | | | | |
| 5-Ethyl-2-picoline $C_8H_{11}N$ | aromatic, sharp, penetrating: XY | .9184 (23/4°C) | | | | ψ! ω! |
| Ethyl propionate $C_5H_{10}O_2$ | fruity, pineapple-like: FPXY | .891 (20/4°C) | 45.2 | | | $Lip_nFru_n$ ψ!! |
| 2-Ethyl-3-propylacrolein $C_8H_{14}O$ | powerful: PX | .8518 (20/20°C) | | | | |
| 4-Ethyl pyridine $C_7H_9N$ | obnoxious: Y | .9404 (22/4°C) | | | | β! |
| Ethyl salicylate $C_9H_{10}O_3$ | faint, methyl salicylate, mild, pleasant, wintergreen: PXY | 1.131 (20/4°C) | 161.5 | | | $He_n$ δ! σ |

| | | | | | | |
|---|---|---|---|---|---|---|
| Ethylselenohydride $C_2H_5Se$ | putrid: A | | | | | β! |
| Ethyl selenomercaptan $C_2H_6Se$ | thiolic: A | | | .0004 | | $Mus_nSse_nSul_n$ β! σ $HU^{3-5}_{4-6}$ 49-121 |
| Ethyl silicate $C_8H_{20}O_4Si$ | faint, sweet alcohol: JPX | .933 (20/4°C) | | | 7.2 | $HU^{1-2}_{2-4}$ 9-36 |
| Ethylsilicontrethoxide | camphor: A | | | | | $Woo_n$ |
| Ethyl sulfide $C_4H_{10}S$ | ethereal, garlic-like, putrid: APXY | .837 (20/4°C) | 35 | .068 | | $All_nSul_n$ β! λ! $HU^{4-5}_{4-6}$ 64-121 |
| Ethyl sulfite $C_4H_{10}O_3S$ | peppermint: M | | | | | $He_n$ δ! |
| α-Ethyl-2-thienylethylamine $C_8H_{13}NS$ | pungent: Y | | | | | ψ! |
| Ethyl thiocyanate $C_3H_5NS$ | onion-like: M | 1.007 (23/4°C) | 10.6 | | | $All_nSul_n$ σ ψ |
| Ethyl trichloroacetate $C_4Cl_3H_5O_2$ | menthol: Y | 1.383 (20/4°C) | 107.4 | | | $Woo_n$ δ! |
| Ethyl valerianate $C_7H_{15}O_2$ | musty, fruity, ester-like: C | | | | | $Mus_nFru_n$ λ σ ψ |
| Ethyl vanillin $C_9H_{10}O_3$ | finer, more intense vanilla odor than vanillin: FXY | | | | | $Mus_nBal_n$ |
| 1-Ethynylcyclohexanol $C_8H_{12}O$ | camphor, faint, sweet: AXY | .967 (20/20°C) | | | | $Woo_n$ α |

| Chemical | Reported Characteristics | Specific Gravity | Vapor Pressure | Detection Threshold | Recognition Threshold | Classification Expression, Factors, HU Value |
|---|---|---|---|---|---|---|
| $\Delta^{16}$-Etiocholon-3-ol | musky: A | | | | | $Mus_n$ |
| Eugenol $C_{10}H_{12}O_2$ | spicy, cloves, musty: CFXY @ | 1.0664 | 182.2 | .000085 | | $Mus_nSpi_n$ σ! ψ $HU^{2-3}_{2-3}$ 16-36 |
| Eugenol acetate $C_{12}H_{14}O_3$ | spicy, cloves: FX | 1.080-1.082 | 209.7 | | | $Spi_n$ |
| Eugenol benzoate $C_{17}H_{16}O_3$ | spicy, cloves: FY | | | | | $Spi_n$ |
| Eugenol formate $C_{11}H_{16}O_3$ | mild, clove: F | | | | | $Spi_n$ |
| Eurazyl $C_{19}ClH_{29}N_2$ | characteristic: Y | | | | | |
| EUROPIUM Eu | no reported odor | | | | | |
| EUROPIUM COMPOUNDS | no reported odors | | | | | |
| Exaltolide† $C_{15}H_{28}O_2$ | amber, strong musk: FMXY @ | .9549 (20/4°C) | | | | $Mus_n$ |
| Exaltone $C_{15}H_{28}O$ | musk: M | | | | | $Mus_n$ |
| Farnesol $C_{15}H_{26}O$ | delicate, rather faint, floral, musk-like, fruity: CFXY | .8871 (20/4°C) | | | | $Fru_nFlo_nMus_n$ ψ |
| Fenchol $C_{10}H_{18}O$ | camphoric, woody: F | .962 | 132.3 | | | $Woo_n$ δ |
| d-Fenchone $C_{10}H_{16}O$ | camphorous: FXY | .984 (18/4°C) | 123.6 | | | $Woo_n$ |

| | | | | |
|---|---|---|---|---|
| Fenthion<br>$C_3H_{12}O_3PS_2$ | slight garlic: Y | 1.250<br>(20/4°C) | | $All_nPho_nSul_n$ $\psi$ |
| Ferric acetate, basic<br>$C_4FeH_7O_5$ | faint, acetic: Y | | | $\phi$ $\psi$ |
| Ferric and ammonium acetate solution | aromatic: Y | | | |
| Ferric ammonium citrate | odorless or slight ammonia: X | | | $Uro_nNit_n$ |
| Ferric chloride hexahydrate<br>$Cl_3Fe \cdot 6H_2O$ | slight odor of hydrochloric acid: Y | | | $Hal_n$ $\phi$ $\psi$ |
| Ferrocene<br>$C_{10}FeH_{10}$ | camphor-like: XY | | | $Woo_n$ |
| Ferrous gluconate<br>$C_{12}FeH_{22}O_{14}$ | slight odor: X | | | |
| Ferrous lactate trihydrate<br>$C_6FeH_{10}O_6 \cdot 3H_2O$ | characteristic: Y | | | |
| Ficin (enzyme) | acrid: XY | | | $\psi$! |
| FLUORINE<br>F | pungent: X | 1.11<br>(-187°C) | -202.7 | $\psi$! |
| Fluorine monoxide<br>$F_2O$ | peculiar: Y | 1.90<br>(-224°C)<br>(liq.) | -165.8 | |
| Fluorine nitrate<br>$FNO_3$ | moldy, acrid: Y | 1.507<br>(-45.9°C)<br>(liq.) | | $Mol_n$ $\sigma$ $\psi$! |

| Chemical | Reported Characteristics | Specific Gravity | Vapor Pressure | Detection Threshold | Recognition Threshold | Classification Expression, Factors, HU Value |
|---|---|---|---|---|---|---|
| Fluorine perchlorate $ClFO_4$ | pungent, acrid: Y | | | | | ψ! |
| Fluoroacetic acid, ethyl ester $C_4FH_7O_2$ | ethyl acetate: Y | 1.0926 (20.5°C) | | | | $Fru_n$ |
| Fluoroacetic acid, methyl ester $C_3FH_5O_2$ | ethyl acetate: Y | 1.1613 (15/4°C) | | | | $Fru_n$ |
| Fluoroacetone $C_3FH_5O$ | pungent: X | .967 (20°C) | | | | $Hal_n$ ψ! |
| Fluoroacetophenone $C_8FH_7O$ | pungent: PX | | | | | ψ! |
| Fluorobenzene $C_6FH_5$ | benzene-like: XY | 1.024 (20/4°C) | 30.4 | | | $Hal_nHyc_n$ |
| Fluoromethane $CFH_3$ | agreeable, ether-like: Y | .8874 (-78°C) (liq.) | | | | $Hal_nHyc_n$ λ |
| p-Fluorophenylisothiocyanate $C_7FH_5NS$ | anise, mustard: D | | | | | $Her_nAll_nHal_nSul_n$ ψ |
| p-Fluorotoluene $C_7FH_7$ | bitter almonds: Y | 1.001 (16°C) | 58.1 | | | $Nut_n$ ν |
| Fluosilicic acid (34% solution) $F_6H_2Si$ | sour, pungent: Y | 1.3162 (17.5/17.5°C) | | | | ψ! |
| Flurothyl $C_4F_6H_4O$ | mild, ethereal, pleasant: Y | 1.41 (20/4°C) | | | | λ |

| | | | | | |
|---|---|---|---|---|---|
| Formaldehyde $CH_2O$ | pungent, suffocating: APXY | .815 (-20/4°C) | -57.3 | 1 | $\phi$! $\psi$! $HU^{2-6}_{4-5}$ 36-121 |
| Formaldehyde p-toluidine $(C_8H_9N)_x$ | aromatic: X | 1.11 | | | |
| Formamide $CH_3NO$ | odorless: Y | 1.146 | 157.5 | 100 | |
| Formic acid $CH_2O_2$ | pungent, penetrating: AFPXY @ | 1.220 (20/4°C) | | | $\psi$! $\omega$! |
| FRANCIUM Fr | no reported odor | | | | |
| Furan $C_4H_4O$ | ethereal: A | .9371 (19.4/4°C) | | | $\lambda$! |
| Furanacrolein $C_7H_8O_2$ | musty, orange: C | | | | $Mus_nFru_n$ |
| Furfural $C_5H_4O_2$ | peculiar, benzaldehyde-like, burnt, new bread: FMPXY | 1.1563 (25/4°C) | 103.4 | | $Nut_nYe_n$ $\sigma$! |
| Furfural acetone $C_7H_6O_2$ | musty, fatty, fruity: C | | | | $Mus_nLip_nFru_n$ $\sigma$ $\psi$ |
| Furfuryl acetate $C_7H_8O_3$ | pungent: X | 1.1175 (20/4°C) | | | $\psi$! |
| Furfuryl alcohol $C_5H_6O_2$ | faint, burning: Y | 1.282 (23/4°C) | 115.9 | | $Hyc_n$ $\nu$ |
| Furfuryl mercaptan $C_5H_6OS$ | roasted coffee beans, burnt: FX | 1.1319 (20/4°C) | | | $Woo_n$ $\sigma$! |
| 2-Furoic acid, methyl ester $C_6H_6O_3$ | agreeable: Y | 1.1786 (21/4°C) | | | |

| Chemical | Reported Characteristics | Specific Gravity | Vapor Pressure | Detection Threshold | Recognition Threshold | Classification Expression, Factors, HU Value |
|---|---|---|---|---|---|---|
| Furoyl chloride $C_5ClH_3O_2$ | powerful lachrymator: XY | | | | | ε!!! |
| 2-Furylbenzothiazole $C_{11}H_7NOS$ | floral, tea-rose, geranium: AM | | | | | $Flo_n$ |
| Fusel oil | disagreeable: XY | | | | | |
| GADOLINIUM Gd | no reported odor | | | | | |
| GADOLINIUM COMPOUNDS | no reported odors | | | | | |
| GALLIUM Ga | no reported odor | | | | | |
| GALLIUM COMPOUNDS | no reported odors | | | | | |
| Gefarnate $C_{27}H_{44}O_2$ | weak turpenic: Y | | | | | $Woo_nHyc_n$ |
| Geosmin $C_{12}H_{22}O$ | strong, actinomycete, earthy, musty: S | | | | | $Ear_nMst_n$ |
| Geraniol $C_{10}H_{18}O$ | sweet rose, floral, geranium, pleasant, musty: ACFXY @ | .8894 (20/4°C) | 165.3 | | | $Mus_nFlo_n$ ψ |
| Geraniol acetate $C_{12}H_{20}O_2$ | sweet, fragrant, mild, rose, oil of lavender: CFXY | .9174 (15/15°C) | 175.2 | | | $Flo_n$ ψ |
| Geraniol benzoate | sweet, rose: C | | | | | $Flo_n$ α! ψ |
| Geraniol butyrate $C_{14}H_{24}O_2$ | characteristic, fragrant, rose-type, sharp, floral: CFXY | .901 (17/4°C) | 193.8 | | | $Flo_nEns_n$ σ ψ!! |

| | | | | |
|---|---|---|---|---|
| Geraniol formate $C_{11}H_{18}O_2$ | roses, green rose leaves, raspberry, bitter rose: FXY | .927 (20/4°C) | 160.7 | $Flo_nEns_nFru_n$ ν |
| Geraniol palmarosa | rosey, citrus, woody: C | | | $Woo_nFru_nFlo_n$ σ ψ |
| Geraniol phenyl-acetate $C_{18}H_{24}O_2$ | honey, rose, sharp, fruity, woody: CF | | | $Car_nWoo_nFlo_nFru_n$ σ ψ! |
| Geraniol propionate $C_{13}H_{22}O_2$ | rose-type, bitter grape: CFX | .896-.913 (25°C) | | $Mst_nFlo_nFru_n$ ν ψ! |
| α-Geranyl-γ-butyrolactone $C_{14}H_{23}O_2$ | musk, fresh peach: A | | | $Mus_nFru_n$ |
| Germander | garlicky: Y | | | $All_n$ ψ |
| GERMANIUM Ge | no reported odor | 5.323 | | |
| Germanium tetra-chloride $Cl_4Ge$ | peculiar acetic odor but can be distinguished from hydrochloric acid: Y | 1.879 (20/20°C) | | $Hal_n$ ϕ ψ |
| Germanium tetra-fluoride $F_4Ge$ | garlic, very irritating to mucous membranes: Y | 2.162 (0°C) (liq.) | | $All_n$ ψ! |
| Gingerol $C_{17}H_{26}O_4$ | pungent: Y | 1.0713 (20/20°C) | | ψ! |
| Glutaric acid, dimethyl ester $C_7H_{12}O_4$ | faint, agreeable: Y | 1.0934 (15/4°C) | | |

| Chemical | Reported Characteristics | Specific Gravity | Vapor Pressure | Detection Threshold | Recognition Threshold | Classification Expression, Factors, HU Value |
|---|---|---|---|---|---|---|
| Glutaric anhydride $C_5H_6O_3$ | suffocating: M | | 212.5 | | | $\phi$! |
| Glycarsamide sodium salt $AsC_8H_9NNaO_5$ | noticeable acid: Y | | | | | $\psi$! |
| Glyceryl p-aminobenzoate $C_{10}H_{13}NO_4$ | faint, aromatic: Y | | | | | |
| Glyceryl tri-(12-acetoxystearate) $C_{63}H_{116}O_{12}$ | mild: X | .955 (25/25°C) | | | | |
| Glycol phenyl-acetal $C_{10}H_{14}O_3$ | floral, roses: AM | | | | | $Flo_n$ |
| Glycyrrhizin $C_{42}H_{62}O_{16}$ | licorice: F | | | | | $Her_n$ |
| Glyoxal $C_2H_2O_2$ | mild: X | 1.26 (20/20°C) | | | | |
| GOLD Au | no reported odor | 19.2 | 2521 | | | |
| Guaiacol $C_7H_8O_2$ | characteristic, aromatic, smokey, burnt: FXY | 1.1395 | 144 | | | $Hyc_nOxy_n$ $\sigma$!!! |
| Guaiacol acetate $C_9H_{10}O_2$ | heliotropin (confectionary odor): F | | | | | $Flo_n$ $\alpha$ $\sigma$ |
| Guaiacol carbonate $C_{15}H_{14}O_5$ | slight aromatic or odorless: X | | | | | |

| | | | | |
|---|---|---|---|---|
| Guaiol $C_{15}H_{26}O_2$ | woody: F | .9074 (100/20°C) | | $Woo_nHyc_n$ |
| Guanethidine sulfate $C_{20}H_{46}N_8O_4S$ | strong, characteristic: X | | | |
| HAFNIUM Hf | no reported odor | | | |
| HAFNIUM COMPOUNDS | no reported odors | | | |
| Halazone $C_7Cl_2H_5NO_4S$ | strong, chlorine: XY | | | $Hal_n$ $\phi$!! $\psi$!! |
| Halibut liver oil | fishy, but not rancid: XY | .920-.930 | | $Ami_n$ |
| Halothane $BrC_2ClF_3H$ | characteristic, sweetish, not unpleasant: XY | 1.871 (20/4°C) | | $Hal_n$ $\alpha$! |
| Hedonal $C_6H_{13}NO_2$ | feeble, aromatic: X | | | |
| HELIUM He | no reported odor | .147 (-270.8°C) (liq.) | -270.3 | |
| Hempa $C_6H_{18}N_3OP$ | mild, amine, spicy: PX | 1.021 (15/15°C) | | $Ami_nSpi_n$ |
| 1,2,4,4,5,6,6-Heptachlorocyclohexene(1)-one(3) $C_7Cl_7HO$ | camphor: A | | | $Woo_n$ |
| 1,1,2,2,3,3,3-Heptachloropropane $C_3Cl_7$ | camphor: A | | | $Woo_n$ |

| Chemical | Reported Characteristics | Specific Gravity | Vapor Pressure | Detection Threshold | Recognition Threshold | Classification Expression, Factors, HU Value |
|---|---|---|---|---|---|---|
| Heptafluorobutyric acid $C_4F_7HO_2$ | sharp, butyric acid-like: PX | 1.641 (25°C) | | | | $Lip_nSeb_n$ ψ |
| Heptanal $C_7H_{14}O$ | penetrating, sweet, fruity, aromatic, sharp, almond: AFXY | .82162 (15/4°C) | 84 | | | $Fru_nNut_n$ α! ψ! ω! |
| Heptane $C_7H_{16}$ | | .684 (20/4°C) | 41.8 | | | |
| Heptanoic acid $C_7H_{14}O_2$ | disagreeable, rancid, unpleasant (faint, tallow-like odor when spectroscopically pure): XY | .9184 (20/4°C) | 160 | | | $Lip_n$ |
| 1-Heptanol $C_7H_{16}O$ | fragrant, fruity: FX | .8187 (25/4°C) | 119.5 | | .509 | $Fru_n$ $HU_2^{2-3}$ 16-25 |
| 2-Heptanone $C_7H_{14}O$ | penetrating, pear, fruity, responsible for the peppery odor in cheeses of the Roquefort type, constituent of artificial carnation oil: FPY @ | .8197 (15/4°C) | 100.0 | | | $Fru_nSpi_n$ ω! |
| Heptyl acetate $C_9H_{18}O_2$ | fruity, apricot: FX | | | | | $Fru_n$ |
| α-Heptyl-γ-butyrolactone $C_{11}H_{20}O_2$ | musky, peach: M | | | | | $Mus_nFru_n$ |

| | | | |
|---|---|---|---|
| Heptyl caproate $C_{13}H_{26}O_2$ | bruised, green leaves: M | | $Ens_n$ |
| Heptyl formate $C_8H_{16}O_2$ | fruity, plum: FX | .894 (0°C) | $Fru_n$ |
| Heptyl geranate $C_{17}H_{30}O_2$ | mimosa, hawthorne: M | | $Woo_nFlo_n$ |
| Heptyl heptoate $C_{14}H_{18}O_2$ | fruity: X | .865 (19°C) | $Fru_n$ |
| Heptyl heptyl ether $C_{14}H_{30}O$ | wet wool: M | | $Lip_nBut_nMus_n$ σ ψ |
| Heptyl hexyl ether $C_{13}H_{28}O$ | bluebell stalks: M | | $Flo_nEns_n$ |
| Heptyl isobutyrate $C_{11}H_{22}O_2$ | cyclamen, chamomile: M | | $Flo_n$ |
| Heptyl pelargonate $C_{16}H_{32}O_2$ | pleasant: X | .866 (15.5/15.5°C) | |
| Heptyl phenyl ether $C_{13}H_{20}O$ | opoponax: M | | |
| Heptyl salicylate $C_{14}H_{20}O_3$ | steel: M | | μ!! |
| Heptyl undecanate $C_{18}H_{36}O$ | smoke, ink: M | | $Hyc_n$ μ σ!! |
| Heptyl undecyl ether $C_{18}H_{38}O$ | fatty aldehyde: M | | $Lip_nHyc_n$ γ |

| Chemical | Reported Characteristics | Specific Gravity | Vapor Pressure | Detection Threshold | Recognition Threshold | Classification Expression, Factors, HU Value |
|---|---|---|---|---|---|---|
| Hexachlorobutadiene $C_4Cl_6$ | mild, characteristic: X | 1.675 (15.5/15.5°C) | | | | |
| 1,2,3,4,5,6-Hexachlorocyclohexane $C_6Cl_6H_6$ | musty (all properties vary with isomeric composition): X | | | | | $Mst_n$ |
| Hexachlorocyclopentadiene $C_5Cl_6$ | pungent: PX | 1.717 (15/15°C) | | | | ψ! |
| Hexachloroethane $C_2Cl_6$ | camphor-like: AMPXY | 2.091 | 124.2 | | | $Woo_n$ |
| Hexachloromethylcarbonate $C_3Cl_6O_3$ | phosgene-like, lachrymator: X | | | | | $Ens_nMol_n$ ε! |
| Hexachloromethyl ether $C_2Cl_6O$ | phosgene-like, very irritant: X | 1.538 (18°C) | | | | $Ens_nMol_n$ ψ!! $HU^{4-6}_{4-6}$ 64-144 |
| Hexadecamethylene imine $C_{16}H_{33}N$ | musky: M | | | | | $Mus_n$ |
| Hexadecanedicarboxylic acid anhydride | musky: A | | | | | $Mus_n$ |
| $\Delta^7$-Hexadecenolactone $C_{16}H_{28}O_2$ | musk: M | | | | | $Mus_n$ |
| Hexahydrobenzaldehyde | almond, high fatty aldehyde: A | | | | | $Lip_nNut_n$ γ |

| | | | | | |
|---|---|---|---|---|---|
| n-Hexaldehyde $C_6H_{12}O$ | sharp, aldehyde: X | .8516 (20/20°C) | 10.5 mm Hg (20°C) | | γ ψ! |
| Hexamethonium bromide $Br_2C_{12}H_{30}N_2$ | faintly aromatic: X | | | | |
| Hexamethyldistan-nane | putrid: A | | | | β! |
| Hexamethylenimine $C_6H_{13}N$ | ammonia-like: X | .8799 (20/4°C) | | | $Uro_n Nit_n$ ψ |
| Hexamethylethane $C_8H_{18}$ | camphor: A | | | | $Woo_n$ |
| n-Hexane $C_6H_{14}$ | faint, peculiar: XY | .65937 (20/4°C) | 15.8 | | |
| 1,6-Hexanediamine $C_6H_{16}N_2$ | piperidine: Y | | | | $Spi_n$ ψ |
| 1-Hexanol $C_6H_{14}O$ | sweet, alcohol, sharp, green, fusel-like: FJW | .8153 (25/4°C) | 102.8 | .09 | $Ens_n Ami_n$ α λ ψ $HU^{3-4}_{2-4}$ 25-64 |
| trans-2-Hexenal $C_6H_{10}O$ | fatty: W | | | | $Lip_n$ |
| cis-Hexenol $C_6H_{12}O$ | fine perfume ingredient for imparting natural green freshness in perfumes, that of isoamyl alcohol, approaching the odor of green leaves when highly diluted: FXY | .846 (22/15°C) | | | $Ens_n$ |

| Chemical | Reported Characteristics | Specific Gravity | Vapor Pressure | Detection Threshold | Recognition Threshold | Classification Expression, Factors, HU Value |
|---|---|---|---|---|---|---|
| Hexyl acetate $C_8H_{16}O_2$ | sweet ester, sharp, citrus: CX | | | | | $Fru_n$ α σ ψ! |
| Hexyl aldehyde $C_6H_{12}O$ | fatty, fruit: F | | | | | $Lip_nFru_n$ |
| n-Hexylamine $C_6H_{15}N$ | amine-like: PX @ | .767 (20/20°C) | | | | $Ami_n$ |
| Hexyl butyrate $C_7H_{20}O_2$ | sweet, fruity, pineapple: CF | | | | | $Fru_n$ α σ ψ! |
| Hexylcaine hydrochloride $C_{16}ClH_{24}NO_2$ | slight, aromatic: X | | | | | |
| Hexyl caproate $C_{12}H_{24}O_2$ | sharp, citrus: C | | | | | $Fru_n$ σ ψ! |
| Hexyl cinnamaldehyde $C_{15}H_{20}O$ | jasmine-like, particularly on dilution, fruity: CX | .953-.959 (25°C) | | | | $Fru_nFlo_n$ ψ! |
| n-Hexyl ether $C_{12}H_{26}O$ | characteristic: X | .7942 (20/20°C) | | | | |
| Hexyl formate $C_7H_{14}O_2$ | plum, ester-like, musty, pungent, fatty: CF | | | | | $Lip_nMus_nFru_n$ σ ψ!! |
| Hexylene glycol $C_6H_{14}O_2$ | mild, sweetish: XY | .924 (15/15°C) | | | | α |
| Hexyl mercaptan $C_6H_{14}S$ | putrid: A | .8450 (25/4°C) | | | | β! |

| | | | | |
|---|---|---|---|---|
| Hexyl methyl ketone $C_8H_{16}O$ | apple-like, pleasant: XY | .820 (20/4°C) | 111.7 | $Fru_n$ |
| p-tert-Hexylphenol $C_9H_{18}O$ | faint, phenol: X | .986 (20/20°C) | | $Mol_n$ |
| Hexyl propionate $C_9H_{18}O_2$ | sharp, pear, citrus: CF | | | $Fru_n$ σ ψ! |
| Hexyl resorcinol $C_{12}H_{18}O_2$ | faint, fatty, pungent: XY | | | $Lip_n$ ψ! |
| Hexyl salicylate $C_{13}H_{18}O_3$ | phenolic: C | | | $Her_nHyc_nOxy_n$ σ!! |
| Hexyltrichloro-silane $C_6Cl_3H_{13}Si$ | sharp, penetra-ting: X | | | ψ! ω! |
| α-n-Hexyl-γ-valerolactone | floral: A | | | $Flo_n$ |
| 1-Hexyne $C_6H_{10}$ | characteristic: X | .7152 (20/4°C) | | |
| Hexynol $C_6H_{10}O$ | slightly piercing: X | .882 (20/20°C) | | ω |
| HN1 (2,2'dichlorotri-ethylamine) $C_6Cl_2H_{13}N$ | faint, fishy, amine: Y | 1.0861 (23/4°C) | | $Ami_n$ |
| HOLMIUM Ho | no reported odor | 8.799 | | |
| HOLMIUM COMPOUNDS | no reported odors | | | |
| Δ-Homoandrostan-3-ol | musky: A | | | $Mus_n$ |

| Chemical | Reported Characteristics | Specific Gravity | Vapor Pressure | Detection Threshold | Recognition Threshold | Classification Expression, Factors, HU Value |
|---|---|---|---|---|---|---|
| Homoveratrylamine $C_{10}H_{15}O_2$ | slight vanilla: X | 1.09 (25/25°C) | | | | $Bal_n$ |
| Humulon $C_{21}H_{30}O_5$ | fatty, green, oily: F | | | | | $Lip_nEns_nHyc_n$ |
| Hydratropaldehyde $C_9H_{10}O$ | characteristic, floral, green, mushroomy, fungal, earthy, hyacinth: CFWX | .998-1.006 (25°C) | | | | $Far_nEar_nFlo_nEns_n$ σ ψ! |
| Hydrazine $H_4N_2$ | penetrating, ammonia-like: Y | 1.011 (15/4°C) | | | | $Uro_nNit_n$ ψ! |
| Hydrocinnamic acid $C_9H_{10}O_2$ | hyacinth-rose: X | | 209 | | | $Flo_n$ |
| Hydrocyanic acid CHN | faint, bitter almonds, pungent, characteristic: APXY @(10% of population cannot detect) | .688 (20/4°C) | -18.8 | | | $Nut_n$ ψ! |
| HYDROGEN H | no reported odor | .0694 (air=1) | -270.3 | | | |
| Hydrogen azide $HN_3$ | intolerable, pungent: Y | 1.09 | | | | ε!! ψ!!! ω |
| Hydrogen bromide BrH | acrid, very irritant to mucous membranes: Y | 3.5 (g/1) | -97.7 | | | ε!! ψ!! |
| Hydrogen chloride ClH | characteristic, pungent, suffocating: XY | 1.187 | -114.0 | | 10 | ϕ! ψ! $HU^{3-6}_{4-6}$ 49-144 |

| | | | | | |
|---|---|---|---|---|---|
| Hydrogen selenide $H_2Se$ | disagreeable, putrid, causing irritation of the eyes, nose, throat: AY | 2.12 (-42/4°C) | -74.2 | | $Sse_n$ β! ε!! ψ!! |
| Hydrogen sulfide $H_2S$ | characteristic, rotten eggs, putrid, offensive (gas deadens sense of smell): APXY | 1.1895 (air=1) | -91.6 | .0047 | $Sul_n$ β!! τ!!! ω! $HU^{4-6}_{4-6}$ 64-144 |
| Hydrogen telluride $H_2Te$ | offensive, garlic-like: Y | 2.68 (-12°C) (liq.) | -45.7 | | $All_n$ |
| Hydrogen tetracarbonyl ferrate (II) $CFeH_2O_4$ | gas has extremely nauseating odor: Y | | | | β!!! |
| Hydroquinone diethyl ether $C_{10}H_{14}O_2$ | anise-like: X | | | | $Her_n$ |
| Hydroquinone dimethyl ether $C_8H_{10}O_2$ | sweet clover, honey: FPX | | | | $Ens_nCar_n$ α |
| Hydrorosyl ethyl ether | green, fatty, weak rose: W | | | | $Ens_nLip_nFlo_n$ |
| Hydroxyacetic acid $C_2H_4O_3$ | burnt sugar (X); odorless (Y) | 1.27 | | | $Car_nHyc_n$ σ |
| o-Hydroxyacetophenone $C_8H_8O_2$ | minty: PX | 1.1307 (20.8°C) | | | $He_n$ δ! |
| Hydroxycitronellal $C_{10}H_{20}O_2$ | sweet, lily, peach, floral, muguet: FX | .925-.930 (15°C) | | | $Flo_nFru_n$ α! |

| Chemical | Reported Characteristics | Specific Gravity | Vapor Pressure | Detection Threshold | Recognition Threshold | Classification Expression, Factors, HU Value |
|---|---|---|---|---|---|---|
| Hydroxycitronellal dimethyl acetal $C_{12}H_{26}O_3$ | light floral: X | .925-.930 (25/25°C) | | | | $Flo_n$ |
| Hydroxycitronellal methyl anthranilate Schiff base $C_{18}H_{27}NO_2$ | linden-orange flower: X | | | | | $Fru_nFlo_n$ |
| Hydroxycitronellol $C_{10}H_{22}O_2$ | floral, fruity, musty: CF | | | | | $Mus_nFru_nFlo_n$ ψ |
| Hydroxyethylethyl-enediamine $C_4H_{12}N_2O$ | mild, ammoniacal: X | 1.0304 (20/20°C) | | | | $Uro_nNit_n$ ψ |
| 5-(Hydroxy-3-methyl) 2-furaldehyde $C_6H_6O_3$ | chamomile flowers: Y | 1.2062 (25/4°C) | | | | $Flo_n$ |
| 5-(Hydroxymethyl)-tetrahydro-2-fur-furylamine $C_6H_{13}NO_2$ | faint, ammoniacal: Y | 1.1021 (25/4°C) | | | | $Uro_nNit_n$ |
| β-Hydroxypropional-dehyde diethyl acetal ether $C_{12}H_{20}O_3$ | watermellons: M | | | | | $Fru_n$ |
| 8-Hydroxyquinoline benzoate $C_{16}H_{13}NO_3$ | saffron: X | | | | | $Her_n$ |
| 8-Hydroxyquinoline citrate $C_{15}H_{15}NO_8$ | saffron-like: Y | | | | | $Her_n$ ν σ! |

| | | | |
|---|---|---|---|
| 8-Hydroxyquinoline sulfate $C_{18}H_{16}N_2O_6S$ | slight saffron: XY | | $Her_n$ |
| 1,4-Hydroxytetra-decane carboxylic acid | @(most men and children cannot detect, overpowering to women) | | |
| Δ-Hydroxy valeraldehyde | musty, fatty, aldehyde: C | | $Mus_n Lip_n$ ψ! |
| Hymecromone 0,0-diethyl phosphorothioate $C_{14}H_{17}O_5$ | weak, aromatic: Y | 1.260 (38/4°C) (liq.) | |
| Hypophosphorous acid $H_3O_2P$ | sour (X); odorless (Y) | 1.493 | ψ |
| Ichthammol | characteristic, empyreumatic, bituminous: XY | | σ! |
| INDIUM In | no reported odor | 7.3 (20°C) | |
| INDIUM COMPOUNDS | no reported odors | | |
| Indole $C_8H_7N$ | intense, fecal, gasey, fragrant, unpleasant in high concentrations but should not show a fecal quality, floral when diluted, putrid when concentrated: AFXY @ | | $\theta^2$: $Fec_n$ β!! $\theta_1$: $Flo_n$ $HU^{5-6}_{5-6}$ 100-144 |

| Chemical | Reported Characteristic | Specific Gravity | Vapor Pressure | Detection Threshold | Recognition Threshold | Classification Expression, Factors, HU Value |
|---|---|---|---|---|---|---|
| Indolebutyric acid $C_{12}H_{13}NO_2$ | slight, characteristic (Y); essentially odorless (X) | | | | | |
| IODINE $I_2$ | characteristic: XY | 4.93 (20°C) | 116.5 | | | $Hal_n$ ψ! |
| Iodine Heptafluoride $F_7I$ | moldy, acrid: Y | 2.8 (6°C) (liq.) | -31.9 | | | $Mol_n$ ψ! |
| Iodine tribromide $Br_3I$ | irritating: Y | | | | | ψ! |
| Iodine trichloride $Cl_3I$ | pungent, irritating: PXY | 3.203 (-4°C) | 760 mm Hg (64°C) =1 Atm | | | ψ! |
| Iodized oil | alliaceous: XY | | | | | $All_n$ ψ |
| Iodoalphionic acid $C_{15}H_{12}I_2O_3$ | faint, characteristic: X | | | | | |
| Iodobenzene $C_6H_5I$ | characteristic: Y | 1.8384 (15/4°C) | 118.3 | | | |
| 4-Iodo-1-tert-butylbenzene $C_{10}H_{13}I$ | aromatic: A | | | | | |
| Iodoform $CHI_3$ | characteristic, penetrating, disagreeable, saffron: MXY @ | 4.08 | | | | $Her_n$ ω |
| Iodoformin $C_7H_{13}I_3N_4$ | faint, iodoform: XY | | | | | $Her_n$ ω |

| | | | | | |
|---|---|---|---|---|---|
| Iodonitromethane $CH_2INO_2$ | pungent: A | | | | ψ! |
| p-Iodophenol $C_6H_5IO$ | characteristic: Y | | | | |
| p-Iodophenyliso-thiocyanate $C_6H_5INS$ | very sweet, anise: AD | | | | $Her_n$ α!! |
| 3-Iodopropanol $C_3H_7IO$ | radish, pungent: A | | | | $All_n$ ψ! |
| Iodosobenzene $C_6H_5IO$ | on contact imparts odor similar to that of chlorinated lime: Y | | | | $Hal_n$ |
| 3-Iodo-2,2,3-trimethylbutane $C_7H_{15}I$ | camphor: A | | | | $Woo_n$ |
| Ionone $C_{13}H_{20}O$ | in very dilute alcohol solution resembles the odor of violets, cedarwood: Y @ | .933-.937 (25/25°C) | | | $\theta_1$: $Woo_n$ |
| α-Ionone $C_{13}H_{20}O$ | woody, violet, floral: AFX | .927-.933 (25°C) | 181.2 | .0031 | $Flo_nWoo_n$ σ! |
| β-Ionone $C_{13}H_{20}O$ | violet, more fruity and woody than α-ionone: CFX | .941-.947 | | | $Flo_nFru_nWoo_n$ σ! ψ |
| Iopanoic acid $C_{11}H_{12}I_3NO_2$ | faintly aromatic: X | | | | |

| Chemical | Reported Characteristics | Specific Gravity | Vapor Pressure | Detection Threshold | Recognition Threshold | Classification Expression, Factors, HU Value |
|---|---|---|---|---|---|---|
| IRIDIUM<br>Ir | no reported odor | 22.42<br>(20°C) | | | | |
| IRIDIUM COMPOUNDS | no reported odors | | | | | |
| Iridomyrmecin<br>$C_{10}H_{16}O_2$ | aromatic, catnip: Y | | | | | $Ens_n$ |
| IRON<br>Fe | no reported odor | 7.86 | 2360 | | | |
| Irone<br>$C_{14}H_{22}O$ | in dilute alcohol solution characteristic, violet, floral, sweet: AXY | .926-<br>.939 | | | | $Flo_n$ α! σ |
| α-Irone<br>$C_{14}H_{22}O$ | characteristic, violet, woody: MY | .9362<br>(20/4°C) | | | | $Flo_nWoo_n$ |
| β-Irone<br>$C_{14}H_{22}O$ | similar to β-ionone: Y | .9434<br>(21/4°C) | | | | $Flo_nFru_nWoo_n$ |
| Isatin<br>$C_8H_5NO_2$ | alcohol solution imparts a persistent disagreeable odor to human skin: Y | | | | | β! ρ |
| Isoamylalcohol<br>$C_5H_{12}O$ | disagreeable, pungent: XY | .813<br>(15/4°C) | 80.7 | | | $Flo_nHer_nMol_nHyc_n$<br>λ μ σ ψ! ω!!! |
| Isoamylamine<br>$C_5H_{13}N$ | strong, ammonia: Y | .751<br>(18°C) | | | | $Uro_nNit_n$ ψ!! |
| Isoamyl benzoate<br>$C_{12}H_{16}O_2$ | fruity, musty, amber: CX | .993<br>(15/4°C) | 186.8 | | | $(MusBil_2)$ $Mst_2$<br>$Fru_3$ 0 α σ ψ |

| | | | | |
|---|---|---|---|---|
| Isoamyl benzyl ether $C_{12}H_{18}O$ | fruity: X | .904-.908 | | $Fru_n$ ψ! |
| Isoamyl butyrate $C_9H_{18}O_2$ | aromatic, pear-like: Y | .866 (19/15°C) | 113.1 | $Fru_n$ |
| α-Isoamylbutyrolactone $C_9H_{16}O_2$ | peach: M | | | $Fru_n$ |
| γ-Isoamylbutyrolactone $C_9H_{16}O_2$ | peach: M | | | $Fru_n$ |
| Isoamylchloramine $C_5ClH_{10}N$ | pungent: A | | | ψ! |
| Isoamylcinnamate $C_{14}H_{18}O_2$ | fruity, spicy, musty, amber: CF | | | $(MuBil_2)$ $Mst_2$ $(Fru_3Spi_2)$ Hyc σ ψ |
| Isoamyl cyanide $C_6H_{11}N$ | very disagreeable: Y | .806 (20/4°C) | | |
| Isoamyldichloroarsine $AsC_5Cl_2H_{11}$ | somewhat agreeable, very irritant: PX | | | ε!! |
| Isoamyl ether $C_{10}H_{22}O$ | pleasant, fruity: Y | .783 (12/4°C) | | $Fru_n$ |
| Isoamyl formate $C_6H_{12}O_2$ | fruity, sweet, plum: FY | .877 (20°C) | 65.4 | $Fru_n$ α! |
| Isoamyl mercaptan $C_5H_{12}S$ | repulsive: Y | .835 (20/4°C) | | β! |
| Isoamyl pelargonate $C_{14}H_{28}O_2$ | fruity: X | .860 (15.5/15.5°C) | | $Fru_n$ |

| Chemical | Reported Characteristics | Specific Gravity | Vapor Pressure | Detection Threshold | Recognition Threshold | Classification Expression, Factors, HU Value |
|---|---|---|---|---|---|---|
| Isoamyl propionate $C_8H_{16}O_2$ | bittersweet, apricot, plum, fruity, musky, apple: CFX | .869-.873 (20/20°C) | | | | $Mus_5$ 0 $Fru_5$ 0 σ ψ!! |
| Isoamyl salicylate $C_{12}H_{16}O_3$ | pleasant, orchid-like, strawberry, clover: CFMXY | 1.048 (19/15°C) | | | | |
| Isoamyl sulfide $C_{10}H_{22}S$ | | .843 (20/4°C) | | | | $A_5$ 0 $(Flo_3Ens_3)_5$ 0 α σ! ψ |
| Isoamyl valerate $C_{10}H_{20}O_2$ | apple-like when diluted with alcohol: XY | .858 (19/4°C) | | | | $Fru_n$ |
| Isoborneol $C_{10}H_{18}O$ | camphor: FX | | | | | $A_nWoo_n$ σ ψ |
| d-Isoborneol $C_{10}H_{18}O$ | camphor: A | | | | | $Woo_n$ |
| 1-Isoborneol $C_{10}H_{18}O$ | camphor (strong), moldy: A | | | | | $Woo_nMol_n$ |
| Isobornyl acetate $C_{12}H_{20}O_2$ | pine needle, woody: FX | .978 ±.001 (20°C) | | | | $Woo_n$ σ |
| Isobornyl salicylate $C_{17}H_{21}O_3$ | sweet: X | | | | | α |
| Isobornyl thiocyanoacetate $C_{13}H_{19}NO_2S$ | terpene-like: XY | 1.1465 (25/4°C) | | | | $Woo_n$ |
| Isobornyl valerate $C_{15}H_{26}O_2$ | peculiar, aromatic: X | .954 | | | | |

| | | | | | |
|---|---|---|---|---|---|
| Isobutane $C_4H_{10}$ | characteristic, natural gas: X | 2.01 (air=1) | -54.1 | | $Hyc_n$ |
| Isobutene $C_4H_8$ | coal gas: X | .6 (20°C) | -49.3 | | $Hyc_n$ |
| Isobutyl acetate $C_6H_{12}O_2$ | sweet, ester, fruit-like, may be mildly irritating to mucous membranes: FJPXY | .871 (20/4°C) | | .50 | $Fru_n$ α ψ $HU^{2-5}_{2-5}$ 16-100 |
| Isobutyl acrylate $C_7H_{12}O_2$ | sweet, musty: J | .884 (25°C) | | .012 | $HU^{3-4}_{2-4}$ 25-64 |
| Isobutyl alcohol $C_4H_{10}O$ | sweet, similar but weaker than amyl alcohol, musty: JPY | .806 (15°C) | 61.5 | 2.05 | $Mil_nFru_n$ α $HU^{2-3}_{2-3}$ 16-36 |
| Isobutylamine $C_4H_{11}N$ | amine: X | .724 (25/4°C) | 18.8 | | $Ami_n$ |
| Isobutyl benzoate $C_{11}H_{14}O_2$ | characteristic: X | 1.002 | 166.4 | | |
| Isobutylchloramine $C_4ClH_9N$ | pungent: A | | | | ψ! |
| Isobutyl cinnamate $C_{13}H_{16}O_2$ | amber fragrance: X | 1.001-1.004 | | | $Mus_nBil_n$ σ |
| Isobutyldichloramine $C_4Cl_2H_8N$ | pungent: A | | | | ψ! |
| Isobutyl ether $C_8H_{18}O$ | characteristic: Y | .761 (15°C) | | | |
| Isobutyl-3-hexenoate $C_{10}H_{19}O$ | cocoa, sweet, fruity: W | | | | $Woo_nFru_n$ α! σ ψ |

| Chemical | Reported Characteristics | Specific Gravity | Vapor Pressure | Detection Threshold | Recognition Threshold | Classification Expression, Factors, HU Value |
|---|---|---|---|---|---|---|
| Isobutyl isovalerate $C_9H_{18}O_2$ | ethereal, apple: FY | .853 (20°C) | 105.2 | | | $Fru_n$ λ! |
| Isobutyl mercaptan $C_4H_{10}S$ | heavy skunk: Y | .8537 (20/4°C) | | | | $Mus_n$ |
| Isobutyl phenylacetate $C_{12}H_{16}O_2$ | rose, honey-like, fruity: CX | .984-.988 (25°C) | | | | $Fru_nFlo_nCar_n$ ψ! |
| Isobutyl propionate $C_7H_{14}O_2$ | agreeable, ethereal: Y | .888 (0/4°C) | 79.5 | | | λ |
| γ-Isobutylpyridine $C_{10}H_{14}N$ | floral, heliotrope: AM | | | | | $Flo_n$ |
| Isobutyl urethane $C_7H_{15}NO_2$ | apple-like: Y | .943 (20/4°C) | | | | $Fru_n$ |
| Isobutraldehyde $C_4H_8O$ | pungent, sweet ester: JPXY @ | .7938 (20/4°C) | | | .236 | α ψ! $HU^{2-4}_{2-4}$ 16-64 |
| Isobutyric acid $C_4H_8O_2$ | pungent, similar to butyric acid: MPY @(2.5% of population cannot detect) | .950 (20/4°C) | 98 | | | $Lip_nSeb_n$ ψ! |
| Isocitronellyl acetate $C_{12}H_{22}O_2$ | fruity, woody, ionone-like: C | | | | | $Woo_nFru_n$ σ |
| Isocyclocitral | green, earthy, fatty, musty, partly rose: W | | | | | $Flo_nEns_nEar_nLip_nMus_n$ |
| Iso-dinitro-2-methyl tert-butylbenzene $C_{11}H_{16}N_2O_4$ | weak musk: A | | | | | $Mus_n$ |

| | | | | | |
|---|---|---|---|---|---|
| Isoeugenol $C_{10}H_{12}O_2$ | spice, clove type, sweet: FXY | 1.080 (25/4°C) | 194 | | $Spi_n$ α! ψ! |
| Isometheptene $C_9H_{19}N$ | amine-like: XY | .794-.798 (25/25°C) | | | $Ami_n$ |
| Isonicotinic acid, ethyl ester | ester-like: Y | 1.0091 (15/4°C) (liq.) | | | |
| Isonicotinic acid, methyl ester $C_7H_7NO_2$ | slight odor similar to mint or oil of winter-green: Y | | | | $Her_n$ δ |
| Isooctane $C_8H_{18}$ | gasoline: Y | .69194 (20/4°C) | 40.7 | | $Hyc_n$ |
| 2-Isooctylamine $C_8H_{19}N$ | fishy: Y | | | | $Ami_n$ |
| Isooctyl isodecyl phthalate $C_{26}H_{42}O_4$ | mild, character-istic: X | .976 (20/20°C) | | | |
| Isooctyl thioglycolate $C_{10}H_{20}O_2S$ | faint, fruity: PX | .9736 (25°C) | | | $Fru_n$ |
| Isopentaldehyde $C_5H_{10}O$ | sharp: X | .8089 (20/20°C) | | | ψ!! |
| Isopentane $C_5H_{12}$ | pleasant: PX | .61967 (20°C) | -20.2 | | |
| Isopentanoic acid $C_5H_{10}O_2$ | penetrating, goaty: JX | .9388 (20/20°C) | .14 mm Hg (20°C) | .026 | $But_n$ ω! $HU^{3-5}_{4-6}$ |

| Chemical | Reported Characteristics | Specific Gravity | Vapor Pressure | Detection Threshold | Recognition Threshold | Classification Expression, Factors, HU Value |
|---|---|---|---|---|---|---|
| Isopentyl acetate $C_7H_{14}O_2$ | S | | | .0033 | | |
| Isophorone $C_9H_{14}O$ | sharp: J | .9229 (20/20°C) | .2 mm Hg (20°C) | | .54 | $HU^{2-5}_{2-5}$ 16-100 |
| Isopropanolamine $C_3H_9NO$ | slight, ammonia: X | .9619 | | | | $Uro_nNit_n$ |
| Isopropenylchloroformate $C_4ClH_5O_2$ | very irritating: X | 1.103 (20°C) | | | | ε!! |
| 4-(5-Isopropenyl-2-methyl-1-cyclopenten-1-yl)-2-butanone $C_{13}H_{20}O$ | citrus-like, woody background: Y | .9218 (25/25°C) | . | | | $Fru_nWoo_n$ |
| Isopropyl acetate $C_5H_{10}O_2$ | sweet, ester, aromatic, may be irritating to mucous membranes: JPXY | .870 (20/4°C) | 35.7 | | .97 | α λ ψ $HU^{2-5}_{2-4}$ |
| Isopropyl alcohol $C_3H_8O$ | sharp, musty, slight odor resembling a mixture of ethanol and acetone, sweet apple: FJY | .78505 (20/4°C) | 39.5 | | 28.2 | $Fru_nMst_nHyc_n$ α! λ σ! ψ $HU^{2-5}_{3-5}$ 25-100 |
| Isopropylamine $C_3H_9N$ | ammonia, amine: JPXY | .694 (15/4°C) | | | .95 | $Uro_nNit_n$ ψ $HU^{2-5}_{3-5}$ 25-100 |
| 5-Isopropylamino-1-pentanol $C_8H_{19}NO$ | faint, amine: X | | | | | $Ami_n$ |

| | | | | | |
|---|---|---|---|---|---|
| Isopropyl N-(3-chlorophenyl) carbamate $C_{10}ClH_{12}NO_2$ | faint, characteristic: P | 1.18 (30°C) | 2 mm Hg (149°C) | | |
| 1-Isopropylcyclopentanone-2 | minty: A | | | | $He_n$ δ! |
| Isopropyl ether $C_6H_{14}O$ | sweet, ethereal: JPX | .7258 (20/4°C) | 13.7 | .053 | α λ! $HU^{3-4}_{2-3}$ 25-49 |
| p-Isopropylhydratropic aldehyde | green, floral, fatty: W | | | | $Ens_nFlo_nLip_n$ |
| Isopropylisothiocyanate $C_4H_4NS$ | pungent: A | | | | ψ! |
| Isopropyl mercaptan $C_3H_8S$ | extremely powerful, unpleasant: X | .814 (15/15°C) | | | |
| Isopulegol $C_{10}H_{18}O$ | mint-like: FX | .930-.936 | | | $He_n$ δ! ψ! |
| Isopulegone $C_{10}H_{16}O$ | mentholic: F | | | | $Woo_n$ |
| Isopulegyl acetate $C_{12}H_{20}O_2$ | woody, fruity, mint-like, pears: FX | .930-.936 | | | $Woo_nFru_nHe_n$ δ! ψ! |
| Isoquinoline $C_9H_7N$ | pungent, aniseed, aromatic, mixture of anise oil and benzaldehyde: AFMY | 1.09101 (30/4°C) | 167.6 | | $Spi_nNut_n$ ψ! |
| trans-Isosafrole $C_{10}H_{10}O_2$ | fragrant, anise: XY | 1.1206 (20/4°C) | | | $Spi_n$ σ |

| Chemical | Reported Characteristics | Specific Gravity | Vapor Pressure | Detection Threshold | Recognition Threshold | Classification Expression, Factors, HU Value |
|---|---|---|---|---|---|---|
| p-Isothiocyanobenzaldehyde | floral: A | | | | | $Flo_n$ |
| Isovaleraldehyde $C_5H_{10}O$ | pungent, apple-like: PXY | .785 (20/20°C) | | | | $Fru_n$ ψ! |
| Isovaleric acid $C_5H_{10}O_2$ | disagreeable, sour, rancid, cheese: FXY @ | .931 (20/4°C) | 118.9 | | | $Lip_n$ ψ! $HU^{3-5}_{4-5}$ 49-100 |
| Isovaleric acid diethylamide $C_{10}H_{19}NO_3$ | minty: A | | | | | $He_n$ δ! |
| Isovalerylazide | pungent: A | | | | | ψ! |
| Isovaleryl diethylamide $C_9H_{19}NO$ | aromatic, characteristic: XY | | | | | |
| Itaconic acid $C_5H_6O_4$ | characteristic (Y); odorless (X) | 1.63 | | | | |
| Jalop resin | slight: X | | | | | |
| Japan wax | tallow-like, rancid: XY | .970-.980 | | | | $Lip_n$ |
| Jasmone $C_{11}H_{16}O$ | floral, green, jasmine: FXY | .944 (22/0°C) | | | | $Flo_nEns_n$ |
| Kaolin | clay odor when moistened: X | 1.8-2.6 | | | | $Ear_n$ |
| Kerosene | characteristic, not disagreeable: Y | | | | | $Hyc_n$ μ σ |

| | | | | |
|---|---|---|---|---|
| Ketene $C_2H_2O$ | penetrating, very irritating, pungent: AXY | | | ε!! ψ! ω! |
| δ-Lactone $C_{11}H_{20}O_2$ | new mown hay: M | | | $Woo_nEns_n$ |
| Lactucarium-"French" | opium-like: Y | | | |
| Lanolin | slight: XY | | | |
| LANTHANUM La | no reported odor | 6.15 (20°C) | | |
| LANTHANUM COMPOUNDS | no reported odors | | | |
| Lard | faint, characteristic: XY | .917 | | $Lip_n$ |
| Lard oil | peculiar: X | .905-.915 | | $Lip_n$ |
| Lauric acid $C_{12}H_{24}O_2$ | bay oil: Y | .869 (5/4°C) | 227.5 | $Her_n$ |
| Lauroyl peroxide $C_{24}H_{46}O_4$ | faint: X | | | |
| Lauryl alcohol $C_{12}H_{26}O$ | floral, fatty, slightly orange: FX | .830-.836 | 192 | $Flo_nLip_nFru_n$ |
| Lauryl aldehyde $C_{12}H_{24}O$ | strong, fatty, waxy, floral, musty, fruity: CFX | .828-.836 | 184.5 | $Mus_nLip_nFlo_nHyc_n$ σ ψ! |
| Lauryl bromide $BrC_{12}H_{25}$ | coconut: Y | 1.026 (25/25°C) | | $Nut_n$ |
| Lauryl formate $C_{13}H_{27}O_2$ | musty, ester: C | | | $Mus_n$ ψ! |

| Chemical | Reported Characteristics | Specific Gravity | Vapor Pressure | Detection Threshold | Recognition Threshold | Classification Expression, Factors, HU Value |
|---|---|---|---|---|---|---|
| Lauryl mercaptan $C_{12}H_{26}S$ | mild, catty, characteristic: X | .85 (20/20°C) | | | | $Mus_n Uro_n$ |
| LEAD Pb | no reported odor | 11.337 (20/20°C) | 1421 | | | |
| Lead acetate $C_4H_{12}O_7Pb$ | slight, acetate: Y | 3.251 (20/4°C) | 2.55 | | | $Fru_n$ |
| Lecithin $C_{42}H_{84}NO_9P$ | characteristic: X | | | | | |
| Lenthionine $C_2H_4S_5$ | odorous principle from mushroom (Shiitake Lentinus edodes): Y | | | | | $Mo_n$ |
| Lepidine $C_{10}H_9N$ | quinoline-like: XY | 1.0826 (20/4°C) | | | | ν |
| Lidocaine $C_{14}H_{22}N_2O$ | characteristic: X | | | | | |
| Lime, sulfurated | hydrogen sulfide: X | | | | | $Sul_n$ β ψ! ω |
| dl-Limonene $C_{10}H_{16}$ | orange, lemon, caraway, pleasant: FY | .8402 (20.85/4°C) | 108.3 | | | $Fru_n Her_n$ |
| Linalool $C_{10}H_{18}O$ | bergamot-French lavender, sweet, woody, citrus, floral: FXY | .858-.868 (25°C) | | | | $Flo_n Her_n Woo_n Fru_n$ α |
| Linalyl acetate $C_{12}H_{20}O_2$ | bergamot, citrus, lavender, woody: CFXY | .895 (20/4°C) | 151.8 | | | $Her_n Woo_n Fru_n Flo_n$ σ |

| | | | | |
|---|---|---|---|---|
| Linalyl anthranilate $C_{17}H_{24}NO_2$ | lychee-orange: C | | | $A_nFru_nFlo_n$ σ ψ! |
| Linalyl benzoate $C_{16}H_{19}O_2$ | floral, canaga, minty: CF | | | $Flo_nHe_n$ δ! σ ψ! |
| Linalyl butyrate $C_{14}H_{24}O_2$ | sweet, honey: F | | | $Car_nWoo_nFru_nFlo_n$ α! σ ψ! |
| Linalyl cinnamate $C_{19}H_{24}O_2$ | spicy, lily, jasmine-like: C | | | $Spi_nFlo_n$ ψ! |
| Linalyl formate $C_{11}H_{18}O_2$ | pineapple, fruity, fatty: CF | .915 (25/4°C) | | $Lip_nFru_n$ σ ψ!! |
| Linalyl methyl anthranilate | fruity, floral: C | | | $Fru_nFlo_n$ σ! ψ! |
| Linalyl propionate $C_{13}H_{22}O_2$ | sweet, floral, black current, similar to bergamot oil: FX | .895-.902 (25°C) | | $Woo_nFru_nFlo_nHer_n$ α! ψ! |
| α-Lindane $C_6Cl_6H_6$ | persistent, acrid: Y | | .06 mm Hg (40°C) | |
| γ-Lindane $C_6Cl_6H_6$ | slight, musty: Y | | .14 mm Hg (40°C) | $Mst_n$ |
| Linoleic acid aluminum salt $AlC_{36}H_{58}O_6$ | linseed oil: Y | | | $He_n$ |
| Linseed oil | peculiar, becomes more and more pronounced when exposed to air: Y | .925-.935 | | $He_n$ |

| Chemical | Reported Characteristics | Specific Gravity | Vapor Pressure | Detection Threshold | Recognition Threshold | Classification Expression, Factors, HU Value |
|---|---|---|---|---|---|---|
| LITHIUM Li | no reported odor | .534 (20°C) | 1097 | | | |
| Lithium amide $H_2LiN$ | ammonia-like: X | 1.178 | | | | $Uro_nNit_n$ ψ |
| Lithium silicon | sharp, irritating: X | | | | | ε ψ! |
| LUTETIUM Lu | no reported odor | 9.849 | | | | |
| LUTETIUM COMPOUNDS | no reported odors | | | | | |
| 2,6-Lutidine $C_7H_9N$ | pyridine and peppermint: XY | .92519 (20/4°C) | | | | $Hyc_nOxy_nHe_n$ β δ ν σ ω |
| Lysidine $C_4H_3N_2$ | mousy: X | | | | | $Uro_nBut_nMus_n$ |
| MAGNESIUM Mg | no reported odor | 1.738 | 909 | | | |
| Magnesium acetate $C_4H_6MgO_4$ | acetic acid: X | 1.45 | | | | φ!! ψ!! |
| Magnesium ricinoleate $C_{36}H_{65}O_6$ | faint, fatty, acid: X | 1.03 (25/25°C) | | | | $Lip_n$ |
| Malathion $C_{10}H_{19}O_6PS_2$ | characteristic: Y | 1.23 (25/4°C) | | | | β ψ |
| Maleic acid $C_4H_4O_4$ | faint, acidulous: PXY | 1.59 | | | | ψ |

| | | | | |
|---|---|---|---|---|
| Maltol $C_6H_6O_3$ | fragrant, carmel-like, sweet, freshly baked, suggestive of a fruity, strawberry aroma in dilute solution: FXY | | | $\theta^2$: $Seb_nCar_nFur_n$ α σ!! <br> $\theta_1$: $Fru_n$ |
| Mandelic acid $C_8H_8O_3$ | faint: X | 1.30 | | |
| MANGANESE Mn | no reported odor | 7.2 | 1792 | |
| MANGANESE COMPOUNDS | no reported odors | | | |
| Mastic gum | slightly balsamic: XY | | | $Bal_n$ |
| Mechlorethamine $C_5Cl_2H_{11}N$ | faint, herring, irritant: Y | 1.118 (25/4°C) | | $Ami_n$ ε ψ |
| Menadiol sodium diphosphate $C_{11}H_8Na_4O_8P_2 \cdot 6H_2O$ | characteristic: X | | | |
| Menadione $C_{11}H_8O_2$ | nearly odorless (X); very faint, acrid, irritating (Y) | | | ψ |
| $\Delta^{1:8(9)}$-o-menthadiene $C_{10}H_{16}$ | lemon, pine wood: A | | | $Fru_nWoo_nHyc_n$ |
| $\Delta^{3:8(9)}$-p-menthadiene $C_{10}H_{16}$ | strong, lemon: A | | | $Fru_n$ ψ! |
| Menthanediamine $C_{10}H_{22}N_2$ | characteristic, terpine: X | | | $Woo_nHyc_n$ |

| Chemical | Reported Characteristics | Specific Gravity | Vapor Pressure | Detection Threshold | Recognition Threshold | Classification Expression, Factors, HU Value |
|---|---|---|---|---|---|---|
| cis-p-Menthanol-8 $C_{10}H_{21}O$ | minty: A | | | | | $He_n$ δ! |
| trans-p-Menthanol-8 $C_{10}H_{21}O$ | minty (stronger than cis-isomer): A | | | | | $He_n$ δ!! |
| $\Delta^1$-o-Menthene $C_{10}H_{18}$ | faint, minty: A | | | | | $He_n$ δ |
| $\Delta^{8(9)}$-o-Menthene $C_{10}H_{18}$ | faint, minty: A | | | | | $He_n$ δ |
| $\Delta^{8(9)}$-p-Menthene $C_{10}H_{18}$ | mainly parsly at first, then lemon: A | | | | | $Ens_nFru_n$ |
| $\Delta^1$-o-Menthenol-8 $C_{10}H_{18}O$ | minty, turpineol: A | | | | | $He_nWoo_n$ δ! |
| 1-Menthol $C_{10}H_{20}O$ | peppermint, cool, strong mint (stronger than d-form): AFPXY @ | .890 (15/15°C) | 149.4 | | | $He_n$ δ!!! ψ |
| d-Menthol $C_{10}H_{20}O$ | minty: A | | | | | $He_n$ δ! |
| Menthol valerate $C_{15}H_{28}O_2$ | mild, pleasant: X | .907 (15/4°C) | | | | |
| 1-Menthone $C_{10}H_{18}O$ | slight peppermint, bittersweet, minty: AFXY | .895 (20/4°C) | | | | $He_n$ α δ ν |
| Menthylacetaldehyde $C_{12}H_{23}O$ | minty: A | | | | | $He_n$ δ! |

| | | | | |
|---|---|---|---|---|
| Menthyl acetate $C_{12}H_{22}O_2$ | characteristic, menthol-like: XY | .919 (20/4°C) | 156.7 | $Woo_n$ |
| Menthyl borate $BC_{30}H_{57}O_3$ | faint borate: Y | | | $Woo_n$ |
| Menthyl-sec-butyl ketone $C_{15}H_{24}O$ | minty: A | | | $He_n$ δ! |
| Menthyl ethoxyacetate $C_{14}H_{26}O_3$ | faint menthol (Y); odorless, less irritating than menthol (X) | | | $Woo_n$ ψ |
| Menthyl salicylate $C_{17}H_{24}O_3$ | slightly fruity: Y | 1.045 (25/25°C) | | $Fru_n$ |
| Menthyl valerate $C_{15}H_{28}O_2$ | menthol and valerian: Y | .906-.908 | | $Woo_n$ |
| Meparfynol $C_6H_{10}O$ | acrid: Y | .8688 (20/4°C) | | ψ! |
| Mephentermine $C_{11}H_{17}N$ | fishy, amine: XY | | | $Ami_n$ |
| Meprobamate $C_9H_{18}N_2O_4$ | characteristic: X | | | |
| 2-Mercaptobenzothiazole $C_7H_5NS_2$ | disagreeable (Y); slight (depends on degree of purification) (X) | 1.42 | | |
| Mercaptoethanol $C_2H_6OS$ | characteristic: X | 1.1168 (20/20°C) | 1 mm Hg 20°C | |
| Mercuric acetate $C_4H_6HgO_4$ | slight acetic: Y | 3.270 | | ψ |

| Chemical | Reported Characteristics | Specific Gravity | Vapor Pressure | Detection Threshold | Recognition Threshold | Classification Expression, Factors, HU Value |
|---|---|---|---|---|---|---|
| Mercuric nitrate $HgN_2O_6 \cdot H_2O$ | nitric acid: Y | 4.3 | | | | $Nit_n$ $\phi$!!! $\psi$!! |
| Mercuric oleate $C_{36}H_{66}HgO_4$ | oleic acid: Y | | | | | $Lip_n$ |
| Mercurous nitrate $HgNO_3 \cdot H_2O$ | slight odor of nitric acid: Y | 4.78 | | | | $Nit_n$ |
| MERCURY Hg | no reported odor | 13.5939 (20/4°C) | 261.7 | | | |
| Mesitylene $C_9H_{12}$ | peculiar: Y | .8637 (20/4°C) | 98.9 | | | |
| 2,4,6-Mesityliso-thiocyanate $C_{10}H_{14}NS$ | floral, spirea-like: M | | | | | $Flo_n$ |
| Mesityl oxide $C_6H_{10}O$ | sweet, honey-like: JXY | .8592 (25/4°C) | 72.1 | | .051 | $Car_n$ $\alpha$ $HU^{2-3}_{2-3}$ 25-36 |
| Mesityl thiocarba-mide $C_{10}H_{14}NS$ | very floral: M | | | | | $Flo_n$ |
| Mesotan $C_9H_{10}O$ | faintly aromatic: Y | 1.2 (15°C) | | | | |
| Metaldehyde $(C_2H_4O)_n$ | refreshing, tonic: | | | | | |
| Metcaraphen $C_{20}H_{31}NO_2$ | faint, amine: Y | | | | | $Ami_n$ |
| Methacholine bromide $BrC_8H_{18}NO_2$ | slight fishy: X | | | | | $Ami_n$ |

| | | | | | |
|---|---|---|---|---|---|
| Methacholine chloride $C_8ClH_{18}NO_2$ | odorless or slight odor of dead fish: XY | | | | $Ami_n$ |
| Methacrylic acid $C_4H_6O_2$ | acrid, repulsive: Y | 1.0153 (20/4°C) | 106.6 | | β! ψ! |
| Methallyl chloride $C_4ClH_7$ | disagreeable: P | | | | |
| β-Methallyl chloride $C_4ClH_7$ | sharp, penetrating: X | .925 (20°C) | | | ψ! ω! |
| Metham sodium dihydrate $C_2H_4NNaS_2 \cdot 2H_2O$ | unpleasant, similar to carbon disulfide: Y | | | | λ! β |
| Methanol $CH_4O$ | sour, sharp, slight alcoholic, crude form may be repulsive, pungent: JY | .8665 (20/4°C) | | 53.3 | $\theta^2$: β! ψ! (crude)<br>$\theta_1$: $Hyc_n$<br>$HU^{2-5}_{3-6}$ 25-121 |
| Methanyl N-butyrate | pungent, musty, fatty: C | | | | $Mus_nLip_n$ σ ψ!! |
| Methapyrilene fumarate $C_{28}H_{38}N_6S_2 \cdot C_{12}H_{12}O_{12}$ | faint, aromatic: X | | | | |
| Metharbital $C_9H_{14}N_2O_3$ | faint, aromatic: X | | | | |
| Methitural $C_{12}H_{19}N_2NaO_2S_2$ | slight, mercaptans: Y | | | | $Mus_nSul_nNit_n$ σ |
| p-Methoxyacetophenone $C_9H_{10}O_2$ | pleasant, sharp, hay-like, fine floral, musty: CDFX | | | | $Mst_nEns_nFlo_n$ σ ψ! |

| Chemical | Reported Characteristics | Specific Gravity | Vapor Pressure | Detection Threshold | Recognition Threshold | Classification Expression, Factors, HU Value |
|---|---|---|---|---|---|---|
| Methoxyamine $CH_5NO$ | fishy, amine: Y | | | | | $Ami_n$ |
| 2-Methoxy-5-chlorophenylisothiocyanate $C_8ClH_8NOS$ | faint, floral: AD | | | | | $Flo_n$ |
| 3-Methoxy-4-chlorophenylisothiocyanate $C_8ClH_8NOS$ | anise, spirea: D | | | | | $Her_n$ |
| 3-Methoxy-5-chlorophenylisothiocyanate $C_8ClH_8NOS$ | geranium, slightly pungent: D | | | | | $Flo_n$ $\psi$ |
| Methoxyethyl oleate $C_{21}H_{40}O_3$ | mild: X | .898 (25°C) | | | | |
| Methoxyethyl stearate $C_{21}H_{42}O_3$ | mild: X | | | | | |
| p-Methoxyphenylisothiocyanate $C_7H_8NOS$ | very pronounced aniseed: AD | | | | | $Her_n$ |
| Methoxytriglycol acetate $C_9H_{18}O_5$ | pleasant, fruity: X | 1.0940 (20/20°C) | | | | |
| Methyl acetate $C_3H_6O_2$ | fragrant, pleasant, sweet, ethereal, fruity: AFXY | .928 (20/4°C) | 9.4 | | | $Fru_n$ $\alpha!$ $\lambda!$ |

| | | | | | |
|---|---|---|---|---|---|
| Methyl acetophenone $C_9H_{10}O$ | fragrant, coumarin, slight musty: CX | 1.001-1.004 | | | $Mst_nFlo_nBal_nEns_n$ σ ψ |
| Methyl acetyl-ricinoleate $C_{21}H_{38}O_4$ | mild: X | .938 (25/25°C) | | | |
| Methyl acrylate (monomer) $C_4H_6O_2$ | acrid, lachrymator: Y | .9561 (20/4°C) | 28 | | ε! ψ |
| Methylal $C_3H_8O_2$ | chloroform, pungent: PXY | .8593 (20/4°C) | | | α λ ψ |
| Methylallyl alcohol $C_4H_8O$ | pungent: X | .8515 (20/4°C) | | | ψ |
| Methylamine $CH_5N$ | strong, putrid, ammoniacal, boiled lobsters: AMPX | .699 (-10.8/4°C) | -56.9 | .021 | $Uro_nNit_n$ β ψ! $HU^{3-5}_{4-6}$ 49-121 |
| Methylamino-dimethylacetal $C_5H_{13}NO_2$ | sharp, ammoniacal: X | .924 (25/25°C) | | | $Uro_nNit_n$ ψ! |
| 2-Methylamino-ethanol $C_3H_9NO$ | fishy: Y | .937 (20°C) | | | $Ami_n$ |
| Methyl amyl acetate $C_8H_{16}O_2$ | sweet, ester, mild, agreeable, pleasant: JPX | .8595 (20/20°C) | | .40 | $HU^{2-3}_{3}$ 25-36 |
| Methyl amyl alcohol $C_6H_{14}O$ | sweet, alcohol: J | .8079 (20/20°C) | 3.8 mm Hg (20°C) | .52 | $HU^{2-3}_{2-3}$ 16-36 |
| Methyl-n-amyl carbinol $C_7H_{16}O$ | mild: X | .8187 (20/20°C) | 1 mm Hg (20°C) | | |

| Chemical | Reported Characteristics | Specific Gravity | Vapor Pressure | Detection Threshold | Recognition Threshold | Classification Expression, Factors, HU Value |
|---|---|---|---|---|---|---|
| 3-Methylandrostan-3α-ol | musky: A | | | | | $Mus_n$ |
| 3-Methylandrostan-3β-ol | musky: A | | | | | $Mus_n$ |
| 17-Methylandrostan-3α-ol | musky: A | | | | | $Mus_n$ |
| 17-Methylandrostan-3β-ol | musky: A | | | | | $Mus_n$ |
| 17-Methylandrostan-3-one | cedar: A | | | | | $Woo_n$ |
| α-Methylanisalacetone $C_{12}H_{14}O_2$ | sharp, dry: X | | | | | $\psi$ |
| p-Methylanisole $C_8H_{10}O$ | strong, floral, suggestive of ylang-ylang: X | .966-.970 | | | | $Flo_n$ |
| Methyl anthranilate $C_8H_9NO_2$ | grape-type, floral, orange neroli, jasmine, orange blossom: ACFX | 1.168 | 187.8 | .059 | | $Flo_nFru_n$ $\sigma$ $HU^{2-3}_{1-2}$ 9-25 |
| Methylazide $CH_3N_3$ | somewhat ethereal: A | | | | | $\lambda$ |
| Methyl benzoate $C_8H_8O_2$ | pleasant, floral, fragrant, harsh, bitter, strawberry, musty: ACFPXY | 1.094 (15/4°C) | 130.8 | | | $Mst_nFlo_nFru_n$ $\nu$ $\sigma!$ $\psi$ |

| | | | | |
|---|---|---|---|---|
| α-Methyl benzyl acetate $C_8H_{11}N$ | plum, very strong, suggesting gardenia: FX | 1.023-1.026 (25/25°C) | | $Fru_nFlo_n$ |
| α-Methyl benzyl alcohol $C_8H_{10}O$ | mild, hyacinth-gardenia, floral, benzophenone, sweet hay: CFX | 1.009-1.014 (25°C) | 140.3 | $Flo_nEns_n$ α |
| α-Methyl benzyl-amine $C_8H_{11}N$ | mild, ammoniacal, aromatic: XY | .9395 (15/4°C) | .5 mm Hg (20°C) | $Uro_nNit_n$ |
| α-Methyl benzyl-diethanolamine $C_{12}H_{15}NO_2$ | ammonia-like: X | 1.0812 (20°C) | | $Uro_nNit_n$ ψ |
| α-Methyl benzyl ether $C_{16}H_{18}O$ | faint: X | 1.0017 (20/20°C) | | |
| Methyl bromide $BrCH_3$ | ethereal, usually odorless, chloro-form-like at high concentrations: AM PXY | 1.730 (0/4°C) | -39.4 | $\theta^2$: $Hal_nHyc_n$ α λ<br>$\theta_1$: $Hal_nHyc_n$ |
| 2-Methyl-6-bromo-benzothiazole $BrC_8H_8NS$ | floral, tea-rose, geranium: AM | | | $Her_nFlo_n$ |
| 2-Methyl-1-butene $C_5H_{10}$ | disagreeable: X | .650 (20/20°C) | -28 | |
| 3-Methyl-1-butene $C_5H_{10}$ | disagreeable: X | .6272 (20°C) | -9.9 | |
| 1-Methyl-2-butenyl-2-methyl butyrate | green, fruity, earth-like: W | | | $Lip_nEar_nFru_nEns_n$ |

| Chemical | Reported Characteristics | Specific Gravity | Vapor Pressure | Detection Threshold | Recognition Threshold | Classification Expression, Factors, HU Value |
|---|---|---|---|---|---|---|
| Methyl butyl ketone $C_6H_{12}O$ | minty, camphor, peppermint, may be irritating: AY | .830 (20/20°C) | 79.8 | | | $Woo_nHe_n$ δ! ε |
| 2-Methyl-4-tert-butylthiophenol $C_{11}H_{16}S$ | non-mercaptan odor: X | .983 (25°C) | | | | |
| Methylbutynol $C_5H_8O$ | fragrant: X | .8672 (20/20°C) | | | | |
| Methyl butyrate $C_5H_{10}O_2$ | sweet, apple: F | .898 (20/4°C) | 48 | | | $Fru_n$ α |
| Methyl carbonate $C_3H_6O_3$ | pleasant: X | 1.065 (17/4°C) | | | | |
| Methyl chloride $CClH_3$ | ethereal, faintly sweet: AMXY | 1.00 (23.7/4°C) (liq.) | -63 | | 10 | $Hal_nHyc_n$ α λ $HU^{1-2}_{2-3}$ 9-25 |
| Methyl chloroformate $C_2ClH_3O_2$ | military poison gas, lachrymator, may be strongly irritating to skin, eyes, mucous membranes: XY | 1.23 (15°C) | | | | $Hal_n$ ε!!! ψ! ω |
| 3-Methyl-4-chlorophenylisothiocyanate $C_8ClH_8NS$ | pungent: D | | | | | $Hal_nNit_nSul_n$ ψ! |
| 4-Methyl-3-chlorophenylisothiocyanate $C_8ClH_8NS$ | pungent, anise: D | | | | | $Her_n$ α ψ! |

| | | | | |
|---|---|---|---|---|
| Methyl chlorosulfonate $CClH_3O_3S$ | pungent, very irritant: PX | 1.492 (10°C) | | $Hal_nSul_n$ ε!! ψ! |
| Methyl cinnamate $C_{10}H_{10}O_2$ | strawberry-like, fruity, sweet, spicy, musty: CFX | 1.0415 | 185.8 | $Mus_nSpi_nFru_n$ α! σ ψ |
| Methyl cinnamic aldehyde $C_{10}H_{10}O$ | characteristic, cinnamon-like: X | 1.6025-1.6070 (20°C) | | $Spi_n$ γ |
| 3-Methyl coumarin $C_{10}H_8O_2$ | like coumarin, heavier: C | | | $Flo_nBal_nEns_n$ |
| Methyl cyanoformate $C_3H_3NO_2$ | ethereal: PX | | | $Hyc_nNit_n$ λ! |
| Methylcyclohexanol $C_7H_{14}O$ | aromatic, menthol-like: PX | | | $Woo_n$ δ! |
| 1-Methylcyclohexanol-1 $C_7H_{14}O$ | camphor: A | | | $Woo_n$ |
| Methylcyclohexanol acetate $C_9H_{16}O_2$ | ester-like: X | .941 | | |
| Methylcyclohexanone $C_7H_{12}O$ | acetone-like: X | .925 | | $He_n$ δ |
| 1-Methylcyclohexanone-2 $C_7H_{12}O$ | minty, weak: A | | | $He_n$ δ |
| 1-Methylcyclohexanone-4 $C_7H_{12}O$ | minty: A | | | $He_n$ δ |
| Methyl cyclohexyl carbinol | camphor: A | | | $Woo_n$ |

| Chemical | Reported Characteristics | Specific Gravity | Vapor Pressure | Detection Threshold | Recognition Threshold | Classification Expression, Factors, HU Value |
|---|---|---|---|---|---|---|
| Methyl cyclohexyl ketone $C_8H_{13}O$ | strong camphor: A | | | | | $Woo_n$ |
| 1-Methylcyclopentadecan-2-one $C_{16}H_{30}O$ | weak, musky: AM | | | | | $Mus_n$ |
| Methylcyclopentanone-2 $C_8H_{14}O$ | minty: A | | | | | $He_n$ δ |
| Methylcyclopentenol-2-one-3 $C_7H_{11}O$ | @ | | | | | |
| Methyl cyclopenten (1)-yl ketone $C_7H_9O$ | almond: A | | | | | $Nut_n$ |
| Methyl cyclopropyl ketone $C_5H_8O$ | strong camphor: A @ | | | | | |
| Methyldichloroacetate $C_3Cl_2H_4O_2$ | ethereal, military poison gas: P | 1.3759-1.3839 (20/20°C) | 85.4 | | | $Hal_n$ λ! |
| Methyldichloroarsine $AsCCl_2H_3$ | agreeable, very irritant, military poison gas: X | | | | | ε!! |
| Methyl dichlorostearate $C_{19}Cl_2H_{35}O_2$ | slight fatty: X | .997 (15.5/15.5°C) | | | | $Lip_nHal_n$ |

| | | | | | | |
|---|---|---|---|---|---|---|
| Methyldiethanolamine $C_5H_{13}NO_2$ | amine-like: X | 1.0418 (20°C) | | | | $Ami_n$ |
| Methyl-2,4-dimethylphenyl ketone $C_{10}H_{10}O$ | minty: A | | | | | $He_n$ δ! |
| Methyl α,β-dimethyl propyl ketone $C_6H_{12}O$ | strong, minty: A | | | | | $He_n$ δ!! |
| Methyl diiodoacetate $C_3H_3I_2O_2$ | pungent: A | | | | | ψ |
| Methyleneandrostan-3-one | cedar: A | | | | | $Woo_n$ |
| Methylene chloride $CCl_2H_2$ | penetrating, ether-like (poisonous when inhaled): AMX | 1.335 (15/4°C) | -6.3 | | 214 | $Hal_n$ α γ λ ω $HU^{4-6}_{5-6}$ 81-144 |
| Methylene glycol $CH_4O_2$ | | | | | | |
| Methylethanolamine $C_3H_9NO$ | musty, ammoniacal: J | .9414 | .7 mm Hg (20°C) | | 3.4 | $HU^{2-6}_{3-5}$ 25-121 |
| Methyl ether $C_2H_6O$ | ethereal: Y | 1.617 (air=1) | -62.7 | | | λ! |
| 1-Methyl-4-ethylcyclohexanone $C_9H_{17}O$ | minty: A | | | | | $Her_n$ δ |
| Methyl ethyl ketone $C_4H_8O$ | acetone-like, sharp, sweet: JXY | .805 (20/4°C) | 25 | | 6 | $Hyc_nHe_n$ α δ λ $HU^{2-4}_{3-4}$ 25-81 |

| Chemical | Reported Characteristics | Specific Gravity | Vapor Pressure | Detection Threshold | Recognition Threshold | Classification Expression, Factors, HU Value |
|---|---|---|---|---|---|---|
| 2-Methyl-5-ethyl-pyridine $C_8H_{11}N$ | sharp, penetrating, sour, pungent: JX | .921 (20/20°C) | | | .01 | $HU^{4-5}_{5-6}$ 81-121 |
| Methyl eugenol $C_{11}H_{14}O_2$ | fatty, spicy, musty: C | 1.032-1.036 (25°C) | 183.7 | | | $Lip_nMus_nSpi_n$ σ |
| Methyl fluorosulfonate $CFH_3O_3S$ | ethereal: P | | | | | $Hal_nSul_n$ α λ ω |
| Methyl formate $C_2H_4O_2$ | agreeable, ethereal: APXY | .987 (15/15°C) | -12.9 | | | $Hyc_n$ α λ |
| 2-Methylfuran $C_5H_6O$ | ether-like: PX | .913 (20/4°C) | | | | $Hyc_n$ λ ω |
| Methyl furfural $C_6H_6O_2$ | coffee: F | | | | | $Fur_n$ σ!! |
| Methyl 2-furoate $C_6H_6O_3$ | coffee, pleasant: FX | 1.1739 (15/15°C) | | | | $Seb_nFur_n$ α σ!! |
| α-Methyl-β-furyl acrolein $C_8H_{10}O_2$ | musty, honey-like: C | | | | | $Car_nMus_n$ σ ψ |
| Methyl heptine carbonate $C_9H_{14}O_2$ | green, grassy, extremely strong, violet type: CFX | .919-.923 | | | | $A_nFlo_nEns_n$ σ! ψ! |
| Methyl heptine carboxylate | floral: A | | | | | $Flo_n$ |

| | | | | | |
|---|---|---|---|---|---|
| 1-Methylhexahydro-acetophenone | strong, camphor: A | | | | $Woo_n$ |
| trans-2-Methylhexa-hydrobenzaldehyde | minty: A | | | | $Her_n$ δ |
| Methylhexylacetal-dehyde | floral: A | | | | $Flo_n$ |
| 4-Methyl-2-hexylamine $C_7H_{17}N$ | amine: X | .762-.765 | | | $Ami_n$ ψ |
| Methylhydrazine $CH_6N_2$ | ammonia-like: X | .874 (25°C) | | | $Nit_nHyc_n$ ψ!! |
| Methylhydroxybu-tanone $C_5H_{10}O_2$ | sweet, camphor-like: X | .9553 (20/20°C) | | | $Woo_n$ α |
| Methyl iodide $CH_3I$ | sweet, ethereal: M | 2.28 (20/4°C) | -7.0 | | $Hal_nHyc_n$ α! λ |
| Methyl iodoacetate $C_3H_6IO_2$ | pungent: A | | | | $Hal_nHyc_n$ ψ!! |
| Methyl isoamyl ketone $C_7H_{14}O$ | pleasant, sweet, sharp: JX | .8132 (20/20°C) | | .07 | $HU_2^{3-4}$ 25-36 |
| Methyl isobutyl carbinol $C_6H_{14}O$ | pleasant: P | .8079 (20/20°C) | 78.0 | | |
| Methyl isobutyl ketone $C_6H_{12}O$ | sweet, faint, sharp, ketonic, camphor, pleasant: AJXY | .8042 (20/20°C) | 70.4 | .28 | $Woo_nHyc_n$ α λ ψ $HU_{2-3}^{2-3}$ 16-36 |

| Chemical | Reported Characteristics | Specific Gravity | Vapor Pressure | Detection Threshold | Recognition Threshold | Classification Expression, Factors, HU Value |
|---|---|---|---|---|---|---|
| Methyl isocyanate $C_2H_3NO$ | pungent: A | .9599 (20/20°C) | | | | ψ! |
| Methyl isocyanide $C_2H_3N$ | pungent: A | | | | | ψ! |
| Methyl isonicotinate $C_7H_7NO_2$ | mild: X | 1.15 (20/20°C) | | | | |
| p-Methylisopropenyl benzene $C_{10}H_{12}O$ | lemon when hot: A | | | | | $Fru_n$ ψ |
| Methyl isopropenyl ketone $C_5H_8O$ | pleasant: X | .854 (20°C) | | | | |
| 2-Methyl-5-isopropylhexahydrobenzaldehyde | floral when dilute: A | | | | | $Flo_n$ |
| Methyl isothiocyanate $C_2H_3NS$ | pungent, horse-radish: A | | 59.3 | | | $All_nNit_n$ γ ψ!! |
| Methyl isovalerate $C_6H_{12}O_2$ | valerian: Y | .881 (20/4°C) | 59.8 | | | |
| Methyl malonate $C_5H_8O_4$ | ethereal: A | 1.154 (20/4°C) | 121.9 | | | λ! |
| 2-Methylmenthene $C_{10}H_{17}$ | camphor: A | | | | | $Woo_n$ |
| Methyl mercaptan $CH_4S$ | putrid, rotten cabbage, powerful, unpleasant, penetrating, rubbery: AFXY @ | .87 (20°C) | -34.8 | | .0021 | $Sul_nHyc_n$ $HU^{4-6}_{4-6}$ 81-144 |

| | | | | | |
|---|---|---|---|---|---|
| Methyl methacrylate $C_5H_8O_2$ | sweet, sharp: J | .940 (25/25°C) | | .3 | $HU^{2-5}_{3-5}$ 25-100 |
| Methyl α-methyl-butyl ketone $C_7H_{12}O$ | minty: A | | | | $He_n$ δ! |
| Methyl-2-methyl-cyclopenten (1)-yl(1) ketone | minty: A | | | | $He_n$ δ! |
| Methyl morpholine $C_5H_{11}NO$ | ammonia: X | .921 (20/20°C) | | | $Uro_nNit_n$ ψ |
| Methylnaphthyldo-decyldimethylammo-nium chloride $C_{26}ClH_{39}N$ | mild: X | | | | |
| Methyl β-naphthyl ketone $C_{12}H_{19}O$ | orange blossom, musty: CX | | 229.8 | | $Mus_nFlo_nFru_n$ |
| Methyl nicotinate $C_7H_7NO_2$ | mild, pleasant: X | | | | |
| Methyl nitrate $CH_3NO_3$ | pleasant, ester: M | 1.2075 (20/4°C) | | | |
| Methyl nitrite $CH_3NO_2$ | powerful, oppres-sive: M | | | | |
| Methyl nonanal $C_{10}H_{20}O$ | sweet, spicy, citrus: F | | | | $Spi_nFru_n$ α |
| Methyl nonanoate $C_{10}H_{20}O_2$ | fruity: X | .877 (18°C) | | | $Fru_n$ |

| Chemical | Reported Characteristics | Specific Gravity | Vapor Pressure | Detection Threshold | Recognition Threshold | Classification Expression, Factors, HU Value |
|---|---|---|---|---|---|---|
| Methyl 2-nonenoate $C_{10}H_{18}O_2$ | strong, violet leaf: X | .893-.898 (25°C) | | | | $Flo_nEns_n$ |
| Methylnonylacetaldehyde $C_{12}H_{24}O$ | fatty orange character: X | .824-.828 | | | | $Lip_nFru_n$ |
| Methyl nonyl ketone $C_{11}H_{22}O$ | strong, rue: MX | .822-.826 | 161.0 | | | |
| Methyl octine carbonate $C_{10}H_{16}O_2$ | sweet, peach, acid: A | | | | | $Fru_n$ α! ψ! |
| Methyl oleate $C_{19}H_{36}O_2$ | faint, fatty: X | .8739 (20°C) | | | | $Lip_n$ |
| Methylol riboflavin $CH_2O_2$ | slight formaldehyde (Y); nearly odorless (X) | | | | | ϕ ψ |
| Methyl paraben $C_8H_8O_3$ | faint, characteristic: X | | | | | |
| 2-Methylpentaldehyde $C_6H_{12}O$ | sweet, rancid: J | .8092 | | | .136 | $HU^{2-3}_{4-5}$ 36-64 |
| 2-Methyl-1,3-pentanediol $C_6H_{14}O_2$ | musty, fatty, aldehyde: C | .9745 | | | | $Mus_nLip_n$ γ ψ! |
| 2-Methyl-1-pentanol $C_6H_{14}O$ | sweet, alcohol: J | .8252 | 1.1 mm Hg (20°C) | | .082 | $HU^{2-3}_{2-3}$ 16-36 |

| | | | | |
|---|---|---|---|---|
| 2-Methyl-2-pentyl-1,3-dioxolane-4-methanol $C_{10}H_{20}O_3$ | fruity: Y | .983 (21°C) | | $Fru_n$ |
| Methyl phenylacetate $C_9H_{10}O_2$ | fine, honey-like, sharp, sweet rose: CFX | 1.062-1.066 (25°C) | | $Car_nFlo_n$ α! ψ! |
| Methylphosphinic acid bisdiethylamide | aromatic: A | | | |
| Methyl phthalyl ethyl glycolate $C_{13}H_{14}O_6$ | slight, characteristic: X | 1.217-1.227 | | |
| 2-Methyl piperazine $C_5H_{12}N_2$ | typical amine-like: P | .8401 (20/20°C) | | $Ami_n$ |
| 1-Methyl-4-piperidinol $C_6H_{13}NO$ | characteristic, amine-like: X | | | $Ami_n$ |
| p-(2-Methylpropenyl)-phenol acetate $C_{12}H_{14}O_2$ | anise: Y | | | $Her_n$ α σ! |
| Methyl propionate $C_4H_8O_2$ | sweet, black currant: F | .915 (20/4°C) | 29 | $Fru_n$ α! |
| 1-Methyl-1-propylcyclohexanone-2 | minty: A | | | $He_n$ δ! |
| Methyl propyl ketone $C_5H_{10}O$ | | .809 (20/4°C) | 56.8 | |

| Chemical | Reported Characteristics | Specific Gravity | Vapor Pressure | Detection Threshold | Recognition Threshold | Classification Expression, Factors, HU Value |
|---|---|---|---|---|---|---|
| Methylpropylnitrosamine $C_4H_{10}N_2O$ | camphor: A | | | | | $Woo_n$ |
| Methylpropylselenide $C_4H_8Se$ | putrid: A | | | | | β! |
| 2-Methyl pyrazine $C_5H_6N_2$ | pyridine-like: P | | | | | $Hyc_nOxy_n$ β! ν σ!! ϕ ω |
| N-Methyl-2-pyrrolidone $C_5H_9NO$ | mild, amine: X | 1.027 | | | | $Ami_n$ |
| N-Methylpyrroline $C_5H_9N$ | unpleasant, ammonia-like: Y | | | | | $Uro_nNit_n$ ψ! |
| Methyl salicylate $C_8H_8O_3$ | wintergreen, gaultheria: FXY | 1.184 (25/25°C) | 150 | | | $He_nFru_n$ δ! |
| α-Methyl styrene $C_9H_{10}$ | sweet, aromatic: J | .9062 (25/25°C) | | | .156 | $HU_2^{2-3}$ 16-25 |
| β-Methyl styrene $C_9H_{10}$ | irritant: H | | | | | |
| Methyltetrahydrofuran $C_5H_{10}O$ | ether-like: PX | .854 (20/4°C) | | | | λ! σ |
| 4-Methyl-5-thiazoleethanol $C_6H_9NOS$ | disagreeable odor of thiazole compound becoming somewhat pleasant at extreme dilution and imparting a nut-like flavor: Y | 1.196 (24/4°C) | | | | $\theta^2$: $Hyc_nOxy_n$ β! σ!! ϕ ω<br>$\theta_1$: $Nut_n$ |

| | | | | | |
|---|---|---|---|---|---|
| Methyl thiocyanate $C_2H_3NS$ | onion: Y | 1.068 (20°C) | 70.4 | 3.2 | $All_nSul_n$ ε ψ! ω $HU^{3-4}_{3-5}$ 36-81 |
| Methyl thiopropanol $C_4H_{10}OS$ | @ | | | | |
| Methyl-β,β,γ-tribromopropyl ether | camphor: A | | | | $Woo_n$ |
| Methyl tuberate | musty, fatty: C | | | | $Mus_nLip_n$ σ ψ! |
| Methyl vinyl ketone $C_4H_6O$ | powerfully irritating, lachrymator: P | .8636 (20/4°C) | | | $Hyc_n$ ε!!! ψ!!! |
| Methyprylon $C_{10}H_{17}NO_2$ | slight, characteristic: X | | | | |
| Methyridine $C_8H_{11}NO$ | sweet: Y | .988 (20°C) | | | α! |
| Metyrapone $C_{14}H_{14}NO_2$ | characteristic: X | | | | |
| MOLYBDENUM Mo | no reported odor | 10.2 | 4109 | | |
| MOLYBDENUM COMPOUNDS | no reported odors | | | | |
| Morphine acetate $C_{19}H_{23}NO_5 \cdot 3H_2O$ | slight acetic: Y | | | | ϕ ψ |
| Morphine valerate $C_{17}H_{19}NO_3 \cdot C_5H_{10}O_2$ | valeric acid: Y | | | | |

| Chemical | Reported Characteristics | Specific Gravity | Vapor Pressure | Detection Threshold | Recognition Threshold | Classification Expression, Factors, HU Value |
|---|---|---|---|---|---|---|
| Morpholine $C_4H_9NO$ | characteristic, fishy, amine-like: JXY | 1.007 (20/4°C) | 6.6 mm Hg (20°C) | | .14 | Amin $HU^{3-5}_{4-6}$ 49-121 |
| 2-(Morpholinothio)-benzothiazole $C_{11}H_{12}N_2OS_2$ | sweet: X | 1.34 (25°C) | | | | α! |
| Mucidone $C_{12}H_{18}O$ | strong, actinomy-cete, earthy, musty: S | | | | | $Ac_nEar_nMst_n$ |
| Muscone (-) $C_{16}H_{30}O$ | musk: XY @ | .9221 (17/4°C) | 241.5 | | | $Mus_n$ ρ! ω |
| Musk ambrette $C_{12}H_{16}NO_5$ | heavy musky, ambrette seed: X | | | | | $Mus_n$ ρ! ω |
| Musk ketone $C_{14}H_{18}NO_5$ | sweet, musk: X @ | | | | | $Mus_n$ α! |
| Musk xylol $C_{12}H_{15}N_3O_6$ | powerful musk, fatty: ACX @ | | | | | $Lip_nMus_n$ ρ! |
| Mustard oil, volatile | pungent, acrid: X | 1.016-1.022 | | | | ψ! |
| Myrcene $C_{10}H_{16}$ | pleasant: XY | .7957 (20/4°C) | 106 | | | |
| Myristic aldehyde $C_{14}H_{28}O$ | sweet, amber, faint fatty, slightly citrus: DF | | 214.5 | | | $Mus_nFru_nLip_n$ α! |
| Naphthalene $C_{10}H_8$ | strong, coal tar, moth balls: XY | 1.162 (20/4°C) | 145.5 | | | $Hyc_n$ μ ρ σ!! ψ! ω! |

| | | | | |
|---|---|---|---|---|
| 1-Naphthlenethiol $C_{10}H_8S$ | strong, mercaptan: Y | 1.607 (20/4°C) | | $Mus_nSul_n$ β! ν σ!! π |
| 2-Naphthlenethiol $C_{10}H_8S$ | disagreeable: Y | | | |
| α-Naphthol $C_{10}H_8O$ | phenolic: Y | 1.0954 (98.7/4°C) | 206 | $Mol_nHyc_n$ ρ σ!! ψ |
| β-Naphthol $C_{10}H_8O$ | slight phenolic: PXY | 1.217 | 209.8 | $Mol_nHyc_n$ σ ψ |
| 1,4-Naphthoquinone $C_{10}H_6O_2$ | benzoquinone-like, pungent: AXY | 1.422 | | $Hyc_nOxy_n$ ν σ!! ψ |
| α-Naphthylamine $C_{10}H_9N$ | unpleasant, putrid: AY | 1.13 | 220 | $Ami_nHyc_n$ β! |
| β-Naphthylamine $C_{10}H_9N$ | aromatic: P | 1.061 (98/4°C) | 224.3 | |
| 2-Naphthylamine-3, 6-disulfonic acid $C_{10}H_9NO_6S$ | characteristic: X | | | |
| β-Naphthyl ethyl ether $C_{12}H_{12}O$ | orange blossom, neroli: FX | | | $Flo_nFru_n$ |
| 1-Naphthylisocyanate $C_{11}H_7NO$ | characteristic of isocyanates, pungent: Y | 1.181 | | ψ! |
| α-Naphthyl methyl ether $C_{11}H_{10}O$ | moderately fragrant, fairly acid, moderately burnt, moderately caprylic: C | | | $But_nFlo_n$ σ! ψ!! |
| β-Naphthyl methyl ether $C_{11}H_{10}O$ | acacia, orange: F | | | $Flo_nFru_n$ |

| Chemical | Reported Characteristics | Specific Gravity | Vapor Pressure | Detection Threshold | Recognition Threshold | Classification Expression, Factors, HU Value |
|---|---|---|---|---|---|---|
| NEODYMIUM<br>Nd | no reported odor | 7.004 | | | | |
| NEODYMIUM COMPOUNDS | no reported odors | | | | | |
| NEON<br>Ne | no reported odor | .6964<br>(air=1) | | | | |
| Neopentyl alcohol<br>$C_5H_{12}O$ | peppermint, minty:<br>AX @ | | -251.0 | | | $He_n$ δ! |
| Nepetalactone<br>$C_{10}H_{14}O_2$ | odor very attractive to cats: Y | 1.0663<br>(25/4°C) | | | | |
| Nerol<br>$C_{10}H_{18}O$ | rose-neroli, sweet, floral: CFXY | .8813<br>(15°C) | 159.8 | | | $Flo_n$ α! σ ψ |
| Nerolidal<br>$C_{15}H_{26}O$ | fruity, pear: F | .8720<br>(25/4°C) | | | | $Fru_n$ |
| Neryl acetate<br>$C_{12}H_{20}O_2$ | sweet, raspberry:<br>F | | | | | $Flo_nFru_n$ α! σ ψ! |
| Neryl butyrate<br>$C_{14}H_{24}O_2$ | sweet, cocoa: F | | | | | $Woo_n$ α! ν σ! ψ |
| Neryl formate<br>$C_{11}H_{18}O_2$ | bitter peach: F | | | | | $Fru_n$ ν! |
| Neryl propionate<br>$C_{13}H_{22}O_2$ | acid, mirabell,<br>plum: F | | | | | $Fru_n$ ψ! |
| Neurine<br>$C_5H_{13}NO$ | fishy: XY | | | | | $Ami_n$ |
| NICKEL<br>Ni | no reported odor | 8.908 | 2364 | | | |

| | | | | | |
|---|---|---|---|---|---|
| Nickel acetate $C_4H_6NiO_4 \cdot 4H_2O$ | acetic: Y | 1.744 | | | $\psi$! |
| Nicotine $C_{10}H_{14}N_2$ | develops odor of pyridine: Y | 1.0097 (20/4°C) | 169.5 | | $Hyc_nOxy_n$ $\beta$! $\nu$ $\sigma$! $\phi$ $\psi$ $\omega$ |
| β-Nicotyrine $C_{10}H_{10}N_2$ | characteristic: Y | 1.241 (20/4°C) | | | |
| NIOBIUM Nb | no reported odor | 8.57 | | | |
| Nitric acid $HNO_3$ | suffocating, choking, caustic, characteristic: XY | 1.50269 (25/4°C) | 62 mm Hg (25°C) | | $Nit_n$ $\phi$!!! $\psi$!! |
| 2-Nitrobenzaldehyde $C_7H_7NO_3$ | almond when cold, pungent when hot: A | | 196.2 | | $\theta^2$: $\psi$!<br>$\theta_1$: $Nut_n$ |
| Nitrobenzene $C_6H_5NO_2$ | coarse, bitter almonds: AMY @ | 1.205 (15/4°C) | 139.9 | .0047 | $Nut_nNit_n$ $\nu$!<br>$HU^{3-4}_{3-5}$ 36-81 |
| m-Nitrobenzotrifluoride $C_7F_3H_4NO_2$ | aromatic: PX | 1.437 (15.5°C) | | | |
| p-Nitrobenzoyl chloride $C_7ClH_4NO_3$ | pungent: Y | | | | $Nit_nHal_nOxy_nHyc_n$ $\psi$! |
| o-Nitrobiphenyl $C_{12}H_9NO_2$ | characteristic, sweet: Y | 1.189 (40/15.5°C) (liq.) | | | $Nit_nHyc_nOxy_n$ $\alpha$! $\lambda$ $\omega$ |
| 3-Nitro-tert-butylbenzene $C_{10}H_{13}NO_2$ | aromatic: A | | | | |
| 2-Nitrocamphane $C_{10}H_{18}NO_2$ | camphor: A | | | | $Woo_n$ |

| Chemical | Reported Characteristics | Specific Gravity | Vapor Pressure | Detection Threshold | Recognition Threshold | Classification Expression, Factors, HU Value |
|---|---|---|---|---|---|---|
| 2-Nitrocymol $C_{10}H_{13}NO_3$ | aromatic: A | | | | | |
| 2-Nitro-2,4-dimethylpentane $C_7H_{14}NO_2$ | camphor: A | | | | | $Woo_n$ |
| Nitroethane $C_2H_5NO_2$ | pleasing: MY | 1.052 (20/20°C) | 57.8 | | | |
| Nitrofurantoin $C_8H_6N_4O_5$ | slight: X | | | | | |
| NITROGEN N | no reported odor | 1.25046 | -209.7 | | | |
| Nitrogen dioxide $NO_2$ | irritating: Y | 1.448 (20/4°C) (liq.) | -14.7 | | | $Nit_nOxy_n$ $\varepsilon$! $\psi$ |
| Nitrogen fluoride $F_3N$ | moldy: XY | 1.537 (-129°C) (liq.) | | | | $Mol_nHal_nNit_n$ $\sigma$! |
| β-Nitrohexane $C_6H_{13}NO_2$ | aniseed: AM | | | | | $Her_n$ $\alpha$ |
| Nitrohydrochloric acid | suffocating, strongly irritant: PXY | | | | | $Sul_nNit_n$ $\varepsilon$!! $\phi$!!! $\psi$!! |
| Nitromethyl $CH_3NO_2$ | pleasant: M | | | | | |
| 3-Nitropentane $C_5H_{11}NO_2$ | fusel oil: Y | .957 (0/4°C) | | | | $Nit_nHyc_n$ $\alpha$ $\lambda$ $\mu$ $\psi$! |

| | | | | |
|---|---|---|---|---|
| o-Nitrophenol $C_6H_5NO_3$ | aromatic, strong characteristic, peculiar, aromatic: MPY | 1.657 (20°C) | 146.4 | |
| γ-Nitropropanol $C_3H_7NO_3$ | weak, pungent: A | | | ψ |
| N-Nitrosodiethyl-amine $C_4H_{10}N_2O$ | aromatic: A | .9422 (20/4°C) | | |
| 2-Nitroso-2-methylbutane $C_5H_{11}NO$ | camphor: A | | | $Woo_n$ |
| 2-Nitroso-2-methyl-propane $C_4H_8NO$ | camphor: A | | | $Woo_n$ |
| Nitrosyl chloride ClNO | irritating, pun-gent: AP | 1.273 (20°C) | -46.3 | ψ! |
| α-Nitrothiophen $C_4H_3NO_2S$ | almond: A | | | $Nut_n$ |
| Nitrous oxide $N_2O$ | slightly sweetish: Y | 1.226 (-89°C) (liq.) | -110.3 | α λ |
| Nitryl chloride $ClNO_2$ | chlorine-like: Y | 1.37 (0°C) (liq.) | | $Hal_n$ ϕ! ψ! |
| Nitryl fluoride $FNO_2$ | pungent (attacks mucous membranes instantly): Y | 1.796 (-72°C) (liq.) | | ε!! ϕ! ψ!!! |
| 2,6-Nonadien-1-ol $C_9H_{16}O$ | sharp, green, violet leaf: FM | | | $Ens_nFlo_n$ ψ! |

| Chemical | Reported Characteristics | Specific Gravity | Vapor Pressure | Detection Threshold | Recognition Threshold | Classification Expression, Factors, HU Value |
|---|---|---|---|---|---|---|
| Nonamethylene carbonate $C_{11}H_{20}O_3$ | camphor, earthy: A | | | | | $Woo_nEar_n$ |
| Nonanal $C_9H_{18}O$ | orange rose, floral, musty, fatty: AFX | .822-.830 | | | | $Lip_nMst_nFru_nFlo_n$ $\sigma$ $\psi$ |
| Nonane $C_9H_{20}$ | powerful, petrol: M | .722 | 88.1 | | | $Hyc_n$ $\mu$ $\omega$ |
| Nonyl acetate $C_{11}H_{22}O_2$ | pungent, strong, suggestive of mushrooms, bitter peach, resembles gardenia when diluted: CFXY | .8785 (15/4°C) | | | | $\theta^2$: $Flo_n$<br>$\theta_1$: $Far_nFlo_nFru_n$ $\nu$ $\psi$!! |
| Nonyl alcohol $C_9H_{20}O$ | rosey, soft citrus, musty, fatty, citronella oil: FXY | .8279 (20/4°C) | | | | $Lip_nMst_nFlo_nFru_n$ $\alpha$ $\sigma$ $\psi$ |
| Nonylal dimethyl acetal | green, fatty, violet, some rose: W | | | | | $Ens_nLip_nFlo_n$ |
| Nonylbenzene $C_{15}H_{24}$ | faint, aromatic: X | .864 (20/20°C) | | | | |
| α-Nonyl-γ-butyrolactone $C_{13}H_{24}O_2$ | peach, cocoa flowers: M | | | | | $Flo_nFru_n$ $\alpha$ $\nu$ $\sigma$!! $\psi$ |
| γ-Nonyl lactone $C_9H_{16}O_2$ | coconut-like, nutty: FX | .956-.963 | | | | $Lip_nNut_n$ $\alpha$ |
| Nonyl nonanoate $C_{18}H_{36}O_2$ | orange rose: X | .863 (25°C) | | | | $Fru_nFlo_n$ |

| | | | |
|---|---|---|---|
| Nonyl phenol $C_{15}H_{24}O$ | phenolic, slight characteristic: XY | .950 (20/20°C) | $Mol_nHyc_n$ σ! |
| Nonyl trichloro-silane $C_9Cl_3H_{19}Si$ | pungent, irritating: X | | ε! ψ! |
| Nootkatone | citrus, grapefruit: | | $Fru_n$ ν ψ |
| A-Norandrostan-2α-ol | musky: A | | $Mus_n$ |
| A-Norandrostan-2β-ol | cedar: A | | $Woo_n$ |
| A-Norandrostan-2-one | cedar: A | | $Woo_n$ |
| Norhexahydrofarne-sol $C_{12}H_{28}O$ | floral, refreshing: D | | $Flo_n$ α δ |
| $\Delta^3$-Normanthenol-8 | minty, cymene: A | | $He_nHyc_n$ δ! |
| $\Delta^{3:8(9)}$-Normenth-adiene | strong, lemon, turpentine: A | | $Fru_nWoo_nHyc_n$ σ ψ! |
| Nornicotine $C_9H_{12}N_2$ | develops slight amine odor, less than nicotine: Y | 1.0737 (20/4°C) | $Ami_n$ ψ |
| Novoldiamine $C_9H_{22}N_2$ | amine: Y | .819 (20/26°C) | $Ami_n$ |

| Chemical | Reported Characteristics | Specific Gravity | Vapor Pressure | Detection Threshold | Recognition Threshold | Classification Expression, Factors, HU Value |
|---|---|---|---|---|---|---|
| Nystatin $C_{46}H_{77}NO_{19}$ | odor suggestive of cereals: X | | | | | $Fur_n Her_n Woo_n$ σ |
| Ocimene $C_{10}H_{16}$ | pleasant: Y | .8006 (20/4°C) | | | | |
| Octadecyltrichlorosilane $C_{18}Cl_3H_{37}Si$ | pungent: X | .984 (25°C) | | | | ψ! |
| Octamethylene carbonate $C_9H_{16}O_3$ | camphor, earthy: A | | | | | $Woo_n Ear_n$ |
| Octamylamine $C_{13}H_{29}N$ | weak, aromatic: Y | | | | | |
| Octanal $C_8H_{16}O$ | strong, fruity: X | .821 (20/4°C) | 145.3 | | | $Fru_n$ |
| 1-Octanol $C_8H_{18}O$ | penetrating, aromatic, characteristic, sharp, powerful, slightly orange, fatty, musty: CFXY | .827 (20/4°C) | 135.2 | | | $(Mus_n But_n)$ 0 $Fru_n$ $Hyc_n$ σ ψ!! ω! |
| 2-Octanol $C_8H_{18}O$ | disagreeable, aromatic, somewhat unpleasant, particularly on heating, fruity, musty: CXY | .8193 (20/4°C) | 119.8 | | | $(Mus_n But_n)$ 0 $Fru_n$ $Hyc_n$ α β! λ σ ψ! ω |
| Octanoyl chloride $C_8ClH_{15}O$ | characteristic, pungent: X | .9576 (15.5/15.5°C) | | | | ψ! |
| Octyl acetate $C_{10}H_{20}O_2$ | strong, floral, fruity, sweet, peach: CFJX | .873 (20/20°C) | .4 mm Hg (20°C) | | .21 | $Flo_n Fru_n$ α! $HU_2^{2-4}16\text{-}36$ |

| | | | | |
|---|---|---|---|---|
| Octyl butyrate $C_{12}H_{24}O_2$ | sweet, melon, fruity, orangey: CF | | | $Fru_n$ $\alpha$! |
| $\gamma$-Octyl-$\gamma$-butyrolactone $C_{12}H_{22}O_2$ | weak, musky, peach: M | | | $Mus_nFru_n$ |
| Octyl crotonyl acetate $C_{13}H_{24}O_2$ | fruity, musty: C | | | $Mus_nFru_n$ $\psi$! |
| Octyl formate $C_9H_{18}O_2$ | fruity, burning, peach: FX | .869-.872 (25°C) | | $Fru_n$ $\gamma$ |
| Octyl mercaptan $C_8H_{18}S$ | mild: X | .8395 (25/4°C) | | |
| Octyl methyl ketone $C_{10}H_{19}O$ | sharp, musty, fatty: C | | | $Mus_nLip_n$ $\psi$! |
| Octyl peroxide $C_8H_{18}O_2$ | sharp: X | | | $\psi$! |
| Octyl phenol $C_{14}H_{22}O$ | phenolic, animal-like: C | .89 (90°C) | | $A_6$ $T_1$ $E_1$ $\beta$! $\sigma$!! $\psi$! |
| Octyl propionate $C_{11}H_{22}O_2$ | melon: F | | | $Fru_n$ $\alpha$ |
| Octyl trichlorosilane $C_8Cl_3H_{17}Si$ | pungent, irritating: X | | | $\varepsilon$! $\psi$! |
| Oleic acid $C_{18}H_{34}O_2$ | nearly odorless, rancid upon oxidation, lard-like: XY | .891 (20/4°C) | 286 | $Lip_n$ |
| OSMIUM Os | elemental odor of Os when heated: X | 22.48 | | $Osm_n$ $\beta$ |

| Chemical | Reported Characteristics | Specific Gravity | Vapor Pressure | Detection Threshold | Recognition Threshold | Classification Expression, Factors, HU Value |
|---|---|---|---|---|---|---|
| Osmium tetroxide $O_4Os$ | very pungent, disagreeable, acrid, chlorine-like, penetrating: MPXY | 4.906 (22°C) | 71.5 | | | $Hal_n$ $\beta$ $\phi$ $\psi$!! $\omega$! $HU^{4-6}_{5-6}$ 81-144 |
| Oxalyl chloride $C_2Cl_2O_2$ | military poison gas, penetrating: XY | 1.488 (13/4°C) | | | | $\omega$!!! |
| Oxeladin $C_{20}H_{33}NO_3$ | acrid: Y | | | | | $\psi$!! |
| 1-Oxo-2-phenyl-2-methylane glycol $C_{11}H_{14}O_2$ | musky: M | | | | | $Mus_n$ |
| OXYGEN O | no reported odor | 1.10535 | -198.8 | | | |
| Ozone $O_3$ | characteristic, pleasant in concentrations less than 2 PPM, irritating in higher concentrations: XY | 1.571 (-180°C) | -141 | .5 | | $\theta^2$: $\varepsilon$! $\theta_1$: $Oxy_n$ $\sigma$!! $HU^{2-6}_{2-6}$ 16-144 |
| PALLADIUM Pd | no reported odor | 12.02 (20/4°C) | | | | |
| PALLADIUM COMPOUNDS | no reported odors | | | | | |
| Pancreatin | characteristic: X | | | | | |
| Parabromdylamine $BrC_{16}H_{19}N_2$ | characteristic, amine-like: Y | | | | | $Ami_n$ |

| | | | | |
|---|---|---|---|---|
| Paracresyl acetate $C_9H_{10}O_2$ | moderately fragrant, very burnt, light moderate acid, fairly caprylic: C | | | $But_n$ σ!! ψ |
| Paraformaldehyde $(CH_2O)_n$ | slight odor of formaldehyde: XY | | 69.0 | ε τ ϕ ψ |
| Paraldehyde $C_6H_{12}O_3$ | aromatic, agreeable: XY | .994 (20/4°C) | 25.3 mm Hg (20°C) | |
| Paramethadione $C_7H_{11}NO_3$ | fruity, ester-like: XY | 1.1180-1.1240 (25/4°C) | | $Fru_nHyc_n$ |
| Parascorbic acid $C_6H_8O_2$ | sweet, aromatic, irritating when heated: Y | 1.079 (18/4°C) | | α! |
| Parathion $C_{10}H_{14}NO_5PS$ | often but not always with characteristic odor: X | 1.26 (25/4°C) | | |
| Peanut oil | mild, pleasant, nutty: PY | .917-.921 (15/15°C) | | $Nut_n$ |
| Pecilocin $C_{17}H_{25}NO_3$ | ester-like: Y | | | |
| Pelargonic acid $C_9H_{18}O_2$ | slight characteristic: XY | .907 (20/4°C) | 184.4 | |
| Pelargonyl peroxide $(C_8H_{17}COO-)_2$ | faint: X | | | |
| Penicillin S potassium | disagreeable: Y | | | β |

| Chemical | Reported Characteristics | Specific Gravity | Vapor Pressure | Detection Threshold | Recognition Threshold | Classification Expression, Factors, HU Value |
|---|---|---|---|---|---|---|
| Pentaborane $B_5H_9$ | bad pungent: PX | .61 | 66 mm Hg (0°C) | | | $\beta$ $\psi$! |
| Pentabromoacetone $Br_5C_3HO$ | penetrating: Y | | | | | $\omega$! |
| Pentachloroethane $C_2Cl_5H$ | chloroform-like, ethereal: AY | 1.6712 (25/4°C) | 93.5 | | | $\lambda$! |
| Pentachloronitro-benzene $C_6Cl_5NO_2$ | musty: X | 1.718 (25/4°C) | | | | $Mst_n$ |
| Pentachlorophenol $C_6Cl_5HO$ | characteristic, very pungent when hot, produces sneezing (dust): PY | 1.718 (25/4°C) | 239.6 | | | $\psi$!! |
| 1,1,2,2,4-Penta-methylcyclopenta-none $C_{10}H_{18}O$ | camphor: A | | | | | $Woo_n$ |
| 1,1,3,3,5-Penta-methyl-4,6-dinitro-indane $C_{14}H_{18}N_2O_4$ | musk-type: X | | | | | $Mus_n$ |
| Pentamethyl ethyl acetate $C_9H_{17}O_2$ | camphor: A | | | | | $Woo_n$ |
| Pentamethyl ethyl alcohol $C_7H_{15}O$ | camphor: A | | | | | $Woo_n$ |
| Pentamethyl phenyl-isothiocyanate $C_{12}H_{14}NS$ | weak, floral: A | | | | | $Flo_n$ |

| | | | | | |
|---|---|---|---|---|---|
| n-Pentane $C_5H_{12}$ | pleasant: X | .62638 (20/4°C) | -12.6 | | |
| 3-Pentanol $C_5H_{12}O$ | characteristic: Y | .815 (25/4°C) | | | |
| Pentyl methacrylate $C_6H_{15}O$ | sweet, floral, anise-like: W | | | | $Flo_n Her_n$ α |
| Pentyl valerate $C_{10}H_{20}O_2$ | S | | | .113 | |
| Peracetic acid $C_2H_4O_3$ | strong, acrid: PXY | 1.15 (20°C) | | | ψ!! |
| Perbenzoic acid $C_7H_6O_3$ | acrid: Y | | | | ψ! |
| Perchloromethyl mercaptan $CCl_4S$ | disagreeable, irritant: X | 1.722 (0°C) | | | ε! |
| Perchloryl fluoride $ClFO_3$ | characteristic, sweet: P | 1.434 (liq.) | | | α! |
| Perilla aldehyde $C_{10}H_{14}O$ | coumin, almond, fruity, green: W | | | | $Spi_n Nut_n Fru_n Ens_n$ |
| α-Phellandrene $C_{10}H_{16}$ | spice, pine: F | | 110.6 | | $Spi_n Woo_n$ |
| d-β-Phellandrene $C_{10}H_{16}$ | pleasant, slight citrus: PX | .8520 (20/4°C) | | | $Fru_n$ |
| Phenethyl alcohol $C_8H_{10}O$ | floral, rose, peach, honey: ACFPXY | 1.017 (25/25°C) | 154.0 | | $Car_n Flo_n Fru_n$ α |
| Phenethylamine $C_8H_{11}N$ | fishy: XY | .9640 (25/4°C) | | | $Ami_n$ ψ |

| Chemical | Reported Characteristics | Specific Gravity | Vapor Pressure | Detection Threshold | Recognition Threshold | Classification Expression, Factors, HU Value |
|---|---|---|---|---|---|---|
| Phenetole $C_8H_{10}O$ | fragrant, floral, aromatic: AM | .967 (20/4°C) | 108.4 | | | $Flo_n$ |
| Pheniramine $C_{16}H_{20}N_2$ | characteristic, amine-like: Y | 1.0081 | | | | $Ami_n\ \psi$ |
| Pheniramine maleate $C_{16}H_{20}N_2 \cdot C_4H_4O_4$ | faint, amine-like: X | | | | | $Ami_n\ \xi$ |
| Phenol $C_6H_6O$ | characteristic, distinctive: PXY | 1.071 | 121.4 | | .047 | $Mol_n\ \sigma!!$ $HU^{3-5}_{3-5}$ 36-100 |
| Phenothiazine $C_{12}H_9NS$ | slight: X | | | | | |
| Phenoxypropylene oxide $C_9H_{10}O_2$ | characteristic: X | 1.1110 (20/20°C) | | | | |
| Phenylacetaldehyde $C_8H_8O$ | very strong, green, hyacinth-like, lilac, honey: WXY | 1.023-1.030 (25/25°C) | | | | $Car_nFlo_nEns_n$ |
| Phenylacetaldehyde dimethylacetal $C_{10}H_{14}O_2$ | very potent green: X | 1.000-1.004 (25/25°C) | | | | $Woo_nEns_n\ \sigma\ \psi$ |
| Phenylacetic acid $C_8H_8O_2$ | sweet, floral, weak civet, honey-like: AFP @ | 1.091 (77/4°C) | 198.2 | | | $Mus_nCar_nFlo_n\ \alpha!\ \sigma\ \psi$ |
| Phenylazide $C_6H_5N_3$ | almond, trace of anise: A | 1.088 (20/20°C) | | | | $Nut_nHer_n$ |
| Phenylazoamide $C_6H_5N_3$ | unpleasant, penetrating: M | | | | | $\omega!$ |

| | | | | |
|---|---|---|---|---|
| Phenyl benzoate $C_{13}H_{10}O_2$ | geranium, musky: CPY | 1.235 | 227.8 | $Mus_nFlo_n$ |
| 2-Phenylbenzothia-zole $C_{13}H_9NS$ | floral, tea-rose: AM | | | $Flo_n$ |
| Phenylbutazone $C_{19}H_{20}N_2O_2$ | very slight aro-matic: X | | | |
| Phenylbutynol $C_{10}H_{10}O$ | camphor-like: XY | 1.0924 (20/20°C) | | $Woo_n$ |
| α-Phenyl-γ-butyrolactone $C_{10}H_{10}O_2$ | floral, balsamic: AM | | | $Flo_nBal_n$ |
| Phenylcarbylamine chloride $C_7Cl_2H_5N$ | very irritant, onion-like: X | 1.30 (15°C) | | $All_n$ ε! ψ!! |
| 2-Phenyl-6-chlorophenol $C_{12}ClH_9O$ | slight, charac-teristic: Y | | | |
| Phenyl cresyl oxide | floral: C | | | $Flo_n$ ψ! |
| Phenylcyclohexane $C_{12}H_{16}$ | slight, pleasant: X | .938 (25/15°C) | 169.3 | |
| Phenyldidecyl phosphite $C_{26}H_{47}O_3P$ | alcohol: X | .940 (25/15.5°C) | | $Hyc_n$ |
| 2-Phenylethyl acetate $C_{10}H_{12}O_2$ | sweet, honey, peach-like: FX | 1.030-1.034 | | $Car_nFru_n$ α! ψ |

| Chemical | Reported Characteristics | Specific Gravity | Vapor Pressure | Detection Threshold | Recognition Threshold | Classification Expression, Factors, HU Value |
|---|---|---|---|---|---|---|
| Phenylethyl acetic acid $C_{10}H_{12}O_2$ | aromatic: X | | | | | |
| Phenylethyl aldehyde $C_8H_8O$ | floral, hyacinth: AM | | | | | $Flo_n$ |
| 2-Phenylethylamine $C_8H_{11}N$ | fishy: X | .9640 | | | | $Ami_n$ |
| 2-Phenylethyl anthranilate $C_{15}H_{15}NO_2$ | grape, orange, floral, winey: CFX | 1.14 (25/25°C) | | | | $Mst_nFer_nFru_nFlo_n$ ψ |
| Phenylethylbenzoate $C_{15}H_{14}$ | bitter, strawberry: F | | | | | $Fru_n$ ν! |
| Phenylethyl cinnamate $C_{17}H_{16}O_2$ | cherry, irritant: F | | | | | $Fru_n$ ε ψ! |
| Phenylethyl dimethyl carbinol $C_{11}H_{15}O$ | floral, citrus: C | | | | | $Flo_nFru_n$ σ ψ |
| Phenylethyl dimethyl carbinyl acetate | floral, rosey: C | | | | | $Flo_n$ σ! ψ |
| Phenylethyl formate $C_9H_{10}O_2$ | green, plum: F | | | | | $Ens_nFru_n$ ψ! |

| | | | | | |
|---|---|---|---|---|---|
| 2-Phenylethyl isobutyrate $C_{12}H_{16}O_2$ | pleasant fragrance resembling a somewhat fruity, tea-rose odor, sweet, pear: CFX | .988 (25/25°C) | | | $Fru_nFlo_nEns_n$ α! ψ! |
| Phenylethylisovalerate $C_{13}H_{18}O_2$ | fruity: F | | | | $Fru_n$ |
| Phenylethyl methoxyacetate $C_{11}H_{13}O_3$ | floral: A | | | | $Flo_n$ |
| 2-Phenylethyl phenyl acetate $C_{16}H_{16}O_2$ | sweet, honey, hyacinth: FX | 1.080-1.082 | | | $Car_nFlo_n$ α! |
| 2-Phenylethyl propionate $C_{11}H_{14}O_2$ | flower, fruit: X | 1.012 (25/25°C) | | | $Flo_nFru_n$ |
| α-Phenylethyl-pyridine $C_{13}H_{13}$ | floral, rose: AM | | | | $Flo_n$ |
| 2-Phenylethyl salicylate $C_{15}H_{14}O_3$ | sweet, peach, very faint aromatic: FX | | | | $Fru_nHyc_n$ α ξ ψ |
| Phenylethyl tiglate $C_{12}H_{16}O_2$ | floral, rose: F | | | | $Flo_n$ |
| Phenylhydrazine $C_6H_8N_2$ | faint aromatic, pleasant: AMY | 1.0978 (20/4°C) | 173.5 | | $Hyc_n$ |
| Phenylhydroxylamine $C_6H_7NO$ | irritant: M | | | | ε! |
| Phenyl isobutyl ketone $C_{11}H_{12}O$ | musty, spicey, green wood: C | | | | $Mst_nSpi_nWoo_nEns_n$ |

| Chemical | Reported Characteristics | Specific Gravity | Vapor Pressure | Detection Threshold | Recognition Threshold | Classification Expression, Factors, HU Value |
|---|---|---|---|---|---|---|
| Phenyl isocyanate $C_7H_5NO$ | acrid, penetrating, pungent, irritating: AXY | 1.092 (15/4°C) | 100.6 | | | ε! ψ! ω! |
| Phenylisocyanide $C_7H_5N$ | offensive, nauseating, narcotic, repulsive: AM @ | | 101.0 | | | β! |
| Phenyl isonitrile $C_7H_5N$ | S | | | .0068 | | |
| Phenylisothiocyanate $C_7H_5NS$ | pungent, strongly pungent: AD | 1.1288 (25/4°C) | 147.7 | .00018 | | ψ!! $HU^{5-6}_{5-6}$ 100-144 |
| o-Phenylphenol $C_{12}H_{10}O$ | mild, characteristic: Y | | 205.9 | | | |
| Phenylpropanolamine hydrochloride $C_9ClH_{14}NO$ | crude benzoic acid: XY | | | | | |
| Phenylpropyl acetate $C_{12}H_{14}O_2$ | bittersweet: F | 1.012-1.016 | | | | $Flo_n$ α ν ψ!! |
| Phenylpropyl alcohol $C_9H_{12}O$ | floral, musty: CX | .998-1.000 | 170.3 | .00065 | | $Mus_nFlo_n$ α σ ψ |
| Phenylpropyl aldehyde $C_9H_{10}O$ | floral, hyacinth, bittersweet almond: CFX | 1.010-1.020 | | | | $Flo_nNut_n$ α ν σ! ψ!! |
| Phenylpropyl cinnamate $C_{18}H_{18}O_2$ | bitter, cherry: F | | | | | $Fru_n$ ν |

| | | | | | |
|---|---|---|---|---|---|
| α-Phenylpropyl pyridine $C_{15}H_{16}N$ | floral, rose: AM | | | | $Flo_n$ |
| Phenyl salicylate $C_{13}H_{10}O_3$ | pleasant, faint, aromatic: PXY | 1.2614 | | | |
| Phlorol $C_8H_{10}O$ | phenol: Y | 1.018 (25/25°C) | 141.8 | | $Mol_n$ |
| Phorone $C_9H_{14}O$ | floral: A | .8791 (20/20°C) | 134 | | $Flo_n$ |
| Phosgene $CCl_2O$ | strongly irritating, new mown hay, green corn, when much diluted with air an odor reminscent of moldy hay, suffocating: PXY | 1.432 (0/4°C) | -35.6 | 1 | $\theta^2$: $Ens_nMol_n$ $\varepsilon$ $\phi$! <br> $\theta_1$: $Ens_n$ $\varepsilon$!! $\phi$!!! <br> $HU^{5-6}_{5-6}$ 100-144 |
| Phosphine $H_3P$ | disagreeable, garlic-like, putrid, decaying fish: AXY | 1.185 | -118.8 | .021 | $All_nAmi_n$ $\beta$! $\psi$! <br> $HU^{5-6}_{5-6}$ 100-144 |
| Phosphoric acid dibromide diisobutylamide | strong camphor: A | | | | $Woo_n$ |
| Phosphoric acid dichloride di-n-amylamide | aromatic: A | | | | |
| Phosphoric acid dichloride diethylamide | strong camphor: A | | | | $Woo_n$ |

| Chemical | Reported Characteristics | Specific Gravity | Vapor Pressure | Detection Threshold | Recognition Threshold | Classification Expression, Factors, HU Value |
|---|---|---|---|---|---|---|
| Phosphoric acid dichloride diisobutylamide | camphor: A | | | | | $Woo_n$ |
| Phosphoric acid dichloride dimethylamide | weak pepper, pungent: A | | | | | $Spi_n$ ψ! |
| Phosphoric acid dichloride dipropylamide | minty: A | | | | | $He_n$ δ! |
| Phosphoric acid dichloride methylamide | pungent: A | | | | | ψ! |
| Phosphoric acid diethyl ester diisobutylamide | aromatic: A | | | | | |
| Phosphoric acid ethyl ester bisdiethylamide | minty: A | | | | | $He_n$ δ! |
| Phosphoric acid ethyl ester chloride dipropylamide | aromatic: A | | | | | |
| PHOSPHOROUS P | no reported odor | | | | | |

| | | | | |
|---|---|---|---|---|
| Phosphorous acid ethyl ester bisdiethylamide | putrid: A | | | β! |
| Phosphorous acid ethyl ester bisdipropylamide | putrid: A | | | β! |
| Phosphorous oxy-chloride $Cl_3OP$ | pungent: XY | 1.675 (20/20°C) | 47.4 | ψ! |
| Phosphorous pentachloride $Cl_5P$ | pungent, unpleasant, irritating: XY | 3.60 | 117.0 | ψ! |
| Phosphorous pentasulfide $P_2S_5$ | peculiar: XY | 2.03 | | |
| Phosphorous tribromide $Br_3P$ | very penetrating: XY | 2.852 (15°C) | 103.6 | ω!! |
| Phosphorous triselenide $P_4Se_3$ | irritating: Y | 1.31 | | ψ! |
| Phthalic anhydride $C_8H_4O_3$ | characteristic, mild, suffocating: MX | 1.527 (4°C) | 202.3 | ϕ |
| Phthalylsulfacet-amide $C_{16}H_{14}N_2O_6S$ | slight: X | | | |
| α-Picoline $C_6H_7N$ | strong, pyridine-like, unpleasant: PXY | .952 | 71.4 | $Hyc_nOxy_n$ β! σ! ϕ ψ |

| Chemical | Reported Characteristics | Specific Gravity | Vapor Pressure | Detection Threshold | Recognition Threshold | Classification Expression, Factors, HU Value |
|---|---|---|---|---|---|---|
| β-Picoline $C_6H_7N$ | sweetish, not unpleasant (Y); unpleasant (J) | .9613 (15/4°C) | | | .046 | α! $HU^{3-5}_{3-5}$ 36-100 |
| γ-Picoline $C_6H_7N$ | obnoxious, sweetish: Y | .957 (15/4°C) | | | | α! β! |
| Pinacol dimethyl ether $C_8H_{18}O_2$ | agreeable: Y | | | | | |
| α-Pinene (dl) $C_{10}H_{16}$ | characteristic, turpene, pine-like, woody: FPXY | .8592 (20/4°C) | 90.1 | | | $Woo_n$ |
| β-Pinene $C_{10}H_{16}$ | characteristic, turpene, pine-like, woody: FX | .8740-.8770 (15.5/15.5°C) | 94 | | | $Woo_n$ |
| Piperazine $C_4H_{10}N_2$ | bitter, dandylion-like, slightly ammoniacal: M | | | | | $Ens_nFlo_nUro_nNit_n$ ν |
| Piperazine citrate $C_{24}H_{46}N_{16}O_4$ | slight: X | | | | | |
| Piperidine $C_5H_{11}N$ | characteristic, pepper, ammoniacal, pungent, amine-like: MPXY | .8622 (20/4°C) | 49 | | | $Ami_nSpi_nUro_nNit_n$ γ ψ! |
| Piperine $C_{17}H_{19}NO_3$ | pungent: F | | | | | ψ! |
| Piperitol | minty: A | | | | | $He_n$ δ! |

| | | | | |
|---|---|---|---|---|
| d-Piperitone $C_{10}H_{16}O$ | peppermint, minty: AY | .9344 (20/4°C) | | $He_n$ δ! |
| Piperonal $C_8H_6O_3$ | sweet, floral, heliotrope: ACXY | | 191.7 | $Flo_n$ α! ρ |
| Piperonyl butoxide $C_{19}H_{30}O_5$ | mild: X | 1.06 (25°C) | | |
| PLATINUM Pt | no reported odor | 21.45 (20°C) | 3714 | |
| PLATINUM COMPOUNDS | no reported odors | | | |
| Polyethylene glycol | characteristic: X | | | |
| Polyoxyl (8) stearate | faint, fatty: X | | | $Lip_n$ ξ |
| Potash, sulfurated | hydrogen sulfide: X | | | $Sul_n$ β! |
| POTASSIUM K | no reported odor | .862 | 586 | |
| Potassium alginate $(C_6H_7KO_6)_n$ | slight, characteristic: X | | | |
| Potassium bisulfite $HKO_3S$ | sulfur dioxide: X | | | $Sul_n$ |
| Potassium cyanide CKN | faint bitter almonds, hydrogen cyanide: PXY | 1.52 (16°C) | | $Nut_n$ ξ ψ |
| Potassium hydrosulfide HKS | hydrogen sulfide-like: X | 1.68-1.70 | | $Sul_n$ β! |
| Potassium metabisulfite $K_2O_5S_2$ | sulfur dioxide: XY | 2.25 | | $Sul_n$ |

| Chemical | Reported Characteristics | Specific Gravity | Vapor Pressure | Detection Threshold | Recognition Threshold | Classification Expression, Factors, HU Value |
|---|---|---|---|---|---|---|
| Potassium stearate $C_{18}H_{35}KO_2$ | slight fat: XY | | | | | $Lip_n$ ξ |
| PRASEODYMIUM Pr | no reported odor | 6.769 (20°C) | | | | |
| PRASEODYMIUM COMPOUNDS | no reported odors | | | | | |
| Pristane $C_{19}H_{40}$ | faintly odored: X | .775-.795 (20°C) | | | | |
| Promazine $C_{17}H_{20}N_2S$ | amine: Y | | | | | $Ami_n$ |
| PROMETHIUM Pm | no reported odor | | | | | |
| PROMETHIUM COMPOUNDS | no reported odors | | | | | |
| 1,3-Propanedithiol $C_3H_8S_2$ | disagreeable: Y | 1.0772 (20/4°C) | | | | |
| Propargyl alcohol $C_3H_4O$ | mild, geranium: PY | .9715 (20/4°C) | | | | $Flo_n$ |
| Propargyl bromide $BrC_3H_3$ | sharp: P | 1.520 (20°C) | | | | ψ! |
| Propenyl guaethol $C_{11}H_{14}O_2$ | strongly similar to vanilla: X | | | | | $Bal_n$ |
| Propenyl sulfonic acid $C_3H_6O_3S$ | alliaceous: A @ | | | | | $All_n$ |

| | | | | | | |
|---|---|---|---|---|---|---|
| β-Propiolactone $C_2H_4O_2$ | pungent: X | 1.1460 (20/4°C) | | | | ψ! |
| Propiolaldehyde $C_3H_2O$ | pungent, intensely irritating: AM | | | | | ψ!!! ε!! |
| Propiolic acid $C_3H_2O_2$ | acrylic odor: M | 1.1380 (20/4°C) | | | | |
| Propionaldehyde $C_3H_6O$ | suffocating, sweet, ester, acetaldehyde, pungent: FJ MPXY | .8071 (20/4°C) | | | .080 | $Fru_n$ α λ φ! ψ! $HU^{3-6}_{4-6}$ 49-144 |
| Propionic acid $C_3H_6O_2$ | pungent, rancid, disagreeable, sour: AFJXY | .99336 (20/4°C) | 85.8 | .000042 | .034 | $Lip_n$ ψ! $HU^{3-6}_{4-6}$ 49-144 |
| Propionic anhydride $C_6H_{10}O_3$ | more pungent than the acid: XY | 1.0169 (15/4°C) | 107.2 | | | ψ!! |
| Propionitrile $C_3H_5N$ | ethereal, sweetish, pleasant: MPXY | .7818 (20/4°C) | 41.4 | | | α! λ! |
| Propionyl chloride $C_3ClH_5O$ | pungent: XY | 1.065 (20/5°C) | | | | ψ! |
| Propiophenone $C_9H_{10}O$ | strong, persistent, agreeable, flowery: XY | 1.0105 (20/4°C) (liq.) | 149.3 | | | $Flo_n$ ρ! |
| n-Propyl acetate $C_5H_{10}O_2$ | pleasant, pears, sweet, ester: FJPXY | .836 (20/4°C) | 47.8 | | .15 | $Fru_n$ α! λ $HU^{2-3}_{2-3}$ 16-36 |
| n-Propyl alcohol $C_3H_8O$ | sweet, ethyl alcohol, alcoholic, slightly stupifying, pungent, ethereal: AFJPXY | .804 (20/4°C) | 52.8 | | .13 | $Mst_nHyc_n$ α! λ! ψ! $HU^{2-3}_{2-4}$ 16-49 |

| Chemical | Reported Characteristics | Specific Gravity | Vapor Pressure | Detection Threshold | Recognition Threshold | Classification Expression, Factors, HU Value |
|---|---|---|---|---|---|---|
| n-Propylamine $C_3H_9N$ | strong ammonia: XY | .719 (20/20°C) | 5.0 | | | $Uro_nNit_n$ ψ!!! |
| p-Propylanisole $C_{10}H_{14}O$ | characteristic, anise-like: X | .940-.943 (25°C) | | | | $Her_n$ |
| Propyl bromide $BrC_3H_7$ | ethereal: M | 1.353 (20/20°C) | 18 | | | λ |
| α-Propyl-γ-butyrolactone $C_7H_{12}O_2$ | cumin, trace anise: M | | | | | $Spi_nHer_n$ |
| n-Propyl chloride $C_3ClH_7$ | chloroform-like, ethereal: AMP | .890 (20/20°C) | -2.5 | | | λ! |
| Propyl chlorosulfonate $C_3ClH_7O_3S$ | lachrymator, military poison gas, very irritant: X | | | | | ε!! |
| 1-Propylcyclohexanol-1 $C_9H_{18}O$ | camphor: A | | | | | $Woo_n$ |
| Propylene $C_3H_6$ | aromatic: J | .5139 (20/4°C) | -84.1 | | 67.60 | $HU^{1-2}_{2-3}$ 9-25 |
| Propylene chlorohydrin $C_3ClH_7O$ | mild, pleasant, non-residual: X | 1.1128 (20/20°C) | | | | |
| Propylene dichloride $C_3Cl_2H_6$ | chloroform-like, sweet: JXY | 1.1583 (20/20°C) | 39.4 | | .60 | α λ! $HU^{2-3}_{2-3}$ 16-36 |
| Propylene glycol $C_3H_8O_2$ | slight: X | 1.0381 (20/20°C) | 132 | | | |

| | | | | | | |
|---|---|---|---|---|---|---|
| Propylene glycol monoricinoleate $C_{21}H_{40}O_4$ | mild: X | .960 (25/25°C) | | | | |
| Propylene oxide $C_3H_6O$ | ethereal, sweet: JPX | .8304 (20/20°C) | -12.0 | | 35.0 | α λ! $HU^2_{2-3}$ 16-25 |
| Propyl formate $C_4H_8O_2$ | pleasant: PY | .9006 (20/4°C) | 29.5 | | | |
| n-Propyl furoate $C_8H_{10}O_3$ | aromatic: X | 1.0745 (25.9/4°C) | | | | |
| Propyl heptyl ketone $C_{11}H_{22}O$ | rue, fruit: M | | | | | $Fru_n$ |
| Propylhexedrine $C_{10}H_{21}N$ | amine: XY | .8501 (25/4°C) | | | | $Ami_n$ |
| Propyl 2-hexenoate $C_9H_{16}O_2$ | fruity, grass, green: W | | | | | $Fru_nEns_n$ |
| Propyl iodide $C_3H_7I$ | ethereal: AM | 1.747 (20/4°C) | 43.8 | | | λ! |
| Propylmalonic acid, diethyl ester $C_{10}H_{18}O_4$ | aromatic: X | .9860 (25°C) | | | | |
| n-Propyl mercaptan $C_3H_8S$ | offensive: X | .8408 | 15.3 | .024 | | β! $HU^{4-6}_{4-6}$ 64-144 |
| n-Propyl nitrate $C_3H_7NO_3$ | ethereal: X | 1.0538 (20/4°C) | | | | λ! |
| α-Propylpyridine $C_8H_{11}N$ | floral: D | | | | | $Flo_n$ |
| γ-Propylpyridine $C_8H_{11}N$ | violets: D | | | | | $Flo_n$ |

| Chemical | Reported Characteristics | Specific Gravity | Vapor Pressure | Detection Threshold | Recognition Threshold | Classification Expression, Factors, HU Value |
|---|---|---|---|---|---|---|
| Propylselenohydride $C_3H_8Se$ | putrid: A | | | | | β! |
| Propyl sulfide $C_6H_{14}S$ | | .814 | | .167 | | $HU^{3-5}_{4-5}$ 49-100 |
| Pseudocyclocitral | green, hay-like: | | | | | $Woo_nEns_n$ |
| Pulegone $C_{10}H_{16}O$ | pleasant, minty, midway between peppermint and camphor: FXY | .9346 (15/4°C) | 143.1 | | | $Woo_nHe_n$ δ! |
| d-Pulegone $C_{10}H_{16}O$ | minty: A | | | | | $He_n$ δ! |
| Putrescine $C_4H_{12}N_2$ | putrid, strong: AX | | | | | β! |
| Pyrazine $C_4H_4N_2$ | strong pyridine-like: MY | 1.031 (61/4°C) | | | | $Hyc_nOxy_n$ β!! ν!!! σ!! ϕ ω! |
| Pyrazole $C_3H_4N_2$ | pyridine: XY | | | | | $Hyc_n$ $Oxy_n$ β! ν!! σ!! ϕ ψ! ω |
| 2-Pyrazoline $C_3H_6N_2$ | faint amine, an odor resembling chocolate has been observed in some preparations: Y | 1.0200 (17/4°C) | | | | $Ami_n$ ξ σ ψ or $Ami_nWoo_n$ σ ψ |
| Pyridine $C_5H_5N$ | characteristic, disagreeable, sharp, penetrating, rank, unpleasant, empyreumatic: MPXY | .9780 (25/4°C) | 57.8 | | 21 | $Hyc_nOxy_n$ β! ν!!! ϕ σ!!! ψ! ω! $HU^{4-6}_{5-6}$ 81-144 |

| | | | | |
|---|---|---|---|---|
| Pyridostigmine bromide $BrC_9H_{13}N_2O_2$ | agreeable: X | | | |
| Pyrilamine maleate $C_{21}H_{27}O_5N_3$ | faint: X | | | |
| Pyrimidine $C_4H_4N_2$ | penetrating: XY | | | ω! |
| Pyrocarbonic acid diethyl ester $C_6H_{10}O_5$ | fruity: Y | 1.12 (20/4°C) | | $Fru_n$ |
| Pyroligneous acid | empyreumatic: Y | 1.018-1.030 | | σ!! |
| Pyrrobutamine phosphate $C_{20}ClH_{22}N \cdot 2H_3O_4P$ | slight: X | | | |
| Pyrrole $C_4H_5N$ | agreeable, ethereal, empyreumatic, chloroform: AXY | .9691 (20/4°C) | | λ! σ! |
| Pyrrolidine $C_4H_9N$ | unpleasant, ammonia-like, penetrating: XY | .8520 (22.5/4°C) | | $Uro_nNit_n$ ψ ω |
| Pyrroline $C_4H_7N$ | unpleasant, ammonia-like: Y | .9097 (20/4°C) | | $Uro_nNit_n$ ψ |
| 2-α-Pyrrylbenzothiazole $C_{11}H_8N_2S$ | floral, tea-rose, geranium: AM | | | $Her_nFlo_n$ |
| Pyruvaldehyde $C_3H_4O_2$ | pungent: PY | 1.0455 (24°C) | | ψ! |
| Pyruvic acid $C_3H_4O_3$ | acetic acid-like: XY | 1.2272 (20/4°C) | 106.5 | φ ψ!! |

| Chemical | Reported Characteristics | Specific Gravity | Vapor Pressure | Detection Threshold | Recognition Threshold | Classification Expression, Factors, HU Value |
|---|---|---|---|---|---|---|
| Pyruvic acid diethylamide $C_8H_{13}NO_4$ | weak, minty: A | | | | | $He_n$ $\delta$ |
| Quinaldine $C_{10}H_9N$ | quinoline: XY | 1.059 (20/4°C) | 176.2 | | | $Her_n$ $\beta$ $\nu$! $\sigma$!! $\omega$! |
| Quinazoline $C_8H_6N_2$ | quinoline-like: Y | | | | | $Her_n$ $\beta$ $\nu$!! $\sigma$! $\omega$! |
| Quinine valerate $C_{25}H_{36}N_2O_5$ | slight, valerian: Y | | | | | |
| Quinoline $C_9H_7N$ | penetrating, peculiar, characteristic, aromatic, aniseed, not as offensive as pyridine: AMPXY | 1.0899 | 163.2 | | | $Her_n$ $\beta$ $\nu$! $\sigma$ $\omega$! |
| Quinoline tartrate $C_{43}H_{45}N_3O_{24}$ | pungent: Y | | | | | $\psi$! |
| Quinone $C_6H_4O_2$ | chlorine-like, pungent, characteristic, irritating vapors: AMPXY | 1.318 (40/4°C) | | | | $Hal_n$ $\varepsilon$! $\nu$ $\psi$!! |
| Quinoxaline $C_8H_6N_3$ | quinoline when cool, piperidine when hot: Y | 1.1334 (48/4°C) (liq.) | | | | $\theta^2$: $Amin_nSpi_nUro_nNit_n$ $\psi$!<br>$\theta_1$: $Her_n$ $\beta$ $\nu$! $\sigma$ $\omega$! |
| Resorcinol acetate $C_8H_8O_3$ | faint, characteristic: X | 1.203-1.207 | | | | |

| | | | | |
|---|---|---|---|---|
| Resorcinol dimethyl ether $C_8H_{10}O_2$ | substantially fragrant, about medium acid, about medium burnt, substantially caprylic: C | 1.063-1.066 (25/25°C) | | $But_n$ σ! ψ! |
| RHENIUM Re | no reported odor | 21.02 (0°C) | | |
| RHENIUM COMPOUNDS | no reported odors | | | |
| Rhodinol $C_{10}H_{20}O$ | pronounced rose-like: FXY | .8549 (20/4°C) | | $Flo_n$ σ ψ! |
| Rhodinyl acetate | rose-like, raspberry, bitter: FX | .895-.908 (25°C) | | $Flo_nFru_n$ ν σ ψ! |
| Rhodinyl butyrate | blackberry, sweet, moss, rose: C | | | $Fru_nFlo_nMoo_n$ α! σ ψ |
| α-Rhodinyl-γ-butyrolactone | musky, peach, mellow: M | | | $Mus_nFru_n$ |
| Rhodinyl formate | bittersweet, red rose, cherry: C | | | $Fru_nFlo_n$ α ν σ ψ!! |
| Rhodinyl phenyl-acetate | rose: C | | | $Flo_n$ σ ψ |
| RHODIUM Rh | no reported odor | 12.42 (20°C) | | |
| D-Ribose $C_5H_{10}O_5$ | slightly sweet: X | | | α |
| RUBIDIUM Rb | no reported odor | 1.525 | 514 | |

| Chemical | Reported Characteristics | Specific Gravity | Vapor Pressure | Detection Threshold | Recognition Threshold | Classification Expression, Factors, HU Value |
|---|---|---|---|---|---|---|
| RUBIDIUM COMPOUNDS | no reported odors | | | | | |
| RUTHENIUM Ru | no reported odor | 12.41 (20°C) | | | | |
| Ruthenium tetroxide $O_4Ru$ | ozone: P | 3.29 | | | | $Oxy_n$ |
| Safrole $C_{10}H_{10}O_2$ | sassafras: XY | 1.096 (20°C) | 165.1 | | | $Her_n$ |
| Salicylaldehyde $C_7H_6O_2$ | bitter almond-like, floral, nutty, phenolic: ACFXY @ | 1.167 (20/4°C) | 129.4 | | | $Nut_nFlo_nHyc_n$ ν σ!!! ψ |
| SAMARIUM Sm | no reported odor | 7.8 | | | | |
| SAMARIUM COMPOUNDS | no reported odors | | | | | |
| Santalol $C_{15}H_{24}O$ | characteristic of oil of sandalwood, woody: FX | .971-.973 | | | | $Woo_n$ α! σ ψ |
| Santalyl acetate $C_{17}H_{26}O_2$ | apricot, light odor of sandalwood: FX | .982-.985 | | | | $Fru_nWoo_n$ σ ψ |
| Santalyl phenyl-acetate $C_{23}H_{31}O_2$ | honey, floral: C | | | | | $Car_nFlo_n$ ψ |
| Santalyl salicylate $C_{22}H_{28}O_3$ | faint, balsamic: Y | 1.07 | | | | $Bal_n$ |
| SCANDIUM Sc | no reported odor | 3.1 | | | | |
| SCANDIUM COMPOUNDS | no reported odors | | | | | |

| | | | | |
|---|---|---|---|---|
| Sebacic dinitrile $C_{10}H_{16}N_2$ | unpleasant, nutty: M | | | $Nut_n$ |
| Sebacic nitrile $C_{10}H_{16}N_2$ | unpleasant, nutty, sweet: M | | | $Nut_n$ α! |
| Selagine $C_{15}H_{18}N_2O$ | coniine: Y | | | $Uro_nBut_nMus_n$ |
| SELENIUM Se | no reported odor | | 554 | |
| Selenium bromide $Br_2Se_2$ | unpleasant: Y | 3.604 (15/4°C) | | |
| Selenium oxide $O_2Se$ | pungent, sour: Y | 3.954 (15/15°C) | | ψ! |
| Selenium oxyfluoride $F_2OSe$ | ozone-like: Y | 2.67 | | $Oxy_n$ |
| Selenium tetrabromide $Br_4Se$ | unpleasant: Y | | | |
| Selenium sulfide $S_2Se$ | faint, at most: X | | | |
| Senecialdehyde $C_5H_8O$ | more pungent than isovaleraldehyde: Y | .8722 (20/4°C) | | ψ!! |
| Silane $H_4Si$ | repulsive: XY | .68 (-185°C) (liq.) | -140.5 | β! |
| Silicoheptane $C_6H_{16}Si$ | petroleum-like: M | | | $Hyc_n$ |
| Silicoheptyl alcohol | camphor: A | | | $Woo_n$ |

| Chemical | Reported Characteristics | Specific Gravity | Vapor Pressure | Detection Threshold | Recognition Threshold | Classification Expression, Factors, HU Value |
|---|---|---|---|---|---|---|
| SILICON Si | no reported odor | 2.330 (25/4°C) | 2083 | | | |
| Silicononane $C_8H_{20}Si$ | light petroleum: M | | | | | $Hyc_n$ |
| Siliconony1 alcohol $C_8H_{20}OSi$ | camphor: A | .768 (22/4°C) | | | | $Woo_n$ |
| Silicon tetra-bromide $Br_4Si$ | disagreeable: PXY | 2.82 (0/4°C) | | | | $HU^{4-5}_{4-5}$ 64-100 |
| Silicon tetra-chloride $Cl_4Si$ | suffocating, may be irritating: PXY | 1.52 (0/4°C) | 5.4 | | | β φ!! $HU^{4-5}_{4-5}$ 64-100 |
| Silicon tetra-fluoride $F_4Si$ | suffocating, similar to hydrogen fluoride, very pungent, similar to hydrogen chloride: PXY | 1.590 (-78°C) (liq.) | -113.3 | | | $HU^{5-6}_{5-6}$ 100-144 |
| SILVER Ag | no reported odor | 10.49 (15°C) | 1865 | | | |
| Silver potassium cyanide $AgC_2KN_2$ | slight odor of hydrocyanic acid: P | | | | | $Nut_n$ ξ ψ |
| Skatole $C_9H_9N$ | extremely fecal, putrid: AFXY @ | | 197.4 | .223 | | $Fec_n$ β!!! σ ω! $HU^{5-6}_{5-6}$ 100-144 |
| SODIUM Na | no reported odor | .9712 | 701 | | | |

| | | | | |
|---|---|---|---|---|
| Sodium alginate $(C_6H_7NaO_6)_n$ | characteristic, slight: X | | | |
| Sodium amide $H_2NNa$ | ammonia: X | | | $Uro_nNit_n$ ψ |
| Sodium benzyl succinate $C_{11}H_{11}NaO_4$ | slight benzyl: X | | | |
| Sodium bisulfide HNaS | hydrogen sulfide: Y | 1.79 | | $Sul_n$ α β!! τ!! φ!! ψ! |
| Sodium bisulfite $HNaO_3S$ | slight sulfurous, sulfur dioxide: XY | 1.48 | | $Sul_n$ φ! ψ! ω |
| Sodium cyanide CNNa | in damp air emits slight odor of hydrocyanic acid, odorless when perfectly dry: Y | | 1214 | $Nut_n$ τ! |
| Sodium diacetate $C_4H_7NaO_4$ | acetic acid: X | | | ε φ ψ!! |
| Sodium formaldehydesulfoxylate $CH_3NaO_3S$ | odorless when freshly prepared but quickly develops a characteristic garlic odor: Y | | | $All_n$ ψ |
| Sodium formate $CHNaO_2$ | slight formic acid: XY | 1.919 | | ψ ω |
| Sodium gluconate $C_6H_{11}NaO_7$ | technical grade may have a pleasant odor: Y | | | |
| Sodium glutamate monohydrate $C_5H_8NNaO_4 \cdot H_2O$ | slight peptone-like: Y | | | |

| Chemical | Reported Characteristics | Specific Gravity | Vapor Pressure | Detection Threshold | Recognition Threshold | Classification Expression, Factors, HU Value |
|---|---|---|---|---|---|---|
| Sodium hydrosulfite $Na_2O_4S_2$ | slight, characteristic: Y | | | | | |
| Sodium hypochlorite solution | sweetish, disagreeable odor of hypochlorites: XY | | | | | $Hal_n$ α β |
| Sodium lauryl sulfate $C_{12}H_{25}NaO_4S$ | slight, characteristic, faint odor of fatty substances: XY | | | | | $Lip_n$ |
| Sodium mandelate $C_8H_7NaO_3$ | slight, aromatic: Y | | | | | |
| Sodium metabisulfite $Na_2O_5S_2$ | sulfur dioxide: Y | | | | | $Sul_n$ τ! φ ω |
| Sodium n-methyl-n-oleoyl taurate $C_{21}H_{40}NaO_4S$ | pleasant, slight, sweet: X | | | | | α |
| Sodium morrhuate | fishy: Y | | | | | $Ami_n$ |
| Sodium oleate $C_{18}H_{33}NaO_2$ | tallow-like, slight: XY | | | | | $Lip_n$ ξ |
| Sodium psylliate $C_{33}H_{65}NaO_2$ | soap-like: Y | .925-.930 | | | | $Lip_n$ |
| Sodium saccharin $C_7H_4NNaO_3S \cdot 2H_2O$ | odorless or faint aromatic: X | | | | | |
| Sodium salicylate $C_7H_5NaO_3$ | faint aromatic: X | | | | | |

| | | | | |
|---|---|---|---|---|
| Sodium stearate $C_{18}H_{35}NaO_3$ | fatty: X | | | $Lip_n$ |
| Sodium sulfoxone $C_{14}H_{14}N_2Na_2O_6S_3 \cdot 2H_2O$ | characteristic: X | | | |
| Sodium thiamylal $C_{12}H_{17}N_2NaO_2S$ | disagreeable: X | | | |
| Sodium thioglyco-late $C_2H_3NaO_2S$ | slight character-istic: XY | | | |
| Sodium thiopental $C_{11}H_{17}N_2NaO_2S$ | disagreeable: X | | | |
| Sparteine $C_{15}H_{26}N_2$ | distinctive, pecu-liar: X | 1.020 (20/4°C) | | |
| Spironolactone $C_{24}H_{32}O_4S$ | faint to mild mercaptan-like: X | | | $Mus_n$ |
| Squalene $C_{30}H_{50}$ | faint, agreeable: XY | .8584 (20/4°C) | | |
| Stearic acid $C_{18}H_{36}O_2$ | odorless or slight, tallow-like: XY | .8390 (80/4°C) | 291.0 | $Lip_n$ ξ |
| Stearyl alcohol $C_{18}H_{38}O$ | faint, characteris-tic: X | .8124 (59/4°C) | 269.4 | |
| Stibine $H_3Sb$ | disagreeable: Y | 2.26 (-25°C) | | |
| STRONTIUM Sr | no reported odor | 2.6 | 1111 | |
| Strontium sulfide SSr | hydrogen sulfide odor in the presence of moist air: XY | 3.70 | | $Sul_n$ |

| Chemical | Reported Characteristics | Specific Gravity | Vapor Pressure | Detection Threshold | Recognition Threshold | Classification Expression, Factors, HU Value |
|---|---|---|---|---|---|---|
| Styrene $C_8H_8$ | sharp, sweet, penetrating, aromatic: JPXY | .9045 (25/25°C) | 82 | | .15 | α λ ρ! ψ $HU^{2-3}_{2-4}$ 16-49 |
| Styrene oxide $C_8H_8O$ | sweet: J | 1.0469 (25/4°C) | | | .40 | $HU^{2-3}_{2-4}$ 16-49 |
| Succinic anhydride $C_4H_4O_2$ | suffocating: M | 1.104 (20/4°C) | 189.0 | | | φ! |
| SULFUR (amorphous) S | no reported odor | 2.046 | 327.2 | | | |
| Sulfur chloride $Cl_2S_2$ | penetrating, irritating: PXY | 1.6885 (15.5/15.5°C) | 75.3 | | | $Hal_nSul_n$ ε! ψ! ω! |
| Sulfur dichloride $Cl_2S$ | pungent, chlorine: PX | 1.638 (15.5°C) | | | .001 | $Hal_n$ ε! τ! φ!! ψ!! $HU^{4-6}_{4-6}$ 81-144 |
| Sulfur dioxide $O_2S$ | suffocating, pungent, extremely irritating: PXY | 1.5 (liq.) | -46.9 | | .47 | $Sul_n$ β! ε!!! τ!! φ!! $HU^{4-6}_{4-6}$ 81-144 |
| Sulfur iodine $I_2S_2$ | iodine: X | | | | | $Sul_nHal_n$ |
| Sulfurous acid $H_2O_3S$ | suffocating, sulfur dioxide, sulfur: XY | 1.0 | | | | $Sul_n$ ε!!! φ!!! ψ!!! |
| Sulfuryl chloride $Cl_2O_2S$ | very pungent: XY | 1.6674 | 17.8 | | | $Sul_nHal_n$ ψ!!! φ! |
| Tabun $C_5H_{11}N_2O_2P$ | fruity, reminiscent of bitter almonds: Y | 1.4250 (20/4°C) | | | | $Fru_nNut_n$ ν |

| | | | | |
|---|---|---|---|---|
| Tannic acid $C_{76}H_{52}O_{46}$ | faint, characteristic (Y); odorless (X) | | | |
| TANTALUM Ta | no reported odor | 16.69 | | |
| TANTALUM COMPOUNDS | no reported odors | | | |
| 1-Tartaric acid $C_4H_6O_6$ | burnt sugar odor when heated to melting point: Y | 1.7598 (20/4°C) | | $Car_n$ σ!! |
| TELLURIUM Te | imparts garlic-like odor to breath of workers: X | 6.11-6.27 | 838 | |
| Tellurium hexafluoride $F_6Te$ | repulsive: Y | 2.499 (-10°C) (liq.) | -67.9 | $Hal_n$ β!! |
| TERBIUM Tb | no reported odor | 8.253 | | |
| TERBIUM COMPOUNDS | no reported odors | | | |
| Terebene $C_{10}H_{16}$ | thyme-like: Y | .860-.865 (25/25°C) | | $Her_n$ |
| α-Terpiene $C_{10}H_{16}$ | pleasant, lemon: Y | .8375 (19.6/4°C) | | $Fru_n$ |
| Terpineol $C_{10}H_{18}O$ | peach, floral, lilac, musty, fruity: ACFX | .930-.936 (25°C) | 150.1 | $Mst_nFru_nFlo_n$ ψ |
| Terpinyl acetate $C_{12}H_{20}O_2$ | bergamot-lavender, sweet, almonds, raspberry, fresh, green, woody: FWX | .958-.968 (15°C) | | $Woo_nFlo_nNut_nFru_n$ α σ! ψ |

| Chemical | Reported Characteristics | Specific Gravity | Vapor Pressure | Detection Threshold | Recognition Threshold | Classification Expression, Factors, HU Value |
|---|---|---|---|---|---|---|
| Terpinyl anthranilate | floral, fruity: C | | | | | $Flo_nFru_n$ ψ! |
| Terpinyl formate | raspberry: F | | | | | $Fru_n$ |
| Terpinyl propionate | woody, fruity, floral: C | | | | | $Woo_nFru_nFlo_n$ σ! ψ |
| Tetraamminecopper sulfate hydrate $CuH_{12}N_4O_4S \cdot H_2O$ | ammonia: Y | 1.81 (20/4°C) | | | | $Uro_nNit_n$ ψ!! |
| Tetraamylbenzene $C_{26}H_{46}$ | faintly aromatic: X | .89 (20°C) | | | | $Woo_n$ |
| 1,1,2,2-Tetrabromochloroethane $Br_4C_2ClH$ | camphor: A | | | | | $Woo_n$ |
| 1,1,2,2-Tetrabromocyclobutane $Br_4C_4H_4$ | camphor: A | | | | | $Woo_n$ |
| 1,1,2,2-Tetrabromodifluoroethane $Br_4C_2F_2$ | strong camphor: A | | | | | $Woo_n$ |
| 1,2,2,2-Tetrabromoethane $Br_4C_2H_2$ | ethereal, weak, naphthalene: A | | | | | $Woo_nHyc_n$ λ σ ω |
| 1,1,1,2-Tetrabromofluoroethane $Br_4C_2FH$ | camphor: A | | | | | $Woo_n$ |
| 1,2,2,3-Tetrabromopropane $Br_4C_3H_4$ | camphor: A | | | | | $Woo_n$ |

| | | | | | |
|---|---|---|---|---|---|
| Tetrabutylthiuram disulfide $C_{18}H_{36}N_2S_4$ | slight, sweet: X | 1.03-1.06 (20/20°C) | | | $\alpha$ |
| sym-Tetrachlorodifluoroethane $C_2Cl_4F_2$ | camphor-like: X | 1.6447 (25°C) | 38.6 | | $Woo_n$ |
| 1,1,1,2-Tetrachlorodifluoroethane $C_2Cl_4F_2$ | camphor: A | | | | $Woo_n$ |
| sym-Tetrachloroethane $C_2Cl_4H_2$ | chloroform-like, sweetish, suffocating, camphor, ethereal: APXY | 1.58658 (25/4°C) | 83.2 | | $Woo_nHal_n$ $\alpha$!! $\lambda$! $\phi$! |
| Tetrachloroethylene $C_2Cl_4$ | ethereal, chloroform: PXY | 1.6311 (15/4°C) | 61.3 | | $\lambda$! |
| Tetrachloromethyl ether $C_2Cl_4H_2O$ | pungent: P | | | 4.68 | $\psi$! $HU^{4-5}_{4-5}$ 64-100 |
| 2,3,4,6-Tetrachlorophenol $C_6Cl_4H_2O$ | strong, characteristic: PX | 1.839 (25/4°C) | 205.2 | | |
| 2,4,5,6-Tetrachlorophenol $C_6Cl_4H_2O$ | phenol: PX | 1.65 | | | $Mol_nHyc_n$ $\sigma$!! |
| Tetradecamethylene carbonate | musky: A | | | | $Mus_n$ |
| Tetradecamethylene formal | musky: A | | | | $Mus_n$ |

| Chemical | Reported Characteristics | Specific Gravity | Vapor Pressure | Detection Threshold | Recognition Threshold | Classification Expression, Factors, HU Value |
|---|---|---|---|---|---|---|
| Tetradecanolactone | musky: A | | | | | $Mus_n$ |
| Tetradecylamine $C_{14}H_{31}N$ | ammonia: X | | 215.7 | | | $Uro_nNit_n$ ψ! |
| Tetraethylene carbonate $C_7H_{10}O_3$ | musky: A | | | | | $Mus_n$ |
| Tetraethyllead $C_8H_{10}Pb$ | pleasant, characteristic: PX | 1.653 (20°C) | 123.8 | | | |
| Tetraethyl pyrophosphate $C_8H_{20}O_7P_2$ | agreeable: Y | 1.185 (20/4°C) | | | | |
| Tetraethyl tetrazine $C_8H_{20}N_4$ | putrid, alliaceous: AM | | | | | $All_n$ β! ψ! |
| Tetraethyltin $C_8H_{20}Sn$ | ethereal: A | 1.187 (23°C) | | | | λ! |
| Tetraethyl trithiopyrophosphate | aromatic, turpentine oil: A | | | | | $Hyc_nWoo_n$ |
| Tetraethylurea $C_8H_{20}N_2O$ | minty: A | | | | | $He_n$ δ! |
| $\Delta^1$-Tetrahydrobenz aldehyde $C_7H_{10}O$ | almond: A | | | | | $Nut_n$ |
| Tetrahydrofuran $C_4H_8O$ | ethereal, etherlike, sweet: AMPXY | .8892 (20/4°C) | | | | α! λ! |

| | | | | |
|---|---|---|---|---|
| 2,5-Tetrahydro-furandimethanol $C_6H_{12}O_3$ | faint, highly irritating: Y | 1.1719 (0/4°C) | | ε!! |
| Tetrahydro-3-furanol $C_4H_8O_2$ | ether-like: Y | 1.0916 (20/4°C) | | α λ! |
| Tetrahydrogeraniol $C_{10}H_{22}O$ | geranium, green: C | | | $Flo_nEns_n$ σ! ψ |
| Tetrahydrolinalool $C_{10}H_{22}O$ | floral, sweet, reminiscent of citronellal, delicate, fatty: CFMX | .832-.837 | | $Lip_nFlo_nHyc_n$ α! |
| 1,2,3,4-Tetrahydro-6-methylquinoline $C_{10}H_{13}N$ | characteristic, civet: X | | | $\theta^2$: $Fec_nMus_nSul_n$ β! |
| Tetrahydronaphthalene $C_{10}H_{12}$ | pungent: X | .891 (13°C) | | ψ! |
| Tetrahydropyran $C_5H_{10}O$ | pungent, sweetish, ether-like: PY | .8814 (20/4°C) | | α! λ! ψ! |
| Tetrahydrothiophene $C_4H_8S$ | @ | 1.0 (15.6/15.6°C) | | |
| Tetraisopropylthiuram disulfide $C_{14}H_{28}N_2S_4$ | amine: X | 1.12 (20/20°C) | | $Ami_n$ |
| Tetralin† $C_{10}H_{12}$ | mixture of benzene and menthol, may be irritating: Y | .9702 (20/4°C) | 135.3 | |
| Tetramethylammonium hydroxide $C_4H_{13}NO$ | strong, ammonia-like: Y | | | $Uro_nNit_n$ ψ!! |

| Chemical | Reported Characteristics | Specific Gravity | Vapor Pressure | Detection Threshold | Recognition Threshold | Classification Expression, Factors, HU Value |
|---|---|---|---|---|---|---|
| Tetramethylcyclo-pentanone-3 | camphor: A | | | | | $Woo_n$ |
| Tetramethyldiamino-butane $C_8H_{20}N_2$ | penetrating: Y | .7861 (20°C) | | | | ω! |
| Tetramethyldiamino-methane $C_5H_{14}N_2$ | pungent: A | | | | | ψ! |
| Tetramethylethyl-enediamine $C_6H_{16}N_2$ | slight ammoniacal: X | .7765 (20/4°C) | | | | $Uro_nNit_n$ |
| Tetramethylguani-dine $C_5H_{13}N_3$ | slight, ammoniacal: X | | | | | $Uro_nNit_n$ |
| Tetramethylphos-phorodiamidic fluoride $C_4FH_{12}N_2OP$ | fishy: Y | 1.1151 | | | | $Ami_n$ |
| Tetramethyltin $C_4H_{12}Sn$ | ethereal: A | | 22.8 | | | λ! |
| Tetranorane (10) $BrH_{10}$ | disagreeable: P | | | | | |
| Tetrapropylthiuram disulfide $C_{14}H_{28}NS_4$ | musty: X | 1.13 (20/20°C) | | | | $Mst_n$ |
| Thalline sulfate $C_{20}H_{26}N_2O_2 \cdot H_2SO_4 \cdot 2H_2O$ | coumarin-like: Y | | | | | |

| | | | | |
|---|---|---|---|---|
| THALLIUM<br>Tl | no reported odor | 11.85 | 1196 | |
| THALLIUM COMPOUNDS | no reported odors | | | |
| Theophylline sodium glycinate | ammoniacal: X | 1.05<br>(20°C) | | $Uro_nNit_n$ ψ |
| Thiamine hydro-chloride<br>$C_{12}ClH_{17}N_4OS \cdot HCl$ | nut-like, slight thiazole: XY | | | $Nut_nHyc_nOxy_n$ β σ |
| Thiamorpholine<br>$C_4H_9NS$ | strong, resembling piperidine: Y | | | $Ami_nSpi_nUro_nNit_n$ ψ! |
| Thiamylal sodium<br>$C_{12}H_{17}N_2NaO_2S$ | disagreeable: X | | | |
| Thianaphthene<br>$C_8H_6S$ | naphthalene-like: Y | | | $Woo_nHyc_n$ ω! |
| 1,4-Thiazane<br>$C_4H_8NS$ | pyridine-like: X | | | $Hyc_nOxy_n$ β! σ!! φ ω |
| Thiazole<br>$C_3H_3NS$ | characteristic, foul, pyridine-like: MXY | 1.198 | | $Hyc_nOxy_n$ β! σ!! φ ω |
| Thimerosal<br>$C_9H_9HgNaO_2S$ | slight character-istic: X | | | |
| Thioacetic acid<br>$C_2H_4OS$ | pungent, acetic, disagreeable, put-rid, hydrogen sulfide odor: APXY | 1.075<br>(10/4°C) | 154.0 | $Sul_n$ β! τ ψ!! |
| Thioacetic acid allylamide<br>$C_6H_9NO_3S$ | weak garlic: A | | | $All_n$ |

| Chemical | Reported Characteristics | Specific Gravity | Vapor Pressure | Detection Threshold | Recognition Threshold | Classification Expression, Factors, HU Value |
|---|---|---|---|---|---|---|
| Thioanisole $C_7H_8S$ | strong, unpleasant: X | 1.053 (25°C) | | | | |
| Thiocarbonyl chloride $CCl_2S$ | irritating, putrid: AP | 1.5085 (15°C) | | | | β! ψ! |
| Thiocresol $C_8H_8S$ | S | | | .019 | | $HU^{4-5}_{4-5}$ 64-100 |
| p-Thiocresol $C_8H_8S$ | unpleasant, musty: X | | | | | $Mst_n$ |
| Thiodiglycol $C_4H_{10}O_2S$ | characteristic: PX | 1.1852 (20°C) | 285 | | | |
| Thioglycerol $C_3H_8O_2S$ | slight sulfidic: Y | 1.295 | | | | $Sul_n$ |
| Thioglycolic acid $C_2H_4O_2S$ | strong, unpleasant: XY | 1.325 | | | | |
| Thiolactic acid $C_3H_6O_2S$ | disagreeable: Y | 1.220 (15/4°C) | | | | |
| Thiomalic acid $C_4H_6O_4S$ | sulfidic, smokey, reminiscent of burning rubber: MXY | | | | | $Sul_nHyc_n$ σ!!! ψ! |
| Thionyl chloride $Cl_2OS$ | sharp, suffocating: XY | 1.638 (20/4°C) | 21.4 | | | ϕ ψ! |
| N′-Thionyl-N,N-diethylhydrazine | aromatic: A | | | | | |
| Thionylethylamine $C_2H_5NOS$ | pungent: A | | | | | ψ! |

| | | | | | |
|---|---|---|---|---|---|
| Thionyl fluoride<br>$F_2OS$ | suffocating: Y | 1.780<br>(-100°C)<br>(liq.) | | | φ! |
| Thiophene<br>$C_4H_4S$ | slight aromatic, resembling benzene, faint, neutral: MY | 1.0873<br>(0/4°C) | 30.5 | | $Hyc_n$ ξ |
| α-Thiophenealdehyde<br>$C_5H_4OS$ | almond-like: AX | 1.210-<br>1.220 | | | $Nut_n$ |
| Thiophenol<br>$C_6H_6S$ | repulsive, penetrating, garlic-like: Y | 1.0728<br>(25/4°C) | 106.6 | .014 | $All_n Sul_n$ β! ψ! ω!<br>$HU^{4-5}_{4-6}$ 64-121 |
| Thiophosphoric acid dibromide diethylamide | aromatic, camphor: A | | | | $Woo_n$ |
| Thiophosphoric acid dichloride di-n-amyl-amide | aromatic: A | | | | |
| Thiophosphoric acid dichloride diethylamide | strong, camphor: A | | | | $Woo_n$ |
| Thiophosphoric acid dichloride ethylamide | camphor: A | | | | $Woo_n$ |
| Thiophosphoric acid dichloride methylamide | weak, pungent: A | | | | ψ |

| Chemical | Reported Characteristics | Specific Gravity | Vapor Pressure | Detection Threshold | Recognition Threshold | Classification Expression, Factors, HU Value |
|---|---|---|---|---|---|---|
| Thiophosphoryl chloride $Cl_3PS$ | penetrating: PX | 1.635 | | | | ω! |
| Thiopropionic acid allylamide $C_7H_{11}NO_2S$ | weak, garlic: A | | | | | $All_n$ |
| Thioxane $C_4H_8OS$ | characteristic: P | | | | | |
| Thiram $C_6H_{12}N_2S_4$ | characteristic: X | 1.29 (20°C) | | | | |
| Thonzylamine hydrochloride $C_{16}H_{22}N_4O \cdot HCl$ | faint: X | | | | | |
| THORIUM Th | no reported odor | 11.3 11.7 | | | | |
| THORIUM COMPOUNDS | no reported odors | | | | | |
| Thujic acid methyl ester $C_{11}H_{14}O_2$ | pleasant: Y | 1.0225 (22/4°C) | | | | |
| Thujone $C_{10}H_{16}O$ | cedar leaf, spicy, tea-like: F | | | | | $Woo_nSpi_nEns_n$ |
| THULIUM Tm | no reported odor | 9.332 | | | | |
| THULIUM COMPOUNDS | no reported odors | | | | | |
| Thymol $C_{10}H_{14}O$ | aromatic, characteristic, pungent, medicinal, burnt, herb-like: CFXY @ | .9699 (25/4°C) | 164.1 | | | $Her_n$ σ!! ψ |

| | | | | | |
|---|---|---|---|---|---|
| Thymol acetate $C_{12}H_{16}O_2$ | characteristic: Y | 1.009 (0°C) | | | |
| Thymol blue $C_{27}H_{30}O_5S$ | thymol: Y | | | | $Her_n$ σ! ψ! |
| Thymol carbonate $C_{21}H_{26}O_3$ | thymol: Y | | | | $Her_n$ σ! ψ! |
| Thymol iodide $C_{20}H_{24}I_2O_2$ | slight, aromatic: X | | | | |
| Thymoquinone $C_{10}H_{12}O_2$ | penetrating: XY | | | | ω! |
| Tiglic acid $C_5H_8O_2$ | spicy: X | .972 | 140.5 | | $Spi_n$ |
| TIN Sn | no reported odor | 7.31 | 1968 | | |
| Tin tetraethyl $C_8H_{10}Sn$ | pleasant: M | | | | |
| TITANIUM Ti | no reported odor | 4.5 (20°C) | | | |
| Titanium tetra-chloride $Cl_4Ti$ | penetrating, acid: Y | 1.726 (liq.) | 71 | | ψ! ω! |
| m-Tolualdehyde $C_8H_8O$ | almond: A | | | | $Nut_n$ |
| o-Tolualdehyde $C_8H_8O$ | almond, burnt, ben-zaldehyde: AC | 1.0386 (19/4°C) | | | $Nut_n$ σ!!! |
| Toluene $C_7H_8$ | sweet, alcohol, benzol-like, ben-zene-like: JPXY | .866 (20/4°C) | 51.9 | 1.74 | $HU^{2-3}_{2-4}$ 16-49 |

| Chemical | Reported Characteristics | Specific Gravity | Vapor Pressure | Detection Threshold | Recognition Threshold | Classification Expression, Factors, HU Value |
|---|---|---|---|---|---|---|
| Toluene-2,4-diisocyanate $C_9H_6N_2O_2$ | sharp, pungent: XY | 1.2244 (20/4°C) (liq.) | | | | ψ! |
| 2-p-Tolylbenzo-thiazole | floral, tea-rose, geranium: AM | | | | | $Flo_n$ |
| p-Tolyl isocyanate $C_8H_7NO$ | S | | | | 2.14 | $HU^{3-4}_{3-5}$ 36-81 |
| m-Tolylisothiocyanate $C_8H_7NS$ | very strongly pungent: D | | | | | ψ!! |
| o-Tolylisothiocyanate $C_8H_7NS$ | strongly pungent: D | | | | | ψ! |
| p-Tolylisothiocyanate $C_8H_7NS$ | aniseed, sweet anise: D | | | | | $Her_n$ α! |
| Toxaphene | pleasant, piney, mild, chlorine, camphor: XY | 1.66 (27°C) | | | | $Woo_nHal_n$ ϕ ψ |
| Triacetin $C_9H_{14}O_6$ | slight, fatty: X | 1.160 (20°C) | | | | $Lip_n$ |
| Triamylamine $C_{15}H_{33}N$ | amine: P | .79 (20°C) | | | | $Ami_n$ |
| Triamylbenzene $C_{21}H_{36}$ | faintly aromatic: X | .87 (20°C) | | | | |
| Triamylborate $BC_{15}H_{33}O_3$ | n-amyl alcohol: P | .845 (20°C) | | | | $Fru_n$ |

| | | | |
|---|---|---|---|
| Triazoacetylazide $C_2N_9O$ | pungent: A | | $\psi$! |
| Tribromoacetyl-nitrile $Br_3C_3NO$ | pungent: A | | $\psi$! |
| 1,2,4-Tribromobenzene $Br_3C_6H_3$ | aromatic: A | | |
| Tribromo-tert-butyl alcohol $Br_3C_4H_7O$ | camphor-like: AXY | | $Woo_n$ |
| 1,1,2-Tribromo-cyclobutane $Br_3C_4H_5$ | camphor: A | | $Woo_n$ |
| 2,2,3-Tribromo-3, 3-dimethylpropane $Br_3C_5H_9$ | camphor: A | | $Woo_n$ |
| Tribromoethanol $Br_3C_2H_3O$ | aromatic, slight: XY | | |
| 1,1,2-Tribromo-1, 2,2-trifluoroethane $Br_3C_2F_3$ | camphor: A | | $Woo_n$ |
| Tributoxyethyl phosphate $C_{18}H_{39}O_7P$ | butyl-like: P | 1.020 (20°C) | |
| Tributylamine $C_{12}H_{27}N$ | characteristic, amine: XY | .7782 (20/20°C) | $Ami_n$ |
| Tri-n-butyl borate $BC_{12}H_{27}O_3$ | n-butyl alcohol-like: P | .8550-.8570 | $Mst_nFru_nAmi_n$ $\psi$! |

| Chemical | Reported Characteristics | Specific Gravity | Vapor Pressure | Detection Threshold | Recognition Threshold | Classification Expression, Factors, HU Value |
|---|---|---|---|---|---|---|
| Tri-sec-butyl borate $BC_{12}H_{27}O_3$ | sec-butyl alcohol odor: P | | | | | $HU^2_{2-3}$ |
| Tributyl(2,4-dichlorobenzyl)phosphonium chloride $C_{19}Cl_3H_{32}P$ | mild, aromatic: X | | | | | |
| Tri-n-butyl phosphine $C_{12}H_{27}P$ | garlic-type: X | | | | | $All_n$ ψ |
| Tributyl phosphorothioate $C_{12}H_{27}O_3PS$ | mild, characteristic: P | | | | | |
| Trichloroacetic acid $C_2Cl_3HO_2$ | slight, characteristic, sharp, pungent: XY | 1.629 (61/4°C) | 137.8 | | | ψ! |
| Trichloroacetic acid diethylamide $C_7Cl_3H_9NO_3$ | minty: A | | | | | $He_n$ δ! |
| Trichloroacrylic acid ethyl ester | minty: A | | | | | $He_n$ δ! |
| 2,4,6-Trichloroanisole $C_7Cl_3H_5O$ | faint, similar to acetophenone: Y | | | | | $A_nMst_nFru_nFlo_nHyc_n$ α! γ σ ψ |
| 1,2,4-Trichlorobenzene $C_6Cl_3H_3$ | similar to o-dichlorobenzene: X | 1.4634 (25/25°C) | 140 | | | |

| | | | | | |
|---|---|---|---|---|---|
| 1,1,2-Trichloro-ethane $C_2Cl_3H_3$ | pleasant, characteristic, sweet: PXY | 1.4416 (20/4°C) | 55.7 | | α! |
| 2,2,2-Trichloro-ethanol $C_2Cl_3H_3O$ | ethereal: AXY | 1.55 (20/20°C) | | | λ! |
| Trichloroethylene $C_2Cl_3H$ | characteristic, chloroform-like, ethereal: APXY @ | 1.4649 (20/4°C) | 31.4 | 21.4 | α λ! $HU^{2-4}_{3-5}$ 25-81 |
| Trichlorofluoro-methane $CCl_3F$ | faint, ethereal, sweet: JY | 1.494 (17.2/4°C) | -23 | 209.0 | λ $HU^{1-3}_{2-4}$ 9-49 |
| Trichloromethyl ether $C_2Cl_3H_3O$ | pungent: PX | 1.5066 (10°C) | | | ψ! |
| Trichloromethyl-phenylcarbinyl acetate $C_{10}Cl_3H_9O_2$ | intense rose: X | | | | $Flo_n$ |
| Trichloronitroso-methane $CCl_3NO$ | unpleasant: CPX | 1.5 (20°C) | | | |
| 3,3,4-Trichloro-pentanol-2 $C_5Cl_3H_9O$ | camphor: A | | | | $Woo_n$ |
| 2,4,5-Trichloro-phenol $C_6Cl_3H_3O$ | strong, phenolic: XY | 1.678 (25/4°C) | 178 | | $Mol_nHyc_n$ σ! ω |
| 2,4,6-Trichloro-phenol $C_6Cl_3H_3O$ | strong, phenolic: PX | 1.675 (25/4°C) | 177.8 | | $Mol_nHyc_n$ σ! ω |

| Chemical | Reported Characteristics | Specific Gravity | Vapor Pressure | Detection Threshold | Recognition Threshold | Classification Expression, Factors, HU Value |
|---|---|---|---|---|---|---|
| sym-Trichlorophenol $C_6Cl_3H_3O$ | iodoform-like: M | | | | | $Her_n$ ω |
| Tri-o-chlorophenyl borate $BC_{18}Cl_3H_{12}O_3$ | o-chlorophenol odor: P | | | | | $Mol_nHyc_nHal_n$ ψ! ω |
| 1,1,1-Trichloro-propanol-2 $C_3Cl_3H_5O$ | camphor: AXY | | | | | $Woo_n$ |
| 2,2′,2′′-Trichloro-triethylamine $C_6Cl_3H_{12}N$ | faint, fish+soap: Y | 1.2347 (25/4°C) | | | | $Ami_nLip_n$ |
| 1,1,2-Trichloro-1,2,2-trifluoro-ethane $C_2Cl_3F_3$ | sweet (J); nearly odorless (X) | 1.42 (25°C) | -1.7 | | 135.0 | $HU^{1-2}_{2-4}$ 9-36 |
| Tri-o-cresyl borate $BC_{21}H_{24}O_3$ | o-cresol odor: P | | | | | $Hyc_nMol_n$ σ!! ω |
| Tri-cresyl borate(s) $BC_{21}H_{24}O_3$ | characteristic: P | | | | | |
| Tricresyl phosphite $C_{21}H_{21}O_3P$ | slight phenolic: X | 1.115 (20/4°C) | | | | $Mol_n$ |
| Tricyclamol chloride $C_{19}H_{29}NO{\cdot}CClH_3$ | faint, characteristic: X | | | | | |
| sym-Tricyclodecane $C_{10}H_{16}$ | camphor: A @ | | | | | $Woo_n$ |

| | | | | | |
|---|---|---|---|---|---|
| Tri-(2-cyclohexyl-cyclohexyl)borate $BC_{36}H_{63}O_3$ | characteristic: P | | | | |
| Tridecamethylene carbonate | musky: A | | | | $Mus_n$ |
| Tridecanolactone | musky: A | | | | $Mus_n$ |
| Tridecyl alcohol $C_{13}H_{28}O$ | pleasant: X | .845 (20/20°C) | | | |
| Tri(decyl) phosphite $C_{30}H_{63}O_3P$ | 1-decanol odor: X | .892 (25/15.5°C) | | | $Fru_nLip_n$ α! ψ |
| Tri-(diisobutyl carbinyl) borate $BC_{27}H_{57}O_3$ | 2,6-dimethyl-4-heptanol **odor**: P | | | | $Hyc_n$ α! |
| Triethanolamine $C_6H_{15}NO_3$ | slight, ammoniacal, oily, slightly fishy: MXY | 1.1242 (20/4°C) | | | $Uro_nAmi_nLip_nNit_nHyc_n$ μ ψ |
| Triethylamine $C_6H_{15}N$ | strong ammoniacal, fishy: JXY | .7255 (25/4°C) | | .28 | $HU^{3-4}_{4-5}$ 49-81 |
| Triethylarsine $AsC_6H_{15}$ | putrid: A | | | | β! |
| Triethyl carbinol $C_7H_{16}O$ | camphor: A | | | | $Woo_n$ |
| Triethyl citrate $C_{12}H_{20}O_7$ | fruity: M | 1.136 (25°C) | 217.8 | | $Fru_n$ |
| Triethylene glycol dimethyl ether $C_8H_{18}O_4$ | mild, ethereal: PX | .9862 (20/20°C) | | | λ |

| Chemical | Reported Characteristics | Specific Gravity | Vapor Pressure | Detection Threshold | Recognition Threshold | Classification Expressions, Factors, HU Value |
|---|---|---|---|---|---|---|
| Triethylene glycol dipelargonate $C_{24}H_{46}O_6$ | mild, characteristic: P | .964 (20/20°C) | | | | |
| Tri(2-ethyl hexyl) borate $BC_{30}H_{51}O_3$ | 2-ethyl hexanol odor: P | | | | | $Mst_n$ |
| Triethyl-orthoformate $C_7H_{16}O_3$ | pungent: PX | .895 (20/20°C) | 88 | | | ψ! |
| Triethyl phosphine $C_6H_{15}P$ | floral, hyacinths: AY | .800 (15/4°C) | | | | $Flo_n$ |
| Triethyl phosphite $C_6H_{15}O_3P$ | ethereal: A | .9687 (20°C) | | | | λ! |
| O,O,O-Triethyl phosphorothioate $C_6H_{15}O_3PS$ | strong, characteristic: PX | 1.074 | | | | |
| Trifluoroacetic acid $C_2F_3HO_2$ | strong, pungent: PX | 1.535 | | | | ψ! |
| Tri-n-hexyl borate $BC_{18}H_{39}O_3$ | 1-hexanol odor: P | | | | | $Ens_nAmi_n$ ψ |
| Trihexylene glycol diborate $B_2C_{18}H_{36}O_6$ | hexylene glycol odor: P | .982 (21°C) | | | | α |
| Trihexyl phosphite $B_2C_{18}H_{39}O_3$ | characteristic: X | .897 (20/4°C) | | | | |

| | | | | | |
|---|---|---|---|---|---|
| Trihydroxyethyl-amine stearate $C_{24}H_{51}N$ | faint, fatty: X | .968 | | | $Lip_n$ |
| Triisobutyl borate $BC_{12}H_{27}O_3$ | isobutyl alcohol odor: P | | | | $Mst_nFru_nHyc_n$ α σ |
| Triisooctyl phos-phite $C_{24}H_{51}O_3P$ | characteristic: X | .891 (20/4°C) | | | |
| Triisopropyl phos-phite $C_9H_{21}PO_3$ | characteristic: X | .914 (20/4°C) | | | |
| Trimethadione $C_6H_9NO_3$ | slight, camphor-like: XY | | | | $Woo_n$ |
| 2,4,5-Trimethoxy-1-propenylbenzene $C_{12}H_{13}O_3$ | spicy, herb-like: F | | | | $Spi_nHer_n$ |
| Trimethylacetic acid diethylamide $C_{10}H_{20}NO_3$ | minty: A | | | | $He_n$ δ! |
| Trimethylacetyl-chloride $C_5ClH_9O_2$ | pungent: A | | | | ψ! |
| Trimethylamine $C_3H_9N$ | fishy, ammoniacal, pungent, putrid, herring brine: AMXY | .6709 (0/4°C) | -40.3 | .00021 | $Ami_nUro_nNit_n$ β!! μ ψ! $HU^{4-6}_{5-6}$ 81-144 |
| Trimethylamine hydrochloride $C_3H_9N \cdot HCl$ | less intense than base: Y | | | | $Ami_nUro_nNit_n$ β μ ψ |
| Trimethyl arsine $AsC_3H_9$ | putrid: A | | | | β! |

| Chemical | Reported Characteristics | Specific Gravity | Vapor Pressure | Detection Threshold | Recognition Threshold | Classification Expressions, Factors, HU Value |
|---|---|---|---|---|---|---|
| Trimethylboron $BC_8H_9$ | pungent: A | | -60.8 | | | ψ! |
| 1,1,4-Trimethyl-cycloheptanone-3 $C_{10}H_{18}O$ | camphor when cold, mint when warm: A | | | | | $\theta^2$: $He_n$ δ! $\theta_1$: $Woo_n$ |
| 1,1,3-Trimethyl-cyclohexanone-5 $C_9H_{16}O$ | minty: A | | | | | $He_n$ δ! |
| 1,1,4-Trimethyl-cyclohexanone-5 $C_9H_{16}O$ | strong mint: A | | | | | $He_n$ δ!! |
| 1,1,2-Trimethyl-cyclopentane $C_8H_{16}$ | camphor: A | | | | | $Woo_n$ |
| 1,1,2-Trimethyl-cyclopentanone-3 $C_8H_{11}O$ | minty: A | | | | | $He_n$ δ! |
| 1,1,2-Trimethyl-cyclopentanone-5 $C_8H_{11}O$ | camphor, mint: A | | | | | $Woo_nHe_n$ δ! |
| 1,1,3-Trimethyl cyclopentanone-2 $C_8H_{11}O$ | camphor, mint: A | | | | | $Woo_nHe_n$ δ! |
| Trimethylene chloro-hydrin $C_3ClH_7O$ | characteristic: X | 1.130-1.150 (25/25°C) | | | | |
| Trimethylene oxide $C_3H_6O$ | agreeable, aromatic: Y | .8930 (25/4°C) | | | | |

| | | | |
|---|---|---|---|
| 2,6,8-Trimethyl-4-nonanone $C_{12}H_{26}O$ | pleasant: X | .8165 (20/20°C) | |
| 2,6,8-Trimethyl-nonyl-4 alcohol $C_{12}H_{26}O$ | characteristic: X | .8913 (20/20°C) | |
| Trimethyl ortho-formate $C_4H_{10}O$ | pungent: P | | ψ! |
| Trimethylphosphine $C_3H_9P$ | putrid, repulsive: AM | | β! |
| 2,4,6-Trimethylpy-ridine $C_8H_{11}N$ | aromatic: Y | .9166 (22.1/4°C) | |
| 2,6,10-Trimethyl-9-undecan-1-al $C_{14}H_{26}O$ | pungent, ozone-like: X | .850 .860 (25/25°C) | $Oxy_n$ ψ! |
| Trinitro-tert-butyltoluene $C_{11}H_{13}N_3O_6$ | @ | | |
| 2,4,6-Trinitro-3-methyl-5-bromo-tert-butylbenzene $BrC_{11}H_{12}N_3O_6$ | musky: A | | $Mus_n$ |
| 2,4,6-Trinitro-3-methyl-tert-butyl-benzene $C_{11}H_{13}N_3O_6$ | musky: A | | $Mus_n$ |
| 2,4,6-Trinitro-3-methyl-5-chloro-tert-butylbenzene $C_{11}ClH_{12}N_3O_6$ | musky: A | | $Mus_n$ |

| Chemical | Reported Characteristics | Specific Gravity | Vapor Pressure | Detection Threshold | Recognition Threshold | Classification Expressions, Factors, HU Value |
|---|---|---|---|---|---|---|
| 2,4,6-Trinitro-3-methyl-di-tert-butylbenzene | weak musky: A | | | | | $Mus_n$ |
| 2,4,6-Trinitro-3-methyl-5-fluoro-tert-butylbenzene $C_{11}FH_{12}N_3O_6$ | musky: A | | | | | $Mus_n$ |
| 2,4,6-Trinitro-1-methyl-3-n-hexyl-benzene | weak, musky: A | | | | | $Mus_n$ |
| 2,4,6-Trinitro-3-methyl-5-iodo-tert-butylbenzene $C_{11}H_{12}IN_3O_6$ | musky: A | | | | | $Mus_n$ |
| 2,4,6-Trinitro-3-methylisopropyl-benzene | weak, musky: A | | | | | $Mus_n$ |
| Tri-n-octylborate $BC_{24}H_{51}O_3$ | 2-octanol odor: P | | | | | $Hyc_n Fru_n Mus_n$ α β! γ σ ψ! ω |
| Trioleyl borate $BC_{53}H_{105}O_3$ | stearyl alcohol odor: P | | | | | |
| Trioxane $C_3H_6O_3$ | ether-alcohol odor: P | | | | | $Hyc_n$ λ |
| sym-Trioxane $C_3H_6O_3$ | formaldehyde: X | 1.17 (65°C) | | | | ε! τ! ϕ!! ω |
| Tripelennamine $C_{16}H_{21}N_3$ | amine: Y | | | | | $Ami_n$ |

| | | | | |
|---|---|---|---|---|
| Triphenyl phosphite $C_9H_{15}O_3P$ | clean, pleasant: X | 1.184 (25/25°C) | | |
| Tripropylamine $C_9H_{21}N$ | amine: X | .754 (20/20°C) | | $Ami_n$ |
| Tri-n-propyl borate $BC_9H_{21}O_3$ | n-propanol odor: P | | | $Mst_nHyc_n$ α! λ! ψ! |
| Tris(2-chloroethyl) phosphite $C_6Cl_3H_{12}O_3P$ | characteristic: X | 1.353 (20/4°C) | | |
| Tris[1-(2-methyl)-aziridinyl]phosphine oxide $C_9H_{16}N_3OP$ | amine: X | | | $Ami_n$ |
| Tristearyl borate $BC_{54}H_{111}O_3$ | stearly alcohol: P | | | $Lip_nHyc_n$ |
| Tri(tetrahydro furfuryl) borate $(C_4H_7O\cdot CH_2O)_3B$ | characteristic: P | | | |
| Trolnitrate phosphate $C_{12}H_{27}N_8O_{13}P$ | banana-like: X | | | $Fru_n$ |
| Tropylene | almond, acetone: A | | | $Nut_nHyc_n$ |
| TUNGSTEN W | no reported odor | 19.3 | 5168 | |
| Turpentine | characteristic: XY | | | |
| Turpentine, spirits of $C_{10}H_{16}$ | rosin-like: X | .860-.875 (15°C) | | $Woo_nHyc_n$ |

| Chemical | Reported Characteristics | Specific Gravity | Vapor Pressure | Detection Threshold | Recognition Threshold | Classification Expressions, Factors, HU Value |
|---|---|---|---|---|---|---|
| Umbelliferone $C_9H_6O_3$ | develops odor of coumarin on heating: Y | | | | | $Spi_n$ |
| γ-Undecalactone $C_{11}H_{20}O_2$ | grassy, pleasant, fruity, peach-like, rancid, fatty, musty: CFX @ | .941-.944 | | | | $Mst_nFru_nLip_n$ σ! |
| Undecamethylene carbonate $C_{12}H_{20}O_3$ | camphor, musk: A | | | | | $Woo_nMus_n$ |
| Undecamethylene oxalate $C_{13}H_{22}O_4$ | musky: M | | | | | $Mus_n$ |
| Undecanal $C_{11}H_{22}O$ | sharp, citrus, sweet, orange, bland: FX | .825-.832 (25°C) | | | | $Fru_n$ α! ψ! |
| 1-Undecanol $C_{11}H_{24}O$ | slightly citrus, musty, fatty: CFX | .829-.834 | | | | $Mst_nLip_nFru_n$ σ ψ |
| Undecenal $C_{11}H_{20}O$ | slightly fatty, citrus, strong, suggesting rose, musty: CFX | .840-.850 (25/25°C) | | | | $Mst_nFlo_nFru_nLip_n$ σ ψ! |
| α-Undecyl-γ-butyrolactone $C_{14}H_{27}O$ | floral, musk, cocoa: AM | | | | | $Bal_nFlo_nMus_nWoo_n$ σ ψ |
| Undecylenic acid $C_{11}H_{20}O_2$ | characteristic, rosey, fruity, suggestive of perspiration: XY | .910-.913 (25/25°C) | | | | $Seb_nLip_nBut_nFru_nFlo_n$ β ψ |

| | | | | | |
|---|---|---|---|---|---|
| Undecylenic alcohol $C_{11}H_{22}O$ | fatty, somewhat citrus: X | | | | $Lip_nFru_n$ |
| Undecylenyl acetate $C_{12}H_{24}O_2$ | floral, fruity-type: X | .876-.883 | | | $Flo_nFru_n$ |
| Uranyl acetate $C_4H_6O_6U \cdot 2H_2O$ | slight acetic: Y | 2.893 | | | ψ |
| Urea $CH_4N_2O$ | ammonia: Y | 1.32 (18/4°C) | | | $Uro_nNit_n$ ε ψ! |
| Valeraldehyde $C_5H_{10}O$ | sharp, penetrating: F | .8095 (20/4°C) | | | ψ! ω! |
| Valeric acid $C_5H_{10}O_2$ | unpleasant, penetrating, rancid: AXY | .9394 (20/4°C) | 128.3 | .0006 | $Lip_n$ β ω! |
| VANADIUM V | no reported odor | 6.11 (18.7°C) | | | |
| VANADIUM COMPOUNDS | no reported odors | | | | |
| Vanillin $C_8H_8O_3$ | pleasant, aromatic, vanilla: FXY @ | 1.056 | 214.5 | | 0 $Mst_2$ $Bal_9$ 0 α!! ξ!! σ |
| Veratraldehyde $C_9H_{10}O_3$ | vanilla bean, chocolate, nutty, coconut: FY | | | | $Nut_nBal_nWoo_n$ ϕ ψ |
| Veratrine (mixture) | exceedingly irritating to mucous membranes, causing violent sneezing when inhaled: Y | | | | ε ψ!!! |
| Veratrole $C_8H_{10}O_2$ | floral, moderately fragrant, moderately acid, burnt, caprylic: AC | 1.084 (25/25°C) | | | $Flo_nBut_n$ σ!! ψ! |

| Chemical | Reported Characteristics | Specific Gravity | Vapor Pressure | Detection Threshold | Recognition Threshold | Classification Expressions, Factors, HU Value |
|---|---|---|---|---|---|---|
| d-Verbenone $C_{10}H_{14}O$ | characteristic: Y | .9780 (20°C) | | | | |
| Vetivert acetate $C_{17}H_{26}O_2$ | pleasant: X | .979-.999 (25/25°C) | | | | |
| Vinbarbital $C_{11}H_{16}N_2O_3$ | characteristic: X | | | | | |
| Vinyl acetate $C_4H_6O_2$ | sour, sharp: J | .9345 (20/20°C) | 23.3 | | .55 | ψ! $HU^{2-5}_{4-5}$ 36-100 |
| Vinyl chloride $C_2ClH_3$ | pleasant, ethereal, faintly sweet: PX | .9121 (20/20°C) (liq.) | -53.2 | | | α! λ! |
| Vinyl ether $C_5H_6O$ | characteristic: XY | .769 | | | | |
| Vinyl-β-ethoxyethyl sulfide $C_6H_{12}OS$ | camphor-like, pungent: X | .9532 (15°C) | | | | $Woo_n$ ψ! |
| Vinylidene chloride $C_2Cl_2H_2$ | sweet, chloroform-like: Y | 1.2129 (20/4°C) | -15 | | | α! λ |
| Vinylidene fluoride $C_2F_2H_2$ | faint, ethereal: X | .617 (g/cc) (24°C) (liq.) | | | | |
| Vitamin A | mild, fishy: X | | | | | $Ami_n$ μ |
| Xylene $C_8H_{10}$ | sweet: J | .864 (20/4°C) | | | .27 | α! $HU^{2-3}_{2-3}$ 16-36 |

| | | | | | |
|---|---|---|---|---|---|
| p-Xylene $C_8H_{10}$ | | .854 (25/4°C) | 75.9 | .47 | |
| 2,4-Xylene-1-ol $C_8H_{12}O$ | weak: D | | | | |
| 2,5-Xylene-1-ol $C_8H_{12}O$ | mild, cresolic: M | | | | $Mol_nHyc_n$ σ! ω |
| 2,6-Xylene-1-ol $C_8H_{12}O$ | wintergreen: D | | | | $He_n$ δ! |
| 3,4-Xylene-1-ol $C_8H_{12}O$ | dull, musty: M | | | | $Mst_n$ |
| 3,5-Xylene-1-ol $C_8H_{12}O$ | strong, phenol: D | | | | $Mol_nHyc_n$ σ!! ω! |
| Xylenol $C_8H_{10}O$ | carbolic, disin-fectant: M | 1.02-1.03 (15°C) | | | $Mol_nHyc_n$ σ!! ω! |
| m-Xylyl bromide $BrC_8H_9$ | powerful lachry-mator: Y | 1.371 (23°C) | | | ε!!! |
| o-Xylyl bromide $BrC_8H_9$ | powerful lachry-mator, war gas: Y | 1.381 (23°C) | | | ε!!! |
| p-Xylyl bromide $BrC_8H_9$ | powerful lachry-mator: Y | 1.324 | | | ε!!! |
| Xylyl bromide (s) $BrC_8H_9$ | pleasant, aromatic, very irritant: X | 1.4 | | | ε!! |
| m-Xylyl chloride $C_8ClH_9$ | powerful lachry-mator: Y | 1.064 (20°C) (liq.) | | | ε!!! |
| o-Xylyl chloride $C_8ClH_9$ | powerful lachry-mator: Y | | | | ε!!! |

| Chemical | Reported Characteristics | Specific Gravity | Vapor Pressure | Detection Threshold | Recognition Threshold | Classification Expressions, Factors, HU Value |
|---|---|---|---|---|---|---|
| p-Xylyl chloride $C_8ClH_9$ | powerful lachrymator: Y | | | | | ε!!! |
| 2,4-Xylylisothiocyanate $C_9H_{11}NS$ | aniseed, delicate anise: AD | | | | | $Her_n$ |
| 2,5-Xylylisothiocyanate $C_9H_{11}NS$ | pungent: D | | | | | ψ! |
| 2,6-Xylylisothiocyanate $C_9H_{11}NS$ | floral, delicate, spirea: AD | | | | | $Flo_n$ |
| 3,4-Xylylisothiocyanate $C_9H_{11}NS$ | harsh, anise-like: D | | | | | $Her_n$ |
| 3,5-Xylylisothiocyanate $C_9H_{11}NS$ | pungent: D | | | | | ψ! |
| Yeast | characteristic, slightly sour: Y | | | | | $Ye_n$ ψ |
| YTTERBIUM Yb | no reported odor | 7.01 | | | | |
| YTTERBIUM COMPOUNDS | no reported odors | | | | | |
| YTTRIUM Y | no reported odor | 4.34 | | | | |
| YTTRIUM COMPOUNDS | no reported odors | | | | | |

| | | | |
|---|---|---|---|
| ZINC<br>Zn | no reported odor | | |
| Zinc acetate<br>$C_4H_6O_4Zn \cdot 2H_2O$ | faint, acetous:<br>XY | 1.735 | ξ ψ |
| Zinc dibutyldi-<br>thiocarbamate<br>$C_{18}H_{36}N_4S_4Zn$ | pleasant: X | 1.24<br>(20/20°C) | |
| Zinc phosphide<br>$P_2Zn_3$ | faint, phosphor-<br>ous: Y | 4.55 | $Pho_n$ ξ |
| Zinc ricinoleate<br>$C_{36}H_{66}O_6Zn$ | faint, fatty acid:<br>X | 1.10<br>(25/25°C) | $Lip_n$ ξ ψ |
| Zinc stearate<br>$C_{36}H_{70}O_4Zn$ | faint, character-<br>istic: XY | 1.095 | $Lip_n$ ξ |
| Zinc valerate<br>$C_{10}H_{18}O_4Zn \cdot 2H_2O$ | disagreeable,<br>valerian: XY | | |
| Zingerone<br>$C_{11}H_{14}O_3$ | spicy, ginger-like:<br>F | | $Spi_n$ γ |
| ZIRCONIUM<br>Zr | no reported odor | 6.4 | |
| ZIRCONIUM COM-<br>POUNDS | no reported odors | | |
| Zolamine<br>$C_{15}H_{21}N_3OS$ | putrid: Y | | β! |

| Chemical | Reported Characteristics | Specific Gravity | Vapor Pressure | Detection Threshold | Recognition Threshold | Classification Expression, Factors, HU Value |
|---|---|---|---|---|---|---|
| *2,4-Dinitro-2,6-dimethyl-4-tert-butylbenzonitrile | musky: A | | | | | $Mus_n$ |
| *2,4-Dinitro-3,5 -dimethyl-6-fluoro-tert-butylbenzene | musky: A | | | | | $Mus_n$ |
| *2,6-Dinitro-3,5-dimethyl-5-fluoro-tert-butylbenzene | musky: A | | | | | $Mus_n$ |

*Addendum

## CONVERSION FORMULAS

GALLONS INTO AVOIRDUPOIS POUNDS: Multiply 8.33 (weight of one gallon of water) by the specific gravity and the result by the number of gallons. Example: What is the weight in pounds of 20 gallons of alcohol, specific gravity: 0.816?

8.33 X 0.816 = 6.797
6.797 X 20 = 135.94 avoirdupois pounds

AVOIRDUPOUS POUNDS INTO GALLONS: Multiply 8.33 (weight of one gallon of water) by the specific gravity and divide the number of pounds by the result. Example: What is the volume in gallons of 236 pounds of phosphoric acid, specific gravity: 1.710?

8.33 X 1.710 = 14.24
236 ÷ 14.24 = 16.57 gallons

MILLILITERS INTO GRAMS: Multiply the number of milliliters by the specific gravity.
Example: What is the weight of 350 milliliters of hydrochloric acid, specific gravity: 1.158?

350 X 1.158 = 405.3 grams

GRAMS INTO MILLILITERS: Divide the number of grams by the specific gravity.
Example: 250 grams of ether, specific gravity: 0.715, equals how many milliliters?

250 ÷ 0.715 = 349.65 milliliters

MILLILITERS INTO AVOIRDUPOIS POUNDS: Multiply the number of milliliters by the specific gravity, and divide the product by 453.59 (weight in grams of avoirdupois pound).
Example: What is the weight in pounds of 750 milliliters of sulfuric acid, specific gravity: 1.835?

750 X 1.835 = 1376.25 grams
1376.25 ÷ 453.59 = 3.03 pounds

AVOIRDUPOIS POUNDS INTO MILLILITERS: Multiply the number of pounds by 453.59 (equivalent in grams of one avoirdupois pound) and divide the product by the specific gravity.
Example: 200 pounds of chloroform, specific gravity 1.476, equals how many milliliters?

453.59 X 200 = 90,718.0 grams
90,718.0 ÷ 1.476 = 61,462.0 milliliters

MILLILITERS INTO AVOIRDUPOIS OUNCES: Multiply the number of milliliters by the specific gravity, and divide the product by 28.35 (weight in grams of one avoirdupois ounce).
Example: What is the weight in ounces of 225 milliliters of ammonia water, specific gravity: 0.958?

225 X 0.958 = 215.55 grams
215.55 ÷ 28.35 = 7.60 ounces

AVOIRDUPOIS OUNCES INTO MILLILITERS: Multiply the number of ounces by 28.35 (weight in grams of one avoirdupois ounce) and divide the product by the specific gravity.
Example: 50 ounces of methyl salicylate, specific gravity: 1.182, equals how many milliliters?

50 X 28.35 = 1,417.5 grams
1,417.5 ÷ 1.182 = 1,199.2 milliliters

## PREFIXES USED IN THE METRIC SYSTEM

| Prefixes | Meaning | | Units |
|---|---|---|---|
| Pico- (one trillionth) | $\frac{1}{1,000,000,000,000}$ | $= 10^{-12}$ | |
| Nano- (one billionth) | $\frac{1}{1,000,000,000}$ | $= 10^{-9}$ | |
| Micro- (one millionth) | $\frac{1}{1,000,000}$ | $= 10^{-6}$ | |
| Milli- (one thousandth) | $\frac{1}{1,000}$ | $= 10^{-3}$ | |
| Centi- (one hundredth) | $\frac{1}{100}$ | $= 10^{-2}$ | |
| Deci- (one tenth) | $\frac{1}{10}$ | $= 10^{-1}$ | Meter for length |
| Unit (one) | 1 | = 1 | |
| Deka- (ten) | 10 | = 10 | Gram for weight or mass |
| Hecto- (one hundred) | 100 | $= 10^{2}$ | |
| Kilo- (one thousand) | 1,000 | $= 10^{3}$ | Liter for capacity |
| Mega- (one million) | 1,000,000 | $= 10^{6}$ | |
| Giga- (one billion) | 1,000,000,000 | $= 10^{9}$ | |
| Tera- (one trillion) | 1,000,000,000,000 | $= 10^{12}$ | |

## U.S. SYSTEM OF MEASURES AND WEIGHTS

### Length

| | |
|---|---|
| 1 International nautical mile | = 6076.1 feet |
| 1 Statute mile (mi.) | = 320 rods = 1760 yards = 5280 feet |
| 1 Rod (rd.) | = 5.5 yards = 16.5 feet |
| 1 Yard (yd.) | = 3 feet = 36 inches |
| 1 Foot (ft.) | = 12 inches |

### Avoirdupois Weight

| | |
|---|---|
| 1 Gross or long ton | = 2240 pounds |
| 1 Ton | = 2000 pounds |
| 1 Hundredweight (cwt.) | = 100 pounds |
| 1 Pound (lb.) | = 16 ounces = 7000 grains |
| 1 Ounce (oz.) | = 16 drams = 437.5 grains |
| 1 Dram (dr.) | = 27.33 grains |

## EQUIVALENTS: U. S. AND METRIC SYSTEMS OF MEASURES AND WEIGHTS

### Length

| | |
|---|---|
| 1 Millimeter | = 0.03937 inch |
| 1 Centimeter | = 0.3937 inch |
| 1 Meter | = 39.37 inches |
| 1 Meter | = 3.2808 feet |
| 1 Meter | = 1.09361 yards |
| 1 Meter | = 0.1988 rod |
| 1 Kilometer | = 0.6214 mile |
| 1 Inch | = 2.540 centimeters |
| 1 Foot | = 30.480 centimeters |
| 1 Foot | = 0.3048 meter |
| 1 Yard | = 0.9144 meter |
| 1 Rod | = 5.0292 meters |
| 1 Mile | = 1.6093 kilometers |

### Area

| | |
|---|---|
| 1 Square centimeter | = 0.155 square inch |
| 1 Square meter | = 1550.0 square inches |
| 1 Square meter | = 10.764 square feet |
| 1 Square meter | = 1.196 square yards |
| 1 Square inch | = 6.4516 square centimeters |
| 1 Square foot | = 929.0341 square centimeters |
| 1 Square foot | = 0.0929 square meter |
| 1 Square yard | = 0.8361 square meter |

Some Multiples and Submultiples of Length

| Inches | Millimeters | Inches | Centimeters |
|---|---|---|---|
| 1/32 | 0.794 | 6 | 15.240 |
| 1/16 | 1.588 | 7 | 17.780 |
| 1/8 | 3.175 | 8 | 20.320 |
| 1/4 | 6.350 | 9 | 22.860 |
| 3/8 | 9.525 | 10 | 25.400 |
| 1/2 | 12.700 | 11 | 27.940 |
| 3/4 | 19.050 | 12 | 30.480 |
| 1 | 25.40 | 24 | 60.960 |
| 2 | 50.80 | 36 | 91.440 |
| 3 | 76.20 | 48 | 121.920 |
| 4 | 101.60 | 60 | 152.400 |
| 5 | 127.00 | 72 | 182.880 |

| Millimeters | Inches | Meters | Feet |
|---|---|---|---|
| 1 | 0.03937 | 1 | 3.2808 |
| 2 | 0.07874 | 2 | 6.5617 |
| 3 | 0.11811 | 3 | 9.8425 |
| 4 | 0.15748 | 4 | 13.1233 |
| 5 | 0.19685 | 5 | 16.4042 |
| 6 | 0.23622 | 6 | 19.6850 |
| 7 | 0.27559 | 7 | 22.9658 |
| 8 | 0.31496 | 8 | 26.2467 |
| 9 | 0.35433 | 9 | 29.5275 |
| 10 | 0.39370 | 10 | 32.8083 |

## THERMOMETRIC EQUIVALENTS

Temperature Scales

| Symbol | Designation (Degree) | Zero Point | Freezing Point of Water | Boiling Point of Water at SAP* |
|---|---|---|---|---|
| °C | Celsius or centigrade | Freezing point of water | 0°C | 100°C |
| °K | Kelvin or absolute temperature in degrees centigrade | Absolute zero | 273.16°K | 373.16°K |
| °F | Fahrenheit | -17.8°C | +32°F | 212°F |
| °Rank | Rankine or absolute temperature in degrees Fahrenheit | Absolute zero | 491.4°Rank | 671.4°Rank |

*SAP: Standard Atmospheric Pressure

## Temperature Conversion Formulas

| Temperature Given In | Temperature Wanted In °C | °K | °F | °Rank |
|---|---|---|---|---|
| °C | C | C + 273.16 | 1.8C + 32 | 1.8C + 491.4 |
| °K | K - 273.16 | K | 1.8K - 459.4 | 1.8K |
| °F | 0.556F - 17.8 | 0.556F + 255.3 | F | F + 459.4 |
| °Rank | 0.556Rank - 273.1 | 0.556Rank | Rank - 459.4 | Rank |

## ANTIFREEZE MIXTURES
(Solutions)

### Freezing Point of Denatured Alcohol-water Solutions

| Denatured Alcohol % v/v | Freezing Point °C | °F |
|---|---|---|
| 5 | -2.8 | 27.0 |
| 10 | -4.0 | 24.8 |
| 15 | -6.0 | 21.2 |
| 20 | -8.5 | 16.7 |
| 25 | -11.5 | 11.3 |
| 30 | -14.8 | 5.4 |
| 35 | -18.3 | -0.9 |
| 40 | -22.1 | -7.8 |
| 45 | -26.9 | -16.4 |
| 50 | -31.1 | -24.0 |

### Freezing Point of Ethylene Glycol-water Solutions

| Ethylene Glycol % v/v | Freezing Point °C | °F |
|---|---|---|
| 5 | -1.1 | 30 |
| 10 | -2.8 | 27 |
| 15 | -5.0 | 23 |
| 20 | -8.3 | 17 |
| 25 | -12.0 | 11 |
| 30 | -16.0 | 3 |
| 35 | -21.0 | -5 |
| 40 | -26.0 | -14 |
| 45 | -31.0 | -23 |
| 50 | -37.0 | -34 |

Freezing Point of Water Solutions of a Commercial Ethylene Glycol Antifreeze Preparation

| % v/v | °C | °F |
|---|---|---|
| 10 | -3.9 | 25 |
| 20 | -8.9 | 16 |
| 30 | -15.5 | 4 |
| 40 | -24.4 | -12 |
| 50 | -36.7 | -34 |
| 60 | -52.2 | -62 |

Freezing Point of Glycerol-water Solutions

| Glycerol | Freezing Point | |
|---|---|---|
| % w/w | °C | °F |
| 10 | -1.6 | 29.1 |
| 20 | -4.8 | 23.4 |
| 30 | -9.5 | 14.9 |
| 40 | -15.4 | 4.3 |
| 50 | -23.0 | -9.4 |
| 60 | -34.7 | -30.5 |

Freezing Point of Water Solutions of a Commercial Methanol Antifreeze Preparation

| % v/v | °C | °F |
|---|---|---|
| 10 | -5.0 | 23 |
| 20 | -11.7 | 11 |
| 30 | -20.6 | -5 |
| 40 | -32.8 | -27 |
| 50 | -46.7 | -52 |

## CONCENTRATIONS OF ACIDS AND BASES

### Common Commercial Strengths

| Chemical | Molecular Weight | Moles per Liter | Grams per Liter | % By Weight | Specific Gravity |
|---|---|---|---|---|---|
| Acetic acid, glacial | 60.05 | 17.4 | 1045 | 99.5 | 1.05 |
| Acetic acid | 60.05 | 6.27 | 376 | 36 | 1.045 |
| Butyric acid | 88.1 | 10.3 | 912 | 95 | 0.96 |
| Formic acid | 46.02 | 23.4 | 1080 | 90 | 1.20 |
| | | 5.75 | 264 | 25 | 1.06 |
| Hydriodic acid | 127.9 | 7.57 | 969 | 57 | 1.70 |
| | | 5.51 | 705 | 47 | 1.50 |
| | | 0.86 | 110 | 10 | 1.1 |
| Hydrobromic acid | 80.92 | 8.89 | 720 | 48 | 1.50 |
| | | 6.82 | 552 | 40 | 1.38 |
| Hydrochloric acid | 36.5 | 11.6 | 424 | 36 | 1.18 |
| | | 2.9 | 105 | 10 | 1.05 |
| Hydrocyanic acid | 27.03 | 25.0 | 676 | 97 | 0.697 |
| | | 0.74 | 19.9 | 2 | 0.996 |
| Hydrofluoric acid | 20.01 | 32.1 | 642 | 55 | 1.167 |
| | | 28.8 | 578 | 50 | 1.155 |
| Hydrofluosilicic acid | 144.1 | 2.65 | 382 | 30 | 1.27 |
| Hypophosphorous acid | 66.0 | 9.47 | 625 | 50 | 1.25 |
| | | 5.14 | 339 | 30 | 1.13 |
| | | 1.57 | 104 | 10 | 1.04 |
| Lactic acid | 90.1 | 11.3 | 1020 | 85 | 1.2 |
| Nitric acid | 63.02 | 15.99 | 1008 | 71 | 1.42 |
| | | 14.9 | 938 | 67 | 1.40 |
| | | 13.3 | 837 | 61 | 1.37 |
| Perchloric acid | 100.5 | 11.65 | 1172 | 70 | 1.67 |
| | | 9.2 | 923 | 60 | 1.54 |
| Phosphoric acid | 98 | 14.7 | 1445 | 85 | 1.70 |
| Sulfuric acid | 98.1 | 18.0 | 1766 | 96 | 1.84 |
| Sulfurous acid | 82.1 | 0.74 | 61.2 | 6 | 1.02 |
| Ammonia water | 17.0 | 14.8 | 252 | 28 | 0.898 |
| Potassium hydroxide | 56.1 | 13.5 | 757 | 50 | 1.52 |
| | | 1.94 | 109 | 10 | 1.09 |
| Sodium carbonate | 106.0 | 1.04 | 110 | 10 | 1.10 |
| Sodium hydroxide | 40.0 | 19.1 | 763 | 50 | 1.53 |
| | | 2.75 | 111 | 10 | 1.11 |

## VAN DER WAAL'S

The general Van der Waal's theory is that the energy of the interreaction of infinitely small volume elements, $dv_1$ and $dv_2$, of two particles is:

$$E = -Q \frac{dv_1\ dv_2}{r^6}$$

where Q is a constant having dimensions of energy, and r is the distance between $dv_1$ and $dv_2$. Integrating the expression, the energy between two spherical particles of distant attraction, each of radius r, their conters being d distance apart, is (H. C. Hamaker, 1937):

$$E = -Qf(x) = -\frac{\pi^2 Q}{6x}\left(\frac{2}{x} + \frac{x-1}{x-2} + \frac{x+1}{x+2} - x \ln \frac{x^2}{x^2-4}\right),$$

where $x = \frac{d}{r}$.

The probability of a collision between two charged particles when the probability between uncharged particles as unity is given by:

$$\frac{1}{p} = \int_0^1 \exp\left(\frac{\psi\left(\frac{2r}{x}\right)}{kT}\right) dx,$$

where $x = \frac{2r}{y}$.

## EFFICIENCY OF ELECTROSTATIC PRECIPITATION

In the absence of turbulence: $\eta = 1 - e^{-\gamma}$,
where $\eta$ is the efficiency and $\gamma$ is a parameter which can be expressed in different ways; for example:

$$\gamma = \frac{2uL}{Rv},$$

where u is the particle velocity, L is the length of the outer electrode, and v is the gas velocity (W. Deutsch, 1922).

## STOKES' LAW

The settling rate through the air of a particle (droplet) of a diameter between 0.1 μ and 100 μ, known as Stokes' Law, is as follows (G. Stokes, 1901):

$$v = \frac{2ga^2(\rho - \rho g}{9\eta}$$

where v is the settling rate in cm/sec, g is the acceleration of gravity (about 980 cm/sec$^2$), a is the radius of the droplet in cm, $\rho$ is its density (1 g/cm$^3$ for water), $\rho g$ is the density of the air or gas (about 0.0012 g/cm$^3$ for air at sea level), and $\eta$ is the viscosity of the air or gas (about 0.00018 poise for air at 68°F):

General form of Stokes' law:

$$f = 6\pi a \eta v,$$

where f is the force in dynes required to pull a droplet or particle of radius a (cm) through a gas of viscosity $\eta$ (poises), at a velocity of v (cm/sec). The force can be any force. For particles having a diameter less than 0.1 µ, the Cunningham correction factor (E. Cunningham, 1910) states:

$$v = \frac{2ga^2(\rho - \rho g)}{9\eta}\left(1 + \frac{0.86L}{a}\right),$$

where L is in cm's if a is in cm's. The correction is used for ordinary particles (about 2 µ in diameter) in high altitudes (50 to 100,000 feet).

## J.N.D.
## (Just Noticeably Different)

The level of an odorant in air is noticeably different in concentrations of the order of $10^5$. The odor level, as with most physiological sensations, is a multiple of the threshold concentration, in this case for odor detection. If $\Delta x$ is the amount by which x must be increased to give a J.N.D., then according to E. H. Weber (1834):

$$\frac{\Delta x}{x} = \text{a Constant}$$

G. T. Fechner (1858) states that if $\frac{\Delta x}{x}$ = a constant for the J.N.D., then:

$$dS = \frac{Cdx}{x},$$

where dS is any increment in the sensation generated by an increment in the stimulus dx, added to an already existing stimulus x, and C is a proportionality constant. Therefore:

$$dS = \frac{Cdx}{x},$$

Then:

$$S = a \log x - a \log x_0,$$

where S is the strength of the sensation, log x is the logarithm of the stimulus that produces the sensation (S), log $x_0$ is the logarithm of the stimulus that produces a just perceptible threshold sensation, and a is a constant. The logarithmic relation between strength of stimulus and strength of sensation is called the Weber-Fechner law and is expressed:

$$P = K \log S,$$

where P is the odor intensity, K is constant and S is odor concentration.

## PERSISTENCE

Persistence P expresses the time an osmogene permeates free air perceptibly (W. Summer, 1971):

$$P = (p_1/p)[\exp(1/2)(TM_1/T_1M)],$$

where p is the vapor pressure, torr, M is molecular weight, T is the air temperature (°K). Indexed values refer to water as a standard:

$$(p_1 = 12.7 \text{ torr}, T_1 = 288°K = 59°F; M_1 = 18, P_1 = 1).$$

## TIME OF ADAPTATION TO OSMOGENE

T is the adaptation time required for the cessation of smell:

$$T = b\sqrt{c - 1},$$

where b is a constant and c is the concentration of the odorant used as the adapting stimulus and has a concentration equal to the concentration at the absolute threshold, c equals 1. For d-octanol, the constant b is approximately 20; for m-xylene, it is approximately 30 (W. Summer, 1971).

## WAVELENGTHS EMITTED FROM SPECIFIC BONDS

(S. Glasstone, 1940)

| Bond | Wavelength (μ) |
|---|---|
| C-C | 12.5 - 11.6 |
| C-O | 12.2 - 11.4 |
| C-N | 11.4 - 10.8 |
| C=C | 6.25 - 6.1 |
| C=O | 6.1 |
| C=N | 5.7 - 5.8 |
| C≡C | 4.75 - 4.45 |
| C≡O | 4.66 |
| C≡N | 4.65 |

## SPECIFIC GRAVITY COMPARISONS

Equivalent of degrees Baumé (American Standard) with specific gravity at 60°F. For liquids lighter than water, to convert Baumé degrees into specific gravity, divide 140 by the sum of 130 plus the degrees Baumé:

$$\left(\text{Specific gravity} = \frac{140}{130 + {}^\circ\text{Bé}}\right)$$

To convert specific gravity into Baumé degrees, substract 130 from the quotient obtained by dividing 140 by the specific gravity:

$$\left(\text{Bé} = \frac{140}{\text{specific gravity}} - 130\right)$$

| °Bé | Sp gr | °Bé | Sp gr | °Bé | Sp gr | °Bé | Sp gr |
|---|---|---|---|---|---|---|---|
| 10.0 | 1.0000 | 29.0 | 0.8805 | 48.0 | 0.7865 | 67.0 | 0.7107 |
| 10.5 | 0.9964 | 29.5 | 0.8777 | 48.5 | 0.7843 | 67.5 | 0.7089 |
| 11.0 | 0.9929 | 30.0 | 0.8750 | 49.0 | 0.7821 | 68.0 | 0.7071 |
| 11.5 | 0.9894 | 30.5 | 0.8723 | 49.5 | 0.7799 | 68.5 | 0.7053 |
| 12.0 | 0.9859 | 31.0 | 0.8696 | 50.0 | 0.7778 | 69.0 | 0.7035 |
| 12.5 | 0.9825 | 31.5 | 0.8669 | 50.5 | 0.7756 | 69.5 | 0.7018 |
| 13.0 | 0.9790 | 32.0 | 0.8642 | 51.0 | 0.7735 | 70.0 | 0.7000 |
| 13.5 | 0.9756 | 32.5 | 0.8615 | 51.5 | 0.7713 | 70.5 | 0.6983 |
| 14.0 | 0.9722 | 33.0 | 0.8589 | 52.0 | 0.7692 | 71.0 | 0.6965 |
| 14.5 | 0.9689 | 33.5 | 0.8563 | 52.5 | 0.7671 | 71.5 | 0.6948 |
| 15.0 | 0.9655 | 34.0 | 0.8537 | 53.0 | 0.7650 | 72.0 | 0.6931 |
| 15.5 | 0.9622 | 34.5 | 0.8511 | 53.5 | 0.7629 | 72.5 | 0.6914 |
| 16.0 | 0.9589 | 35.0 | 0.8485 | 54.0 | 0.7609 | 73.0 | 0.6897 |
| 16.5 | 0.9556 | 35.5 | 0.8459 | 54.5 | 0.7588 | 73.5 | 0.6880 |
| 17.0 | 0.9524 | 36.0 | 0.8434 | 55.0 | 0.7568 | 74.0 | 0.6863 |
| 17.5 | 0.9492 | 36.5 | 0.8408 | 55.5 | 0.7547 | 74.5 | 0.6846 |
| 18.0 | 0.9459 | 37.0 | 0.8383 | 56.0 | 0.7527 | 75.0 | 0.6829 |
| 18.5 | 0.9428 | 37.5 | 0.8358 | 56.5 | 0.7507 | 75.5 | 0.6813 |
| 19.0 | 0.9396 | 38.0 | 0.8333 | 57.0 | 0.7487 | 76.0 | 0.6796 |
| 19.5 | 0.9365 | 38.5 | 0.8309 | 57.5 | 0.7467 | 76.5 | 0.6780 |
| 20.0 | 0.9333 | 39.0 | 0.8284 | 58.0 | 0.7447 | 77.0 | 0.6763 |
| 20.5 | 0.9302 | 39.5 | 0.8260 | 58.5 | 0.7427 | 77.5 | 0.6747 |
| 21.0 | 0.9272 | 40.0 | 0.8235 | 59.0 | 0.7407 | 78.0 | 0.6731 |
| 21.5 | 0.9241 | 40.5 | 0.8211 | 59.5 | 0.7388 | 78.5 | 0.6715 |
| 22.0 | 0.9211 | 41.0 | 0.8187 | 60.0 | 0.7368 | 79.0 | 0.6699 |
| 22.5 | 0.9180 | 41.5 | 0.8163 | 60.5 | 0.7349 | 79.5 | 0.6683 |
| 23.0 | 0.9150 | 42.0 | 0.8140 | 61.0 | 0.7330 | 80.0 | 0.6667 |
| 23.5 | 0.9121 | 42.5 | 0.8116 | 61.5 | 0.7311 | 80.5 | 0.6651 |
| 24.0 | 0.9091 | 43.0 | 0.8092 | 62.0 | 0.7292 | 81.0 | 0.6635 |
| 24.5 | 0.9061 | 43.5 | 0.8069 | 62.5 | 0.7273 | 81.5 | 0.6619 |
| 25.0 | 0.9032 | 44.0 | 0.8046 | 63.0 | 0.7254 | 82.0 | 0.6604 |
| 25.5 | 0.9003 | 44.5 | 0.8023 | 63.5 | 0.7235 | 82.5 | 0.6588 |
| 26.0 | 0.8974 | 45.0 | 0.8000 | 64.0 | 0.7216 | 83.0 | 0.6573 |
| 26.5 | 0.8946 | 45.5 | 0.7977 | 64.5 | 0.7198 | 83.5 | 0.6557 |
| 27.0 | 0.8917 | 46.0 | 0.7955 | 65.0 | 0.7179 | 84.0 | 0.6542 |
| 27.5 | 0.8889 | 46.5 | 0.7932 | 65.5 | 0.7161 | 84.5 | 0.6527 |
| 28.0 | 0.8861 | 47.0 | 0.7910 | 66.0 | 0.7143 | 85.0 | 0.6512 |
| 28.5 | 0.8833 | 47.5 | 0.7887 | 66.5 | 0.7125 | 85.5 | 0.6497 |

## SPECIFIC GRAVITY COMPARISONS

Equivalent of degrees Baumé (American Standard) to specific gravity at 60°F. For liquids heavier than water, to convert Baumé degrees into specific gravity, divide 145 by the difference between 145 and the number of Baumé degrees:

$$\left(\text{Specific gravity} = \frac{145}{145 - {}^{\circ}\text{Bé}}\right)$$

To convert specific gravity into Baumé degrees, subtract from 145 the quotient obtained by dividing 145 by the specific gravity:

$$\left(\text{Bé} = 145 - \frac{145}{\text{specific gravity}}\right)$$

| °Bé | Sp gr | °Bé | Sp gr | °Bé | Sp gr | °Bé | Sp gr |
|---|---|---|---|---|---|---|---|
| 0.5 | 1.0035 | 19.0 | 1.1508 | 37.5 | 1.3488 | 56.0 | 1.6292 |
| 1.0 | 1.0069 | 19.5 | 1.1554 | 38.0 | 1.3551 | 56.5 | 1.6384 |
| 1.5 | 1.0105 | 20.0 | 1.1600 | 38.5 | 1.3615 | 57.0 | 1.6477 |
| 2.0 | 1.0140 | 20.5 | 1.1647 | 39.0 | 1.3679 | 57.5 | 1.6571 |
| 2.5 | 1.0175 | 21.0 | 1.1694 | 39.5 | 1.3744 | 58.0 | 1.6667 |
| 3.0 | 1.0211 | 21.5 | 1.1741 | 40.0 | 1.3810 | 58.5 | 1.6763 |
| 3.5 | 1.0247 | 22.0 | 1.1789 | 40.5 | 1.3876 | 59.0 | 1.6860 |
| 4.0 | 1.0284 | 22.5 | 1.1837 | 41.0 | 1.3942 | 59.5 | 1.6959 |
| 4.5 | 1.0320 | 23.0 | 1.1885 | 41.5 | 1.4010 | 60.0 | 1.7059 |
| 5.0 | 1.0357 | 23.5 | 1.1934 | 42.0 | 1.4078 | 60.5 | 1.7160 |
| 5.5 | 1.0394 | 24.0 | 1.1983 | 42.5 | 1.4146 | 61.0 | 1.7262 |
| 6.0 | 1.0432 | 24.5 | 1.2033 | 43.0 | 1.4216 | 61.5 | 1.7365 |
| 6.5 | 1.0469 | 25.0 | 1.2083 | 43.5 | 1.4286 | 62.0 | 1.7470 |
| 7.0 | 1.0507 | 25.5 | 1.2134 | 44.0 | 1.4356 | 62.5 | 1.7576 |
| 7.5 | 1.0545 | 26.0 | 1.2185 | 44.5 | 1.4428 | 63.0 | 1.7683 |
| 8.0 | 1.0584 | 26.5 | 1.2236 | 45.0 | 1.4500 | 63.5 | 1.7791 |
| 8.5 | 1.0623 | 27.0 | 1.2288 | 45.5 | 1.4573 | 64.0 | 1.7901 |
| 9.0 | 1.0662 | 27.5 | 1.2340 | 46.0 | 1.4646 | 64.5 | 1.8012 |
| 9.5 | 1.0701 | 28.0 | 1.2393 | 46.5 | 1.4721 | 65.0 | 1.8125 |
| 10.0 | 1.0741 | 28.5 | 1.2446 | 47.0 | 1.4796 | 65.5 | 1.8239 |
| 10.5 | 1.0781 | 29.0 | 1.2500 | 47.5 | 1.4872 | 66.0 | 1.8354 |
| 11.0 | 1.0821 | 29.5 | 1.2554 | 48.0 | 1.4948 | 66.5 | 1.8471 |
| 11.5 | 1.0861 | 30.0 | 1.2609 | 48.5 | 1.5026 | 67.0 | 1.8590 |
| 12.0 | 1.0902 | 30.5 | 1.2264 | 49.0 | 1.5104 | 67.5 | 1.8710 |
| 12.5 | 1.0943 | 31.0 | 1.2719 | 49.5 | 1.5183 | 68.0 | 1.8831 |
| 13.0 | 1.0985 | 31.5 | 1.2775 | 50.0 | 1.5263 | 68.5 | 1.8954 |
| 13.5 | 1.1027 | 32.0 | 1.2832 | 50.5 | 1.5344 | 69.0 | 1.9079 |
| 14.0 | 1.1069 | 32.5 | 1.2889 | 51.0 | 1.5426 | 69.5 | 1.9205 |
| 14.5 | 1.1111 | 33.0 | 1.2946 | 51.5 | 1.5508 | 70.0 | 1.9333 |
| 15.0 | 1.1154 | 33.5 | 1.3004 | 52.0 | 1.5591 | 70.5 | 1.9463 |
| 15.5 | 1.1197 | 34.0 | 1.3063 | 52.5 | 1.5676 | 71.0 | 1.9595 |
| 16.0 | 1.1240 | 34.5 | 1.3122 | 53.0 | 1.5761 | 71.5 | 1.9728 |
| 16.5 | 1.1284 | 35.0 | 1.3182 | 53.5 | 1.5847 | 72.0 | 1.9863 |
| 17.0 | 1.1328 | 35.5 | 1.3242 | 54.0 | 1.5934 | 72.5 | 2.0000 |
| 17.5 | 1.1373 | 36.0 | 1.3303 | 54.5 | 1.6022 | 73.0 | 2.0139 |
| 18.0 | 1.1417 | 36.5 | 1.3364 | 55.0 | 1.6111 | 73.5 | 2.0280 |
| 18.5 | 1.1462 | 37.0 | 1.3426 | 55.5 | 1.6201 | 74.0 | 2.0423 |

NUCLEATING EFFICIENCY OF SOME SALTS
(Condensation of Water Vapor)

In Order of Efficiency:

LiCl
NaCl
CaCl
$MnCl_2$
$CuSO_4$
AgI

In Order of Electrochemical Series:

Na
Li
Mn
Cu
Ag

Atomization of liquids, both polar and non-polar, gives rise to charged droplets, so-called "spray electricity." Non-polar liquids give rise to charged droplets several orders of magnitude lower than those of polar liquids.

M. von Smoluchowski (1912) states that the droplet charge depends on the number of positive and negative ions which happen to be in the volume of liquid when it is released. There is random distribution of charges; however, on the average:

$$\overline{\sigma^2} = 2\ NV,$$

where $\overline{\sigma^2}$ is the mean square charge, expressed in terms of the number of elementary charges, N is the concentration of ions of the same sign, and V is the volume of the droplet. The mean absolute value of the charge is given by:

$$|\bar{\sigma}| = 2 \exp\ (-2NV) \sum_{\sigma=0}^{\infty} \sigma I_{\sigma}\ (2NV),$$

where $I_{\sigma}$ (2NV) is a Bessel function of the imaginary argument of the first kind and of the order $\sigma$. Where the value of NV is sufficiently large:

$$|\bar{\sigma}| = \frac{\sqrt{4NV}}{\pi},$$

and the distribution of charges is expressed by the Gaussian equation:

$$\frac{dN}{d\sigma} = \frac{\quad}{\sqrt{4\pi NV}} \cdot \exp\ (-\sigma^2/4NV);$$

verification of the theory has been confirmed by G. L. Natanson (1949), N. Fuchs (1950) and E. E. Dodd (1953).

## EYE IRRITATION INDEX

The amount of time in seconds recorded for subjects to notice eye irritation when exposed to 2 PPM of tested hydrocarbon plus 1 PPM of irritant at 26% relative humidity and 98°F is defined as follows (J. M. Heuss, W. A. Glasson, 1968):

$$I = \frac{(240 - t) \times 10}{240}$$

Values for I

| | |
|---|---|
| Allyl benzene | 8.4 |
| Aromatic olefins | 8 - 9 |
| Benzene | 1.0 |
| Benzyls | 4.5 - 6.5 |
| non-Benzyls | 1 - 2 |
| Butadiene | 7.0 |
| 1,3-Butadiene | 6.9 |
| n-Butane | 0 |
| 1-Butene | 1.3 |
| cis-2-Butene | 1.6 |
| trans-2-Butene | 2.3 |
| n-Butylbenzene | 6.4 |
| sec-Butylbenzene | 1.8 |
| tert-Butylbenzene | 0.9 |
| Ethylbenzene | 4.3 |
| Ethylene | 1.0 |
| n-Hexane | 0 |
| 1-Hexene | 3.5 |
| Iso-butylbenzene | 5.7 |
| Iso-octane | 0.9 |
| Isopropylbenzene | 1.6 |
| 2-Methyl-2-butene | 1.9 |
| α-Methylstyrene | 7.4 |
| β-Methylstyrene | 8.9 |
| Multi - alkylbenzenes | 2 - 3 |
| Olefins (internal) | 1.5 - 2.5 |
| Olefins (terminal) | 1 - 4 |
| Paraffins | 0 - 1 |
| n-Propylbenzene | 5.4 |
| Propylene | 3.9 |
| Styrene | 8.9 |
| Tetramethylethylene | 1.4 |
| Toluene | 5.3 |
| 1,3,5-Trimethylbenzene | 3.1 |
| m-Xylene | 2.9 |
| o-Xylene | 2.3 |
| p-Xylene | 2.5 |

# PATENT INDEX

The following table is a review of selected patents from the patent bibliography. Copies of any patent may be obtained by sending the patent title, number, date and inventor's name to the Commissioner of Patents, Patent Office, Washington, D. C. 20025. Fifty cents should be enclosed for each patent copy requested. Patents are also filed at many public libraries:

Libraries with Files of Patents (by Number)

| | |
|---|---|
| California | |
| Los Angeles | Public Library |
| Georgia | |
| Atlanta | Georgia Tech Library |
| Illinois | |
| Chicago | Main Branch, Public Library |
| Massachusetts | |
| Boston | Public Library |
| Michigan | |
| Detroit | Public Library |
| Minnesota | |
| Minneapolis | Public Library |
| Missouri | |
| Kansas City | Linda Hall Library |
| St. Louis | Public Library |
| New Jersey | |
| Newark | Public Library |
| New York | |
| Albany | University of State of New York Library |
| Buffalo | Grosvenor Library |
| New York | Public Library |
| Ohio | |
| Cincinnati | Public Library |
| Cleveland | Public Library |
| Columbus | Ohio State University Library |
| Toledo | Public Library |
| Pennsylvania | |
| Philadelphia | Franklin Institute Library |
| Pittsburgh | Carnegie Library |
| Rhode Island | |
| Providence | Public Library |
| Wisconsin | |
| Madison | Public Library |
| Milwaukee | Public Library |

All patents in the Index are United States patents except where otherwise indicated.

Patent 168,219: 1875

| | |
|---|---|
| Potassium permanganate: $KMnO_4$ | 1 Ounce |
| Boric acid: $H_3BO_3$ | 1/2 Ounce |
| Thymol: $(CH_3)_2ChC_6H_3(CH_3)OH$ | |

Comments:

The invention teaches the formula as a disinfecting, deodorizing, antiseptic composition. The potassium permanganate is an odor neutralizer of excellent quality for many odors, and the thymol has a penetrating and characteristic odor sufficiently strong to classify it as a deodorant of the masking class. The ingredients in general are of good antiseptic qualities and would contribute to deodorization through the prevention of formation of malodorants due to the antiseptic qualities. This formula is unquestionably a contact formula and due to the strong properties of the ingredients involved should be used with care. It should be pointed out that partial oxidation of some compounds will result in an increase in intensity and diversity of malodorants.

Patent 184,700: 1876

| | |
|---|---|
| Sulfur: S | 6 Parts |
| Carbolic acid: $C_6H_5OH$ | 1 Part |
| Iodine: I | |

Comments:

The mixture taught is used for a disinfecting, deodorizing, fumigant. There is little of true odor control quality inherent in this formula excepting that phenol is a strong osmogene. The iodine in vapor form unquestionably is an excellent catalyst for many malodorants.

Patent 222,453: 1879

| | |
|---|---|
| Sodium hypochlorite: $NaOCl$ | 10 Parts |
| Alum: $K_2SO_4 \cdot Al_2(SO_4)_3$ | 2 Parts |
| Ferric chloride: $FeCl_3$ | 5 Parts |

Comments:

This patent teaches disinfection and deodorization. Unquestionably the chlorine components represent excellent deodorizing capacities for many malodors. Additionally, it is likely that any iron ions available would act as a catalyst for some malodorants, especially sulfur bearing ones. It is unclear as to what, if any, part the alum would play in overall odor control efficiency.

Patent 860,456: 1907

Comments:

This patent proposes the neutralization of formaldehyde fumes by use of ammoniacal vapor. It proposes the use of ammoniacal vapor of about 20% strength in atmospheric contact with any space impregnated with formaldehyde vapors, and thereafter neutralizing the compounds created by the reaction of formaldehyde and ammoniacal vapors by introducing into the atmosphere a vaporous solution of a weak, volatile acid, specifically benzoic acid.

Patent 975,354: 1910

Comments:

This patent teaches the addition to soap stock of partially dehydrated perborates and acid substances which combine a bleaching, disinfecting and deodorizing effect of hydrogen peroxide. The degree of odor control is dependent upon the release of oxygen for oxidation of malodorants.

Patent 1,346,337: 1920

Comments:

This patent teaches the use of paradichlorobenzene ($C_6H_4Cl_2$); as with orthodichlorobenzene ($C_6H_4Cl_2$) and methadichlorobenzene ($C_6H_4Cl_2$), it is unlikely that much more than masking takes place, but these materials have been favored over the years, especially the paradichlorobenzene form, due to the ease of preparation into a solid form which, because of its volatile nature, results in a controlled release of aromatics. The use of this material from a health standpoint is questionable and little can be gained except the replacement of a malodor with a potentially dangerous pollutant.

Patent 1,408,535: 1922

| | |
|---|---|
| Plaster of Paris: $CaSO_4 \cdot 2H_2O$ | 10 Pounds |
| Formaldehyde: HCHO | 6 Ounces |
| Chlorinated lime: $CaCl(ClO) \cdot 4H_2O$ | 8 Ounces |
| Oil of eucalyptus | 12 Ounces |
| Oil of thyme | 6 Ounces |
| Oil of lavender | 4 Ounces |
| Water | 5 Pints |
| Salt | 6 Ounces |

Comments:

This patent teaches disinfection and deodorization, the material being formed into solid blocks and used in urinals. The antiseptic properties of formaldehyde are unquestionably good, but as an odor control agent its sole effectiveness is a result of partial paralysis of the olfactory epithelium and its use is deplored. The essential oils, of course, contribute a masking component to the odor control effectiveness, and the chlorinated lime contributes to some small extent as an oxidizing odor control agent, as well as a malodorant preventative from bacterial degradation.

Patent 1,576,106: 1926

Comments:

The use of common salt, NaCl, for the control of malodors encountered in garbage containers and in garbage is taught in this patent. The use suggested is to thoroughly impregnate the garbage with the salt which, of course, due to its antiseptic qualities in high concentrations is a good, inexpensive preservative of organic materials. There are no other known odor control properties of common salt excepting the dissociation of the chlorine component by electrolysis for use in oxidation malodor control.

Patent 1,593,485: 1926

Comments:

This patent teaches the use of the odorless zinc salts, preferably zinc sulfate, $ZnSO_4$, plus an alkaline acetate such as sodium acetate, $2NaCH_3CO_2$, for the control of hydrogen sulfide and ammoniacal gases. Hydrogen sulfide is reacted with the zinc salt in the alkaline form by the following equation:

$$ZnSO_4 + H_2S = ZnS + SO_4H_2$$

When sodium acetate is added to this:

$$2SO_4H_2 + 2NaCH_3CO = SO_4Na_2 + 2CH_3COOH$$

the deodorization process is completed. Modern odor control must be sensitive to the addition to the environment of any heavy metals; therefore, in spite of the excellent deodorizing properties of this process for hydrogen sulfide, it may only be incorporated in certain limited uses in the odor control field.

Patent 1,648,259: 1927

Comments:

The method of deodorizing taught by this patent is the destruction of malodorants associated with the degradation of nitrogenous materials such as proteins, the destruction of malodorants associated with rubber, or vegetation decomposition malodorants resulting from nitrogenous components by the use of oxy-n-butyl thiocarbonic acid disulfide, or as alternatives oxyethyl thiocarbonic acid disulfide, dithiobenzoyldisulfide, benzoyl peroxide, acid anhydrides or thio-acid anhydrides, tetra sulfides prepared by the interaction of sulfur chloride with salts of non-nitrogenous dithioacids. Benzoyl peroxide is recommended when combined with water.

Patent 1,729,752: 1929

Comments:

This patent suggests baker's yeasts (Saccharomyces cerevisiae) for use as a deodorant for body odors of all sorts. It further recommends the characteristic odor of the yeast being masked since it in itself represents to many people a malodor. Yeasts represent abundant enzyme content and strong reducing capabilities which might play an important role in the biodegradation of normally malodorous body components. Additionally, viable yeast could compete with other organisms which would normally yield malodorants as a result of their metabolism.

Patent 1,922,416: 1933

Comments:

This patent teaches the combination of various charcoals as a more efficient gas adsorbent, specifically charcoals formed from sour cherry (Prunus cerasus) which will adsorb 280.11 cc's of air per cc of charcoal, coconut (Cocus nucifera) which will adsorb 251.80 cc's of air per cc of charcoal, and common boxwood (Buxus sempervirens) which will adsorb 138.50 cc's of air per cc of charcoal. A mixture of equal parts of the charcoals will adsorb 327.20 cc's of air per cc of the mixed charcoal. The ability of chars to adsorb malodorous gases is unquestioned in odor control; all that remains is to find suitable circumstances for their use from an economical and practicable point of view, bearing in mind that in many instances of application the charcoal forms a matrix wherein secondary reactions occur among the adsorbed gases resulting in the release from the charcoal of more toxic and more malodorous components than those being entrapped.

Patent 2,091,497: 1937

Comments:

This patent teaches the use of essential oil of cardamon as a specific Zwaardemaker for tobacco smoke as well as most odors encountered in the breath.

Patent 2,131,235: 1938

Comments:

This patent teaches that the principal malodorant components of menstrual secretions is methylamine, dimethylamine and trimethylamine, and that the reaction of these components with aromatic acids such as benzoic salicylic and phenyl acetic will combine to neutralize completely all malodor associated with menstruation. The use of such compounds over a long period of time on the human body for the purpose of malodor control is a questionable practice; however, the application of this phenomenon to industrial uses where the contaminants methylamine, dimethylamine and trimethylamine occur should not be overlooked.

Patent 2,168,523: 1939

Comments:

This patent discloses a method for treating seeds, bulbs, tubers and roots, particularly of floriferous types, which imparts a required color or odor.

Patent 2,310,099: 1943

Comments:

This patent teaches the neutralization of all classes of offensive and unwanted odors. The basis of the odor neutralizing quality is the use of potassium mercuric iodide, $K_2HgI_4$, claiming a surprising deodorizing property. The odor control efficiency is claimed to be enhanced by alkalizing the aqueous solution of potassium mercuric iodide as well as stabilizing against deterioration. The use of sodium hydroxide, NaOH, or potassium hydroxide, KOH, are recommended for this purpose. The effect of this composition is unquestionably due to the profound and probably catalytic effect of heavy metals in active or ionic form on most odors. Obviously, the use of heavy metals is disadvantageous under most odor control application circumstances.

Patent 2,326,672: 1943

Chlorophyll A: $C_{55}H_{72}MgN_4O_5$
Chlorophyll B: $C_{55}H_{72}MgN_4O_6$
Formaldehyde: HCHO

Comments:

This patent concerns the use of chlorophyll combined with formaldehyde. No differentiation of the type of chlorophyll is stated. The chlorophyll is not claimed to act as an odor control agent but as an atmospheric refreshent or vitiating agent which, when combined with formaldehyde, becomes an odor neutralizing compound. Experience has proven that chlorophyll does have certain odor neutralizing capacities, apparently as an adsorbent and in chemical reaction with some malodorants. On the other hand, formaldehyde has little or no malodor neutralizing capacity, and it is therefore likely that the proposed combination, in view of the polluting and irritating effect of formaldehyde, is not an efficacious one.

Patent 2,356,062: 1944

Comments:

This patent discloses the use of ozonized glycerine trioleate as an odor control composition and antiseptic for use on the body. The ozone is released under body heat and then combines with malodorants or oxidizes antiseptically wounds or other applications. The ozonized glycerine trioleate is capable of absorbing 1.85% of available oxygen added to its molecule which is 50% higher than the corresponding maximum of 1.3% of oxygen capable of being combined with olive oil. The oxidation capacity of nascent oxygen with respect to many malodorants has been discussed elsewhere.

Patent 2,527,029: 1950

Comments:

This patent teaches for the purpose of freshening the environmental atmosphere or improving stale indoor atmospheres the use of a solid extract of forest soil. The composite extractive, it is claimed, will vitiate the air, restoring to it a desirable element of freshness. The patent does not claim odor control or any odor control mechanisms.

Patent 2,546,898: 1951

Comments:

This patent discloses that sulfonated castor oil exhibits remarkable deodorizing properties, stating that it is especially efficient in eliminating odors resulting from garbage cans, toilet bowls, pets, cess pools, sewers, clothing and linens, kitchens, urinals, public restrooms and baby diapers. Unquestionably, the efficacy of this material is based upon the odor control principle of adsorption.

Patent 2,562,042: 1951

Comments:

This patent teaches the use of tetrahydropyranyl sulfides, $C_{6-12}H_{12-16}OS$ as odor masking compositions.

Patent 2,683,074: 1954

Comments:

This patent teaches that an alkaline solution of potassium permanganate is advantageous over an acidic solution due to (1) disinfectant qualities are increased, (2) deodorant qualities are increased, (3) the potassium permanganate is less corrosive in alkaline solution, and (4) potassium permanganate has no tendency to spontaneous breakdown in alkaline solution.

Patent 2,715,611: 1955

Comments:

This patent teaches that malodorous air may be effectively neutralized by diffusion into the malodorous air of solutions or suspensions of organic hydroperoxides, and that the efficiency of the organic peroxidic compounds is not dependent upon the presence of extraneous decomposing or oxygen liberating agents other than the malodorant material to be destroyed. Examples given suggest the use of cumene hydroperoxide, 69% strength, with a contact time in the malodorous air of 20 seconds, resulting in a substantial reduction in malodorant content.

Patent 2,719,129: 1955

Comments:

This patent teaches that cationic surface active agents, generally known as quaternary morpholinium alkyl sulfates, have powerful deodorant properties, although being odorless in themselves. The patent states that said materials destroy odors upon which they act and do not function as masking agents or perfumery materials.

Patent 2,762,822: 1956

Comments:

This patent discloses the use of copper gluconate and an alkali metal salt of an amino benzoic acid (sodium, potassium or lithium) in an aqueous water solution as an excellent deodorizing, enzyme inhibiting, bacteriacidal composition. Unquestionably, the odor neutralizing component is the catalytic reaction of the copper ions. The composition is suggested for use in odor control of ammonium thioglycolate, a solution normally encountered in hair permanents and hair waving lotions.

Patent 2,815,260: 1957

Comments:

This patent claims the use of lithium carbonate, $Li_2CO_3$, as an odor neutralizing composition of high effectiveness for use in absorbent materials, such as diapers, bedding, rugs, or any materials retaining urine odors or urinary excreta from humans or animals. The method taught is a soaking procedure in a rinse containing 100 to 200 parts per million of lithium carbonate and is undoubtedly specific in its antagonism for urine odors.

Patent 2,856,330: 1958

Comments:

This patent teaches the use of copper salts of sulfate, chloride, acetate or nitrate in a pH range of 3.0 to 6.0 as a cotton impregnating substance which will prevent the formation of unpleasant odors in the fabric.

Patent 2,893,958: 1959

Comments:

This patent discloses a method of odor neutralization for most objectionable odors arising from industrial processes and products including odor control procedures regarding fats, oils, rendering, synthetic plastics, pulp and paper, etc. First, small amounts (0.002% to 0.05%, by weight) of aliphatic alcohols of from six to nine carbon atoms are added to the malodorant until the objectionable odor is amplified to its maximum. Then, a ketone is selected from aliphatic methyl ketones ranging from hexyl to nonyl and is added in relatively small amounts until great reduction, or total neutralization in some cases, is achieved. An example for use in rendering plants is given which includes a mixture of 50% methyl-hexyl ketone and 50% n-hexanol to which is added 1% of Tergitol, a wetting agent. A 3% aqueous solution is recommended for use to spray empty collecting drums, trucks, cans, floors, walls, etc. of rendering plants which will remove or neutralize the putrid odor associated with these products.

Patent 2,922,747: 1960

Comments:

This patent teaches that any primary mixture of vegetable oils, animal fats, carotenoids and/or waxes activated by the addition of sodium lauryl sulfoacetate will substantially neutralize most malodorants by adsorption.

Patent 3,074,891: 1963

Comments:

α,β-Unsaturated monocarboxylic acids are claimed to be especially effective deodorants. The invention teaches that space odor control may be achieved by use of these acids solely by chemical reaction with the malodors. An example formula is given:

0.5 Parts by weight of geranyl crotonate
12.5 Parts by weight of isopropyl alcohol
4.0 Parts by weight of triethylene glycol
3.0 Parts by weight of propylene glycol
80.0 Parts by weight of a mixture of equal parts of trichloro-mono-fluoro-methane and dichloro-difluoro-methane

Other α,β-unsaturated monocarboxylic acids preferred are octyl crotonate, benzyl crotonate, 2-ethylhexyl crotonate, senecioic acid geranyl ester, ethyl cinnamate, tiglic acid geranyl ester. These compositions will chemically react with and neutralize tobacco smoke, kitchen odors, room odors and general household odors.

Patent 3,074,892: 1963

Comments:

Odor control agents having activated methylene groups such as esters of β-keto carboxylic acid (a diketone) in which the carbonyl groups are separated by a methylene group or an ester of malonic acid are taught to neutralize by masking which is considered by the inventor as an effective method of odor control due to the broad spectrum capability of masking compounds to deal with largely diversified malodors encountered by a general odor control agent. Materials preferred are 2-ethylhexyl-aceto-acetate, geranyl aceto-acetate, anisyl-aceto-acetate, ethyl-benzoyl acetate, isoamyl benzoyl acetate and di-n-hexyl-malonate.

Patent 3,077,457: 1963

Comments:

Fumaric acid esters as odor control agents causing neutralization due to chemical reaction are taught in this patent. The preferred esters are di-butyl fumarate, di-hexyl furarate. These compounds are claimed to react with tobacco smoke odors, kitchen odors and other general household odors with a substantial reduction upon treatment of malodorous contaminants.

Patent 3,080,295: 1963

Comments:

Pycnanthemum albescens (Michx-mint family) volatile oil extracts are claimed to be odor destructive, especially for objectionable or malodors. The breadth of effect of the volatile oil principle is taught to be completely effective against all odors including irritants such as formaldehyde, hydrogen sulfide, methyl mercaptan, onion, garlic, ammonia, etc. Additionally, it is taught that asthma, hay-fever and many allergies are relieved or prevented when the oils of Pycnanthemum albescens are volatized into the atmosphere.

Patent 3,091,511: 1963

Comments:

Salicylic acid esters of phenol and p-acetylaminophenol combined in a powder base such as talc, kieselguhr, kaolin, or combined with appropriate propellents as a space deodorant. The efficacy of the components is claimed to remove or destroy malodors from confined quarters, cigar, cigarette or pipe smoke and as a foot deodorant. Text examples indicate the efficacy of the foregoing components when used against butyric acid.

Patent 3,102,101: 1963

Comments:

Dodecene, tetradecene, hexadecene, octadecene, dodecane, tetradecane, hexadecane, octadecane, octene-1 dimer, propylene tetramer, 3,6-dimethyldecane, 2,5,4,7-tetramethyloctane, octadecyne and 1,3-tetradecadiene are taught to be odor control agents which will control objectionable malodors and which are non-corrosive, non-toxic, non-irritating and odor neutralizing by virtue of chemical reactivity. The malodors claimed to be affected are a wide variety, the more common odors being bathroom odors, frying food odors, fish odors, ethyl mercaptan odors and cigarette odors. The materials are suggested for use as an aerosol.

Patent 3,124,459: 1964

Comments:

Water soluble ferrous and cupric compounds, specifically ferrous iron and cupric copper, in a ratio from 1000:1 to 1:10, preferably from 100:1 to 1:1, when ingested are claimed to be effective deodorizing agents for all systemic body odors such as perspiration, breath, urine, butyric acid, indole, skatole, etc.

Patent 3,172,817: 1965

Comments:

Water soluble β-diketone metal salts of polyvalent metals, the preferred forms being 2,4-pentanedione, 3-chloro-2,4-pentanedione, 4-p-methylphenyl-2,4-butanedione, 4-p-aminophenyl-2,4-butanedione, 3-n-dodecyl-2,4-pentanedione and 4-phenyl-2,4-butanedione, are taught to neutralize malodors associated with hygienic articles such as sanitary napkins, diapers, shoe insoles, or most materials which might become contaminated with malodors of a systemic nature.

Patent 3,183,645: 1965

Comments:

In this patent odoriferous gases resulting from rendering vessels or cookers are passed into a spray chamber and thereafter into a demisting zone before passing through a bed of adsorbent material such as activated carbon. The non-condensible gases are forced through the bed by a vacuum applied on the opposite side of the adsorbent bed, preferably by a steam ejector.

Patent 3,198,251: 1965

Comments:

This invention claims the use of a water soluble benzethonium quaternary salt such as benzethonium halides, i.e., benzethonium chloride, in addition to a water soluble nitrate such as sodium nitrite as a synergist in combination which is believed to eliminate by neutralization on contact and thereafter suppress such odors as those occurring around urinals, toilet bowls, lavatories, restrooms, garbage containers, decomposable foodstuffs, livestock, etc.

Patent 3,250,724: 1966

Comments:

Odor control through chemical reaction of malodors is claimed in this invention for a polyester acid dissolved in solvent such as alcohol, glycol or a hydrocarbon where the polyester has less than 27 carbon atoms. The preferred materials are diisobutyl citraconate, dibenzyl citraconate, dihexyl citraconate, diisobutyl mesaconate, dihexyl mesaconate, tripropyl aconitate, triisobutyl aconitate, and trihexyl aconitate. These odor control ingredients are to be used in aerosols as space deodorants, and are claimed to be effective against most household odors including tobacco smoke odors, kitchen odors, etc.

Patent 3,328,312: 1967

Comments:

Odor control agents of perchloryl fluoride, $ClFO_3$, and an aerosol propellent are taught to eliminate by oxidation most ordinary household odors such as bathroom odors, kitchen odors, etc. when used in a concentration of approximately 0.025 PPM of air of perchloryl fluoride. Odors claimed to be oxidized are fish odors, frying food odors, cabbage odors, ethyl mercaptan odors and cigar and cigarette odors.

Patent 3,376,219: 1968

Comments:

This patent discloses the use of Bacillus cereus in combination with a substantially nitrogen free starch medium favorable to the growth of Bacillus cereus. The culture and media are added to water containing malodorous components as a result of the presence of actinomycetes. The resulting water is essentially free of the actinomycetes odor.

Patent 3,413,218: 1968

Comments:

Biphenyl, $C_6H_5C_6H_5$, in amounts ranging from 0.5 to 15 PPM are claimed to eliminate through neutralization malodors from sewage, fats, oils, greases, proteins, carbohydrates, rendering odors and in general destroying odors found in the atmosphere substantially without regard to the type or origin of the odor. It is not clear how, or if, biphenyl causes neutralization of odors however, it is capable of causing central nervous system depression and has been observed to cause convulsions. Its lethal dosage for 50% of animals tested ($LD_{50}$) in rats is 2.2 grams per kilogram and should be considered from an odor control aspect as a potential pollutant.

Patent 3,459,852: 1969

Comments:

Sewage disposal plant malodor control is claimed to be effectuated by the use of a sulfide active α,β-unsaturated aldehyde or ketone in an amount sufficient to form sulfur containing reaction products of the sulfide active aldehyde or ketone, especially of the -SH groups; i.e., hydrogen sulfide. The introduction of sulfide active aldehydes and ketones does not interfere with other processes of sewage treatment such as oxidation by aeration, bacterial action, etc. The addition of sulfide active aldehydes is claimed to reduce the BOD of sewage and industrial wastes in addition to elimination of the -SH malodor constituents. The use of such agents as α,β-unsaturated ketones as 3-buten-2-one, 3-hydroxy-2-cyclohexen-1-one, 4-methoxy-3-buten-2-one, 4-(2-furyl)-3-buten-2-one and 5-phenyl-2,4-pentadienophenone is suggested:

Reactive α,β-aliphatical unsaturated aldehyde ketone portion:

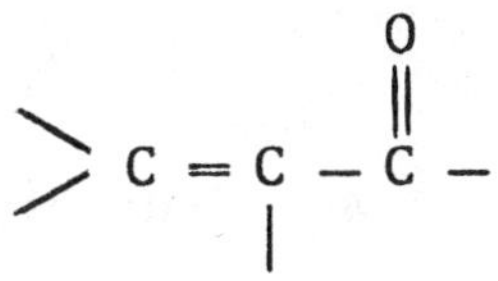

General formula:

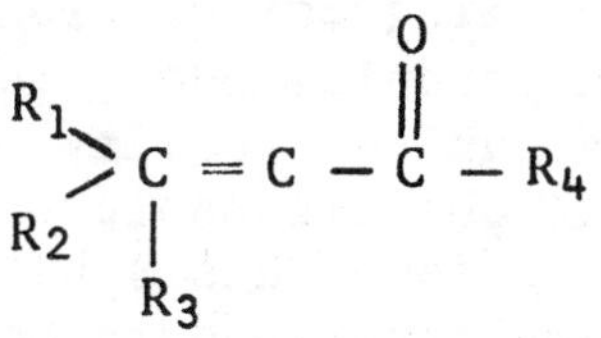


Any R substituents may be hydrogen or alkyl, with hydrogen and alkyl preferred in $R_1$, $R_2$, and $R_3$; or $R_1$ or $R_4$ may be a simple aryl radical. Certain R groups may be substituted with alkyl or aryl such as $R_4$-OH, and $R_4$ may be replaced by hydroxy, methoxy, amine or chloride. The theory of the reaction is as follows: When an α,β-unsaturated aldehyde or ketone is reacted with hydrogen sulfide, the following adduct may be one of the reaction products:

$$
\begin{array}{c}
R_1 \\
\diagdown \\
C = C - \overset{O}{\overset{\|}{C}} - R_4 - R_2 - \overset{R_1}{\underset{\underset{SH}{|}}{\overset{|}{C}}} - \overset{H}{\underset{\underset{R_3}{|}}{\overset{|}{C}}} - \overset{O}{\overset{\|}{C}} - R_4 \quad \rightarrow \\
\diagup \\
R_2 \quad R_3
\end{array}
\qquad
\begin{array}{c}
R_1 \quad H \quad O \\
\diagdown \quad | \quad \| \\
\underset{R_2 \ | \ R_3}{\overset{|}{C}} - \overset{|}{C} - C - R_4 \\
S \\
\text{YIELDS} \quad R_1 \quad H \quad O \\
\diagdown \quad | \quad \| \\
\underset{R_2 \quad R_3}{\overset{|}{C}} - \overset{|}{C} - C - R_4
\end{array}
$$

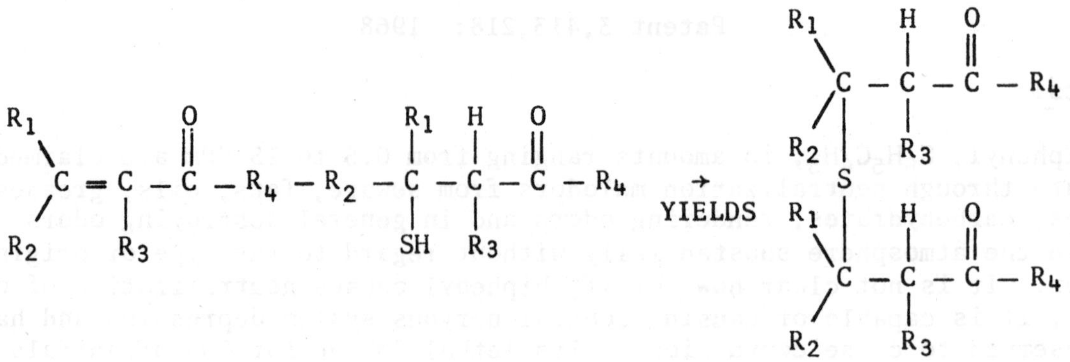

Patent 3,479,297:  1969

Comments:

    Room deodorants consisting of 0.5% to 5% of a cyclic acetal or ketal of a monounsaturated aldehyde or ketone having at least 3 carbon atoms and an aliphatic alcohol (1,2-diol or 1,3-diol), having 8 to 24 carbon atoms is claimed in this invention. The constituents are essentially odorous themselves but are believed to react within a short period of time with malodorous substances and retain their effectiveness over a comparatively long period of time. Additionally, they are not irritating to human mucous membranes, are believed to react with most common malodorants, and are sufficiently stable to retain their effectiveness over a long period of time. The compounds of choice are decane-1,2-diol-acroleinacetal, hexadecane-1,2-diol-crotonaldeacetal, dodecane-1,2-diol crotonaldehydeacetal, pentadecane-1,3-eiol-cyclohexenoneketal, eikosane-1,2-diol-acroleinacetal, hexadecane-1,2-diol-crotonaldehydeacetal, pentadecane-1,3-diol-cyclohexenoneketal, coconut fatty acid-glycerol-monoesteracrolein acetal, acrolein or acetaldehyde and propellants, binders or bases, which claims to be effective against tobacco, burnt milk, burnt fat, fish, onion, etc. odors.


Patent 3,493,650:  1970

Comments:

    A novel perfume and deodorizing composition containing citronellyl senecioate, characterized by a geranium odor, is taught to be a malodor neutralizer. Citronellyl senecioate has the ability of quickly eliminating malodors permanently without creating an objectionable odor of its own through combination with the malodors. The reason this substance is so effective as a deodorizing material is not completely understood; however, it is believed by the inventor that the citronellyl senecioate reacts chemically with many functional groups found in common malodors and thereby destroys them permanently, in contrast to masking or otherwise altering them. Citronellyl senecioate is recommended for use as a space deodorant as well as for personal contact odor neutralization and systemic odor neutralization.

Citronellyl senecioate:

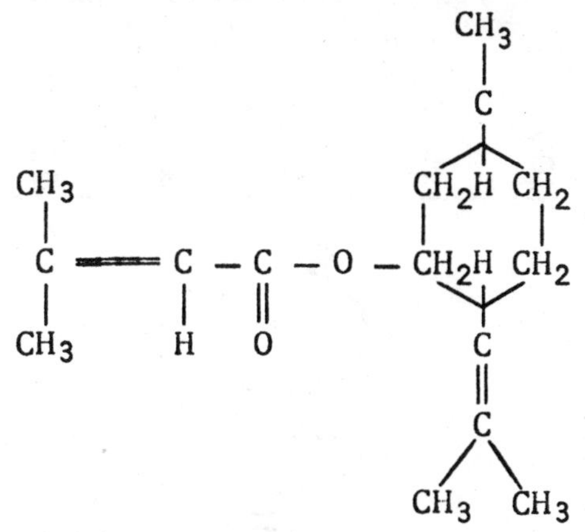

Patent 3,499,722: 1970

Comments:

Odorous gases are removed by introducing an oxidant and in selected instances a fuel into a combustion chamber located in a low pressure region between a cooker and a condenser in this patent.

Patent 3,509,254: 1970

Comments:

Odor control agents for neutralizing fecal odors and reducing bacterial contamination in chemical toilets comprising the use of a mixture of zinc sulfate monohydrate and citric acid in a ratio of 4:1 and in an overall concentration of 50 to 100 PPM is claimed in this patent. The invention proposes the use of water soluble zinc salts and a water soluble chelating acid for the zinc ions with a range for the zinc salt of from 0.001 to 1.3 pounds per gallon of water, and the chelating acid being in the concentration of 0.0001 to 1 pound per gallon of water. The preferred zinc salts are among the following: zinc sulfate, zinc chloride, zinc nitrate, zinc acetate. A chelating agent should be selected from the following recommended group: malic acid, citric acid, fumaric acid, hydroxyacetic acid, tartaric acid, lactic acid, gluconic acid, racemic acid, succinic acid, oxalic acid, malonic acid, glutaric acid, adipic acid and ethylene diamine tetraacetic acid.

Patent 3,527,798: 1970

Comments:

The use of cis-form active calcium succinates is proposed as a useful deodorant, especially for the removal of fish odors, and additionally as an anti-carcinogenic, blood pressure lowering agent, agent for regulating aliphatic acid metabolism, deanesthesiant, agent for lowering hyper-blood sugar

ACTIVE CALCIUM SUCCINATES IN CIS-FORM AND A PROCESS FOR THE PREPARATION THEREOF

Filed Dec. 12, 1966 6 Sheets-Sheet 1

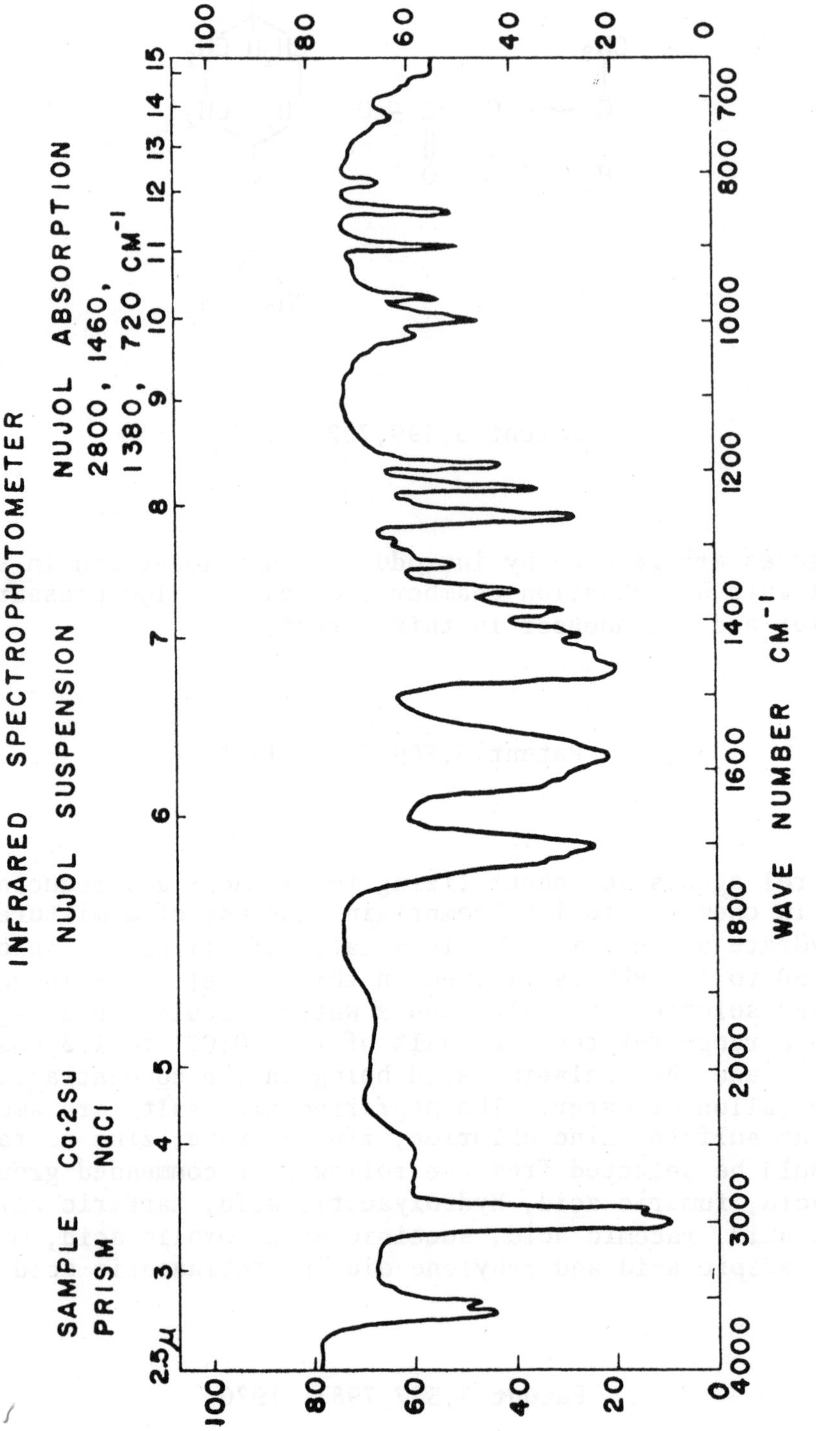


FIG. 1.

INVENTOR.
TADATAKA HARA

BY

Stevens, Davis, Miller & Mosher
ATTORNEYS

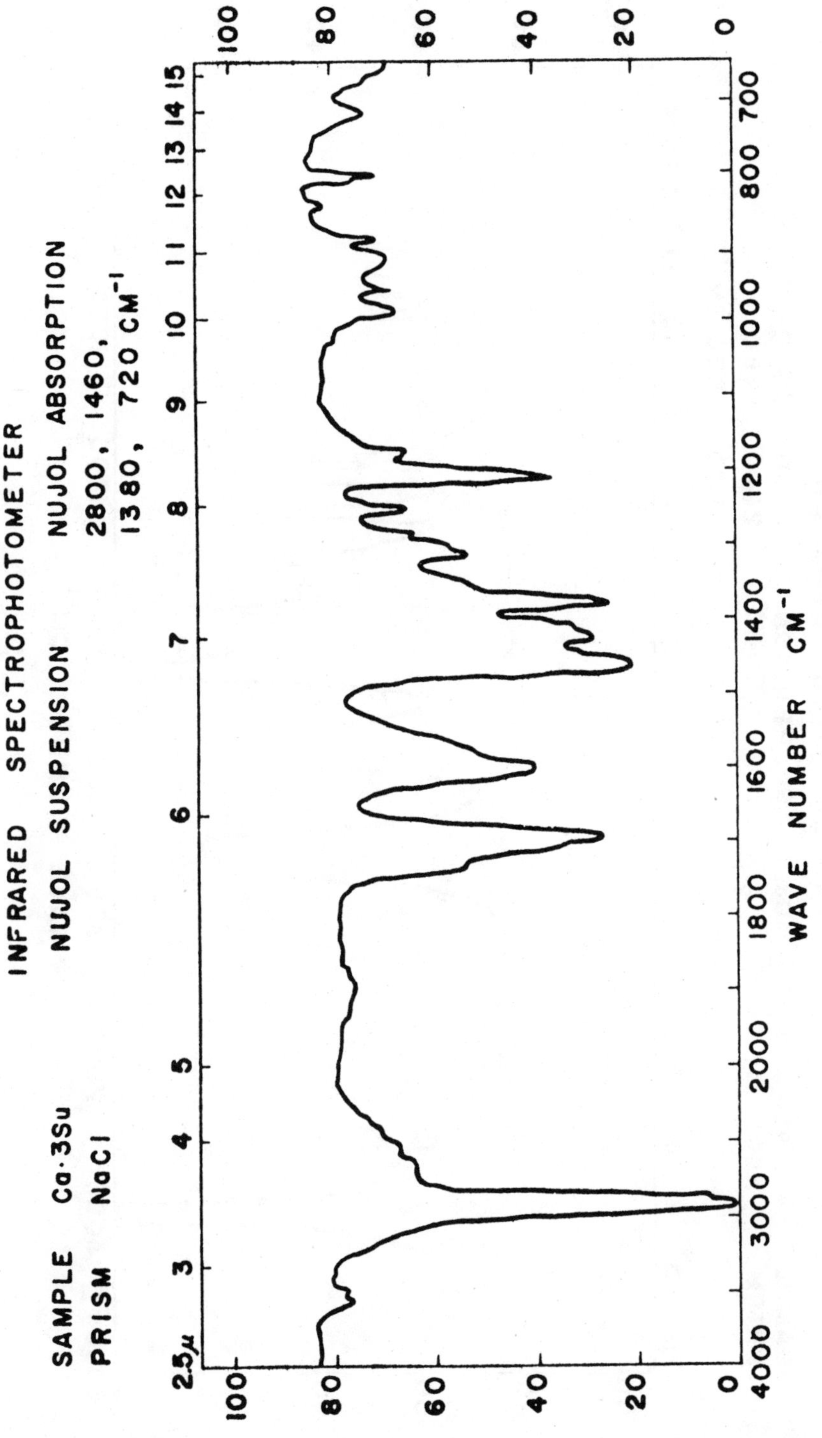


FIG. 2.

INVENTOR.
TADATAKA HARA

BY

Stevens, Davis, Miller & Mosher
ATTORNEYS

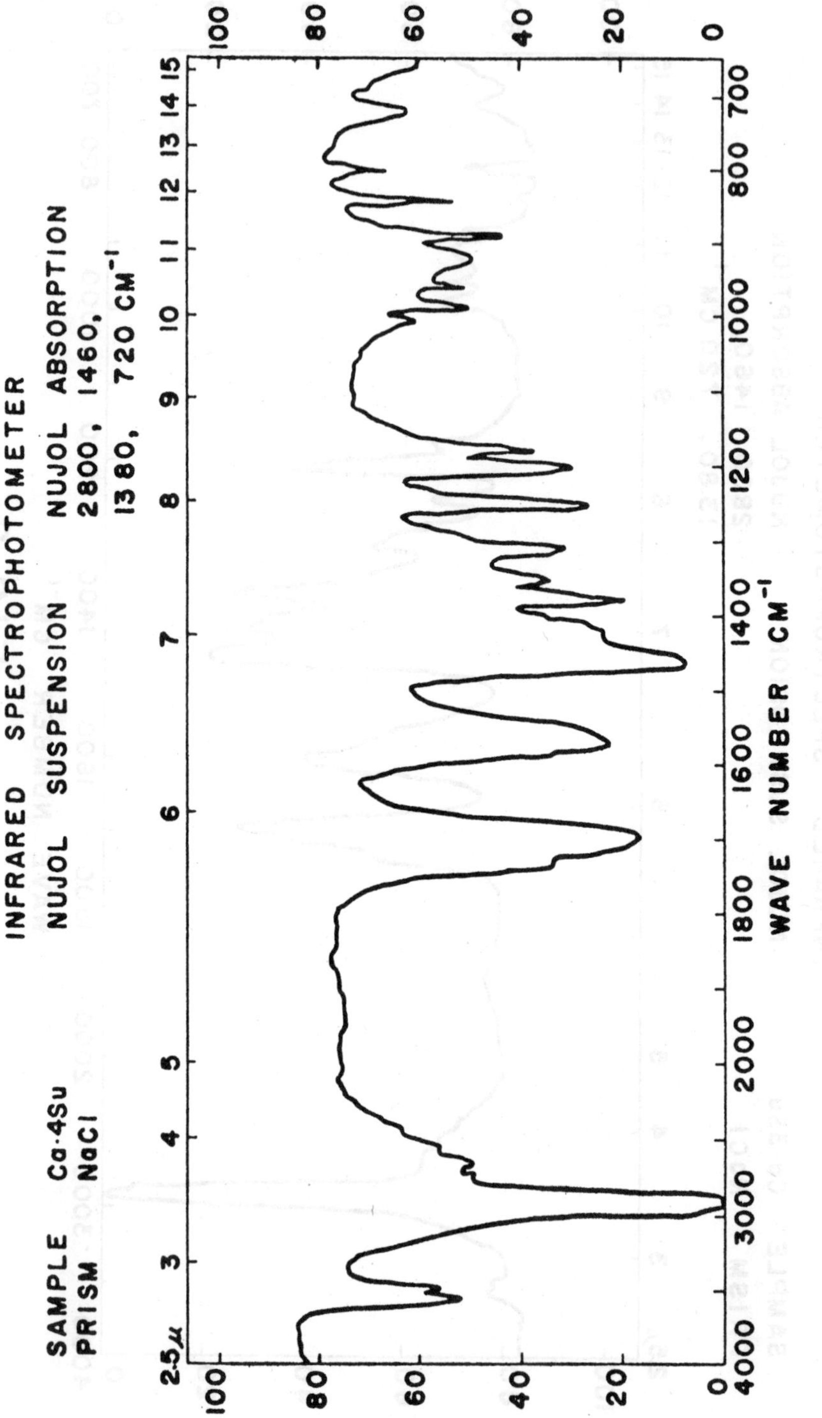


FIG. 3.

INVENTOR.
TADATAKA HARA

BY

Stevens, Davis, Miller & Mosher
ATTORNEYS

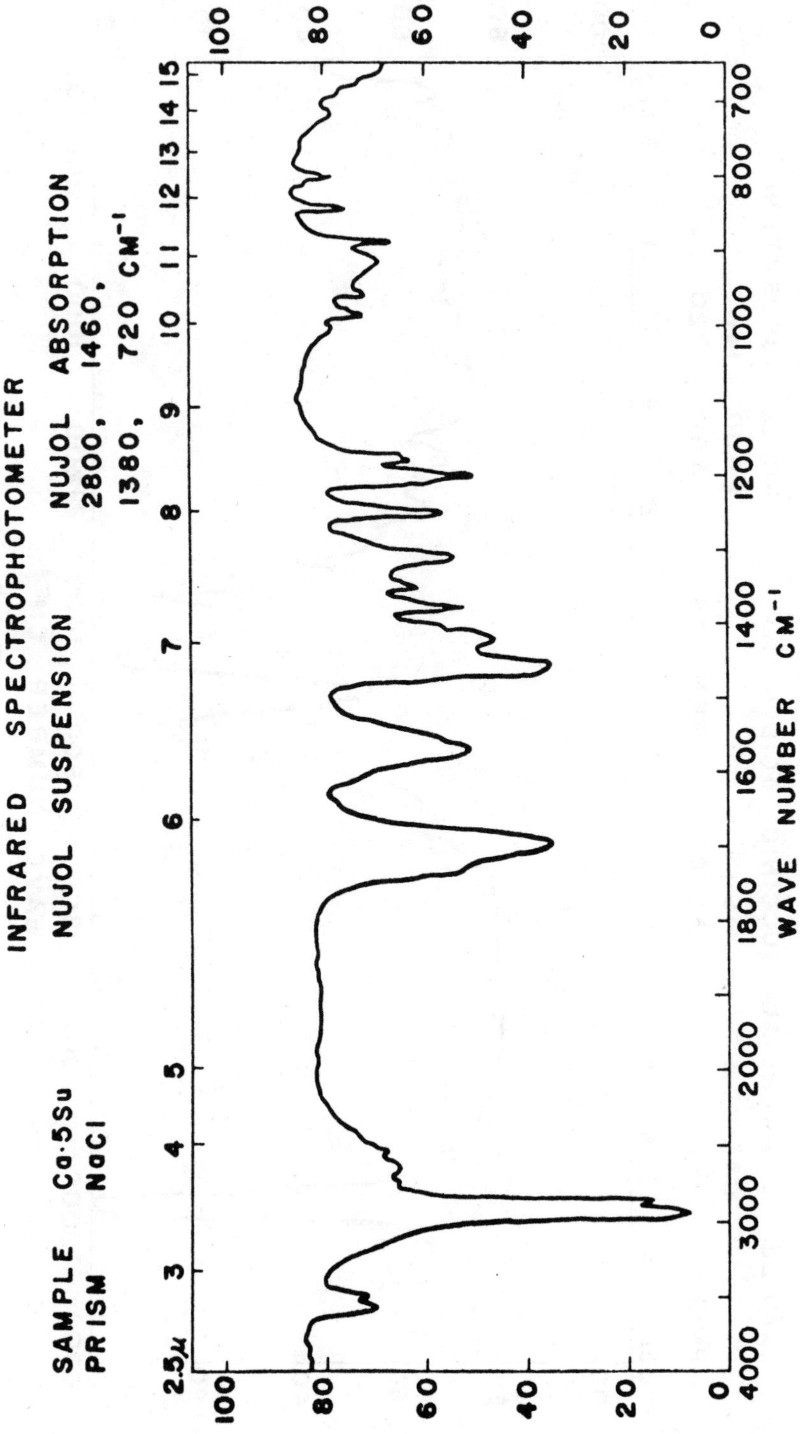


FIG. 4.

INVENTOR.
TADATAKA HARA

BY

Stevens, Davis, Miller & Mosher
ATTORNEYS

ACTIVE CALCIUM SUCCINATES IN CIS-FORM AND A PROCESS FOR THE PREPARATION THEREOF

Filed Dec. 12, 1966 6 Sheets-Sheet 5

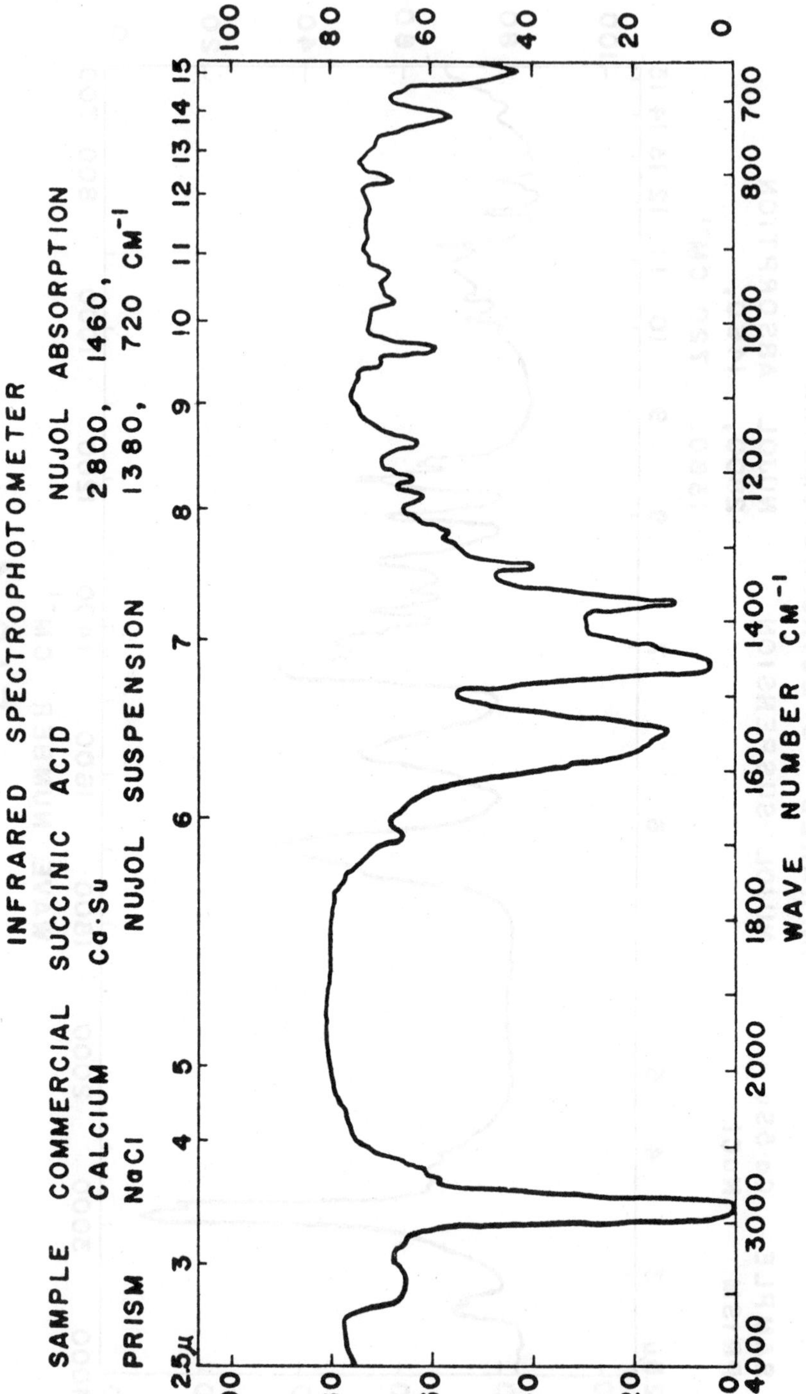


FIG. 5.

INVENTOR.
TADATAKA HARA

BY

Stevens, Davis, Miller & Mosher
ATTORNEYS

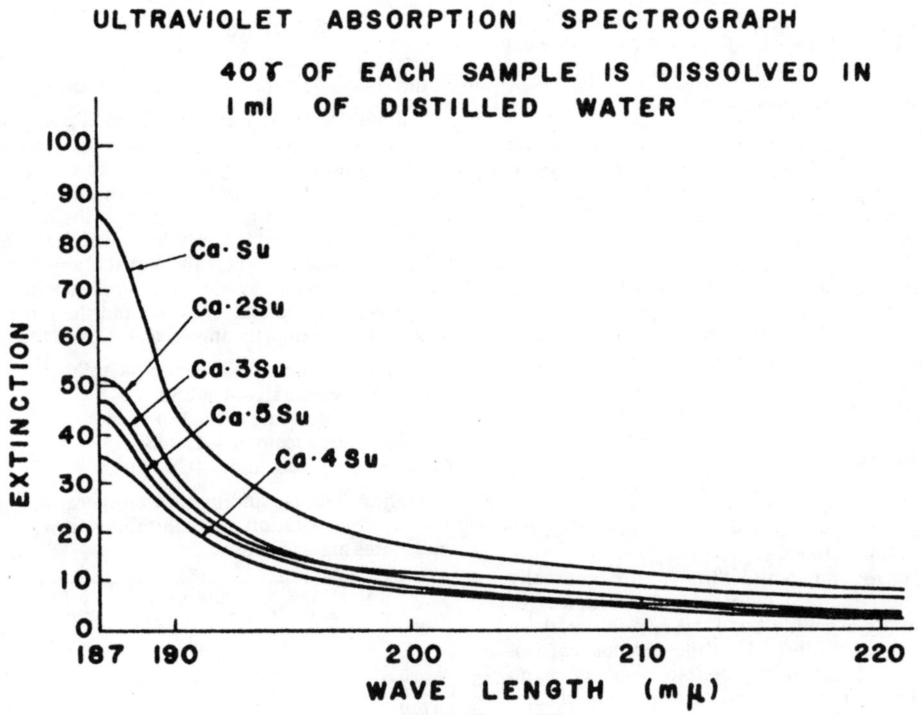


FIG. 6.

INVENTOR.
TADATAKA HARA
BY
Stevens, Davis, Miller & Mosher
ATTORNEYS

**1**

**3,527,798**
**ACTIVE CALCIUM SUCCINATES IN CIS-FORM**
**AND A PROCESS FOR THE PREPARATION**
**THEREOF**
Tadataka Hara, 988 4-chome, Shimotakaido,
Suginami-ku, Tokyo, Japan
Filed Dec. 12, 1966, Ser. No. 600,949
Claims priority, application Japan, Dec. 16, 1965,
40/77,042
Int. Cl. C07c *55/10*
U.S. Cl. 260—537          3 Claims

---

### ABSTRACT OF THE DISCLOSURE

Active calcium succinates in cis-form and a process for the preparation thereof comprising combining commercial succinic acid with calcium in a molar ratio of at least 2:1. The active calcium succinates possess anticarcinogenic activity and are also useful as deodorants for the removal of fish odor or as refreshing agents for fishes.

---

The present invention relates to novel, active calcium succinates in cis-form and to a process for the preparation thereof, and more particularly it relates to the succinates prepared by combining commercial succinic acid with calcium in a molar ratio of at least 2:1 and to the process therefor.

As to processes for preparing active succinic acid in cis form, the present inventor has already been given Japanese Pat. Nos. 310,374, 314,923, 494,465, and 465,057.

The active succinic acid in cis-form obtained by these processes has superior anticarcinogenic activity and is stable in the crystal form, while it is unstable to light and heat in the form of aqueous solution and is eventually denatured if in the form of 1% aqueous solution at a pH above 5.2 whereby it loses its deodorant property and medical effect. Therefore, I have studied to obtain active succinic acid in cis-form which is still stable even if in the form of aqueous solution thereof.

Although the terms "cis-" and "trans-" are generally used to express the structural difference of substances of the same kind having a double bond, we herein use them for the convenience of distinguishing the geometrical isomers of succinic acid having no double bond since no other suitable terms for this purpose are thought of.

According to the present invention, the active calcium succinates in cis-form is prepared by reacting at least two molecules of commercial succinic acid (trans-form) with a molecule of calcium salt. Calcium is a fundamentally divalent element, but in this process it seems to react as a tetra-, hexa-, octa- or deca-valent element.

The conventional calcium succinate is obtained by the reaction as follows:

$$H_2C-COOH$$
$$HOOC-CH_2 + CaCO_3 \longrightarrow$$
succinic acid     calcium
(trans-form)     carbinate

$$\begin{array}{c} H_2C-COO \\ | \\ OOC-CH_2 \end{array}Ca + CO_2 + H_2O$$
calcium succinate    carbon   water
(trans-form)       dioxide

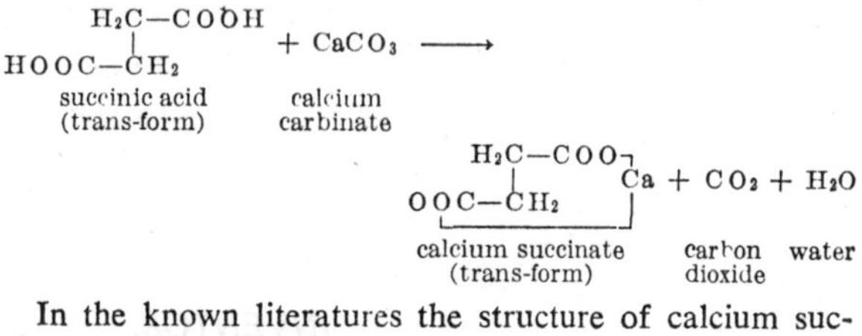

In the known literatures the structure of calcium succinate is shown as follows:

$$\begin{array}{c} H_2C-COO \\ | \\ H_2C-COO \end{array}Ca$$

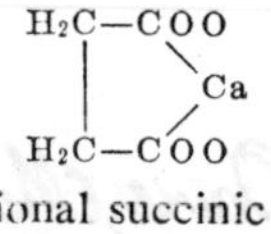

However, the conventional succinic acid is in trans-form, and so it should be expressed as shown in the above reaction formula.

**2**

The following reaction is presumed to take place in the process of this invention, and more particularly the following active calcium succinate in cis-form is obtained by dissolving in water one molecule of calcium salt and 2, 3, 4, or 5 molecules of commercial succinic acid and heating the resulting solution to 70° C.–100° C. (preferably 80° C.) for as long a time as possible (preferably 3–6 hours) to liberate one molecule of formaldehyde, one molecule of carbon dioxide and one molecule of water from the acid used.

$$\begin{array}{c} H_2-H_2 \\ C-C \\ | \quad | \\ C \quad C \\ \| \quad \| \\ O \quad O \\ | \quad | \\ H_2C-COO \quad O \quad O \\ Ca \left\{ \begin{array}{c} HOOC-CH_2 \\ HOOC-CH_2 \end{array} \right\}_{n-2} \\ H_2C-COO \end{array}$$

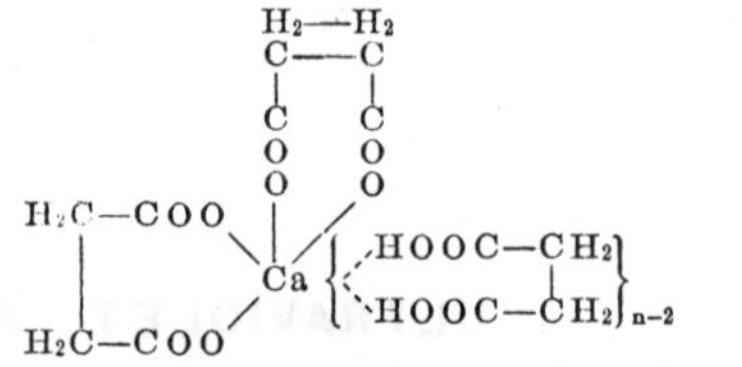

wherein $n$ represents an integer of 2, 3, 4, or 5, and dotted line (-----) represents hydrogen bond.

Calcium salts used in such reaction may be calcium carbonate $CaCO_3$, calcium hydroxide $Ca(OH)_2$ or the like.

The formation of these new types of calcium succinate according to the present invention can be proved by the fact that, on washing with alcohol, the succinic acid portion which is bound by only hydrogen bond is eluted from the active calcium succinate, but the amount of the eluate corresponds to (molecular weight of succinic acid) $(n-2)$.

For brevity, the conventional and the novel calcium succinates are hereinafter shown as follows:

Commercial calcium succinate—Ca.Su
Calcium disuccinate—Ca.2Su
Calcium trisuccinate—Ca.3Su
Calcium tetrasuccinate—Ca.4Su
Calcium pentasuccinate—Ca.5Su

Melting points, sublimation temperatures, pH values of 1% aqueous solution and solubilities in water of the above succinates are as follows:

| | M.P. (°C.) | Subl. temp. (° C.) | pH (1% solution) | Solubility (water) |
|---|---|---|---|---|
| Ca.Su | [1] 310 | ---------- | 5.79 | Extremely low. |
| Ca.2Su | 180 | [2] 135 | 4.8 | 1 g.:10 ml. |
| Ca.3Su | 180 | 135 | 4.4 | 7 |
| Ca.4Su | 175 | 135 | 4.2 | 5. |
| Ca.5Su | 175 | 135 | 4.2 | 5. |

[1] Decomp.
[2] A small amount.

FIGS. 1 to 4 show infrared absorption spectra of active calcium succinates in cis-form, FIG. 5 shows infrared absorption spectra of commercial calcium succinate (transform), and FIG. 6 shows ultraviolet absorption spectra of active calcium succinates in cis-form and commercial calcium succinate.

Infrared absorption spectra of the above succinates were determined with a Hitachi Infrared spectrophotometer.

Common absorptions of the products of this invention were at 3,500, 1,700, 1,570, 1,300–1,200 and 1,000–90 cm.$^{-1}$ (FIGS. 1–4). However, as shown in FIG. 5, absorptions of Ca.Su were not at 3,500 and 1,700 (carboxyl group) but 1,545 cm.$^{-1}$, and the absorptions at 1,300–1,200 and 1,000–900 cm.$^{-1}$ were very weak. From these results, the Ca.Su was presumed to be in transform. Each example was suspended in Nujol.

Ultraviolet absorptions were determined with a self-recording spectrophotometer made by Hitachi Co. The results are shown in FIG. 6. A sample of each of said succinates was weighed precisely with Mettler (micro balance) and dissolved in distilled water to obtain an aqueous solution with the concentration of 40 $\gamma$/ml. Determination was initiated at wave length of 187 m$\mu$ and continued at greater wave lengths, no peak appearing during the determination. It was found that the higher the absorbancy of a sample at 187 mμ is, the less the anticarcinogenic effect of the sample is (the samples have each the same concentration), which agrees with the correlation of ultraviolet absorbancy and the anticarcinogenic effect as shown in Japanese Pat. No. 465,057 (process for preparing new cis-succinic acid) given to the inventor.

Ehrlich anticarcinogenic test for mouse abdominal cancer is stated below.

Mice which were of ddN series and weighing 20±1 g. each, were used in the tests irrespective of sex. Each of groups comprised 10 mice, and three groups were used in each of the tests made on the succinates and the control which is hereinafter mentioned. The following was the procedure of the tests. Cancer cells were obtained from the mice 10 days after the transplantation therein, and suspended in saline solution. About 4 millions of the cells were transplanted into the abdomen of each of the animals, and 250 mg. (about 0.5 ml.) of 1% aqueous solution of the test compound (without adjusting pH value) per kg. of body weight were daily injected into the same abdomen over a period of 10 days, 48 hours after the transplantation of the cancer cells. Observation of these tests was continued for 50 days after this transplantation. The anticarcinogenic effect of each of the succinates was determined from mean survival time and percentage of the mice which survived for 50 days. Mice which died during the test were anatomized to confirm the causes of their death.

Mean values of the results obtained by the three tests made on each of the succinates, and on physiological salt solution which was injected to each mouse of the control group in amount of 0.5 ml. per kg. of body weight are shown below.

| | Mean survival time (day) | Mean longest period of time during which all members of group had been alive after the start of the test (day) | Mean survival rate 50 days after the start of the test (percent) |
|---|---|---|---|
| Control | 14.5 | 11 | 0 |
| Ca.Su | 17.0 | 11 | 0 |
| Ca.2Su | (*) | 25 | 28 |
| Ca.3Su | (*) | 35 | 71 |
| Ca.4Su | (*) | 47 | 96 |
| Ca.5Su | (*) | 41 | 88 |

*Mean survival time could not be calculated because there were some mice which were still alive after the completion of the 50 days' test.



## EXAMPLE

One hundred and eighteen grams of commercial succinic acid (molecular weight: 118) and 25 g. of calcium carbonate (molecular weight: 100) are weighed out and then dissolved in 600 ml. of distilled water at an ambient temperature. The solution is filtered through a filter paper. After allowing to stand for 24 hours, the filtrate is heated gradually to 100° C. Then the water is evaporated from the filtrate as slowly as possible at 100° C. under stirring to form crystals. The crystallization begins about 3 hours after and ends about 6 hours after the initiation of the heating of the filtrate, when the evaporation of the water is completed. The collected crystals are then dried in a dryer for 24 hours. The crystals weigh about 129 g.

The cis-calcium succinates thus obtained are stable in the form of aqueous solution, and are not denatured by light or heat. The cis-calcium succinates may be widely used as medicines (anticarcinogen, blood pressure lowering agent, agent for regulating aliphatic acid metabolism, deanesthesiant, agent for lowering hyper blood sugar content, antiviral agent, antiallergenic agent, cardiac tonic, diuretic drug, breath-recovering agent, etc.), as deodorants (fishy odor, odor of whale, odor of excrements, etc.) or as refreshing agents for fishes.

What I claim is:

**1.** A process for the preparation of calcium succinates in cis-form characterized by dissolving calcium carbonate and from two to five moles of trans succinic acid per mole of calcium carbonate in water to form a solution, heating said solution at a temperature of from 70° C. to 100° C. for a sufficient time to liberate formaldehyde, carbon dioxide and water from said solution, and recovering calcium succinates in cis-form.

**2.** A process according to claim **1** wherein said solution is heated for from three to six hours.

**3.** Active calcium succinates in cis-form obtained by the process as claimed in claim **1**.

**References Cited**

Johnston, C. A. 50:8362 (1956).
Schubert, C. A. 46:7400 (1942).
Schubert et al., J.A.C.S., July 20, 1962, pp. 3529–3532. 3532.

LORRAINE A. WEINBERGER, Primary Examiner
V. GARNER, Assistant Examiner

U.S. Cl. X.R.

260—601, 999; 424—76, 317

content, antiviral agent, antiallergenic agent, cardiac tone, diuretic drug, and breath recovering agent. The requirements for use as an effective anticarcinogenic or as an odor control agent require that an aqueous solution be present in plus 1% quantities and at a pH below 5.2. The invention provides for the preparation of five forms of calcium succinate: calcium succinate (Ca.Su), calcium disuccinate (Ca.2Su), calcium trisuccinate (Ca.3Su), calcium tetrasuccinate (Ca.4Su) and calcium pentasuccinate (Ca.5Su). Calcium tetrasuccinate is the preferred form. Due to the interesting claims made in this patent, it is included in the text.

Patent 3,592,614: 1971

Comments:

In this patent non-condensable gases from a cooking device are incinerated by the intensely hot, high velocity flame of an afterburner which is self-contained and may be associated with any exhaust pipe in which non-condensable gases are present. The flame of the device is produced in an area in which water from the incinerated gases cannot extinguish the flame.

Patent 3,650,968: 1972

Comments:

A composition for fishermen's soap incorporating citric acid or citrus juices as a specific for the removal of fishy odors is disclosed. Citric acid is used in proportions from 0.1% to 5.0% of soap compositions, and citrus juice from 0.1% to 15% by weight, of composition within an effective pH range is claimed. It is interesting to note that folklore has long proposed the use of tomato juices and orange juices for pet baths to eliminate the methyl mercaptan or skunk odor.

Patent 3,706,663: 1972

Comments:

Feedlot odor control utilizing sulfa drugs and sulfaguanidine, applied as solid mixtures with inert diluents in acid solution are claimed to be effective odor control agents. The action of effective odor control is through selective inhibition of the formation of malodorous compounds which result from the normal decomposition of the animal waste. The odors from animal wastes are produced by compounds formed from microbial action on organic compounds present therein. In particular, low molecular weight nitrogen containing compounds, such as the skatoles and indoles, and sulfur containing compounds such as the mercaptans are produced from microbial degradation of protein and other materials present in the animal waste. The invention provides a method of controlling the formation of these malodorous products by treating the waste with a compound which will selectively inhibit undesirable types of microbial decomposition. The addition of the compounds, at the same time, is claimed not to sterilize the waste material which subsequently may still be used as a fertilizer, since it is claimed that the microbial flora, aside from the malodorant forming ones, will otherwise proceed with the normal decomposition of the waste material.

Patent 3,708,421: 1973

Comments:

A process for the removal of mercaptan sulfur in the manufacture of petroleum products is described in this patent. Sour gasolines and other petroleum distillates in the boiling range of 100° to 400°F are treated with a reagent which is formed by reacting a water soluble metal salt with a mixture of a glycinate derivative in an alkaline solution in which the metal salt in an alkaline solution combines with mercaptan sulfur compounds in a sour gasoline and distillate stream. They are then prewashed with a caustic-hydrogen sulfide solution. The mercaptan sulfur compounds are extracted in the presence of the alkaline reagent and are then oxidized in the spent alkaline reagent with a gas containing oxygen to regenerate it for recycling. The disulfide sulfur is then extracted from the regenerated reagent.

Patent 3,709,171: 1973

Comments:

An afterburner for burning combustible particles in smoke and exhaust gases from stationary installations is taught. A heater is disposed adjacent to an intake opening of a water cooled combustion chamber and brings the smoke to its combustion temperature. Particulate matter is removed from the smoke by filters before the clean, non-polluting gas is discharged to the atmosphere. Surfaces of the combustion chamber contacted by smoke or cooling water are coated with Teflon to inhibit substantially all accumulation of particulate matter on such surfaces and prevent clogging of the device. The chamber can be mounted on top of a smoke discharging stack or device, or it can be placed on the ground and provided with suitable conduits and blowers for passing the smoke to and through the combustion chamber. Openings are provided to supply the necessary additional combustion air to the combustion chamber.

Patent 3,709,660: 1973

Comments:

In this patent, a water soluble, inorganic thiosulfate compound is reduced to the corresponding sulfide compound by contacting an aqueous solution of thiosulfate compound and hydrogen with a catalyst, comprising a catalytically effective amount of cobalt sulfide combined with a porous carrier material, at reduction conditions. The principal utility of this treatment procedure is associated with the clean-up or regeneration of aqueous streams containing undesired thiosulfate compounds so that they can be reused in the process which originally produced them. Alternatively, they can be discharged into a suitable sewer without causing a pollution problem. A key feature of the method disclosed is the use of a unique catalyst which has the extraordinary capacity for converting thiosulfate to sulfide in an aqueous solution when hydrogen is utilized as the reducing agent.

Patent 3,709,977: 1973

Comments:

A method for the removal of sulfur dioxide from a gas stream which also contains sulfur trioxide by contacting the gas stream with a solid basic ion exchange resin is disclosed. The gas stream is initially contacted with an alkali prior to contact with the resin. This removes sulfur trioxide and prevents sulfur trioxide adsorption by the resin which would deplete resin activity and result in a tightly bound chemical union which prevents resin regeneration by simple thermal means.

Patent 3,716,620: 1973

Comments:

A process for purifying a gas containing hydrogen sulfide or a mercaptan is taught wherein the gas is contacted with a solution of iodine in an organic solvent which also contains an amine.

Patent 3,720,606: 1973

Comments:

A formulation comprising an aqueous solution containing one or more aerobic, mesophilic, spore-forming bacterial agents, an odor suppressing agent including a perfumant initially effective to suppress and/or mask any undesirable odors, and a carrier containing an emulsifier into which the perfumant is dissolved is taught. The bacterial agent should be selected from Group I of the genus Bacillus, specifically, such as Bacillus megaterium and/or Bacillus subtilis, to induce aerobic decomposition of odor causing waste matter to an odor-free form.

Patent 3,727,375: 1973

Comments:

A continuous process for removal of gaseous contaminants, particularly carbon dioxide, from an atmosphere containing the same in which the contaminant laden atmosphere is subjected to contact with a strongly basic ionic polymer sheet under the influence of an applied electrical field is disclosed. The apparatus for accomplishing this comprises at least one and preferably several cylindrically shaped perforated reinforced sheets, in strip form, of strongly basic ionic polymeric material partially suspended at the lower end into a circulating stream of sea water. The polymeric cylindrically shaped sheets are interspersed between a source of an appiable electric field, e.g., a cathode and an anode, and a cation-exchange membrane and an anion-exchange membrane being in turn interspersed between the cathode and the upper exposed ends of the polymeric sheets.

Patent 3,740,349: 1973

Comments:

In this patent, the gas exhausted from internal combustion or similar engines is treated to convert harmful or pollutant components such as nitrogen oxides, carbon monoxide and unburned hydrocarbons to innocuous compounds. This is accomplished by contacting the exhaust gas with a catalyst composition containing nickel, cobalt and manganese in catalytically effective amounts, deposited on a carrier such as α-alumina.

Patent 3,741,725: 1973

Comments:

A platinum catalyst system is described which is effective in removing oxides of nitrogen from auto exhaust emissions. In a three bed system, the oxides of nitrogen are reduced in the first bed, the hydrocarbons and carbon monoxide are partially oxidized in the second bed, and the hydrocarbon and carbon monoxide oxidation is completed in the third bed.

Patent 3,749,032: 1973

Comments:

An antipollution or smoke control device is disclosed comprising an afterburner for the output of an incinerator which has means of controlling combustion to meet control standards of the various pollution control agencies.

Patent 3,751,386: 1973

Comments:

In this patent catalyst compositions are provided containing aluminum oxide and from 50% to 90%, by weight, of oxide of copper, chromium and nickel, which may optionally be doped with Group II-A metal compounds, the oxide of nickel amounting from 2% to 20%, by weight, of the catalyst. The catalysts are manufactured by mixing powdered calcined oxide of copper and chromium with aluminium oxide or aluminium oxide hydrate, forming catalyst granules with a nickel compound which on calcination will form the catalyst. The catalysts are used in the oxidative purification of waste gases, particularly motor vehicle exhaust gases.

Patent 3,755,534: 1973

Comments:

A method of converting the noxious components of auto exhaust gases to innocuous entities is disclosed by contacting the gases with a palladium catalyst on a suitable support and then passing the gases over a catalyst active for hydrocarbon conversion on a suitable support. The use of this particular configuration results in improved conversion of the carbon monoxide and hydrocarbons in the exhaust gases.

Patent 3,816,577: 1974

Comments:

Water soluble constituents of cherry pits have been found to provide a surprisingly effective animal waste deodorizer, and may be readily obtained by a water extraction process. It is claimed that in regard to the composition it is the protein portion which is the main active ingredient of the extract, and therefore it is most important that the protein portion be conserved without degradation in order to work effectively as an animal waste deodorizer. The exact reasons or means whereby cherry pit water extract becomes an effective odor control agent are not taught.

Chemical Neutralization Compounds and Process
Grillo-Werke Aktiengesellschaft,
Duisburg, Germany
Dr. N. Lowicki, Director
(Patents Pending)

Comments:

While being studied for use as a fungicide, zinc ricinoleate was found to neutralize many odors. Additional experimental work showed that the addition of between 0.1% and 2% of substances as zinc compounds of polyhydroxylated fatty acids, resin acids, and similar groups of compounds are recited as effective synergists. The compounds found effective have been given the name "Grillocin." The odor neutralization effects of Grillocin combinations are claimed to be selective. Odor neutralization has been reported among the following classes of compounds, decreasing in the order given: mercaptans, thioethers, aldehydes, and amines. There is almost no effect on branched compounds, polynuclear, highly substituted, aromatic compounds and esters, although there are some exceptions. Gas chromatography studies showed that pure zinc ricinoleate as well as Grillocin is able to bind n-butylamine and ethyl mercaptan; acetone passes through without being affected. Additional gas chromatographic studies using two separating columns, each two meters long and eight millimeters in diameter, were packed with pure kieselgur for gas chromatography. One of the two packings previously had been impregnated with 20% of the odor-annihilating substance. The carrier gas was hydrogen, the pressure was two atmosphere guage, the quantity of sample was 0.2 to 0.5 milliliter, and the column temperatures were 40 and 80°C. The retention times in the unimpregnated column were 30 seconds for acetone, 24 seconds for ethyl mercaptan, and 54 seconds for butylamine. In the impregnated column, a retention time of 80 seconds was found for acetone. For ethyl mercaptan and butylamine, on the other hand, the measurements were stopped after more than two hours, at which time these two substances had not yet been released from the column.

Vapor pressure measurements were also carried out to investigate the binding of n-butylamine on grated zinc ricinoleate. n-Butylamine has a vapor pressure of 96 mm Hg at 29°C. At molar ratios of butylamine to zinc ricinoleate of less than 0.5, the vapor pressure at 32°C is at most 2 mm Hg. Practically no amine odor was perceptible over the preparation. Molar ratios between 0.5 and 0.8 gave vapor pressures of 2 mm Hg at 21°C, 3 mm Hg at 28°C and 11 mm Hg at 41°C. With a molar ratio of 1.5 butylamine to zinc ricinoleate, a vapor pressure of about 10 mm Hg is obtained for a period of four hours at temperatures between 40 and 50°C. The unusually low molar ratios result from the fact that the grated preparation, with an average grain size of two to three millimeters, can react only at the surface.

The quantities of ethyl mercaptan and butylamine that can be bound by Grillocin at room temperature were checked with a packed column, through which air containing an average of 10 milligrams of ethyl mercaptan or butylamine per liter was passed at various flow rates.

The column was a glass tube 22 millimeters in diameter with a useful capacity of almost exactly 100 milliliters and with an aluminium oxide packing. The interstitial volume of the packed column, on average, was 32%. For the binding tests, the packing was impregnated with approximately 3% of Grillocin. The impregnated packing and the untreated packing were compared by measurement of the time taken or the quantity of gas that had to be passed through the column to bring about the color change in an indicator solution. The indicator used for ethyl mercaptan was 10 milliliters of 0.03 N $J_2$ solution with 1 milliliter of sodium azide and starch. Aqueous solutions of methyl orange and phenolphthalein were used in parallel for the detection of butylamine.

The average times and flow volumes found for the blanks and the absorption tests show the slight influence of measuring errors. The values for ethyl mercaptan were 50 to 65 seconds, corresponding to 0.8 to 1.1 liter of gas, as against 27 to 165 minutes, corresponding to 90 to 1300 liters of gas. Results of investigations are shown in Table I:

Table I: Binding of Ethyl Mercaptan and Butylamine with Grillocin in Gas Phase

| | | | | |
|---|---|---|---|---|
| Column: | Height | = 250 m/m | Volume | = 98.91 cm |
| | $\phi$ | = 22.5 m/m | Packing Weight | = 95.0 g |

| Test No. | Odoriferous Substance | Gas Rate l/h | Concentration of Odoriferous Substance in Gas mg/l | Breakthrough Time (Min.) | Quantity Bound mg | mg/g | $mg/cm^3$ |
|---|---|---|---|---|---|---|---|
| 70 | Ethyl mercaptan | 200 | 11.2 | 26.55 | 1010 | 340 | 10.2 |
| 68 | " " | 100 | 11.1 | 65.23 | 1210 | 430 | 12.2 |
| 66 | " " | 50 | 12.6 | 165.35 | 1650 | 580 | 16.6 |
| 86 | Butylamine | 10 | 7.85 | 38.40 | 47.1 | 16 | 0.47 |
| 87 | " | 25 | 7.85 | 4.10 | 13.03 | 4.7 | 0.14 |

It can be seen from the data in Table I that the binding of ethyl mercaptan begins even at very high flow rates corresponding to residence times of 0.6 to 1.5 seconds, and increasing quantities are bound with increasing residence time.

The reaction time of butylamine is considerably longer, and much smaller quantities are bound by the Grillocin. However, an exothermic effect is observed for both ethyl mercaptan and for butylamine. This is a clear indication that a reaction has occurred.

Corresponding to the results of the vapor pressure measurements, desorption experiments were carried out by passage of air through the column at temperatures of 60 to 65°C. The results are shown in Table II:

Table II: Desorption of Ethyl Mercaptan and Butylamine

Column: Height = 250 m/m; Volume = 98.91 $cm^3$
$\phi$ = 22.5 m/m; Packing Weight = 95.0 g

| Test No. | Odoriferous Substance | Gas Rate 1/h | Desorption Temperature °C | Desorption Time (Min.) | Quantity Bound mg | mg/$cm^3$ | % |
|---|---|---|---|---|---|---|---|
| 70/a | Ethyl mercaptan | 200 | 60 | 26.36 | 93.2 | 0.94 | 9.3 |
| 68/a | " " | 100 | 60 | 26.02 | 93.2 | 0.94 | 7.5 |
| 66/a | " " | 50 | 60 | 266.37 | 84.0 | 0.85 | 5.1 |
| 86/a | Butylamine | 10 | 60 | 72.08 | 25.9 | 0.27 | 53.5 |
| 87/a | " | 25 | 60 | 92.30 | 7.06 | 0.07 | 54.5 |

It is again clear that butylamine is much less strongly bound than ethyl mercaptan. A maximum of only 10% of the latter was desorbed at the highest flow rate, whereas in the case of n-butylamine, approximately 50% was released by the Grillocin at the same temperature for all flow rates. However, the remaining 50% of the bound amine cannot be removed even if air is passed through for several hours. The emerging air remains odorless.

If the continuous decrease in the partial pressure by the air passing through the column is taken into account, the quantities of butylamine released agree well with the results of the vapor pressure measurements.

It is interesting to note that odor neutralization is possible not only in the gas phase but also in the liquid phase, e.g., in an aqueous medium, if ethyl mercaptan is led in.

In this case a column packed with Raschig rings was used. The diameter of the column was 45 millimeters and its useful capacity was 387 cubic centimeters. An aqueous emulsion of Grillocin (concentration or 4.6 grams per liter) was allowed to trickle through the column at a rate of 56 liters per hour. To avoid irregularities in the trickling, the entire column was kept full. The quantity of emulsion used was 650 milliliters, and this was kept in circulation. The results are shown in Table III:

Table III: Binding of Ethyl Mercaptan with Grillocin in Liquid Phase

Column: Height = 280 m/m; Volume = 387 cm

$\phi$ = 44 m/m; Packing Weight = Raschig rings

| Test No. | Odoriferous Substance | Gas Rate l/h | Concentration of Odoriferous Substance in Gas mg/l | Absorption Solution l/h | Concentration of Grillocin in Solution g/l | Breakthrough Time (Min.) | Quantities Absorbed mg | Quantities Absorbed mg/g | Quantities Absorbed mg/cm$^3$ |
|---|---|---|---|---|---|---|---|---|---|
| 72 | Ethyl mercaptan | 50 | 12.6 | 56 | 4.6 | 88.52 | 929.88 | 319 | 2.46 |
| 74 | " " | 100 | 12.6 | 56 | 4.6 | 56.10 | 1181.88 | 416 | 3.06 |
| 76 | " " | 200 | 12.6 | 56 | 4.6 | 29.16 | 1013.00 | 350 | 2.6 |

In blank tests with pure water, breakthrough occurred between three and seven minutes. Subtraction of these blank times gives the values shown in Table III. The breakthrough times are between 30 and 90 minutes, and the quantities absorbed are even higher than those obtained in the gas phase.

Desorption cannot be achieved with odor neutralization in the aqueous phase. If the emulsion is heated to about 60 to 65°C and air passed through it, no ethyl mercaptan can be detected even after several hours.

Similar experiments with butylamine do not give such a spectacular breakthrough in the blank test. The difference is thus not so clear as in the case of the mercaptan.

Some speculation regarding the action of zinc ricinoleate and zinc ricinoleate with synergists is given:

Homopolar Bonding by Chemical Reactions: Complete odor elimination could be explained if the energy required to break these newly formed bonds was about 80 to 100 kilocalories per mole. Such processes are unlikely on purely chemical grounds, and are directly refuted by the fact that partial liberation of the bound substances is possible by ionic bonding.

Ionic Bonding: Ionic bonding might be assumed in some cases, but by no means in all. For example, zinc mercaptides could be formed from the mercaptans. Since a zinc mercaptide and free fatty acid would be formed in this case from a zinc salt of a fatty acid, the energy of reaction would not be particularly high and could possibly be sufficient. This possibility is opposed, however, by the fact that zinc salts of other fatty acids do not have a similar effect.

Complex Formation with the Zinc: This is much more general in character. It would allow nearly all functional groups in organic molecules to react to a more or less pronounced degree. This is again opposed by the fact that other zinc compounds do not have a corresponding effect. Nevertheless, complex formation may undoubtedly be considered as a contributory factor.

Hydrogen Bonding: The reaction energy liberated here is about eight to ten kilocalories per mole. This is not enough to explain the observed binding strength. Here again, at least one other factor would have to be involved.

Bonding by Van der Waal's Forces: The bonding energy here is lower by a factor of 10 than in the case of hydrogen bonds. It would be conceivable that under the conditions of use of a deodorant spray, the binding could be reinforced by hydrophobic association as a result of water saturation in the atmosphere. In this case, the odor annihilation would result from micelle formation between the odoriferous substances and the Grillocin components. However, this idea is also in conflict with the fact that compounds with similar structures are inactive.

The possibility of another type of binding must therefore be considered. One such type is found in inclusion compounds or clathrates. The first inclusion compounds to be discovered and used technically were those formed by urea with unbranched aliphatic hydrocarbons. In the presence of such hydrocarbons, urea forms a special crystal lattice containing tubular cavities into which the hydrocarbon molecules fit.

A second type consists of the cage inclusion compounds formed, e.g., by hydroquinone. Small molecules can be very securely imprisoned within the lattice of a special modification hydroquinone as if in a cage, so that the odor of the trapped compound, e.g., hydrogen sulfide, cannot be perceived immediately, but becomes noticeable only when the crystals are crushed.

A third type consists of the layer inclusion compounds such as are formed, e.g., between the bile acids and fatty acids. Lattice forces are always involved in the formation of these inclusion compounds.

These compounds quickly lost their technical importance with the development of molecular sieves containing fixed cavities of a definite, pre-determined size.

The odor neutralization here is undoubtedly due to an action mechanism such as that leading to the formation of inclusion compounds.

It can be seen from the formula of zinc ricinoleate (Table IV) that the zinc is attached to the carboxylate group by an ionic bond and to the hydroxyl group by a coordinate bond. The intra-molecular bonding, i.e., the formation of two 14-membered rings, is favored by the double bond. The cavity inside these rings probably does not have a rigid shape, but can adapt itself to the size of a compound to be trapped by movement of ring atoms.

The individual zinc ricinoleate molecules are presumably fitted together like steps to form tubes. The coordinate bonding of the hydroxyl group in this form corresponds to a chelate linkage. Alkaline earth metal ions have a much lower tendency to form such chelate linkages; this could explain why the magnesium salt of ricinoleic acid has no odor-neutralizing effect.

The simultaneous occurence of polar forces between the molecule to be trapped and the trapping structure in the formation of inclusion compounds in

Grillocin could explain a certain selectivity that exists with regard to the compounds to be trapped. Thus unlike aldehydes, aliphatic ketones and esters are not bound. This suggests that the formation of hydrogen bonds between the hydroxyl groups of ricinoleic acid and the trapped compound also plays a part.

Table IV: Zinc Ricinoleate

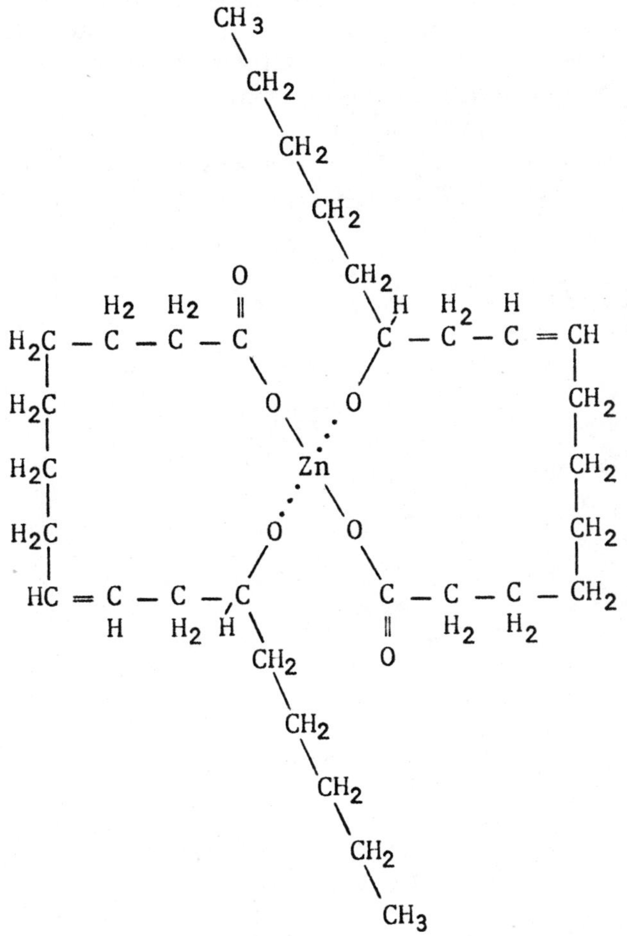

The desorption of bound substances presented in Table III may be regarded as evidence that inclusion compounds are in fact formed.

It was also attempted to find IR-spectroscopic evidence of the formation of inclusion compounds. The stretching vibrations are not expected to be appreciably influenced by the formation of inclusion compounds. On the other hand, vibrations that result in displacement from the bond axis, i.e., wagging vibrations, will be affected, and will in fact be weakened in most cases. However, these vibrations lie in the long-wave region above 10 pm, where certain difficulties are encountered in evaluation and assignment. Deviations have been found in this range that at least do not conflict with the presence of inclusion compounds.

The attempt to explain the odor neutralizing action of zinc ricinoleate by the formation of inclusion compounds has certainly not been successful in every respect. However, this assumption still offers the best explanation for the effects observed. Several effects, some of which have been previously mentioned, undoubtedly occur together, as is also suggested by the possibility of synergistically increasing the activity.

Grillocin is claimed to be completely harmless when applied to the skin as confirmed by a series of dermatological and toxicological investigations.

Two methods are possible for the binding of odoriferous substances from the air. One is to atomize Grillocin in the gas phase, and the other is to recirculate the air, with passage of a side stream over Grillocin on a support. To allow binding to occur, it is necessary to ensure that the molecules of the odoriferous substance come into contact with the Grillocin. Since Grillocin has no appreciable vapor pressure at temperatures below its melting point, one cannot expect self-diffusion into the air as in the masking of odors with perfumery oils. Contact must be made mechanically, e.g., by spraying to produce the greatest possible number of suspended particles.

## PATENT BIBLIOGRAPHY

| NUMBER | DATE | INVENTOR | TITLE |
|---|---|---|---|
| 51,216 | November 28, 1865 | Rankin | Improved Deodorizing Composition |
| 93,607 | August 10, 1869 | Fish | Improved Deodorizing Compound |
| 97,469 | November 30, 1869 | Dayton | Improved Compound for Disinfecting and Deodorizing |
| 168,219 | September 28, 1875 | Bowen | Improvement in Disinfecting, Deodorizing, and Antiseptic Compositions |
| 173,607 | February 15, 1876 | Fehr | Improvement in Deodorizing, Disinfecting, and Antiseptic Powders |
| 184,700 | November 28, 1876 | Commins | Improvement in Disinfectant, Deodorizer, and Fumigator |
| 191,476 | May 29, 1877 | Seligman | Improvement in Deodorizing, Disinfecting, and Fertilizing Compounds |
| 222,451 | December 9, 1879 | Burchardt | Improvement in Antiseptic and Deodorizing Compounds |
| 222,453 | December 9, 1879 | Caffall | Improvement in Disinfectants and Deodorizers |
| 406,700 | July 9, 1889 | Caldwell | Deodorant and Disinfectant |
| 490,797 | January 31, 1893 | Woolf | Disinfectant and Deodorizer |
| 860,456 | July 16, 1907 | Fournier | Disinfecting and Deodorizing Process |
| 975,354 | November 8, 1910 | Gruter, Pohl | Stable Mixture for Producing Hydrogen Peroxide |
| 1,336,272 | November 29, 1916 | Billing | Disinfectant, Antiseptic, Deodorant, or Detergent |
| 1,346,337 | July 13, 1920 | Roark | Deodorizing Material |
| 1,408,535 | March 7, 1922 | Ressler | Deodorant and Disinfectant Compound |
| 1,410,249 | March 21, 1922 | Henderson, Haggard | Process of Deodorizing Offensive Gaseous Emanations from Organic Matter |
| 1,459,036 | June 19, 1923 | Reinhold | Deodorizing Material |
| 1,515,364 | November 11, 1924 | Roark | Deodorant and Insecticide |
| 1,576,106 | March 9, 1926 | Fetherston | Treatment of Garbage Containers and Garbage |
| 1,593,485 | July 20,1926 | Crosnier | Antiseptic Product |
| 1,648,259 | November 8, 1927 | Cadwell | Method of Deodorizing |
| 1,729,752 | 1929 | Southgate | Deodorant Composition |
| 1,922,416 | August 15, 1933 | Block | Gas Adsorbent |
| 1,950,286 | March 6, 1934 | Barkow | Means for Deodorizing Sanitary Napkins |
| 1,953,526 | April 3, 1934 | Dow, McKeown | Absorbent Material |
| 2,024,145 | December 17, 1935 | Cline | Deodorant |
| 2,054,966 | September 22, 1936 | Crites | Means and Method for Deodorizing |
| 2,071,094 | February 16, 1937 | Vincent | Chemical Manufacture |
| 2,077,060 | April 13, 1937 | White | Deodorizing Composition |

| NUMBER | DATE | INVENTOR | TITLE |
|---|---|---|---|
| 2,091,497 | August 31, 1937 | Bane | Cardamon Treated Tobacco |
| 2,131,235 | September 27, 1938 | Randall, Grunenberg | Deodorizing Material |
| 2,168,523 | August 8, 1939 | Heyl | Process for Treating Seeds, Bulbs, Tubes, and Roots. |
| 2,228,993 | January 14, 1941 | Goldstein | Deodorant |
| 2,261,924 | November 4, 1941 | Pittman, Bottoms | Bentonite Treatment |
| 2,310,099 | February 2, 1943 | Loetel | Deodorant |
| 2,317,908 | April 27, 1943 | Grady | Deodorant |
| 2,326,672 | August 10, 1943 | Paschal | Method and Composition for the Treatment of Air |
| 2,356,062 | August 15, 1944 | Johnson | Therapeutic Composition |
| 2,464,043 | March 8, 1949 | Kamlet | Air-deodorizing Compositions |
| 2,527,029 | October 24, 1950 | Paschal | Composition for Freshening Air and Method Therefor |
| 2,546,791 | March 27, 1951 | Slifkin, Sulich | Masking the Odor of Ammonia in Developing Diazotypes |
| 2,546,898 | March 27, 1951 | Mark | Deodorizing Method |
| 2,562,042 | July 24, 1951 | Kipnis | Tetrahydropyran-sulfide Compounds |
| 2,602,042 | July 1, 1952 | Abbott | Processing Methyl Cellulose and the Products Thereof |
| 2,683,074 | July 6, 1954 | Kuehner | Process for Deodorizing and Sterilizing Air |
| 2,691,615 | October 12, 1954 | Turner, Raske | Air Treating Gel |
| 2,715,611 | August 16, 1955 | Weeks | Air Deodorant |
| 2,719,129 | September 27, 1955 | Richardson | Pressurized Liquid Room and Air Deodorant Compositions |
| 2,762,822 | September 11, 1956 | Vagenius | Copper Nitrogenous Organic Compound |
| 2,773,774 | January 22, 1957 | Buslik | Granular Vermiculite Deodorants |
| 2,781,350 | February 12, 1957 | Mannheimer | Cycloimidine Derivatives and Process for Preparing Same |
| 2,781,351 | February 12, 1957 | Mannheimer | Certain Imidazoline Alkanoic Acid Salts of Certain Detergent Acids and Process |
| 2,781,357 | February 12, 1957 | Mannheimer | Imidazoline Derivatives and Process |
| 2,789,078 | April 16, 1957 | Trusler | Disinfecting and Deodorizing Compositions and Method of Using Same |
| 2,793,973 | May 28, 1957 | Cheronis | Treatment of Garbage and Other Wastes and Compositions Therefor |
| 2,794,762 | June 4, 1957 | Westcott | Body Deodorant for Internal Use |
| 2,815,260 | December 3, 1957 | Melander | Process for Eliminating Urine Odors in Textile Materials by Applying Lithium Carbonate |

| NUMBER | DATE | INVENTOR | TITLE |
|---|---|---|---|
| 2,853,475 | September 23, 1958 | Murphey | N-Chlorinated Polysulfonamides |
| 2,856,330 | October 14, 1958 | Vagenius | Method of Treating Cotton Fabrics |
| 2,865,806 | December 23, 1958 | Bulloff | Solidified Air Odor Control Liquids |
| 2,893,958 | July 7, 1959 | Phillips | Reduction of Objectionable Odors of Materials |
| 2,894,876 | July 14, 1959 | Scanlan, Harrison | Deodorant Composition |
| 2,922,747 | January 26, 1960 | Scanlan | Deodorant Composition |
| 2,927,055 | March 1, 1960 | Lanzet | Air Treating Gel and Method of Preparing the Same |
| 2,998,390 | August 29, 1961 | Hamilton | Recirculating Toilet Sump Fluid |
| 3,001,997 | September 26, 1961 | Mannheimer | Carboxylic Acid Amides of N-Amino-alkylene-heterocyclic Amines |
| 3,074,891 | January 22, 1963 | Kulka | Compositions and Methods for the Deodorization of Spaces |
| 3,074,892 | January 22, 1963 | Kulka | Space Deodorant Composition and Method of Using Same |
| 3,077,457 | February 12, 1963 | Kulka | Fumaric Acid Ester Space Deodorant and Method of Using Same |
| 3,080,295 | March 5, 1963 | Goorley | Odor Destroying Agent Derived from Pycnanthemum Albescens (Labiatae) |
| 3,091,511 | May 28, 1963 | Calhoun | Process of Deodorizing |
| 3,093,546 | June 11, 1963 | Atkinson | Absorbent Product |
| 3,102,101 | August 27, 1963 | Hawley, Laycock | Deodorant Compositions and the Methods of Use |
| 3,104,205 | September 17, 1963 | Hainer, Berdick, Morawetz | Deodorant Composition Comprising the Copper Complex of the Copolymer of Allylamine and Methacrylic Acid |
| 3,124,459 | March 10, 1964 | Erwin | Organoleptic Compositions |
| 3,124,460 | March 10, 1964 | Erwin | Organoleptic Compositions |
| 3,150,132 | September 22, 1964 | Symes | Novel Chlorocyanurate Compounds |
| 3,172,817 | March 9, 1965 | Leupold, Kellner, Hellmuth | Method of Deodorizing the Human Body and Materials Therefor |
| 3,183,645 | May 18, 1965 | Teller | Process for Deodorization of Gases from Rendering Vessels or Cookers |
| 3,198,251 | August 3, 1965 | Shore | Deodorant Preparation |
| 3,226,332 | December 28, 1965 | Lincoln, Osment | Production of Potassium Permanganate Activated Alumina Composite |
| 3,236,726 | February 22, 1966 | Ross | Surface Chlorination Composition |

| NUMBER | DATE | INVENTOR | TITLE |
|---|---|---|---|
| 3,248,255 | April 26, 1966 | Bode | Process Precipitating Conditions which Enable the Simultaneous Precipitation or Coagulation of Dispersed or Colloidally Suspended Non-starch Materials |
| 3,250,724 | May 1966 | Kulka | Polyester Space Deodorant and Method of Using Same |
| 3,255,078 | June 7, 1966 | Heinroth, Schegg, Steinlatt, Wiegand | Process for the Treatment of Fiber Articles of Synthetic Polyamides and Composition Produced |
| 3,255,082 | June 7, 1966 | Barton | Method of Preparing Stable Aluminum Chlorhydrate-alkali Metal and Alkaline Earth Metal Salt Complex Antiperspirant Stick |
| 3,271,242 | September 6, 1966 | McNicholas | Stable Chlorine Dioxide Composition and Method of Making Same |
| 3,314,880 | April 18, 1967 | Rubin | Process for Flocculation of Contaminants and Removal of Flocculated Contaminants by Air Flotation |
| 3,317,382 | May 2, 1967 | Hart | Household Deodorant |
| 3,328,312 | June 27, 1967 | Laycock, Tucker | Deodorant Composition and Process of Deodorizing Air |
| 3,339,343 | September 5, 1967 | Van Buuren | Process for Purification of Polluted Air |
| 3,350,301 | October 31, 1967 | Hoffman | Process for Purification of Wastewater Containing Fat, Oil, Greases |
| 3,354,225 | November 21, 1967 | Kane | Novel Camphane Derivatives |
| 3,371,984 | March 5, 1968 | Kelly, Fuller | Air Freshener |
| 3,376,219 | April 2, 1968 | Silvey | Removing Taste and Odor Compounds from Water |
| 3,413,218 | November 26, 1968 | Einsel | Process of Deodorizing Using Biphenyl |
| 3,431,208 | March 4, 1969 | Bailey | Denture Spray |
| 3,446,893 | May 27, 1969 | Hanford, Newman | Solid Deodorizing Compositions |
| 3,452,028 | June 24, 1969 | Shapiro | Quaternary Ammonium Compounds |
| 3,459,852 | August 5, 1969 | Roehm | Deodorizing Treatment of Aqueous Solutions |
| 3,479,297 | November 18, 1969 | Rutzen, Lowenstein | Room Deodorants |
| 3,493,650 | February 3, 1970 | Dunkel | Perfume and Deodorizing with Citronellyl Senecioate |
| 3,499,722 | March 10, 1970 | Ashley | Process for Removing Atmosphere Polluting Odors from Systems |

| NUMBER | DATE | INVENTOR | TITLE |
|---|---|---|---|
| 3,509,254 | April 28, 1970 | Krotinger, Nusbaum | Deodorizing and Bactericidal |
| 3,511,224 | May 12, 1970 | Porwancher | Process for Exhausting Smoke from a Food Product Smoke-house Incinerator |
| 3,520,802 | July 21, 1970 | Pavia | Process for Treatment of High Protein Liquid Wastes |
| 3,527,798 | September 8, 1970 | Hara | Active Calcium Succinates in Cis-form and a Process for the Preparation Thereof |
| 3,591,515 | July 6, 1971 | Lovely | Pulverulent Chlorine Dioxide Compositions |
| 3,592,614 | July 13, 1971 | Schmidt | Process for Incineration of Noncondensable Gases from a Cooking Device |
| 3,632,514 | January 4, 1972 | Blocher | Sawdust Material with Quaternary Ammonium Halide Odor-retardant |
| 3,650,968 | March 21, 1972 | Hoffman | Fisherman's Soap |
| 3,673,065 | June 27, 1972 | Anderson | Process for Deemulsification of Fat-water Emulsion Systems |
| 3,681,464 | August 1, 1972 | Theimer | Saturated Indane Derivatives and Processes for Producing Same |
| 3,697,419 | October 10, 1972 | Grant | Process for Purification of Waste Effluents |
| 3,706,663 | December 19, 1972 | Peterson | Method of Controlling Odor |
| 3,708,421 | January 2, 1973 | Rippie | Process to Remove Mercaptan Sulfur from Sour Oils |
| 3,709,660 | January 9, 1973 | Urban | Catalytic Treatment of Thio-sulfate Containing Solution with Hydrogen to Produce Sulfide |
| 3,725,311 | April 3, 1973 | Grubb | Low-temperature Extrudable Odor-neutralizing Composition |
| 3,726,062 | April 10, 1973 | Hungate, Ogletree, Nickell | Process for Controlling Emission of Odors and Particulate Matter |
| 3,740,349 | June 19, 1973 | Negra, Warshaw | Catalyst for Treating Combus-tion Exhaust Gas |
| 3,741,725 | June 26, 1973 | Graham | Catalytic Control of Auto Exhaust Emissions |
| 3,751,386 | August 7, 1973 | Koberstein, Alzenau, Lakatos | Catalyst for Purification of Waste Gases |
| 3,762,875 | October 2, 1973 | Burmeister | Odor Sealing Method |
| 3,801,709 | April 2, 1974 | Augsburger, Marvel | Fragrance Retention by Chelating Agent Coated Talc |
| 3,816,577 | June 11, 1974 | Neckerman, Hammer | Method of Deodorizing Animal Waste with Cherry Pit Extract |

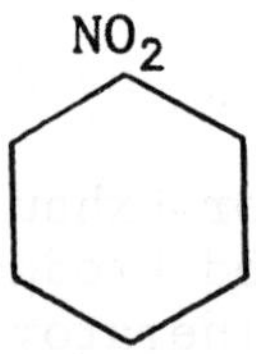


Bitter almond

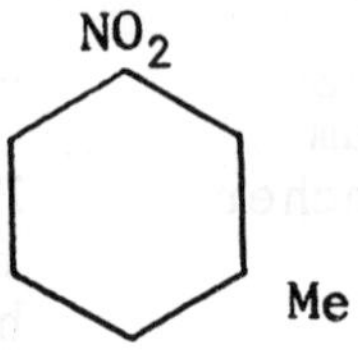


Bitter almond

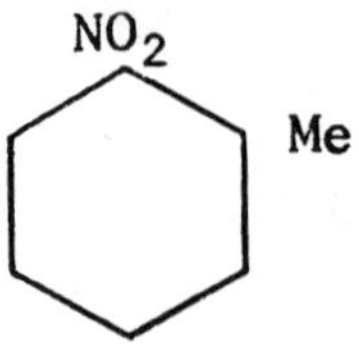


Bitter almond

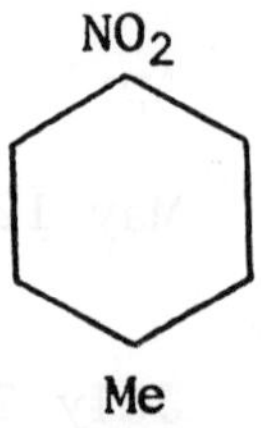


Bitter Almond (Hard)

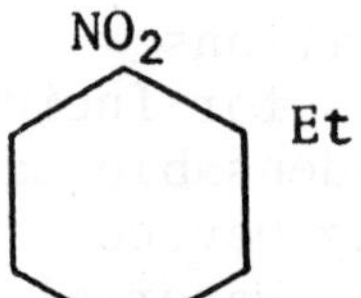


Weak almond, similar to ethyl benzene

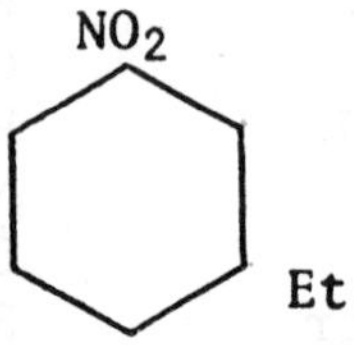


Weak almond (trace coumarin and sassafras)

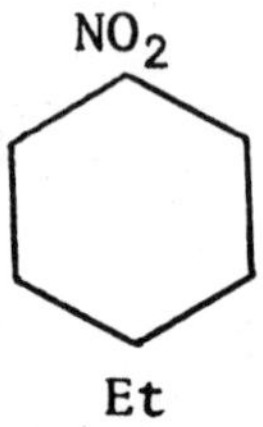


Sassafras, weak cumin

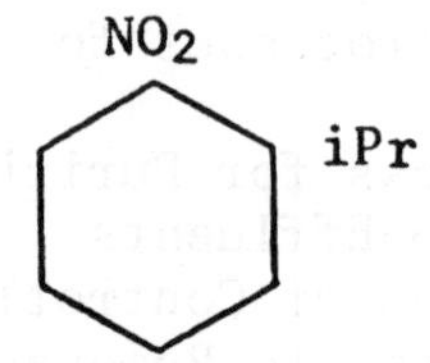


Cuminic

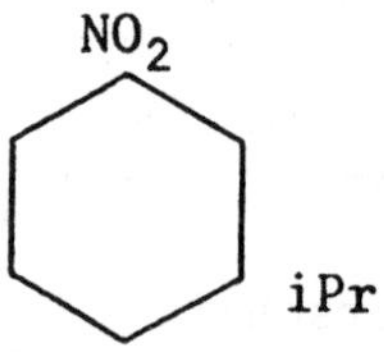


Cuminic, weak sassafras

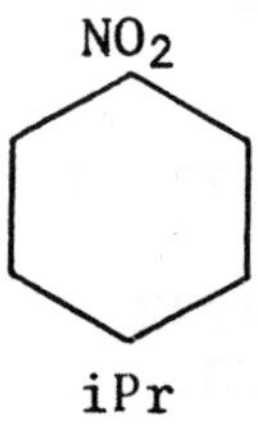


Cumin

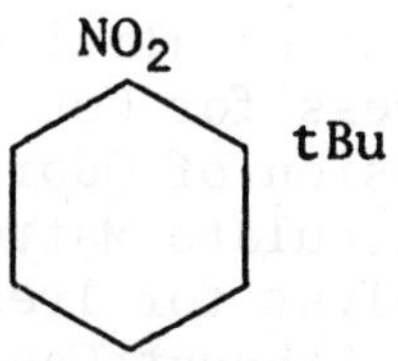


tert. Butyl benzenic

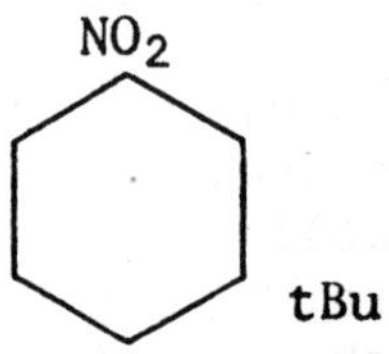


Cumin, strong, carrot

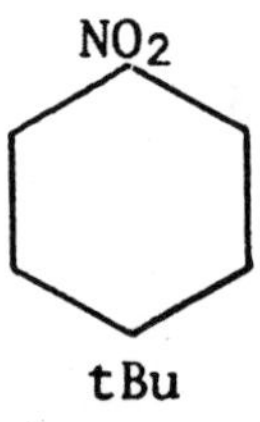


Cumin, carrot

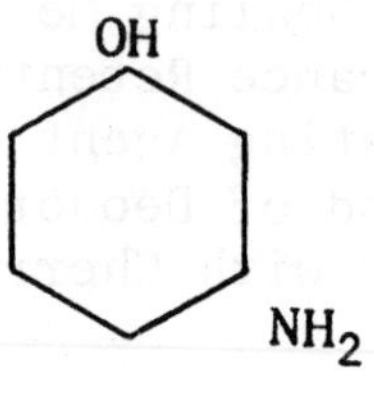


Aromatic m-Nitrophenol

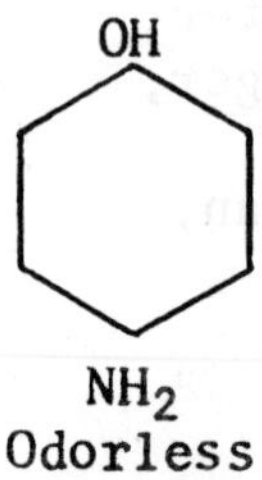


Odorless p-nitrophenol

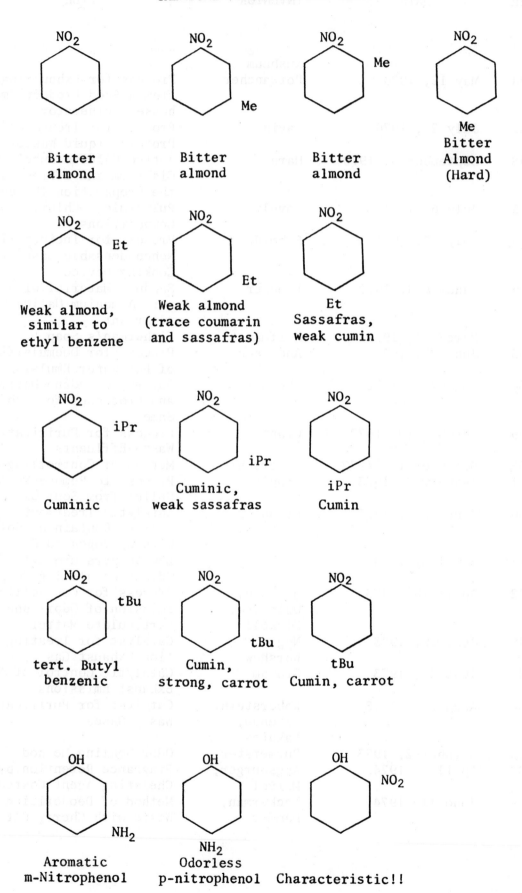

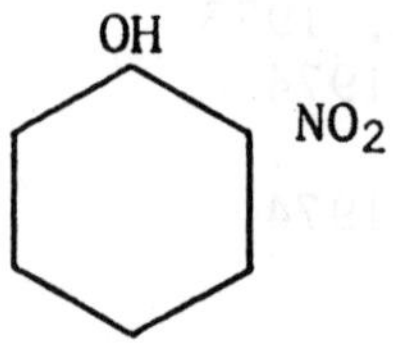


Characteristic!!

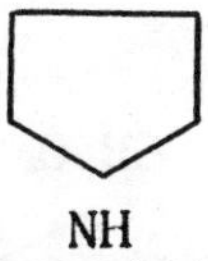

Pyrrolidine
unpleasant,
ammonia

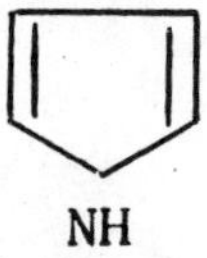

Pyrrole
empyreumatic,
chloroform

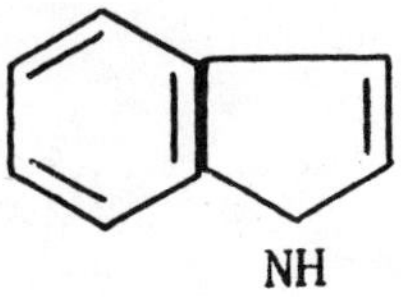

Indole
fecal!!!

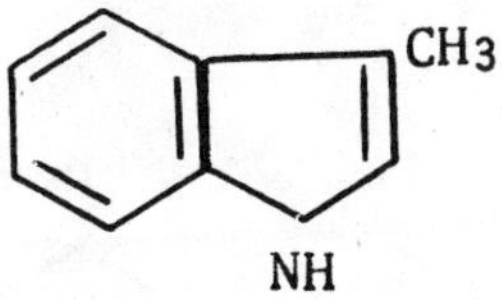

Skatole
fecal!

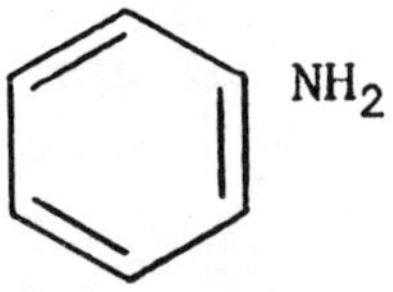

Aniline
gas-lime

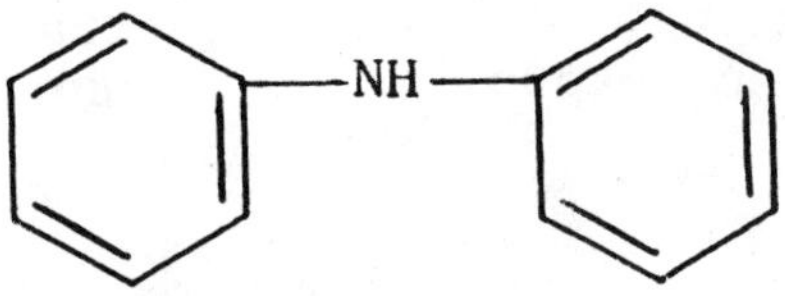

Diphenylamine
floral

$CH_3NHCH_3$ — $(CH_3)_3N$
Dimethylamine Trimethylamine

$NH_3$ → $CH_3NH_2$
Ammonia Methylamine

$NH_2(CH_5)_5NH_2$
Cadaverine

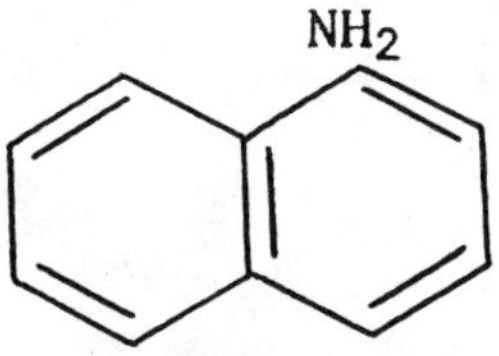

1-Naphthylamine
resembles indole,
unpleasant
$C_{10}H_9N$

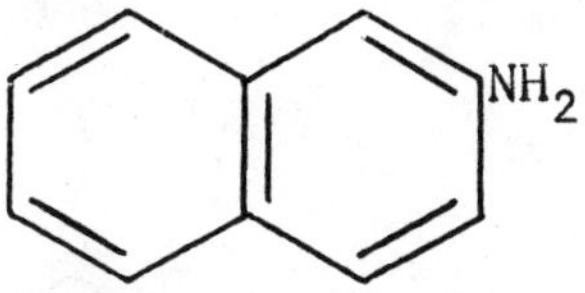

2-Naphthylamine
Slight
acetic odor
$C_{10}H_9N$

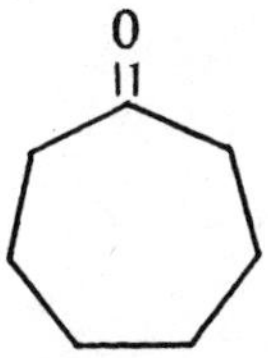

Cyclo-
heptanone
oil of
peppermint
odor

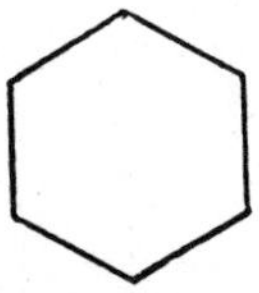

Cyclohexane
solvent
odor;
pungent
when impure

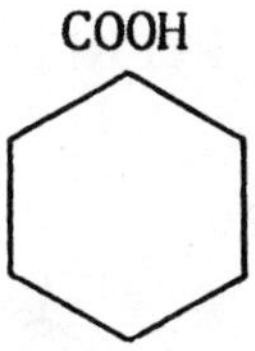

Cyclohexanecar-
boxylic acid
odorless; but
valerian odor
when in solution

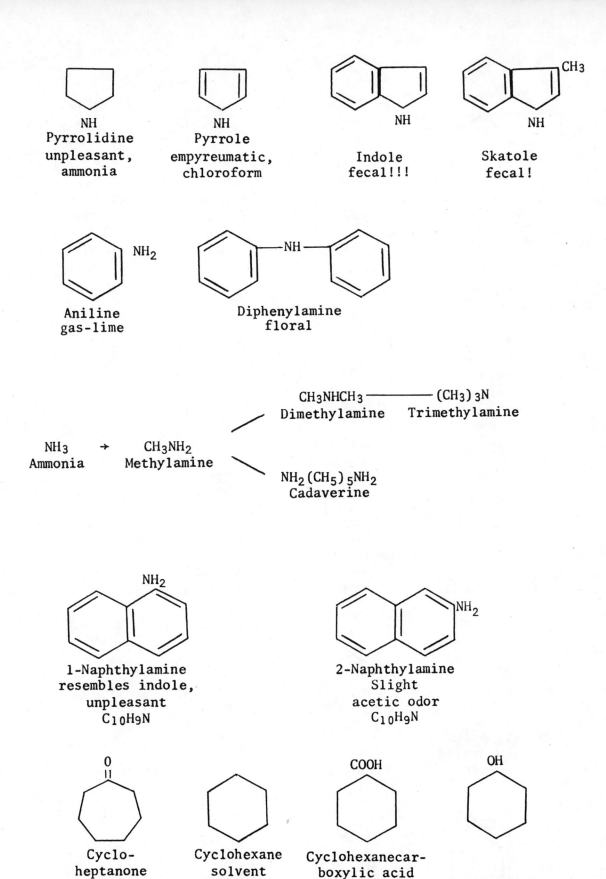

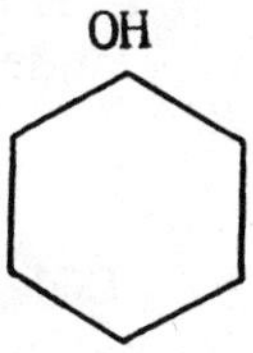

Cyclohexanol
camphor
odor

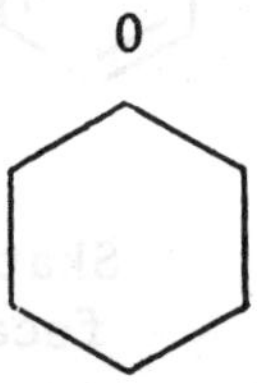


Cyclohexanone
odor reminiscent of peppermint & acetone

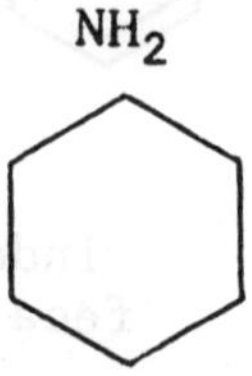


Cyclohexylamine
strong, fishy, amine odor

Cyclohexyl bromide
penetrating odor

Cyclohexylcarbinol
slight odor of camphor

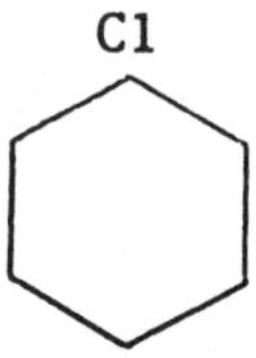


Cyclohexyl chloride
suffocating odor

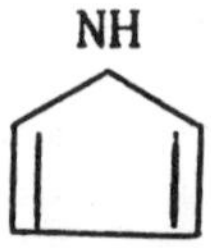


Pyrrole
agreeable, empyreumatic, chloroform-like

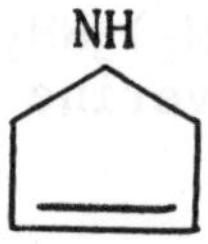


Pyrroline
unpleasant, ammonia-like odor

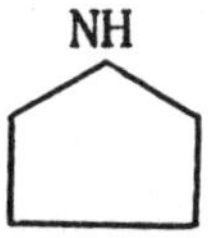


Pyrrolidine
unpleasant, ammonia-like odor

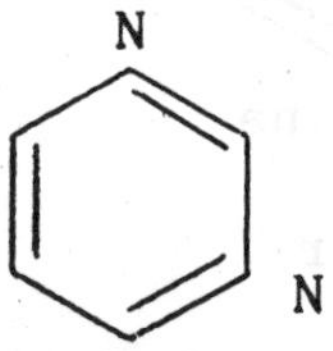


Pyrimidine
penetrating odor

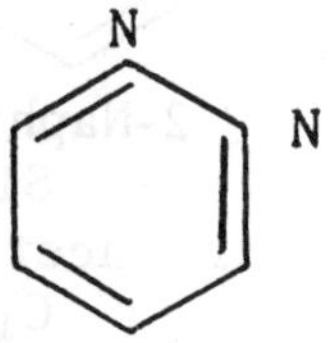


Pyridazine

Benzotrichloride
highly irritant, penetrating odor

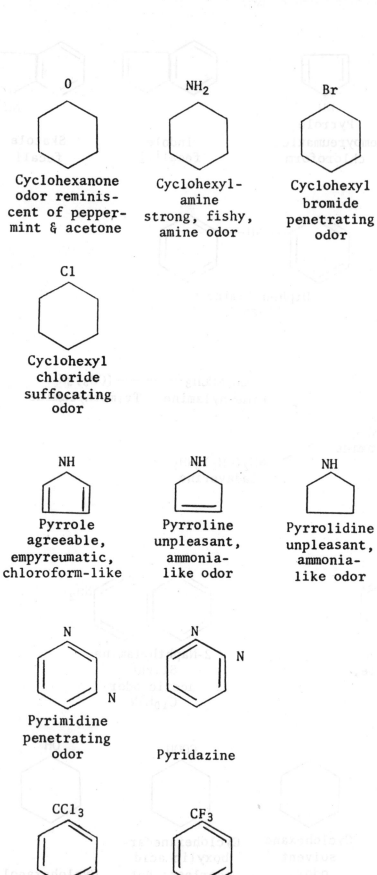

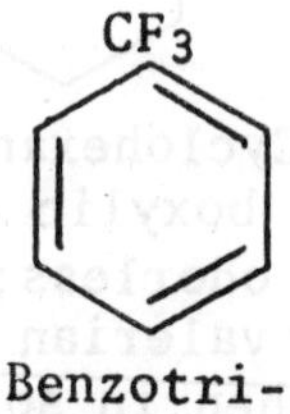


Benzotrifluoride
aromatic odor

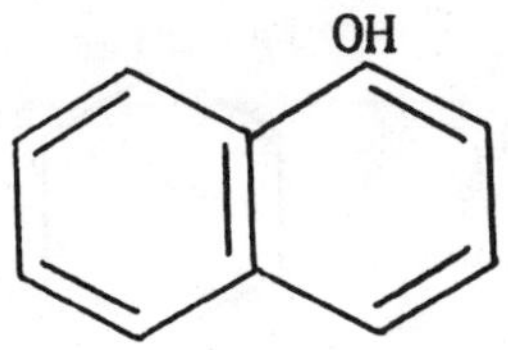


1-Naphthol
phenolic odor

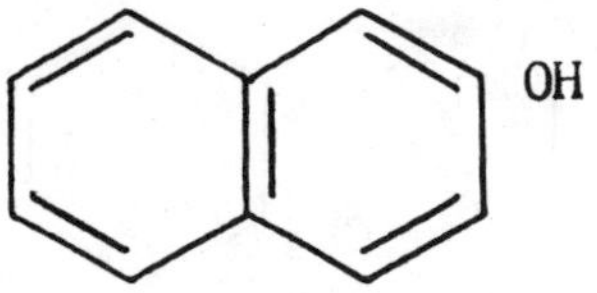


2-Naphthol
slight
phenolic odor

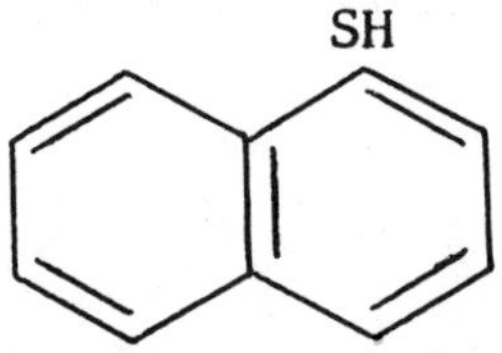


1-Naphthalenethiol
strong mercaptan
odor

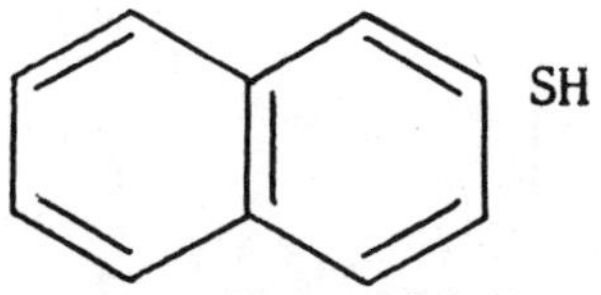


2-Naphthalenethiol
disagreeable
odor

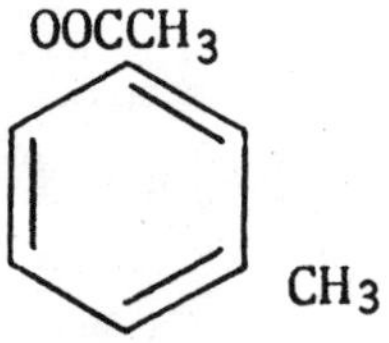


m-Cresyl
acetate
phenolic odor,
reminiscent
of acetone

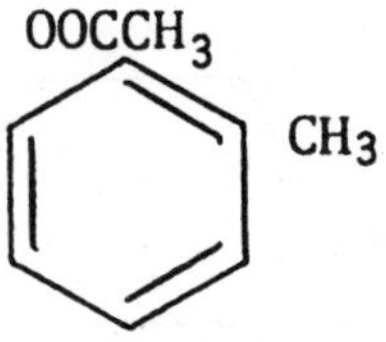


o-Cresyl
acetate
almost
odorless

p-Cresyl
acetate
heavy floral
(narcissus-like)

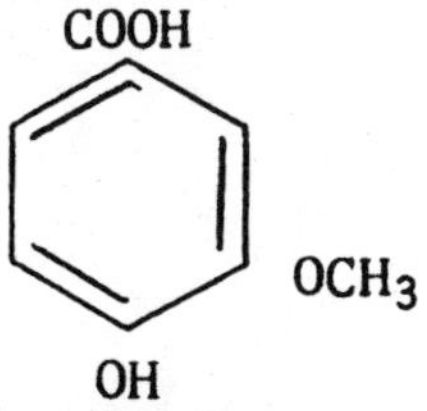


Vanillic
acid
odorless

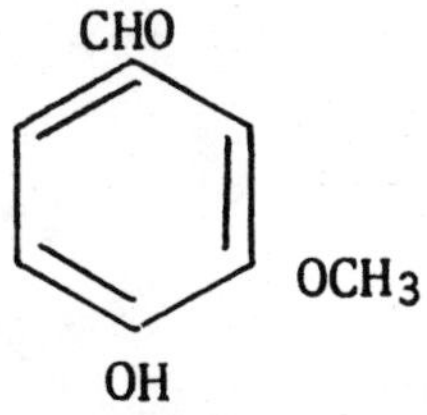


Vanillin
pleasant
vanilla odor

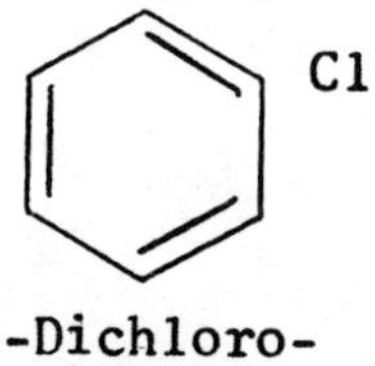


o-Dichloro-
benzene
pleasant,
aromatic
odor

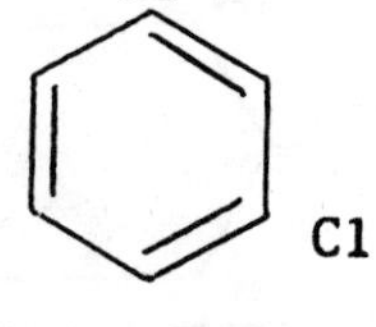


m-Dichloro-
benzene
nearly
odorless

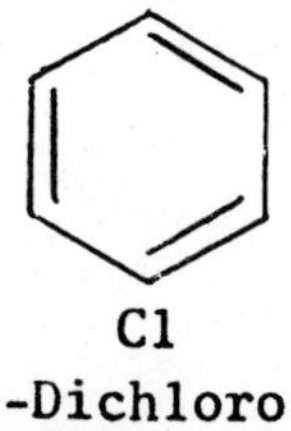


p-Dichloro-
benzene
penetrating
odor

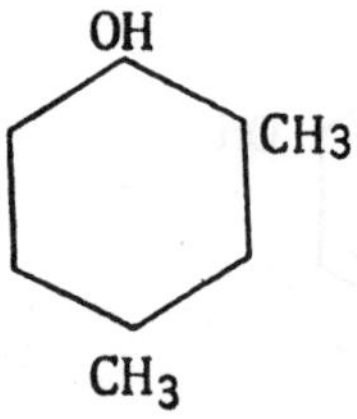


2,4-Xylenol
faint

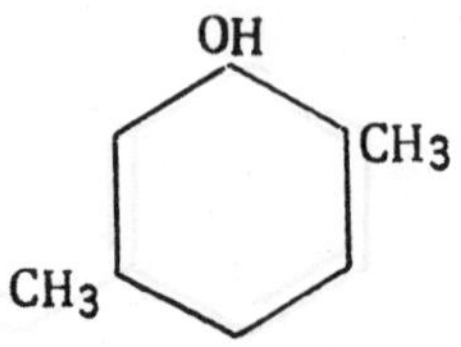


2,5-Xylenol
mild, cresolic
odor

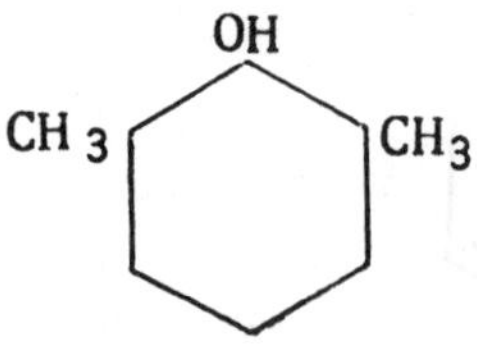


2,6-Xylenol
oil of
wintergreen

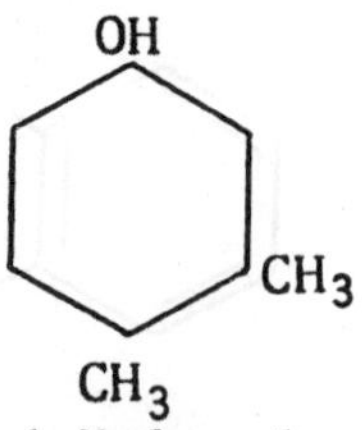


3,4-Xylenol
dull, musty
odor

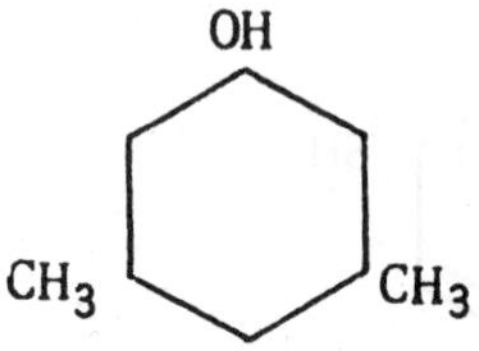


3,5-Xylenol
strong phenol

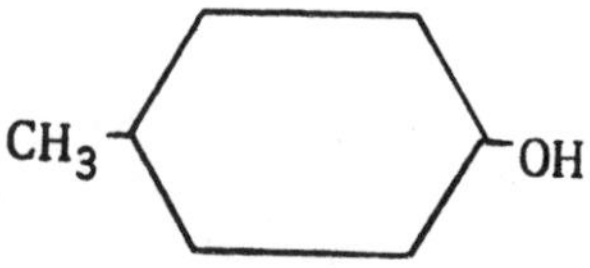


p-Cresol
strong!!!
(Moncrieff)

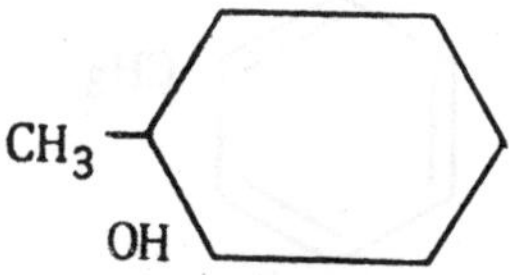


o-Cresol
strong!!
(Moncrieff)

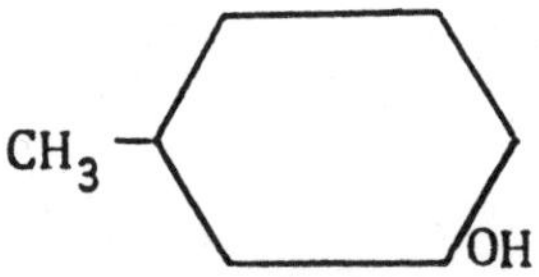


m-Cresol
strong!
(Moncrieff)

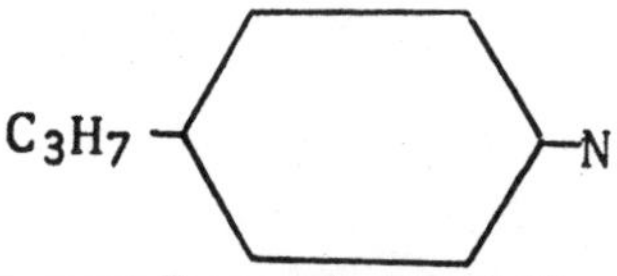


γ-Propyl pyridine
violets
(Moncrieff)

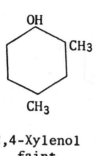

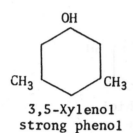

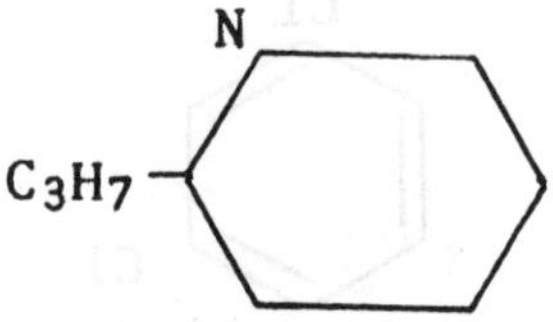


α-Propyl pyridine
flowery
(Moncrieff)

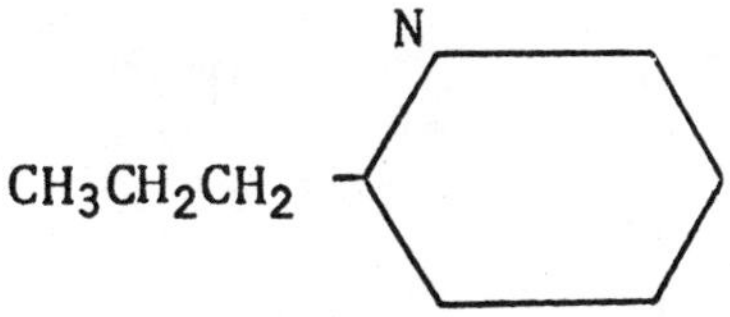


α-Propyl pyridine
floral
(Moncrieff)

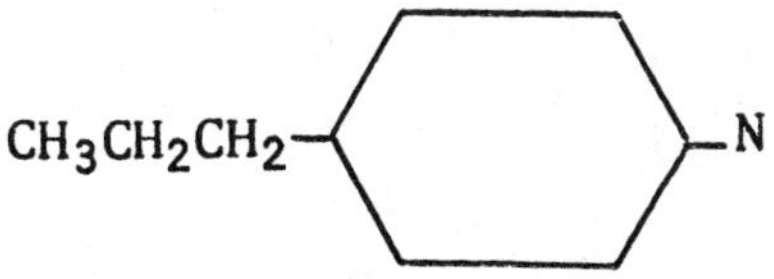


γ-Propyl pyridine
violets
(Moncrieff)

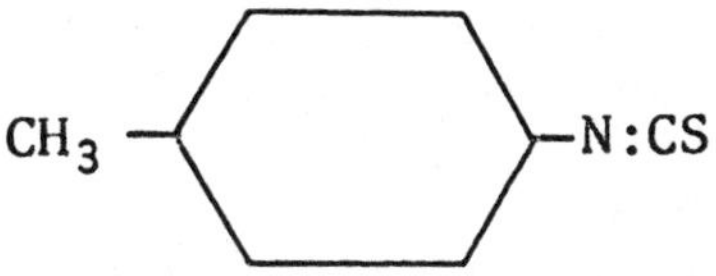


p-Tolyl isothiocyanate
sweet anise
(Moncrieff)

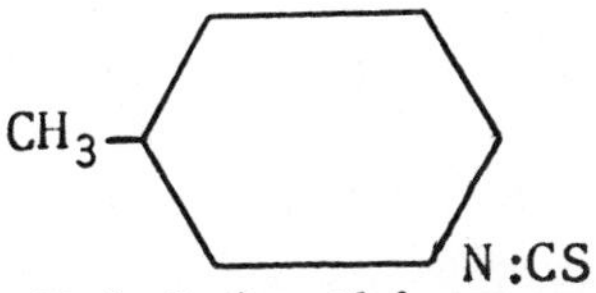


m-Tolyl isothiocyanate
pungent
(Moncrieff)

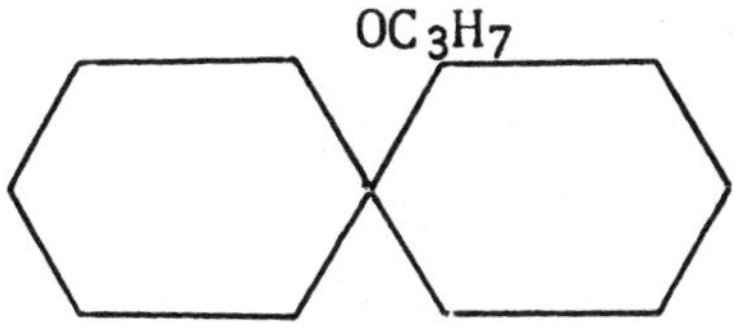


2-Biphenyl propyl ether
faint aromatic
(Moncrieff)

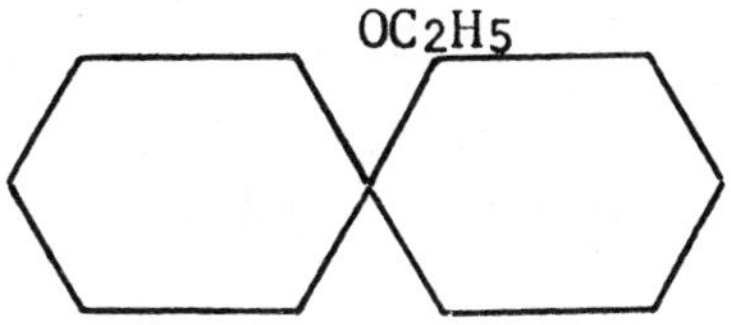


2-Biphenyl ethyl ether
faint, sweet, floral
(Moncrieff)

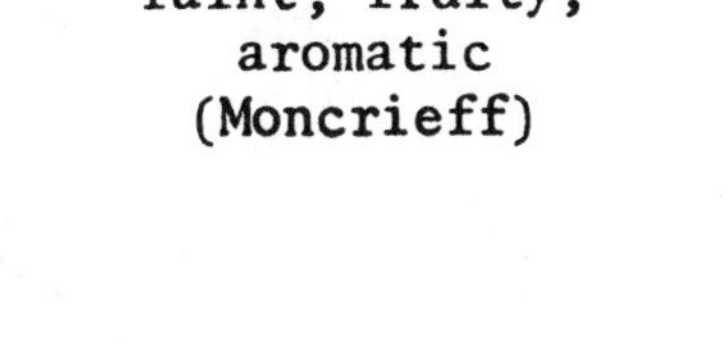

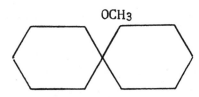

2-Biphenyl methyl ether
faint, fruity,
aromatic
(Moncrieff)

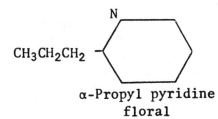

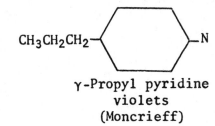

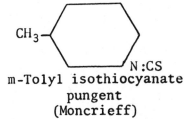

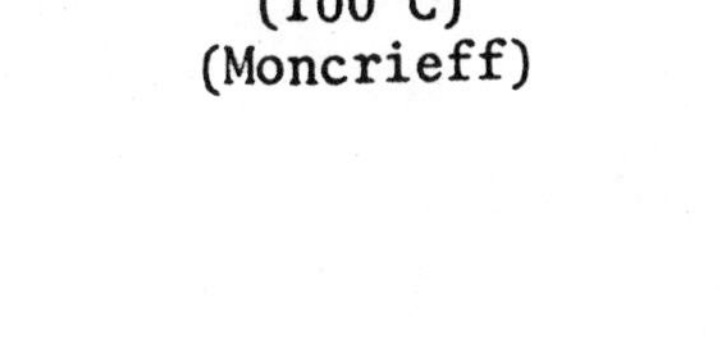

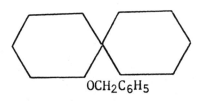

2-Biphenyl benzyl ether
pleasant, nut-like
(100°C)
(Moncrieff)

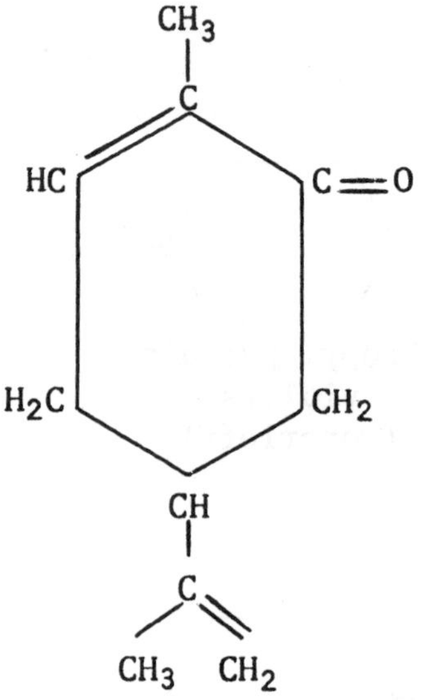

Carvone (carvol)

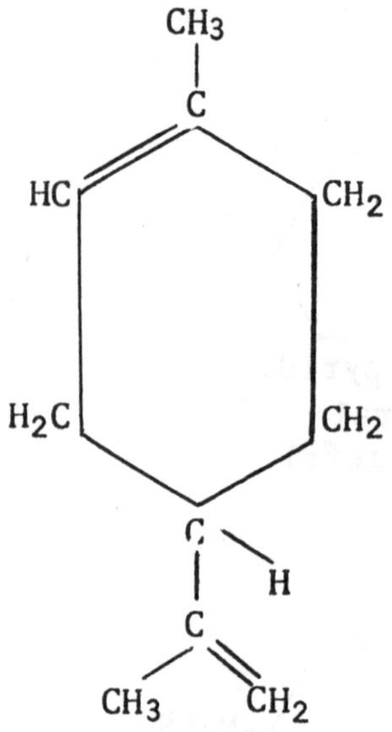

Limonene

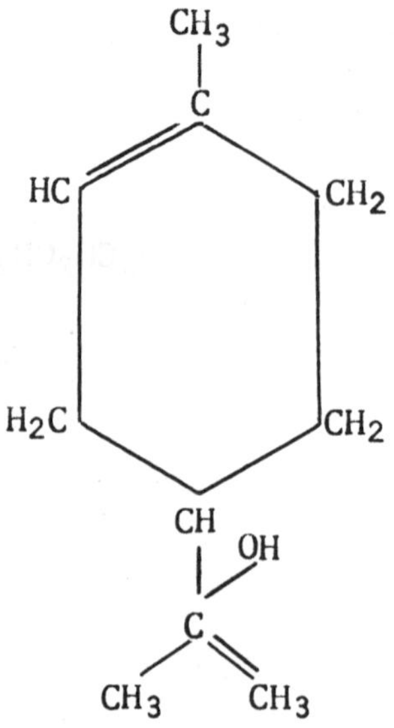

α-Terpineol

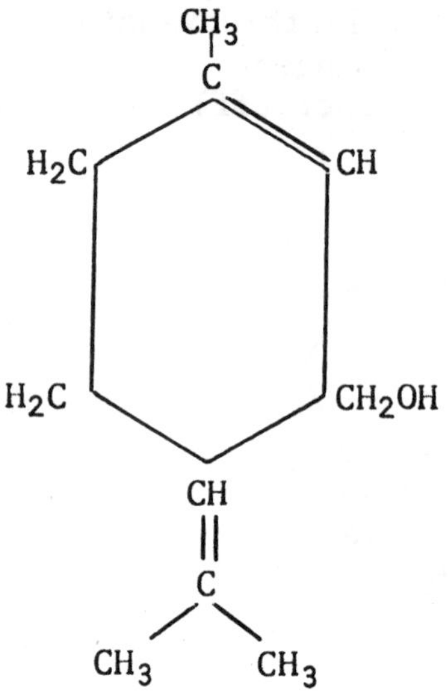

β-Geraniol

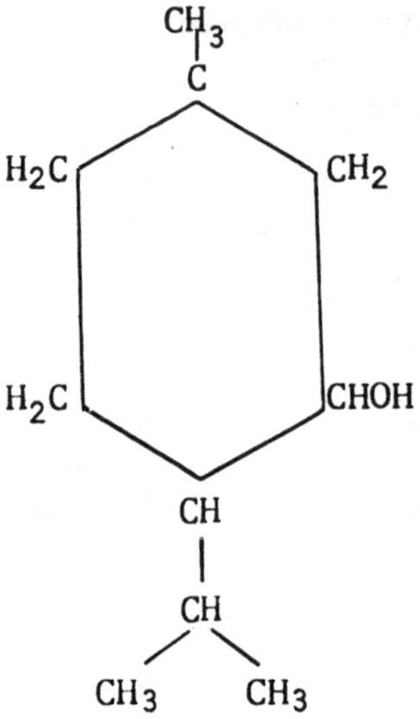

Menthol

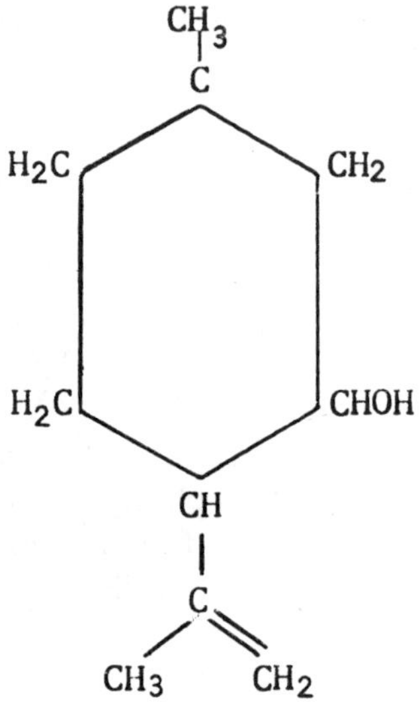

iso-Pulegol

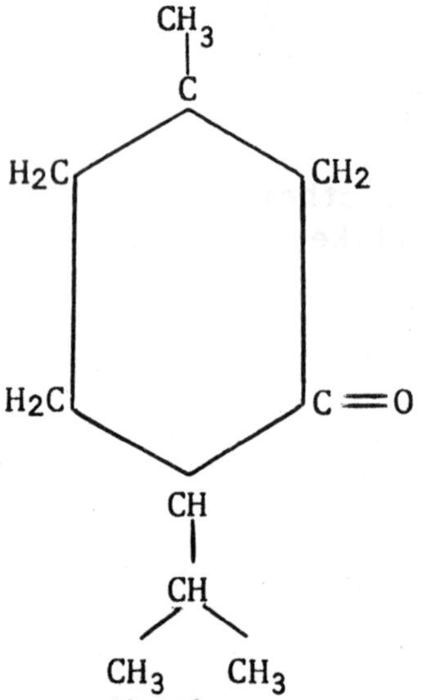

Menthone

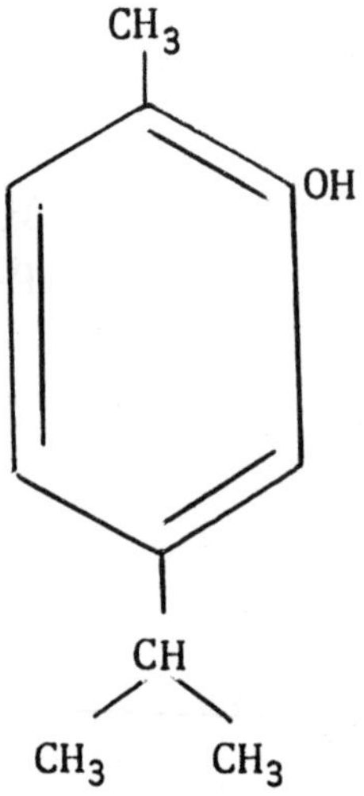

Carvacol

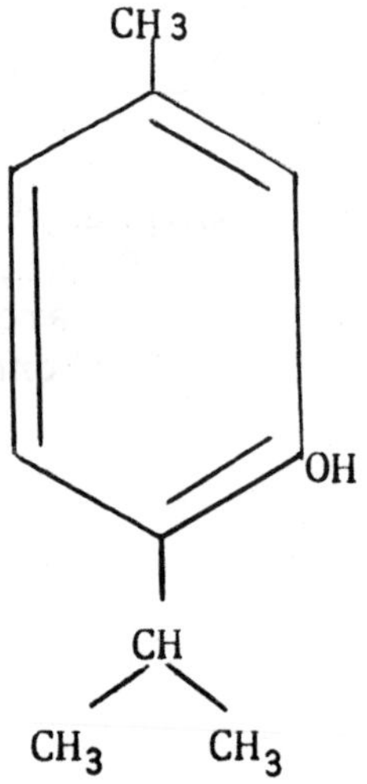

Thymol

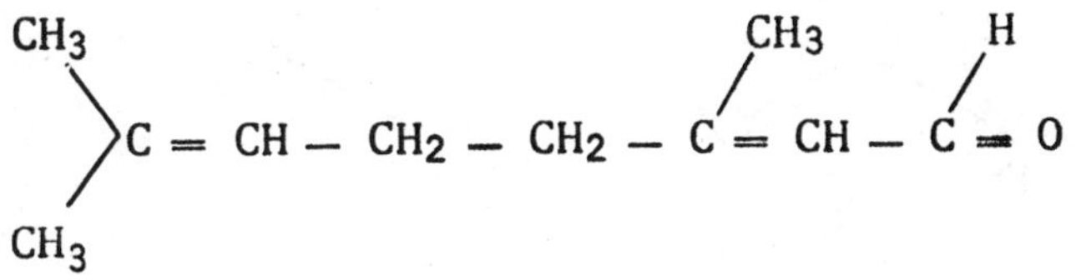

$$CH_3 \diagdown C = CH - CH_2 - CH_2 - \underset{CH_3}{\overset{CH_3}{C}} = CH - \overset{H}{C} = O \qquad \text{Citral}$$

$$CH_3 \diagdown C = CH - CH_2 - CH_2 - \overset{CH_3}{C} = CH - CH_2OH \qquad \text{β-Geraniol}$$

$$CH_3 \diagdown C - CH_2 - CH_2 - CH_2 - \overset{CH_3}{CH} - CH_2OH \qquad \text{α-Citronellol (rhodinol)}$$
with CH₂ below

$$CH_3 \diagdown C = CH - CH_2 - CH_2 - \overset{CH_3}{CH} - CH_2 - CH_2OH \qquad \text{β-Citronellol (rhodinol)}$$

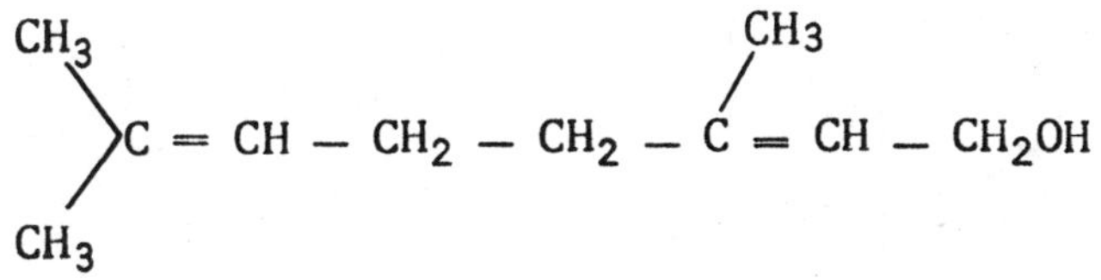

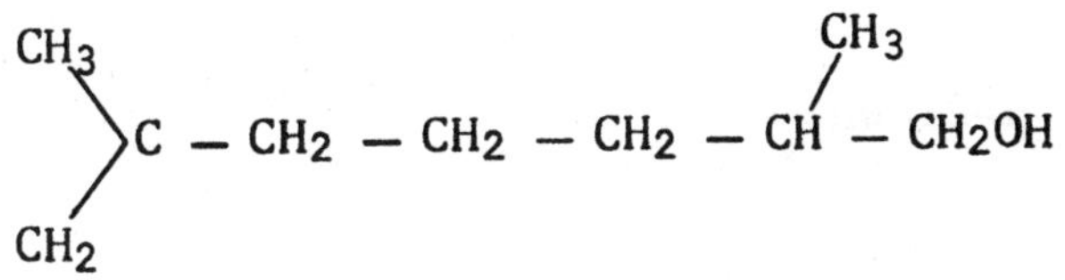

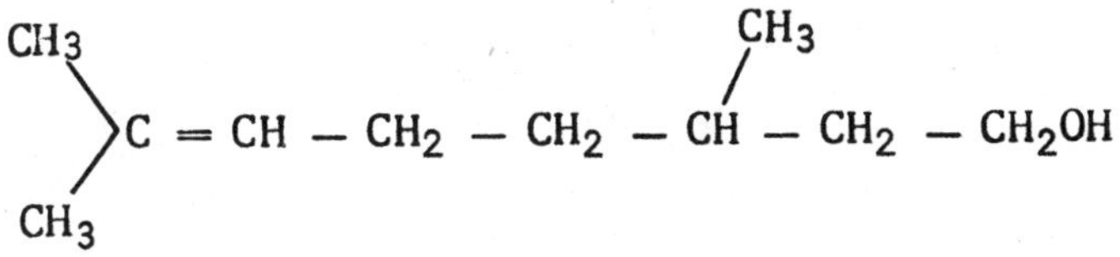

$$CH_3 \diagdown C - CH_2 - CH_2 - CH_2 - \overset{CH_3}{CH} - CH_2 - \overset{H}{C}\diagdown_O \qquad \text{Citronellal (rhodinal)}$$

$$CH_3 \diagdown C = CH - CH_2 - CH_2 - \overset{CH_3}{CH} - CH_2 - \overset{H}{C} = O \qquad \text{Citronellal (rhodinal)}$$

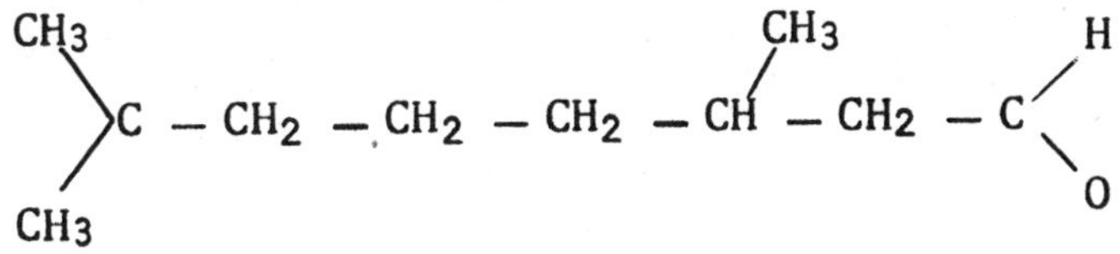

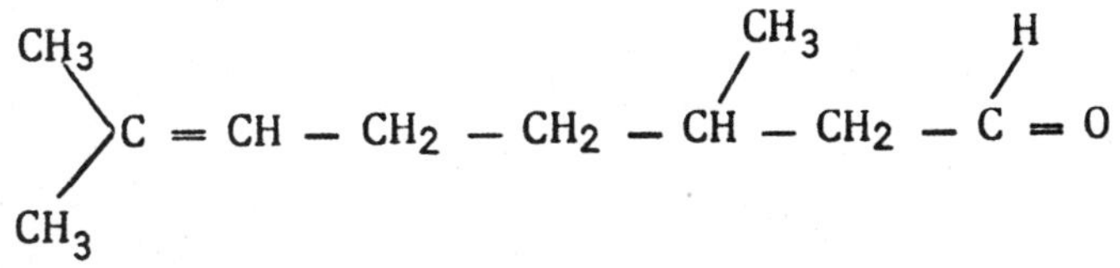

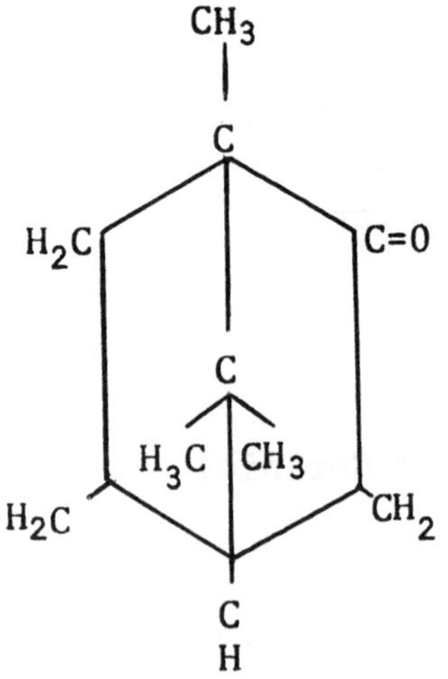

Camphor

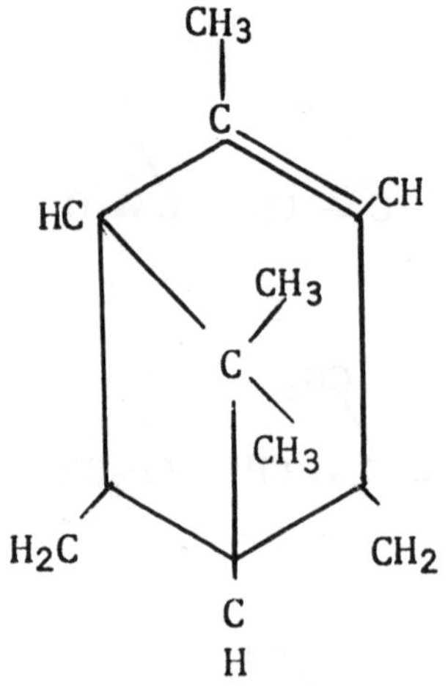

α-Pinene

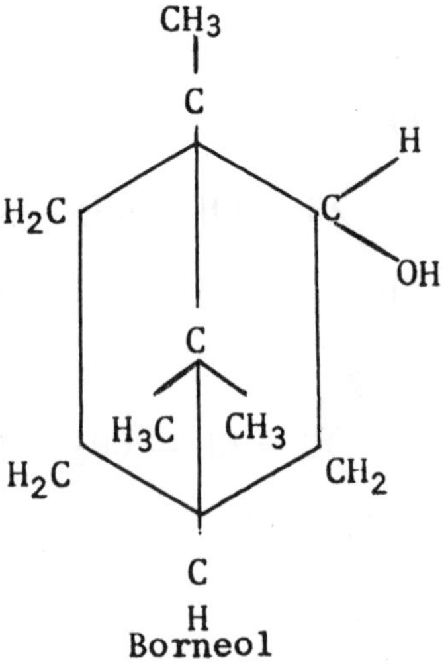

Borneol

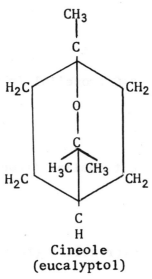

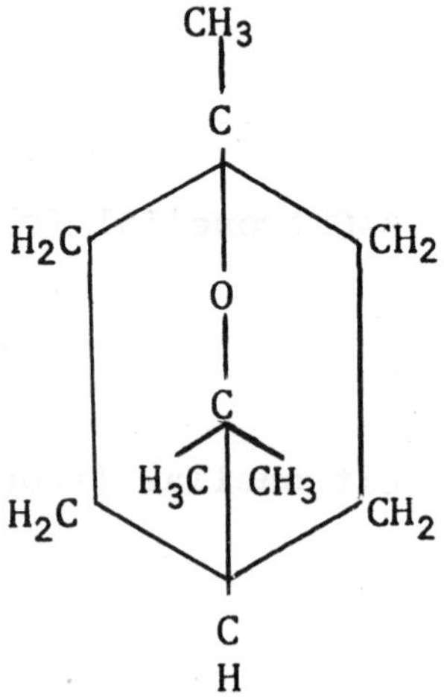

Cineole
(eucalyptol)

Dyson's Study of Phenyl Mustard Oil

Structure as it Relates to Odor

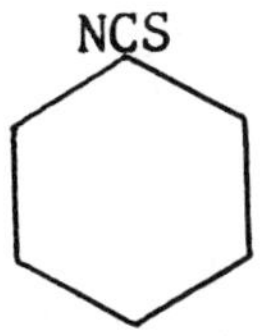

Pungent!

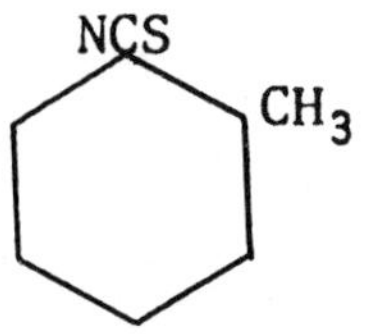

Pungent!

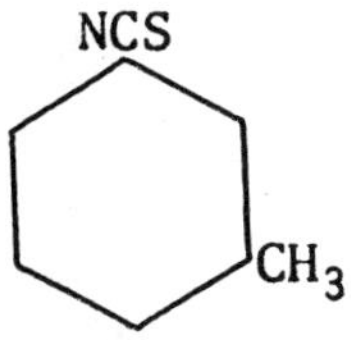

Pungent!!

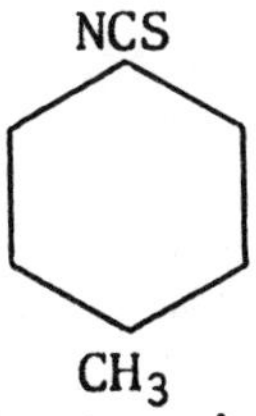

Sweet anise

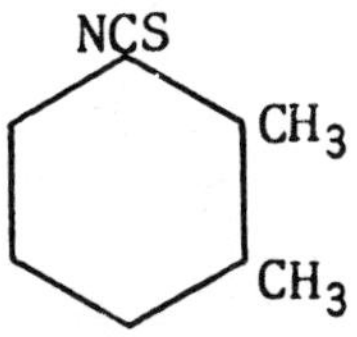

Pungent

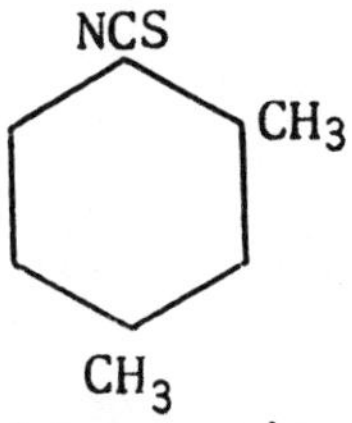

Delicate anise

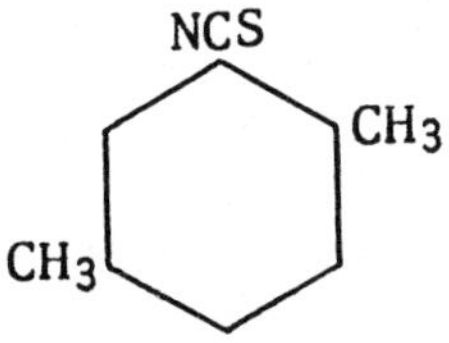

Pungent

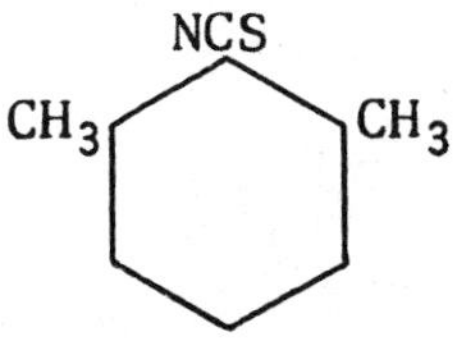

Delicate spiraea

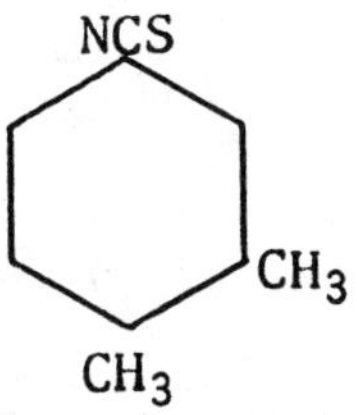

Harsh anise note

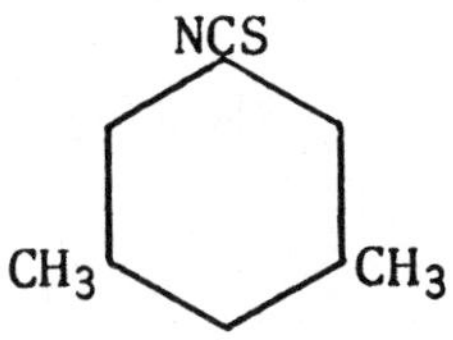

Pungent

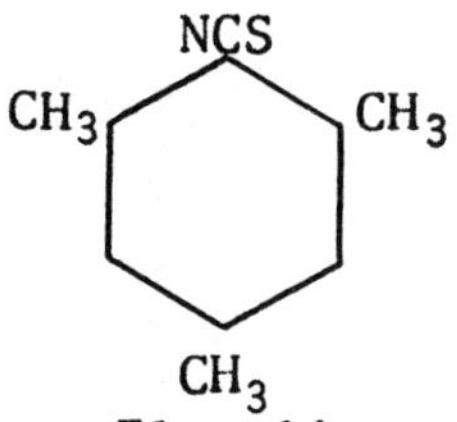

Floral!

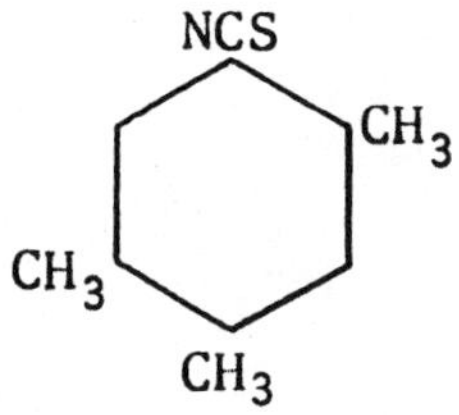

Anise, faint pungent

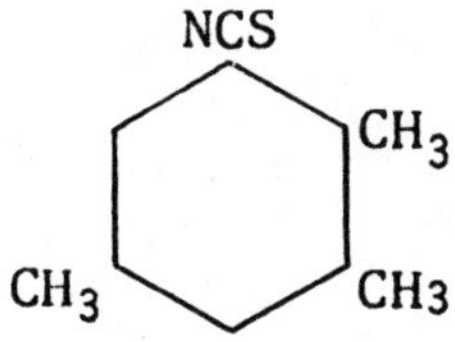

Pungent

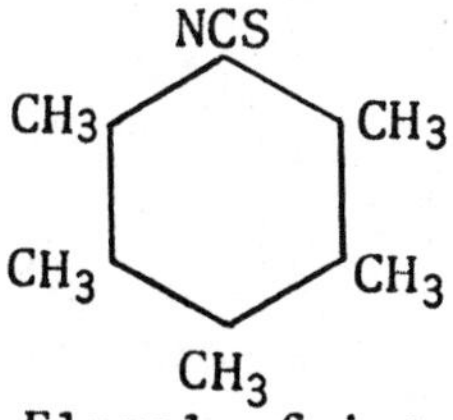

Floral, faint

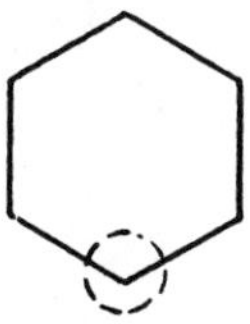
1, 2, 3, 5,
7, 10, 13:
Pungent

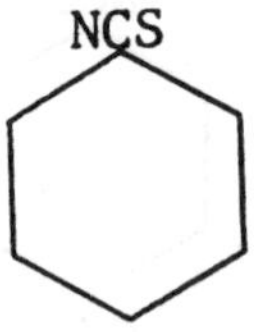


Pungent!

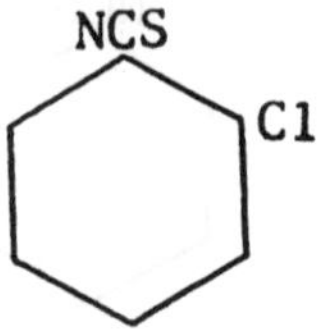


Pungent

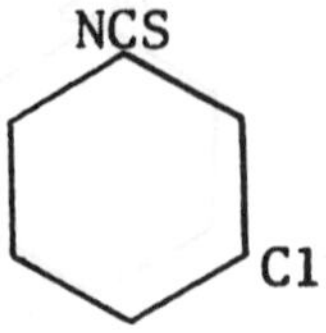


Pungent!

Sweet anise

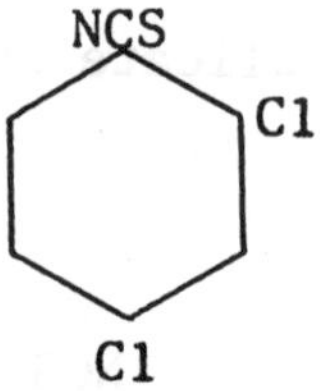


Sweet anise

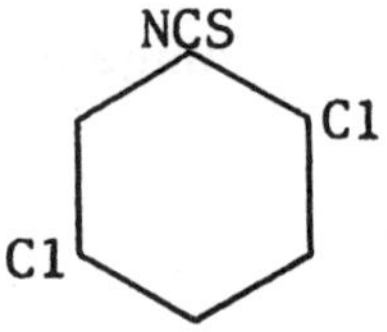


Pungent

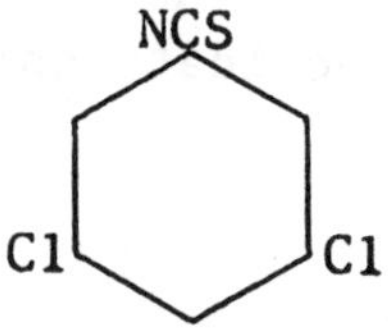


Pungent

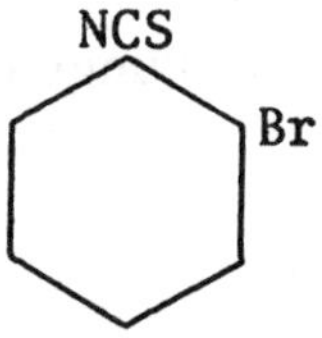


Slight pungent

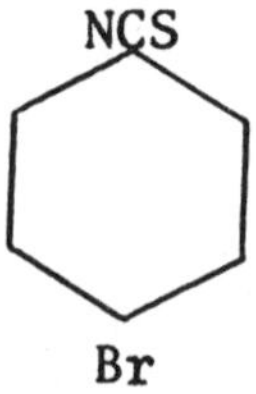


Sweet anise

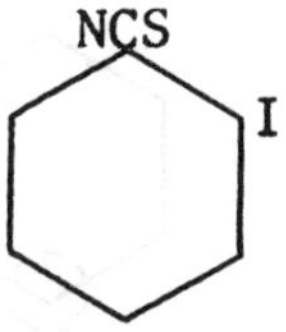


Nearly odorless

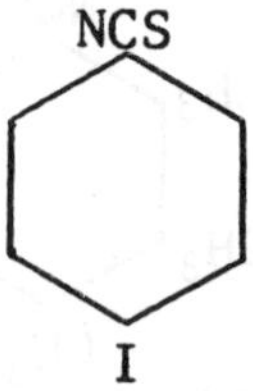


Very sweet anise

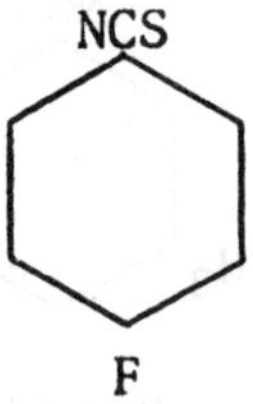


Anise-mustard

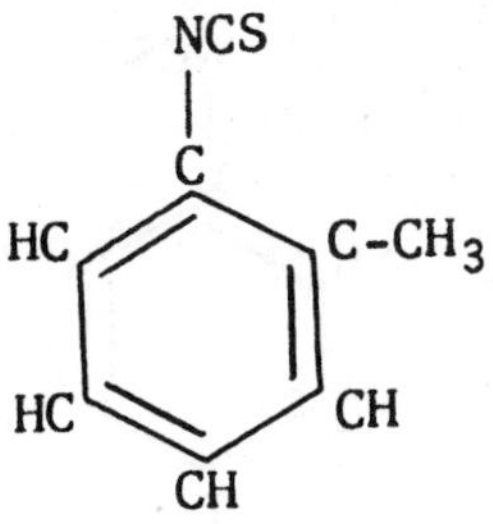

Sweet,
mustard

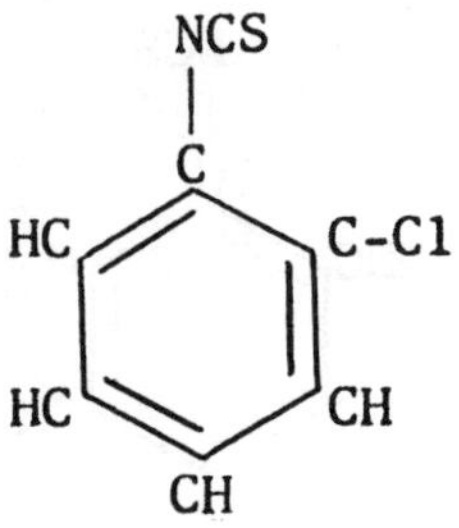

Mustard

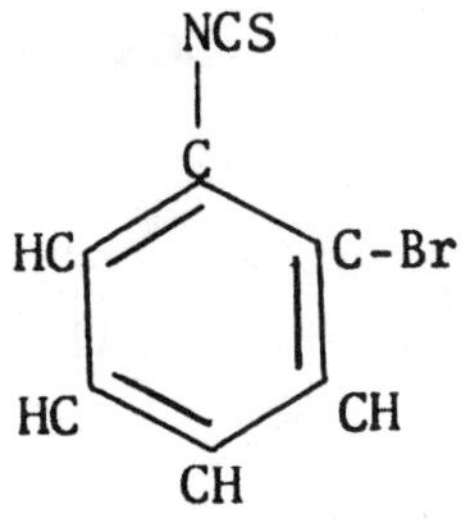

Less pungent,
anise-like

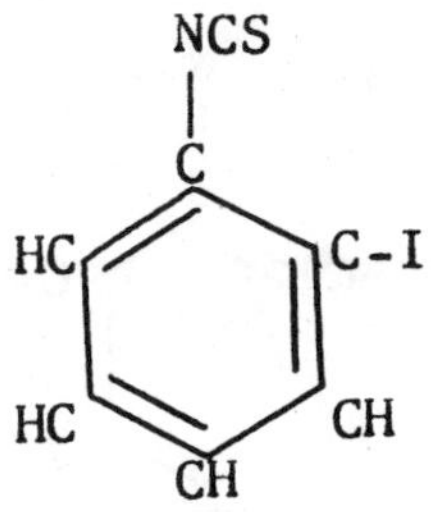

Sweet,
anise-like

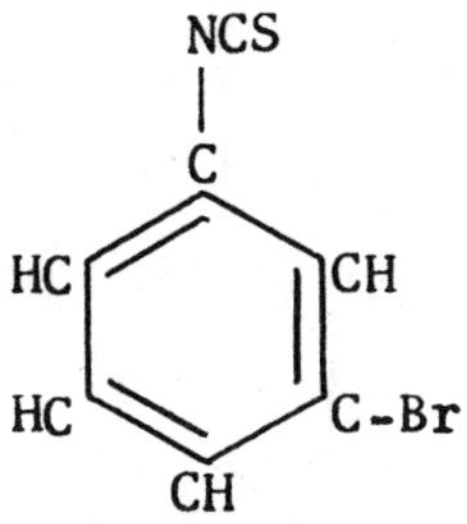

Slight,
pungent

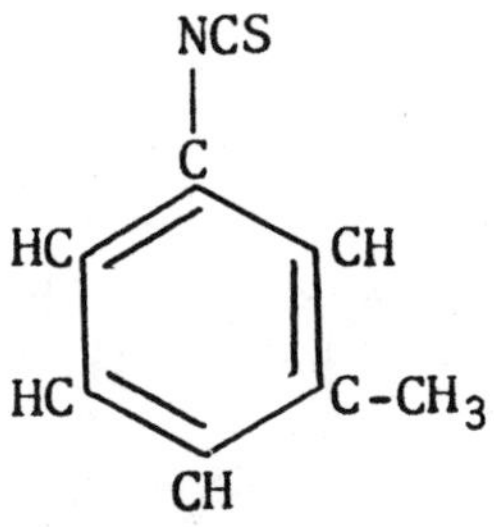

Mustard,
pungent!

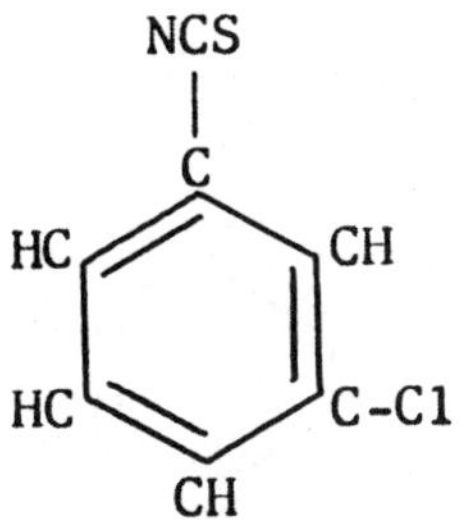

Pungent!!

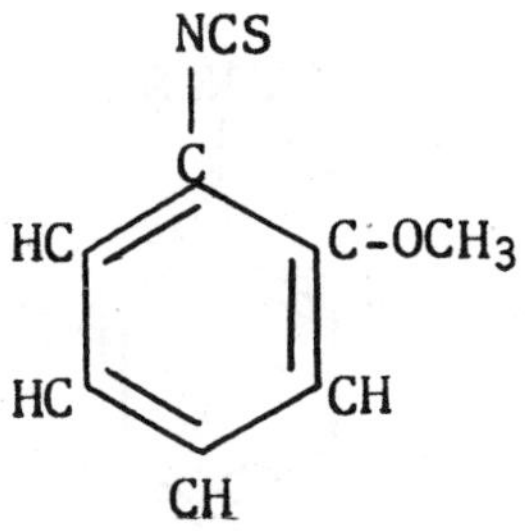

Harsh,
pungent

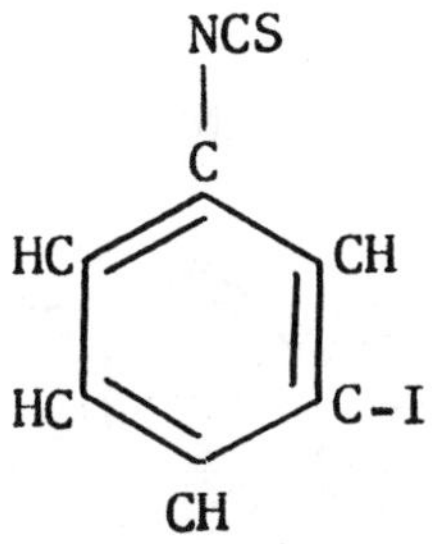

Pungent,
anise-like

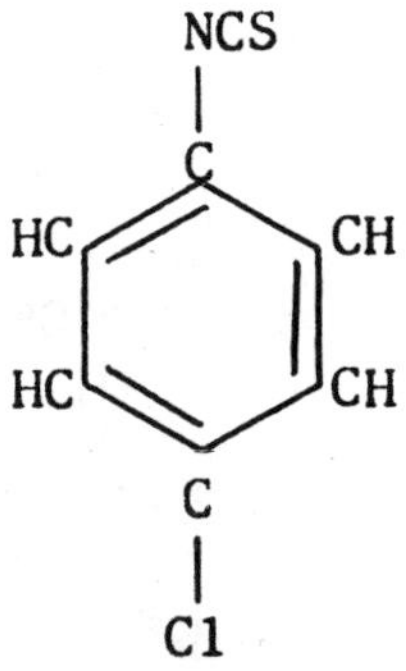

Pungent,
anise-like

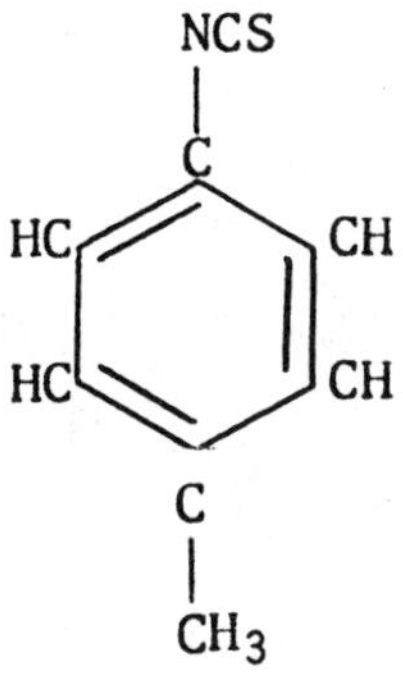

Anise-like

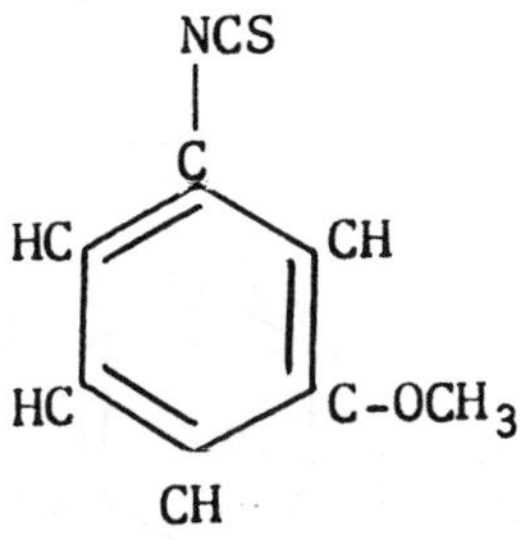

Harsh,
pungent

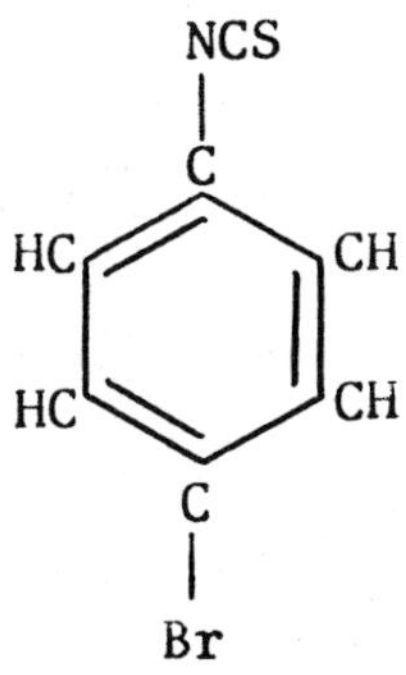

Anise

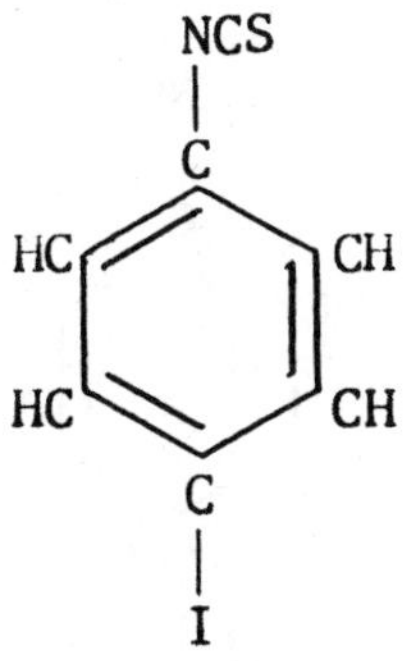

Sweet,
anise

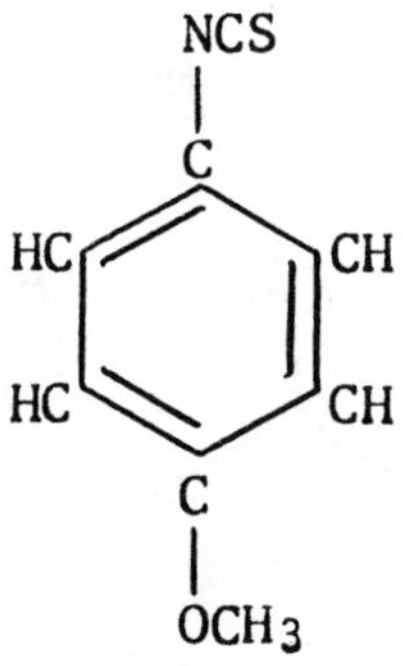

Strong,
anise

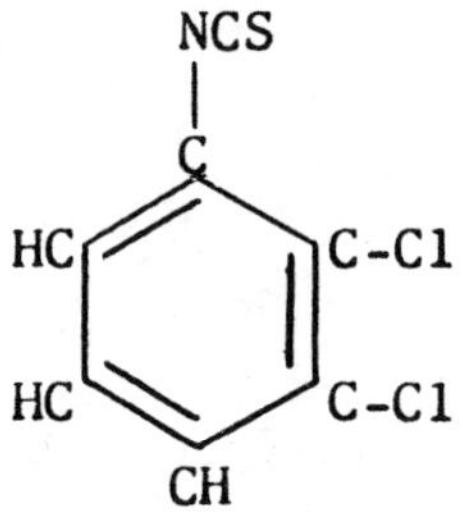

Pungent, sweet,
mustard

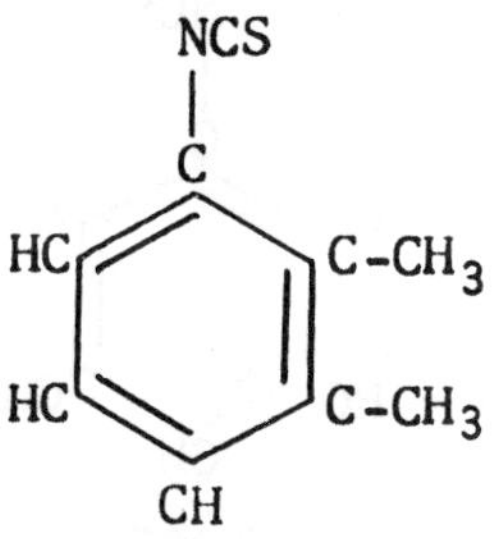

Pungent, sweet, mustard

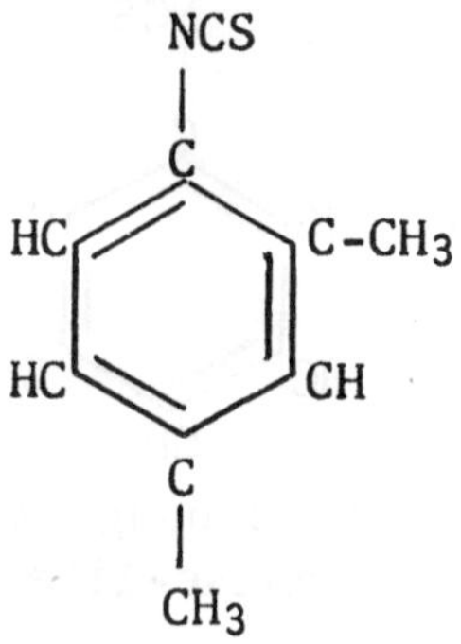

Anise-like

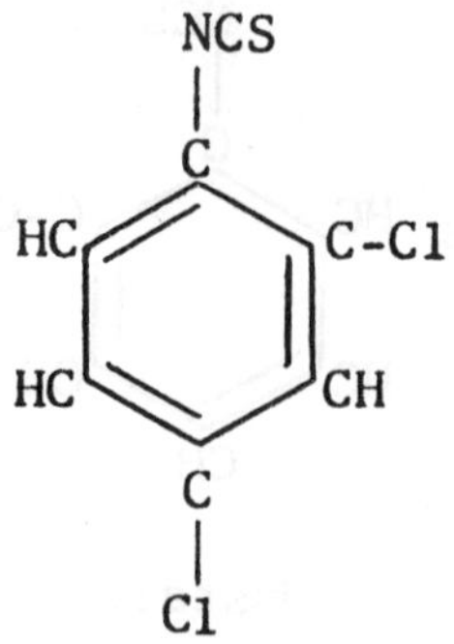

Sweet, anise

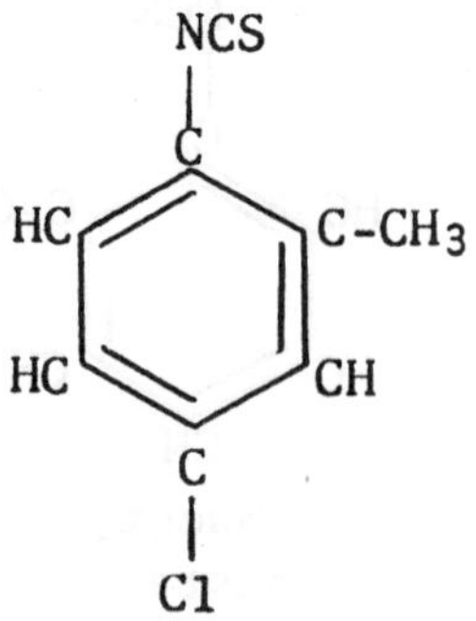

Anise

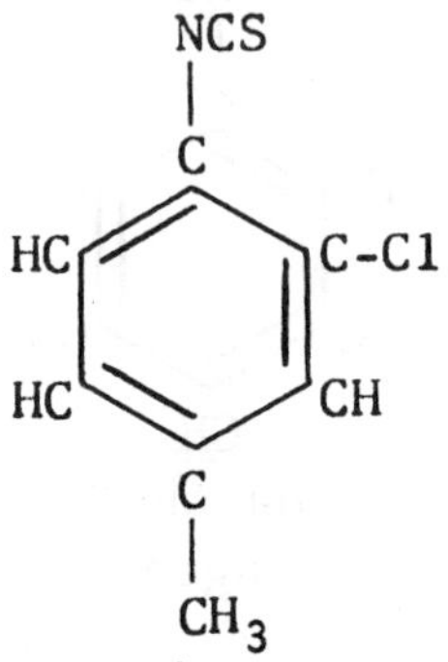

Delicate spiraea

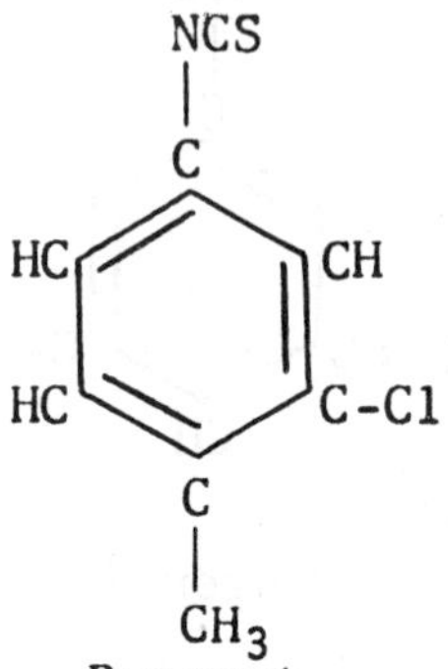

Pungent, anise

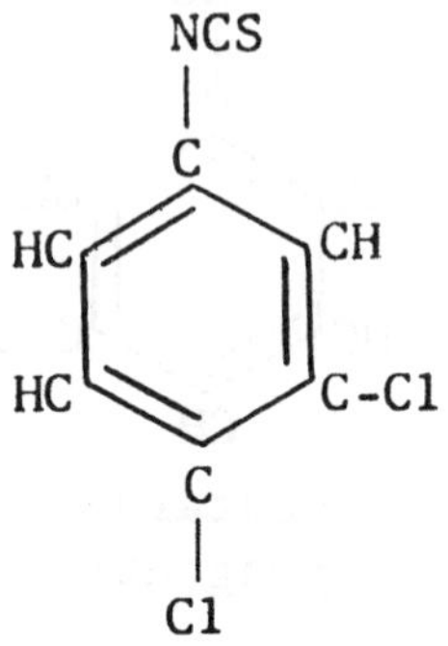

Pungent, anise

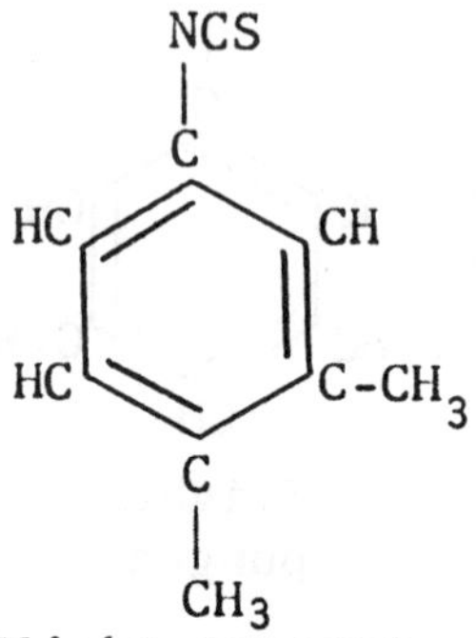

Slight pungent, anise

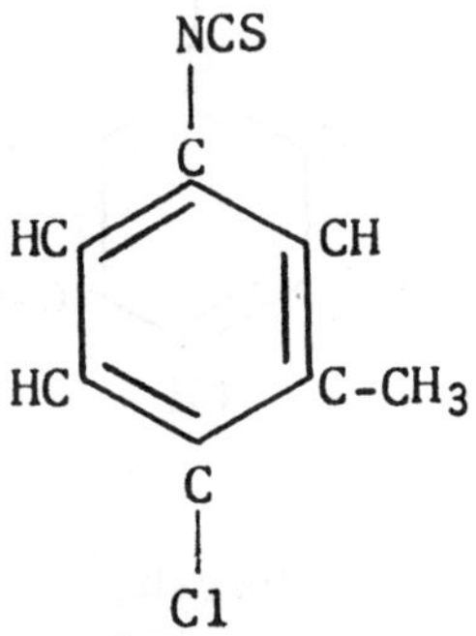

Slight pungent, anise

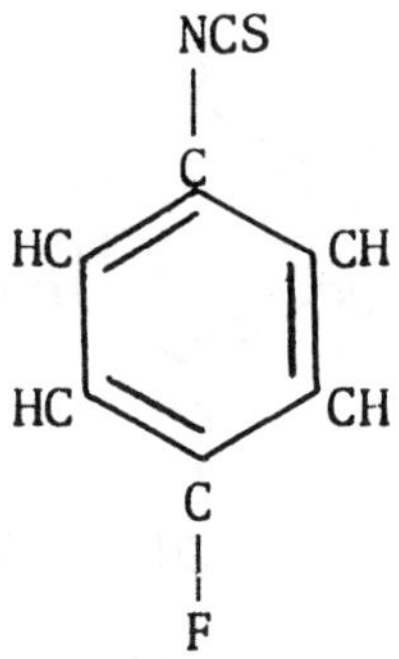

Mustard, slight anise

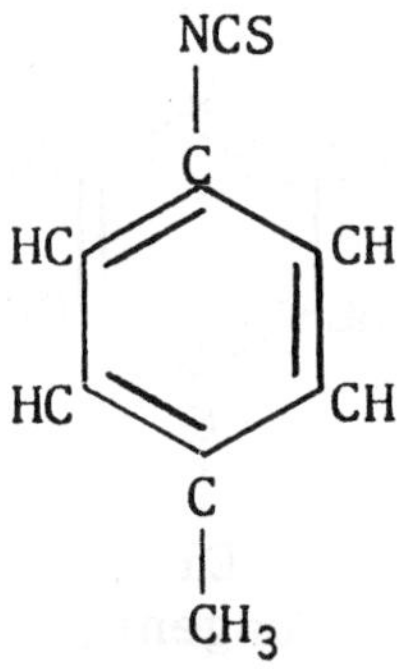

Pungent, anise

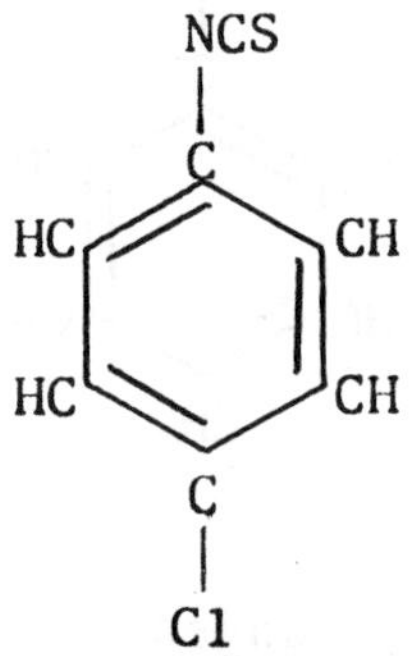

Weak, pungent, anise

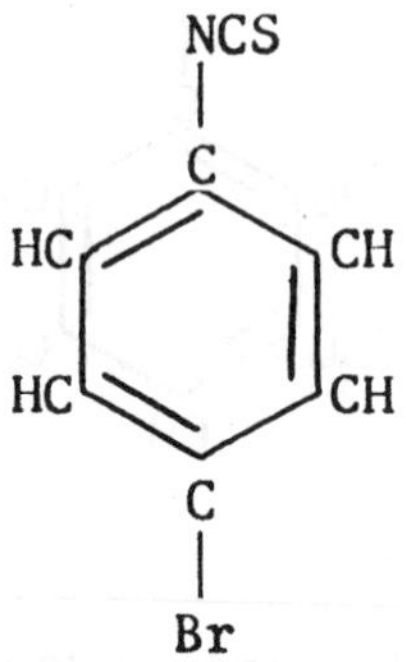

Anise

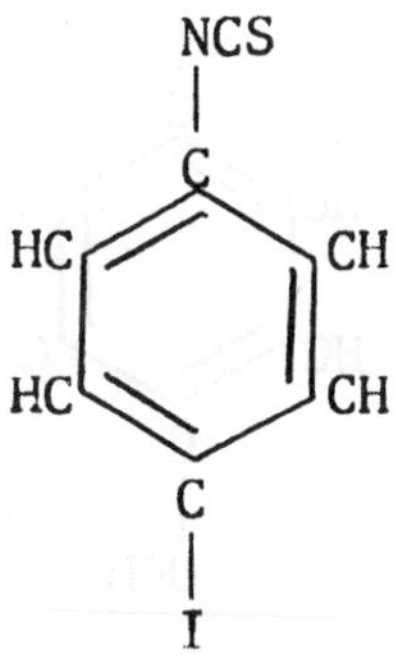

Very sweet, anise-like

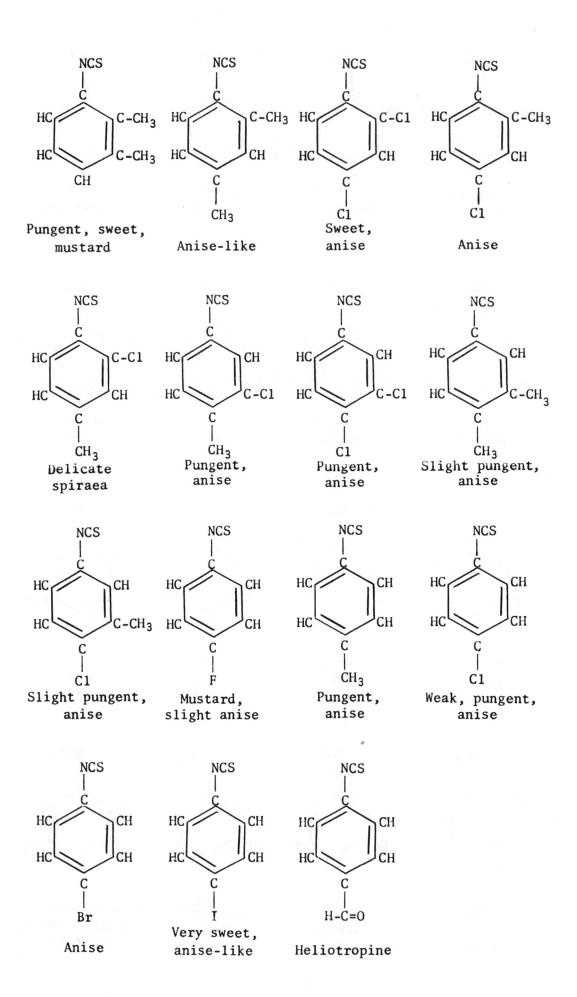

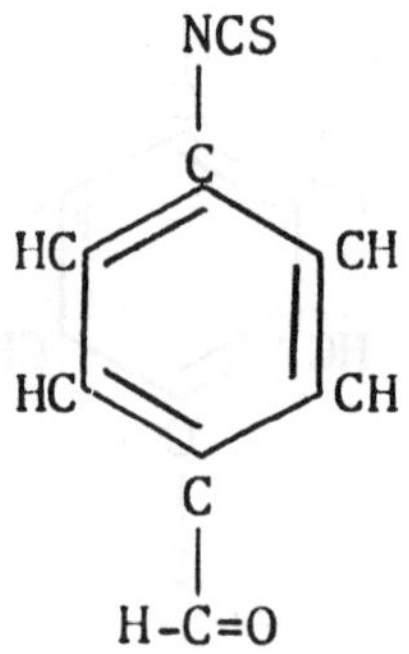

Heliotropine

# GLOSSARY

ABSOLUTE: Alcoholic extract of a flower, etc., freed from wax and from which the alcochol has been removed, leaving the "absolute" odorous principle.

ABSORPTION: The penetration of one substance (the absorbate) into the inner structure of another (the absorbent), with a resulting loss of identity of the original substance.

ABSORPTION BANDS: Dark lines in the spectrum of light caused by the neutralization of vibrations of certain frequencies.

ACETIC ACID: $CH_3COOH$, a clear, colorless organic acid with a distinctive pungent odor, used as a solvent and in the manufacture of rubber, plastics, acetate fibers, pharmaceuticals, and photographic chemicals. When at least 99.8 percent pure, it is also called glacial acetic acid.

ACIDITY: The capacity of a substance for neutralizing a base. It is normally associated with the presence of carbon dioxide, mineral and organic acids and salts of strong acids or weak bases.

ACIDOGEN: Sour-producing group: e.g. --COOH or $--SO_3H$.

ACID-WASHED ACTIVATED CARBON: Carbon which has been contacted with an acid solution with the purpose of dissolving ash in the activated carbon.

ACRE-FOOT: The volume of water (43,560 cubic feet) that will cover an area of one acre to a depth of one foot. A term used in sewage treatment in measuring the volume of material in a trickling filter.

ACTINOMYCES: Any of numerous generally filamentous and often pathogenic microorganisms of the family Actinomycetaceae, resembling both bacteria and fungi.

ACTION, BIOCHEMICAL: Chemical changes resulting from the metabolism of living organisms.

ACTIVATED CARBON: Highly adsorbent carbon obtained by heating granulated charcoal to exhaust contained gases, used in gas absorption, solvent recover, or deodorization, and as an antidote to certain poisons. Also called activated charcoal. The internal surface area of granular activated carbon is estimated to be about 3,600 square feet per gram.

ACTIVATION: The generation of zoogleal organisms under aerobic conditions capable of absorbing organic matter from the sewage in the activated-sludge process.

ACUITY: Keenness; sharpness; acuteness.

ADAMSITE: A yellow, crystalline compound used dispersed in air as a poison gas, $(C_6H_4)_2(NH)Cl$. A heterocyclic arsine.

ADAPTION: Anything that is changed or changes so as to become to a new or special use or situation. A change in the state of receptors on continued stimulation, causing fatigue.

ADENOIDS: Lymphoid tissue growths in the nose above the throat that when swollen may obstruct nasal breathing, induce postnasal discharge, and make speech difficult.

ADSORPTION: The assimilation of gas, vapor, or dissolved matter by the surface of a solid.

ADSORPTION ISOTHERMS (activated carbon): A measurement of adsorption determined at a constant temperature by varying the amount of carbon used or the concentration impurity in contact with the carbon.

ADVANCED WASTE TREATMENT: Any treatment method or process employed following biological treatment (1) to increase the removal of pollution load, (2) to remove substances that may be deleterious to receiving waters or the environment, (3) to produce a high-quality effluent suitable for reuse in any specific manner or for discharge under critical conditions. The term tertiary treatment is commonly used to denote advanced waste treatment methods.

AERATION: The bringing about of intimate contact between air and a liquid by one of the following methods: Spraying the liquid in the air, bubbling air through the liquid, or agitation of the liquid to promote surface absorption of air.

AERATION, DIFFUSED AIR: The aeration produced in a liquid by passing air through a diffuser (porous tile or tube).

AERATION, MECHANICAL: (1) The mixing, by mechanical means, of sewage and activated sludge, in the aeration tank of the activated-sludge process, to bring fresh surfaces of liquid into contact with the atmosphere. (2) The introduction of atmospheric oxygen into a liquid by the mechanical action of paddles or spray mechanisms.

AERATOR: A device that promotes aeration.

AEROBIC: An organism, such as a bacterium, requiring molecular oxygen or air to live.

AEROBIC BIOLOGICAL OXIDATION: Any waste treatment or process utilizing aerobic organisms, in the presence of air or oxygen, as the agent for reducing pollution lead or oxygen demand of organic substances in waste. The term is used in reference to secondary treatment of wastes.

AEROFILTER: A commercial term applied to a trickling filter containing a relatively coarse filtering material and operating at a high rate which may be maintained, if necessary, at times of low sewage flow by recirculation of the filter effluent or other diluting liquids.

AFFECTIVE REACTION: A reaction based on "feeling" tone or mood.

AFFERENT NERVE FIBER: A nerve fiber which transmits messages from the peripheral receptors to the central nervous system.

AFTERBURNER: In incinerator technology, a burner located so that the combustion gases are made to pass through its flame in order to remove smoke and odors.

AFTERODOR: An "odor image" that persists after the actual odor stimulus has ceased, similar to afterimage.

AGEUSIA: Loss of the sense of taste.

AGGLOMERATION: The process by which precipitation particles grow larger by collision or contact with cloud particles or other precipitation particles.

AGGLUTINATION: The process of uniting solid particles coated with a thin layer of adhesive material or of arresting solid particles by impact on a surface coated with an adhesive.

ALBINISM: Absence of normal pigmentation in a person, animal, or plant, usually accompanied by anosmia in man.

ALKALI: A hydroxide or carbonate of an alkali metal, the aqueous solution of which is bitter, slippery, caustic, and characteristically basic in reactions.

ALKALINE: Of, relating to, or containing an alkali; having a pH of greater than 7. Pertaining to water or soils that contain a sufficient amount of alkali to raise the pH value above 7 or to be harmful in the growth of crops.

ALKALINITY: The alkali concentration or alkaline quality of an alkali-containing substance; a term which represents the presence of salts of weak acids. The hydroxides, carbonates, and bicarbonates of calcium, sodium and magnesium are the common impurities that cause alkalinity. They are expressed in milligrams per liter of calcium carbonate.

ALLIACEOUS: Characteristic of garlic.

ALPHA IONONE: A synthetic very similar to irone, the active principle of violets, with a sweet odor much like that of orris root, $C_{13}H_{20}O$

ALUM: Any of various double sulfates of a trivalent metal such as aluminum, chromium, or iron and a univalent metal such as potassium or sodium, especially aluminum potassium sulfate, widely used in industry and medicinally.

AMAROGEN: Bitter-producing groups, e.g. --SH.
AMBERGRIS: A waxy, grayish substance formed in the intestines of sperm whales and found floating at sea or washed ashore. It is used as a fixation in perfumes. Regurgitated squid.
AMBROSIAL: Fragrant, delicious; worthy of the gods.
AMMONIA: A colorless, pungent gas extensively used to manufacture fertilizers and wide variety of nitrogen-containing organic and inorganic chemicals. A solution of ammonia in water. $NH_3$.
AMORPHOUS: Without definite form; lacking a specific shape. Of no particular type or character; unorganized.
AMPHIRHINE: Having paired nostrils.
AMYGDALINE: Of, pertaining to, or resembling an almond.
ANAEROBIC: Without oxygen; living, or active only in the absence of free oxygen.
ANAEROBIC BIOLOGICAL TREATMENT: Any treatment method or process utilizing anaerobic or facultative organisms, in the absence of air, for the purpose of reducing the organic matter in wastes or organic solids settled out of wastes; commonly referred to as anaerobic digestion or sludge digestion when applied to the treatment of sludge solids.
ANALYSIS: (1) The record of an examination of water, sewage, or industrial wastes. In industrial wastes, the determination of chemical composition, concentration, BOD, suspended-solids content, etc. (2) The separation of an intellectual or substantial whole into constituents for individual study.
ANATOMIC: Of or pertaining to the anatomy.
ANESTHETIZING: Inducing total or partial loss of sensation, especially tactile sensibility, induced by disease or an anesthetic.
ANGSTROM UNIT: A unit of length equal to $10^{-10}$ meters, used especially to specify radiation wavelengths. Symbol: Å
ANOSMIA: Total loss of the sense of smell.
ANOSMIC: Without the ability to detect odors.
ANTENNAE: Paired, jointed, flexible sensory appendages on the heads of insects, myriapods or crustaceans.
ANTERIOR NARES: The nostrils.
ANTHOPHILOUS: Flower-loving.
ANTIOXIDANT: A chemical substance or compound that inhibits oxidation.
APHASIA: Partial or total loss of the ability to articulate ideas in any form, resulting from brain damage.
APHRODISIAC: That which stimulates or intensifies sexual desire.
APPARATUS, DOSING: Apparatus for regulating the application of industrial wastes to filters or for applying the required quantity of chemicals (coagulants) to wastes.
APPARENT DENSITY (activated carbon): The weight per unit volume of activated carbon.
APPURTENANCES, SEWER: Structures, devices, and appliances other than pipe or conduit, which are integral parts of a sewerage system, such as manholes, flush tanks, surface inlets.
AQUIFER: A water-bearing rock, rock formation, or group of formations.
ARGOSMIN: An oxidation product of HCl and geosmin. It is inodorous. Argosmin is found in cultures of numerous actinomycetes: $C_{12}H_{20}$
AROMA: A pleasant, characteristic odor, as of a plant, spice, food.
ARRESTOR, FLAME: A safety device on a gas line which allows gas, but not a flame, to pass.
ARSENICAL SMOKES: War gases.
ASAFOETIDA (Devil's dung): Gum-resin with objectionable odor.
ASCLEPIAD: A genus of plants including the vanilla tree.

ASPHYXIANT: Inducers of unconsciousness or death caused by lack of oxygen; suffocant.
ASTRINGENCY: Tending to draw together or constrict tissue; contracting; styptic.
ATOMIC OXYGEN: An exceptionally active form of oxygen: $O_2$.
ATTAR OF ROSES: A fragrant essential oil or perfume obtained from the petals of roses.
AUBEPINE: Anisaldehyde.
AUDIBLE: Capable of being heard.
AUTOSMIA: An odor hallucination; a perception without a source, without external stimulation.
AUTOTOX: Group which if present in a substance with a toxophore group confers toxicity.
AUXOCHROME: Autotox.
AUXOGLUC: Group which if present with a glucophore group confers sweetness.
AVOGARDO'S NUMBER: The number of molecules in a mole of a substance, approximately $6.0225 \times 10^{23}$.
AXIS CYLINDER: The nerve fiber. The term does not include the medulla or sheath.
AXON: The core of a nerve fiber that generally conducts impulses away from the nerve cell.

BACKSIPHONAGE: The flowing back of contaminated or polluted water from a plumbing fixture or cross connection, into a water supply line, due to a lowering of the pressure in such line.
BACKWASHING: The process of cleaning a rapid sand or mechanical filter by reversing the flow of water.
BACTERIA: Any of numerous unicellular microorganisms of the class Schizomycetes, occurring in a wide variety of forms existing either as free-living organisms or as parasites, and having a wide range of biochemical, often pathogenic properties.
BACTERIA, AEROBIC: Bacteria which require free (elementary) oxygen for their growth and life.
BACTERIA, ANAEROBIC: Bacteria which grow and function in the absence of free oxygen and derive oxygen from breaking down complex substances.
BACTERIACIDES: Substances that destroy bacteria.
BACTERIASTAT: Substances that reduce or temporarily stop the reproductive capacity of bacteria.
BAFFLES: Deflector vanes, guides, grids, gratings, or similar devices constructed or placed in flowing water or sewage, to (1) check or effect a more uniform distribution of velocities; (2) absorb energy; (3) divert, guide, or agitate the liquids; and (4) check eddy currents.
BALSAM: An oily or gummy oleoresin, usually containing benzoic or cinnamic acids, obtained from the exudations of any of various trees and shrubs, and used as a base for cough syrups, other medications and perfumes.
BANKS, SLUDGE: Accumulations on the bed of a waterway of deposits of solids of sewage or industrial waste origin.
BASIN, SETTLING: A structure designed to hold wastes in a quiescent state or at a reduced velocity for a sufficient length of time to permit the gravational deposition of suspended matter, with or without the aid of previous flocculation or coagulation.
BASIN, STILLING: A structure or excavation that reduces velocity or turbulence in flowing wastes.

BED, BACTERIA: A bed of sand, gravel, broken stone, or medium through which wastes flow or trickle and which depends upon biological action for its effectiveness.

BED, COVERED SLUDGE-DRYING: A sludge-drying bed with a glass cover or enclosure for protection against rain or snow and for increasing radiant heating as an aid to evaporation of water in the sludge. Frequently used in built-up sections to remove objections of neighboring residents.

BED DEPTH (activated carbon): The amount of carbon expressed in length units, which is parallel to the flow of the stream and through which the stream must pass.

BED, SLUDGE-DRYING: An uncovered area comprising natural or artificial layers of porous material, usually sand, upon which digested sludge is dried by drainage and evaporation.

BETA FACTOR: A cacosmic or painful molecule.

BIOCHEMICAL: Pertaining to biologic growth or activity and measured by, or expressed in terms of, the ensuing chemical change.

BIOCHEMICAL OXYGEN DEMAND (BOD): A measure of the dissolved oxygen in a water supply needed to depose organic materials in a measured time and at a constant temperature.

BIPOLAR CELL: Nerve cells relatively few in number and well embedded in the supporting and basal cells which are believed to be the true olfactory sensory cells.

BIVANE: A sensitive wind vane used in turbulence studies to obtain a record of the horizontal and vertical components of wind.

BLAST INJECTION TEST: A method of measuring the minimum indentifiable odor.

BLOWDOWN: Hydrocarbons purged during refinery shutdowns and startups which can be manifolded to blowdown systems for recovery, safe venting or flaring.

BLOWOFF: A controlled outlet on a pipeline, tank, or conduit which is used to discharge water or accumulations of material carried by the water.

BOUQUET: The fragrance typical of a wine or liquor or flower.

BOWMAN'S GLANDS: In animals these secrete a pigmented fluid in the nasal cavities.

BRANCH: (1) A special form of citrified sewer tile and cast iron pipe used for making connections to a sewer or water main. They are called T.Y. T-Y, double Y, and V branches, according to their respective shapes. (2) Any part of a piping system other than a main.

BREAKER, SCUM: A device to disintegrate or prevent the formation of surface scum in a sludge-digestion tank.

BREECHING: A passage or conduit to conduct products of combustion to the stack or chimney.

BREEZE: The refuse left when coal, coke or charcoal is burned, used in brickmaking and as a concrete filler.

BRIGHTNESS OF SMELL: Concept of quality of smell similar to evanescence or volatility. Opposite to "dull".

BROMIDROSIS: A condition of the skin in which the sweat glands are overactive and exudate a malodorous substance.

BROWN FUMES/BROWN SMOKE: Smoke emitted by air-blown, superoxygenated air-blown, or oxygen-blown iron or steel converters.

BUCCAL: Of or pertaining to the cheeks or mouth cavity.

BUCCAL GLANDS: Cheek glands.

BUFFER SOLUTION: Solution, e.g. of an acid to which a salt is added to depress the ionization of the acid. The salt acts as a buffer between the solvent and the acid.

BULKING, SLUDGE: A phenomenon that occurs in activated-sludge plants wherein the sludge swells and overflows the tanks.
BURNER, WASTE GAS: A device for burning the waste gas from a sludge-digestion tank.
2,3-BUTANEDIONE: Diacetyl; a yellow liquid with a strong odor which in extremely dilute solutions possesses a distinct aroma of butter: $CH_3COCOCH_3$.
BUTYRIC ACID: Either of two colorless isomeric acids occurring in animal milk fats and used in disinfectants, emulsifying agents, and pharmaceuticals: $C_3H_7COOH$.
BY-PASS: An arrangement of pipes, channels, etc., whereby the flow may be passed around any unit in the plant.

CACHALOT: The sperm whale.
CACODYL: (1) The arsenic group, $As(CH_3)_2$. (2) A poisonous oil with an obnoxious garlicky odor.
CACOSMIA: Trigeminal odors, odors associated with pain response.
CAFFEINE: The alkaloid of tea and coffee, trimethylxanthine.
CAKE, SLUDGE: (1) The material resulting from the drying of sludge on open or covered drying beds. (2) The dewatered cake from a vacuum-sludge filter.
CAMERA INODORATA: A large box, normally quite free from odor, in which odors are measured.
CAPRILIC: Goat-like, empyreumatic.
CARBON, ACTIVATED: Carbon particles, usually obtained by carbonization of cellulose material in the absence of air, possessing a high adsorptive capacity. Used in waste treatment for suppressing odors and removing color.
CARBON, BLACK: Finely divided forms of carbon made by the incomplete combustion or thermal decomposition of natural gas or liquid hydrocarbons. Principal types, according to the method of production, are channel black, furnace black, and thermal black.
CARBON COLUMN: A column filled with granular activated carbon whose primary function is the preferential adsorption of a particular type or types of molecules.
CARBON DIOXIDE: A colorless, odorless, incombustible gas formed during respiration, combustion, and organic decomposition and used in food refrigeration, carbonated beverages, inert atmospheres, fire extinguishers, and aerosols: $CO_2$.
CARBON TETRACHLORIDE: A poisonous, nonflammable, colorless liquid used in fire extinguishers and as a solvent: $CCl_4$.
CARBON TETRACHLORIDE ACTIVITY: The maximum percentage increase in weight of a bed of activated carbon after air saturated with carbon tetrachloride is passed through it at a given temperature.
CARMINATIVE: Inducing expulsion of gas from the stomach and intestines.
CASCADE IMPACTOR: Sampling device in which air is drawn through a series of jets against a series of slides. Air particles then adhere to the microscope slides which are coated with an adsorbing medium. Jet openings are sized to obtain a size distribution of particles.
CASTOR: An oily, brown, odorous substance obtained from glands in the groin of the beaver and used as a perfume fixative.
CASUSOSMIC: An odorant which is perceivable due to its reactive similarities to biologically significant osmogenes, but in itself, is not in the Darwinian sense of biological importance.
CATALYSIS: A process in which the speed of a reaction is altered by the presence of an added substance which remains unchanged at the end of the reaction. Catalysts are usually employed to accelerate reactions and are

called "positive" catalysts; in some cases retarding or "negative" catalysts are employed to reduce the rate of a reaction.

CATALYST: A substance, usually present in small amounts relative to the reactants, that modifies, especially increases, the rate of a chemical reaction without being consumed in the process.

CATALYTIC POISONS: Atmospheric dust, dirt and other residue from catalytic reactions that accumulate in the catalysts over a period of time and which must regularly be reclaimed.

CATALYTIC OXIDATION: Oxidation conducted over a catalyst, usually metallic, which requires lower ignition temperatures than thermal combustion and which effects high reduction of pollutant concentrations without excessive fuel charges.

CATCHER, GRIT: A chamber placed at the end of a sewer or at the entrance to a treatment plant to reduce the velocity of the flow sufficiently to permit grit and heavy inorganic matter to settle out.

CEILOMETER: A photoelectric instrument for ascertaining cloud heights.

CELL: The smallest structural unit of an organism that is capable of independent functioning, consisting of one or more nuclei, cytoplasm, various organelles, and inanimate matter, all surrounded by a semipermeable plasma membrane.

CENTRAL NERVOUS SYSTEM: The portion of the vertebrate nervous system consisting of the brain and spinal cord.

CENTRIFUGE: Any apparatus consisting essentially of a compartment spun about a central axis to separate contained materials of different density or to simulate gravity with centrifugal force.

CERAMIC FILTER: Component of a stack sampling system. These are also known as ceramic thimbles and are suitable for high temperature use.

CEREBELLUM: The hind-brain controlling muscular activity.

CEREBRUM: The forebrain controlling association, reflection, etc.

CESSPOOL: An underground pit or covered hole for receiving sediment or drained sewage.

CHAMBER, CHLORINATION: A detention basin or tank in which chlorine is diffused through a liquid.

CHAMBER, DETRITUS: A detention chamber larger than a grit chamber, usually with provision for removing sediment without interrupting the flow of liquid. A settling tank of short detention period designed, primarily, to remove heavy settleable solids.

CHAMBER, FLOWING-THROUGH: The upper compartment of a two-story sedimentation tank.

CHAMBER, GRIT: A small detention chamber or an enlargement of a sewer designed to reduce the velocity of flow of the liquid, to permit the separation of mineral from organic solids by differential sedimentation (same as catcher, grit).

CHAMBER, MIXING: A basin or tank to facilitate the mixing of chemicals with a liquid, usually equipped with mechanical paddles or impellers.

CHARCOAL: A black, porous carbonaceous material, produced by the destructive distillation of wood and used as a fuel, filter, and adsorbent.

CHECKWORK: A pattern of multiple openings in a refractory wall to promote turbulent mixing of products of combustion.

CHELATING: Of or pertaining to a heterocyclic ring containing a metal ion attached by coordinate bonds to at least two non-metal ions in the same molecule.

CHEMICAL OXYGEN DEMAND (COD): (1) A test based on the fact that all organic compounds, with few exceptions, can be oxidized to carbon dioxide and water by the action of strong oxidizing agents under acid conditions. Organic matter is converted to carbon dioxide and water regardless of the biological assimilability of the substances. One of the chief limitations is the inability to differentiate between biologically oxidizable and biologically inert organic matter. The major advantage of this test is the short time required for evaluation (two hours). (2) The amount of oxygen required for the chemical oxidation of organics in a liquid.

CHEMICAL SENSES: Taste and smell.

CHEMISORPTION: To take up and chemically bind a substance on the surface of another substance.

CHEMORECEPTOR: A nerve ending or sense organ, as of smell or taste, sensitive to chemical stimuli.

CHEMOTROPISM: Movement or growth of an organism, especially a plant, in response to chemical stimuli.

CHI FACTOR: Cacosmic odors.

CHIMNEY EFFECT: A phenomenon consisting of a vertical movement of a localized mass of air or other gases due to temperature differences.

CHIMNEY, STACK: Stacks or vertical steel flue for conducting cooled combustion products of a process to the atmosphere, sometimes movement activated by an induced-draft fan.

CHIMNEY SUPERELEVATION: As used in dispersion calculations, effective chimney height denotes the maximum height of the center of a plume path above the ground.

CHIRALITY: Denoting "handedness", used to describe isomers which are chemically left-handed and right-handed structurally.

CHLORINATION: The application of chlorine to water, sewage, or industrial wastes, generally for the purpose of disinfection but frequently for accomplishing other biological or chemical results. Prechlorination is chlorination prior to treatment, and postchlorination follows treatment.

CHLORINATION BREAK POINT: The application of chlorine to water, sewage, or industrial waste containing free ammonia, to the point where free residual chlorine is available.

CHLORINATION, FREE RESIDUAL: The application of chlorine to water, sewage, or industrial wastes to produce directly or through the destruction of ammonia, or of certain organic nitrogenous compounds, a free available chlorine residual.

CHLORINE: A highly irritating greenish-yellow gaseous halogen, capable of combining with nearly all other elements, produced principally by electrolysis of sodium chloride and used widely to purify water, as a disinfectant, a bleaching agent, and in the manufacture of many important compounds: Cl.

CHLORINE, AVAILABLE: A term used in rating chlorinated lime and hypochlorites as to their total oxidizing power. Also a term formerly applied to residual chlorine; now obsolete.

CHLORINE, COMBINED AVAILABLE RESIDUAL: That portion of the total residual chlorine remaining in water, sewage, or industrial wastes at the end of a specified contact period, which will react chemically and biologically as chloramines, or organic chloramines.

CHLORINE, DEMAND: The quantity of chlorine absorbed by waste water (or water) in a given length of time.

CHLORINE, TOTAL RESIDUAL: Free residual plus combined residual.

CHLORITE, HIGH-TEST HYPO: A combination of lime and chlorine consisting largely of calcium hypochloride.

CHLORITE, SODIUM HYPO: A water solution of sodium hydroxide and chlorine, in which sodium hypochlorite is the essential ingredient.

CHOANA: The passage joining the back of the nose to the throat.

CHORDA TYMPANI: Part of the seventh cranial (facial) nerve concerned with taste.

CHROMALOID: Color-like.

CHROMATOGRAPHY: The separation of complex mixtures by percolation through a selectively adsorbing medium, as through a column of magnesia, gelatin, or starch, yielding stratified, sometimes chromatically distinct, constituent layers.

CHROMOLIPOSPECIFICITY: The preferential adsorption specificity for colored, oil or fat impregnated materials.

CHROMOSORPTION: Adsorption on an object solely because of its color, providing it is electrically neutral.

CILIA: Hairs carried by cells.

CIRCUMVALLATE: Large papillae towards the back of the tongue which contain many taste-buds.

CITRAL: A mobile, pale yellow liquid derived from lemongrass oil and used in perfume and as a flavoring: $C_{10}H_{16}O$.

CIVET: A glandular secretion of the civet cat used as a perfume fixative.

CLARIFICATION: Process of removing turbidity and suspended solids by settling. Chemicals can be added to improve and speed up the settling process through coagulation.

CLARIFIER: A sedimentation tank.

CLASSIFICATION SYSTEM: The grouping of items into categories based on shared characteristics or traits.

CLEAR WELL: A reservoir containing water which has been previously filtered or purified before going into the standpipes or distribution system.

CLOGGING, FILTER: The effect of fine particles filling the voids of biological beds or of growths forming mats on the surface of stone filters, which retard the passage of liquid through the filter.

CLOTH, FILTER: A fabric stretched around the drum of a vacuum filter. May be cotton, wool, rayon, or woven-metal mesh.

CLOUD CHAMBER: A device in which the formation of chains of droplets on ions generated by the passage of charged subatomic particles through a supersaturated vapor is used to detect such particles, to infer the presence of neutral particles, and to study certain nuclear reactions.

COAGULANT: A material which, when added to industrial wastes, will combine with certain substances ordinarily present and form a precipitate consisting of more or less gelatinous floc particles and having the capacity to remove colloids from the liquids.

COAGULATION: The agglomeration of colloidal or finely divided, suspended matter by the addition to the liquid of an appropriate chemical coagulant, by biological processes or by other means.

COALESCE: To grow together, fuse.

COILS, DIGESTER: A system of pipes for hot water or steam installed in a sludge digestion tank for the purpose of heating the sludge being treated.

COLLECTION EFFICIENCY: The percentage of a specified substance retained on passage through a gas cleaning or sampling device.

COLLECTOR: A device for removing and retaining contaminants from air or other gases.

COLLECTOR, GRIT: A device placed in a grit chamber to collect and convey deposited grit to a common discharge point.

COLLECTOR, SCUM: A mechanical device for collecting and removing scum from the surface of sedimentation tanks.

COLLECTOR, SLUDGE: A mechanical device for collecting the sludge deposited on the bottom of a sedimentation tank and conveying it to a sludge hopper from which it can be drawn by hydrostatic pressure or by pumps.

COLLOIDS: A suspension of finely divided particles in a continuous medium, especially a gaseous, liquid, or solid substance containing suspended particles that are approximately 5 to 5,000 angstroms in size, do not settle out of the substance rapidly, and are not readily filtered.

COLOR BODIES: Those complex molecules which impart color (usually undesirable) to a solution.

COLUMNAR CELL: The most common olfactory cell which provides the bed or support for the more important basal and bipolar cells.

COMBINING FACTOR: The combination of acids and alcohols resulting in the formation of esters. By the addition of the proper acid to a malodorous effluent containing an alcohol, for example, a pleasant aromatic can oft times result.

COMBUSTION, AIR (INCINERATOR TERMINOLOGY): Air introduced to the primary chamber of an incinerator through the fuel bed by natural, induced, or forced draft.

COMBUSTION CHAMBER: An enclosure in which combustion of combustible solids, vapors, and gases from the primary chamber are burned and settling of fly ash occurs.

COMBUSTION GAS: Gases and vapors produced in furnaces, combustion chambers or open burning.

COMMINUTION: The process of screening wastes and reducing the retained solids to particles sufficiently fine to pass through the screen openings.

COMMON CHEMICAL SENSE: Sensibility to chemical irritants.

COMPACT, INTERSTATE: A compact or agreement between two or more States to cover the development and utilization of interstate streams, to abate pollution, and to control industrial waste treatment.

COMPACTION: Compressing metallic or nonmetallic powders, as a briquette in a die.

CONCENTRATION: The amount of a given substance in a stated unit of a mixture, solution or ore. Common methods of stating concentration are percent by weight or by volume, normality, weight by unit volume.

CONCENTRATION, HYDROGEN ION (pH): The weight of hydrogen ions in grams per liter of solution. Commonly expressed as the pH value that represents the logarithm of the reciprocal of the hydrogen ion concentration. pH 7.0 is neutral. Below 7.0 indicates acidity and above 7.0 indicates alkalinity.

CONCRETE: The alcoholic extract from the enfleurage wax, after the alcohol has been evaporated. Contains wax as well as the odorous principles.

CONDENSATION: The physical process of converting a material from a gaseous phase to a liquid or solid state by decreasing temperature, by increasing pressure, or both.

CONDENSATION FACTOR: The reduction of malodorous effluents through the use of condensers to remove condensible odorants from gas streams.

CONDENSATION SAMPLING: Gas sampling technique in which the gas is drawn through trapping tubes immersed in refrigerants. By use of different refrigerant solutions, various fractions of the components of the gas can be measured.

CONDENSORPTION: Adsorbency wherein the adsorbant has a cooler surface and the adsorbate is condensed to its liquid or solid phase.

CONDITIONED REFLEX: An unnatural reflex, induced by habit.

CONDITIONING, SLUDGE: Treatment of fluid sludge, to facilitate dewatering by the addition of ferric chloride, alum, lime, etc.

CONIINE: A poisonous, colorless liquid alkaloid obtained from the poison hemlock and formerly used in the treatment of spasmodic disorders: $C_8H_{17}N$.

CONSTRUCTION FACTOR: Any chemical reaction which causes the odorant molecule (osmogene) to become complexed, resulting in a loss of odorant property.

CONTENT, MOISTURE: The quantity of water, usually expressed in percentage by weight, present in sludge from waste treatment, screenings, etc.

COUNTER: An instrument for measuring the size and number of dust particles in the atmosphere as dust counters.

CONVECTION CURRENTS: The phenomenon occurring when masses of warm liquid rise upward in a tank, the bulk of the volume at lower depths being colder.

COPPERAS: A common name for ferrous sulfate: $FeSO_4 \cdot 7H_2O$.

CORPORATION COCK: A valve for joining a service pipe to a street water main; it is generally owned and operated by the water utility or department and cannot be operated from the surface.

CORPS EPUISES: Enfleurage wax after removal of the bulk odorous principles by extraction; suitable for pomades.

CORPUS CALLOSUM: A wide arched band of white matter connecting the cerebral hemispheres at the base of the longitudinal fissure.

CORPUSCLE: A cell such as an erythrocyte or leukocyte that is capable of free movement in a fluid or matrix as distinguished from a cell fixed in tissue.

CORTEX: Layer of gray matter on the outside of the brain; receiving station of the brain.

COUNTERCURRENT EFFICIENCY (activated carbon): The unique advantage of a carbon column that permits partially spent activated carbon to adsorb impurities before the semiprocessed stream comes in contact with fresh carbon. This allows the maximum capacity of the activated carbon to be utilized.

CRANIAL: Of or pertaining to the skull.

CRANIAL NERVE: Any of several nerves that arise in pairs from the brainstem and reach the periphery through openings in the skull.

CRITICAL BED DEPTH (activated carbon): In a carbon column the critical bed depth is the depth of granular carbon which is partially spent. It lies between the fresh carbon and the spent carbon and is the zone where adsorption takes place. In a single-column system, this is the amount of carbon that is not completely utilized.

CRITICAL FLICKER FREQUENCY: That at which a flickering light appears to fuse into a continuous light.

CRITICAL FREQUENCY OF GUSTATION: Frequency of the nerve impulses on tasting.

CROSS-SECTIONAL BED AREA (activated carbon): The area of activated carbon through which the stream flow is perpendicular.

CRYPTOSMIA: The perception of odors imperceptable to normal persons.

CRYSTALLOSE: Sodium salt of saccharin.

CUBIC FOOT PER SECOND: A unit of measurement for flowing liquids, equal to a flow of one cubic foot per second past a given section of channel.

CURVE, OXYGEN SAG: A curve that represents the profile of dissolved oxygen content along the course of a stream, resulting from deoxygenation associated with biochemical oxidation of organic matter, and reoxygenation through the absorption of atmospheric oxygen and through biological photosynthesis.

CYANIC ACID: A poisonous, unstable, highly volatile organic acid used to prepare certain cyanates: HOCN.

CYANIDE: Any of various salts or esters of hydrogen cyanide containing a CN group.

CYCLONE: A cyclone collector is a structure without moving parts in which the velocity of an inlet gas stream is transformed into a confined vortex from which centrifugal forces tend to drive the suspended particles to the wall of the cyclone body.

CYCLONE SEPARATOR: A separator which utilizes centrifugal force to arrest all or part of the particles suspended in a current of gas.

DDT: A colorless contact insecticide toxic to man and animals when swallowed or absorbed through the skin: $(ClC_6H_4)_2\ CHCCl_3$.

DECOMPOSITION FACTOR: The dismemberment and simplification of odorant molecules until they no longer exhibit the odorous property. Also referred to as destruction, combustion, catalytic combustion, incineration, chemical oxidation, scrubbing oxidation, ultraviolet, sonics, etc.

DECOMPOSITION OF SEWAGE: The breakdown of organic matter first by aerobic activity and then by anaerobic oxidation.

DECYL ACETATE: A liquid with floral orange-rose odor used in perfumery: $CH_3(CH_2)_9OOCCH_3$.

DEGREASING: The process of removing greases and oils from sewage, waste and sludge.

DELTA FACTOR: Cold odors such as menthol.

DENDRITES: Branched parts of nerve cells which transmit impulses toward the cell body.

DEODORIZE: To disguise or absorb the odor of.

DEPOLYMERIZE: The breaking down of polymers into short chains.

DEPTH, SIDE WATER: The depth of a liquid measured along the inside of the vertical exterior wall of a tank.

DESORPTION: The opposite of adsorption. A phenomenon where an adsorbed molecule leaves the surface of the adsorbant.

DETENTION PERIOD: The period of flow through a tank equal to a given number of hours of the hourly volume of flow, i.e., two hours detention equals the amount of flow reaching the tank in two hours.

DETRITUS: The sand, grit and other coarse material removed by gravitational sedimentation in a relatively short period of detention.

DEWATERING: The removal of a large part of the occluded water content of sludge by draining or by mechanical means, such as vacuum filters or sludge presses.

DEXTROSE: A sugar found in plant and animal tissue and derived synthetically from starch: $C_6H_{12}O_6.H_2O$.

DIACETYL: 2,3-butanedione.

DIFFERENTIATION: A change whereby organs become specialized.

DIFFUSED AERATION: The aeration produced in a liquid by passing air through a diffuser (porous tube or tile).

DIFFUSER: A porous plate or tube through which air is forced and divided into minute bubbles for diffusion in liquids. Commonly made of carborundum, alundum, or silica sand.

DIFFUSION, RIDGE AND FURROW AIR: A method of air diffusion in an aeration tank of the activated sludge process where porous tile diffusers are placed in depressions created by the sawtooth construction of the tank bottom, in rows across the tank at right angles to the direction of flow.

DIFFUSION, SPIRAL FLOW AIR: A method of diffusing air in an aeration tank of the activated sludge process, where by means of properly designed baffles and the proper location of diffusers, a spiral helical movement is given to both the air and the liquor in the tank.

DIGESTION: The primarily enzymatic bodily process by which foodstuffs are decomposed into simple, assimilable substances; the process of decomposing organic matter in sewage by bacteria.

DIGESTION, MESOPHILIC: Digestion at or below 113$^{\circ}$ F.

DIGESTION, SEPARATE: The digestion of sludge in two or more tanks arranged in series.

DIGESTION, SLUDGE: The process by which organic or volatile matter in sludge is gasified, liquefied, mineralized or converted into more stable organic matter through the activities of living organisms.

DIGESTION, STAGE: The progressive digestion of sludge in several tanks arranged in series.
DIGESTION, THERMOPHILIC: Digestion carried on at a temperature generally between 113 to 145° F.
DILUTION: A method of disposing of industrial wastes or plant effluent by discharge into a stream or body of water.
DILUTION FACTOR: The addition of non-odorous substances to malodorous ones to achieve sub-threshold levels, generally achieved through the use of one of various available industrial stacks.
DIPOLE: In substances containing reactive groups, these groups may arrange themselves like the two poles of a magnet. Such substances are dipolar.
DIRHINE: Two nostrils.
DISCOMFORT THRESHOLD: A value at which a stimulus just produces a discomfort sensation or comes just within the limits of perception.
DISGUISING: The use of masking, deodorizing, counteracting, perfuming, etc., to conceal or alter malodorants.
DISINFECTION: The killing of the larger portion (but not necessarily all) of the harmful and objectionable microorganisms in or on a medium by means of chemicals, heat, ultraviolet light, etc.
DISPERSION: The dilution of a pollutant by diffusion, or turbulent action, etc.
DISSOLVED OXYGEN (D): The oxygen dissolved in sewage, water, or other liquid usually expressed in milligrams per liter or percent of saturation. It is the test used in BOD determination.
DISTILLATION: The process of raising the temperature of a liquid to the boiling point and condensing the resultant vapor to liquid form by cooling. It is used to remove substances from a liquid or to obtain a pure liquid from one which contains impurities or which is a mixture of several liquids having different boiling temperatures. Used in the treatment of fermentation products, yeast, etc., and other wastes to remove recoverable products.
DISTRIBUTOR: A device used to apply liquid to the surface of a filter. There are two general types, fixed and movable. The fixed type may consist of perforated pipes or sprinkler nozzles. The movable type may consist of rotating, reciprocating, or traveling perforated pipes or pipe arms fitted with spray nozzles or rotating disks.
DISTRIBUTOR, ROTATING: A distributor consisting of rotating pipe arms from which the liquid is discharged in the form of a spray or thin sheets.
DIURETICS: Medicines causing urination.
DIURNAL: Recurring daily.
DOME, GAS: In sludge-digestion tanks, a steel cover floating on the gas above the sludge, or a fixed metal dome to contain the gas.
DORSAL: Belonging to the back of the tongue, the upper surface.
DOSAGE: Concentration of pollutants in an exposure chamber.
DOSE, CHLORINE: The amount of chlorine applied to a liquid, usually expressed in parts per million.
DRIER, FLASH: A device for vaporizing water from partly dewatered and finely divided sludge through contact with a current of hot gas or other vapor. Usually includes a squirrel-cage mill for separating the sludge cake into fine particles.
DRIER, ROTARY: A long steel cylinder, lying horizontally, with its long axis on a slight incline, through which sludge passes to be dried in an upgoing current of hot air or gas.
DRIER, SPRAY: A drier in which the liquid containing the solids to be dried is sprayed or atomized into a hot chamber.

DUALITY: The characteristic of some odors of causing different sensations in various concentrations. At a low concentration, for example, one substance might cause a sensation of pleasure or attraction whereas at higher concentrations the same substance might create sensations of actual repulsion.

DUFOURS GLANDS: Insect glands which discharge odorous substances to repell and identify the enemy.

DULCIGEN: A group of sweet-tasting chemicals.

DULCIN: A white powder with a taste about two hundred times as sweet as sugar: $H_2NOCNHC_6H_4OC_2H_5$.

DUST: Fine, particulate matter.

EARTH, DIATOMACEOUS: A white or cream-colored siliceous earth composed of the shells of diatoms, extremely minute, unicellular or colonial algae. Used as a coagulant or filter aid in the conditioning of sludge.

EDDY: A current moving contrary to the direction of the main current, especially in a circular motion.

EDUCTOR (activated carbon): A device with no moving parts used to force an activated carbon water slurry through pipes to the desired location.

EFFERENT NERVE FIBER: Nerve fibers which convey messages from the brain to the muscles.

EFFICIENCY, FILTER: The operating results of a filter as measured by various criteria, such as percentage reduction in suspended matter, total solids, BOD, bacteria or color.

EFFLUENT: A liquid which flows out of a containing space. Sewage, water, or other liquid partially or completely treated, or in its natural state, as the case may be, flowing out of a reservoir, basin, or treatment plant, or part thereof.

EFFLUENT, STABLE: A treated waste which contains enough oxygen to satisfy its oxygen demand.

EFFLUVIA: Disagreeable vapors.

ELECTROCHEMICAL SERIES: Table in which the elements are arranged in order, from the electropositive, e.g. halogens, at the bottom.

ELECTROMAGNETIC RECEPTOR: An extended resonator of a natural or multiple of natural frequency of an osmogene.

ELECTROSTATIC PRECIPITATION: A process to separate particulate matter from air or other gases using an electrostatic field.

ELECTROSTATIC PRECIPITATOR: Devices that separate particles from a gas stream by passing the carrier gas between the two electrodes across which a unidirectional, high-voltage potential is effected. The particles pass through this field, becoming charged and migrating to the oppositely charged electrode.

ELUTRIATION: A process of sludge conditioning in which certain constituents are removed by successive flushing with fresh water or plant effluent, thereby reducing the need for using conditioning chemicals.

EMISSIONS: The total amount of a solid, liquid, or gaseous pollutant emitted into the atmosphere from a given source in a given time, and indicated in grams per cubic meter of gas or by a relative measure upon discharge from the source.

EMISSIONS, PRIMARY: Fine solids (less than 100 microns in diameter), coarse particles (greater than 100 microns in diameter), sulfur compounds, organic compounds, nitrogen compounds, oxygen compounds, halogen compounds and radioactive compounds.

EMISSIONS, SECONDARY: Emissions of polluted air reactants such as those which occur in atmospheric photochemical reactions, including ozone, formaldehyde, organic hydroperoxides, etc.

EMPYREUMATIC: Burnt.
ENFLEURAGE: A process in the making of perfume by which odorless fats or oils are exposed to the exhaled fragrance of fresh flowers.
EPIGLOTTIS: Cartilage at the root of the tongue that folds over the glotis to prevent food from entering the windpipe during the act of swallowing.
EPITHELIUM: Skin or mucous membrane.
EPSILON FACTOR: Lachrymatory odors.
ERECTILE TISSUE: Tissue that may be swollen, e.g. that surrounding the air passages in the nose.
ERKENNEMGSSCHWELLE: (German) Just below the threshold level of perception.
ESSENTIAL OIL: A volatile oil, usually having the characteristic odor or flavor of the plant from which it is obtained, used to make perfumes and flavorings.
ETHEREAL: Spirit-like, volatile, similar to ether.
ETHMOID: One of the cranial bones which extends to the bridge of the nose.
ETHYL ALCOHOL: A colorless, volatile liquid used widely in industry: $C_2H_5OH$.
EUCALYPTOL: A colorless, oily liquid derived from eucalyptus oil and used in pharmaceuticals, flavoring, and perfumery: $C_{10}H_{18}O$.
EUTRIFICATION: A condition found in a body of water in which the increase of mineral or organic nutrients reduces the dissolved oxygen producing an aquatic environment favoring plant over animal life.
EXALTOLIDE: A musk compound responsible for the pleasant odor of angelica root oil and used as a fixative in perfumes: $C_{15}H_{28}O_2$.
EXALTONE: Synthetic musk-like substance: $C_{15}H_{28}O$.
EXOTHERMIC: A chemical reaction which gives off heat.
EXPANDED REACTION: A mental process moving from the particular to the general, e.g. on smelling pine oil to think of Norway.
EXPRESSION: The method of separating the essential oil from fruit rinds.
EXTEROCEPTORS: Distance receptors of the nose and ear.

FATIGUE: Unresponsive state of receptors on continued stimulation, due to adaptation.
FAUCES: The space between the mouth and pharynx bounded by the soft palate, the base of the tongue, and the palatine arches.
FEEDER, DRY CHEMICAL: A mechanical device for applying dry chemicals to wastes at a rate controlled manually, or automatically, by the rate of flow of liquid or by quantity per unit of time.
FILIFORM: A kind of papillae covering the dorsum of the tongue. Not connected with gustation.
FILM, MICROBIAL: The gelatinous film of zoogleal growths covering the medium of a biological bed, trickling filter, etc.
FILTER, HIGH-RATE: A trickling filter operated at a high average daily dosing rate, usually between ten and thirty mgd/acre, sometimes including recirculation of effluent.
FILTER, INTERMITTENT: A natural or artificial bed of sand or other fine grained material, to the surface of which sewage is intermittently applied in flooding doses and through which it passes, opportunity being given for filtration and the maintenance of aerobic conditions.
FILTER, LOW-RATE: A trickling filter designed to receive a small load of BOD per unit volume of filtering material and to have a low dosage rate per unit of surface area (usually one to four mgd/acre). Also called a standard rate filter.
FILTER, RAPID SAND: A filter for the purification of water where water which has been previously treated, usually by coagulation and sedimentation, is

passed downward through a filtering medium consisting of a layer of sand or prepared anthracite coal or other suitable material, usually from 24 to 30 inches thick and resting on a supporting bed of gravel or a porous medium such as carborundum. The filtrate is removed by an underdrain system. The filter is cleaned periodically by reversing the flow of the water through the filtering medium, sometimes supplemented by mechanical or air agitation during backwashing to remove mud and other impurities that are lodged in the sand.

FILTER, ROUGHING: A sewage filter of relatively coarse material operated at a high rate as a preliminary treatment.

FILTER, SLUDGE VACUUM: A device in which wet sludge, previously conditioned by a coagulant, is partially dewatered by means of a vacuum or pressure. Commonly in the form of a rotating drum, covered with cotton, nylon, wool, or wire cloth or tightly stretched metal springs or strings.

FILTER, SPRINKLING: A trickling filter to which the sewage is applied by sprays from fixed nozzles or rotating arms. An old term, now considered obsolete, trickling filter being preferred.

FILTER, TRICKLING: A filter consisting of an artificial bed of coarse material, such as broken stone, clinkers, slate, slats or brush, over which sewage is distributed and applied in drops, films, or spray, from troughs, drippers, moving distributors, or fixed nozzles, and through which it trickles to the underdrains, giving opportunity for the formation of zoogleal slimes which clarify and oxidize the sewage.

FILTER, VACUUM: A filter consisting of a cylindrical drum mounted on a horizontal axis, covered with a filter cloth, revolving with a partial submergence in liquid. A vacuum is maintained under the cloth for the larger part of a revolution to extract moisture, and the cake is scraped off continuously.

FILTRATION, BIOLOGICAL: The process of passing a liquid through a biological filter containing media on the surfaces of which zoogleal films develop which absorb and adsorb fine suspended, colloidal, and dissolved solids, and which release various biochemical end-products.

FIXATIVE: Relatively non-volatile substances which added to a perfume, fix or render more permanent the odor of the volatile constituents.

FLAGELLA: Olfactory hairs.

FLAVOR: Combined sensation of odor and taste.

FLOAT CONTROL: A device installed in a channel or tank to operate a screen or pumps. In screening wastes, one form of float control operates on the difference of head between the approaching and discharge side of the screen bars.

FLOC: Small, gelatinous masses formed in a liquid by the addition of coagulants, or through biochemical processes, or by agglomeration.

FLOCCULATION: Floc formation by a mechanical unit to stimulate the formation of compact, quick settling flocs. Usually in the form of revolving shafts with paddle blades operating at slow speed to cause the forming flocs to pass in a multitude of paths through all zones of the flocculation basis.

FLOCCULATOR: An apparatus designed for the formation of floc in water or sewage.

FLOTATION: A method of raising suspended matter to the surface of the liquid in a tank as scum by aeration, vacuum, evolution of gas, chemicals, electrolysis, heat, or bacterial decomposition and the subsequent removal of the scum by skimming.

FLOW, RADIAL OUTWARD: The flow of liquid in a circular or square tank from an inlet at the center to an overflow weir or apertures at the periphery of the tank.

FLUME, PARSHALL: A device, developed by an engineer by that name for measuring the flow of liquid in an open channel. It consists of a contracting length, a throat and an expanding length. At the throat is a sill over which the flow passes. The upper and lower heads are each measured at a definite distance from the sill.

FLUORIDE: Any binary compound of fluorine with another element.
FOAMING, SLUDGE: An increase in the gas in separate sludge digestion tanks causing large quantities of froth, scum and sludge to rise and overflow from openings at or near the top of the tanks.
FOETID: Having a strong offensive odor.
FOETOR: A stink.
FOEHN WINDS: A warm, dry wind coming off the slopes of a mountain range.
FOLIATE: A kind of papillae consisting of vertical ridges on edge of the back of the tongue, connected with gustation.
FORMICARY: An ant hill.
FRANKINCENSE: An aromatic gum resin obtained from African and Asian trees and used chiefly for incense; synonym: olibanum.
FREEBOARD: The vertical distance between the normal maximum level of the liquid in a tank, channel, etc., and the top of the tank or channel or of a mechanism or structure spanning the tank.
FREE ELECTRONS: An electron that is not bound to an atom.
FREQUENCY: The number of times a specified phenomenon occurs within a specified interval.
FREQUENCY, SYNERGISTIC: Mutually reinforcing frequencies.
FUNGIFORM: A kind of mushroom-like papillae on the tongue, concerned with gustation.
FUSEL OIL: Objectionable impurities in alcohol, chiefly amyl alcohols.

GAMMA FACTOR: The presence of a hot sensation in odors such as that of cloves.
GANGLIA: Swellings on nerves just before they enter the central nervous system.
GAS, SLUDGE: The gas produced during the digestion of organic solids from industrial wastes or sewage. Commonly called sludge-digester gas, it may be collected and utilized for heating purposes or for the generation of power for operating vehicles, domestic purposes, etc. The gas normally contains 60 to 65 percent methane and has an average value of 600 to 650 BTU's per cubic foot.
GASOLINE: A volatile mixture of flammable liquid hydrocarbons derived chiefly from crude petroleum and used principally as a fuel for internal-combustion engines.
GEOSMIN: An odorous volatile (extreme musty) resulting from certain water-borne Streptomyces: $C_{12}H_{22}O$.
GLOSSOPHARYNGEAL: The ninth cranial nerve, dealing with a part of gustation.
GOBLET CELLS: Cells which discharge mucous.
GREASE: In sewage, grease includes fats, waxes, free fatty acids, calcium and magnesium soaps, mineral oils, and other non-fatty materials. The type of solvents to be used for its extraction should be stated.
GRINDER, SCREENINGS: A device for grinding, shredding, or macerating material removed from wastes by coarse or fine screens.
GRIT: The heavy mineral matter in water or sewage, such as sand, gravel and cinders.
GULLET: The passage from the mouth to the stomach.
GUSTATION: The sense of taste or act of tasting.
GUSTATORY HAIR: Protoplasmic hair carried by a taste cell. Analogous to olfactory hair.
GYMNEMIC ACID: An acid which abolishes the sense of sweetness and restricts that of bitterness, but leaves the tastes salty and sour more or less unchanged.

HARDNESS: (1) A measure of the capacity of the water for precipitating soap.

(2) A characteristic of water which represents the total concentration of just the calcium and magnesium ions expressed as calcium carbonate.

HARD PALATE: The front part of the roof of the mouth.

HARMONIC RESONANCE: "Action at a distance" phenomenon resulting from a transmitter and receiver where the receiver has the natural wavelength being transmitted.

HEAD, LOSS OF: The decrease in the level of a liquid.

HEAD, STATIC: The vertical distance between the free level of the source of supply and the point of free discharge or the level of the free surface.

HEAD, WEIR: The distance from the crest of a weir to the water surface at a given point ahead of the weir.

HEAT OF ADSORPTION: The heat given off when molecules are adsorbed.

HEAVY METALS: A general name given to the ions of metallic elements such as copper, zinc, iron, chromium, and aluminum. They are normally removed from a waste water by forming an insoluble precipitate.

HEDONICS: The study of pleasant and unpleasant sensations.

HELIOTHROPIN: Piperonal, a white powder having a floral odor, used as flavoring and in perfume: $C_8H_6O_3$.

HEREDITARY CONFORMATION: A genetically inherited characteristic.

HEDONIC UNIT ($HU^a_x y$): An expression of the hedonic value of an odor where HU is a Hedonic Unit. "a" is the numerical value of the odor strength measured on an arbitrary scale of zero through six, "x" is the aesthetic quality of the odor, measured on the same scale, and "y" is the best physical description. For example, the HU value of acetic acid would be $HU^6_6$vinegar.

HORMONE: A substance formed by one organ and conveyed, as by the blood stream, to another, which it stimulates to function by means of its chemical activity.

HUILES ANTIQUES: Perfumes with an olive-oil base.

HYALURONIDASE: An enzyme that catalyzes the hydrolysis of hyaluronic acid. The cement substance of the tissues. It is formed in leeches, in snake and spider venom, and in the testes and malignant tissues, and is produced by a variety of pathogenic bacteria. Also called Duran-Reynals factor, or spreading factor. Used to promote absorption and diffusion of solutions injected subcutaneously.

HYDROTROPISM: Growth or movement of an organism in response to water.

HYOID: A U-shaped bone between the mandible and the larynx at the base of the tongue.

HYPERACUTE: Extremely perceptive.

HYPERGLYCEMIA: The presence of an extremely high concentration of sugar (glucose) in the blood.

HYPEROSMIA: Unusually keen olfaction.

HYPERTROPHIED: A nontumorous increase in the size of an organ or part as a result of the enlargement, without increase in number of constituent.

HYPOGLOSSAL: Located under the tongue; of or pertaining to the hypoglossal nerve, a nerve attached to the medulla oblongata and innervating the muscles of the tongue.

HYPOGLYCEMIA: An abnormally low level of glucose in the blood.

HYPOPLASIA (Hypo + Gr.plasis=formation + ia): Defective or incomplete development.

HYPOSMIA: Reduced olfaction.

HYPOTHALAMUS: The portion of the diencephalon which forms the floor and part of the lateral wall of the third ventricle. It includes the optic chiasm, mammilary bodies, tuber cinereum, infundibulum, and hypophysis. The nuclei of this region exert control over visceral activities, water balance, temperature, sleep, etc.

HYSTERIA: A neurosis characterized by conversion symptoms, a calm mental attitude, and episodes of hallucination, somnambulism, amnesia, and other mental aberrations; excessive or uncontrollable fear or other strong emotion.

IMHOFF CONE: A conically shaped graduated glass vessel used to measure the approximate volume of settleable solids in wastes or other liquids.

IMHOFF TANK: (Also referred to as Emscher tank) Tanks in which the settling solids slide down the incline of a trough-shaped false bottom of the settling compartment and through slots at the apex of the trough into the underlying digestion compartment. The slope of the false bottom is made as steep as possible in order to keep it clean. The slots overlap or are otherwise trapped to keep gases or solids that rise within the digestion compartment out of the settling compartment. However, a small interchange of liquid does occur.

IMPINGE: To collide, strike, dash, to push against. The act of bringing matter forcibly in contact.

INCINERATE: To consume by burning.

INDEX, POLLUTIONAL: A criterion by which the degree of pollution in a stream may be measured, as indicated by bacterial counts, plankton, BOD, or quantity of dissolved oxygen.

INDEX, PURIFICATION: A criterion by which may be measured the degree of oxidation, reduction, or nitrification accomplished in sewage treatment.

INDEX, SLUDGE: The volume in milliliters occupied by aerated mixed liquor containing 1 gram of dry solids after settling 30 minutes commonly referred to as the Mohlman index. The Donaldson index, which is also commonly used, is obtained by dividing 100 by the Mohlman index.

INDOLE: A white, crystalline compound obtained from coal tar and used in perfumery, medicine, and as a flavoring. Odor is extremely unpleasant in high concentrations: $C_8H_7N$.

INERTIAL SEPARATOR: Dry type collectors utilizing the relatively greater inertia of the particle to effect particulate gas separation. Two types of equipment utilize this principle; cyclonic separators which produce continuous centrifugal force as a means of exerting the greater inertial effects of the particle; and simple inertial or impaction separators which employ incremental changes of direction of the carrier gas stream to exert the greater inertial effects of the particle. Included in this category, besides cyclonic and impingment separators, are gravity settling chambers and high velocity gas reversal chambers.

INFERIOR CONCHA: One of three nearly horizontal folds of cartilaginous material on the inside lateral walls of the nose.

INFLUENT: Sewage, water, or other liquid, either raw or partly treated, flowing into a reservoir, basin or treatment plant, or any part thereof.

INFRA-RED: Light waves of lower frequency than the visible spectrum.

INFRA-RED ABSORPTION BANDS: The portion (infra-red) of the electromagnetic spectrum generally considered to lie on the long wave side of the human eye's sensitivity, from 0.7 to about 1000 microns, (where optical and radio microwave techniques overlap) if necessary.

INNERVATION: The supply or service of nerve endings on any part of the body.

INSISTENCE: The characteristic of an odor whereby they are perceptible at very low concentrations but are not strong even at high concentrations.

INTEGRATION: The fusing to a composite whole of impulses from different receptors.

INTERFERENCE FACTOR: The combining of two odorants whose osmic frequencies cancel each other thereby eliminating the individual odors involved.

INTERMOLECULAR: Between molecules.

INTEROCEPTOR: A specialized sensory nerve receptor responding to stimuli

originating in internal organs; receptors requiring contact of the stimulating substance.
INTRAMOLECULAR VIBRATION: The internal, vibratory movements of individual molecules.
INVERSION: A state in which the air temperature increases with increasing altitude, holding surface air down along with its pollutants.
INVERT: The floor, bottom, or lowest portion of the internal cross section of a closed conduit.
ION: An atom, group of atoms, or molecule that has acquired or is regarded as having acquired a net electric charge by gaining electrons in or losing electrons from an initially electrically neutral configuration.
IONIZATION: The process of the formation of one or more ions by the addition of electrons to or the removal of electrons from an electrically neutral atomic or molecular configuration by heat, electrical discharge, radiation, or chemical reaction.
IONONE: Either of two colorless to yellowish liquid isomers having a strong odor of violets and used in perfumes: $C_{13}H_{20}O$.
IRONE: Colorless to amber-yellow liquid, with soft violet odors: $C_{14}H_{22}O$.
IRRIGATION, SPRAY: Irrigation by means of nozzles along a pipe on the ground or from perforated overhead pipes.
ISOLATE: A pure chemical isolated from natural products.
ISOMER: The possession by two or more distinct compounds of the same molecular formula, each molecule possessing an identical number of atoms of each element, but in different arrangement.
ISOTONIC SALT SOLUTION: Equal concentration of salts to that in the blood.

JACOBSON'S ORGAN: The vomero-nasal organ.

LACHRYMATORY: Of, pertaining to, or causing tears.
LAGOON, SLUDGE: A relatively shallow basin, or natural depression, used for the storage or digestion of sludge, sometimes for its ultimate detention or dewatering.
LAMBDA FACTOR: The characteristic in an odor of insistence.
LECITHIN: Any of a group of phosphatides found in all plant and animal tissues, produced commercially from egg yolks, soybeans, and corn, and used in the processing of foods, pharmaceuticals, cosmetics, etc.
LEMON: A spiney, evergreen tree whose fruit yields an aromatic rind and an acid, juicy pulp.
LEMONGRASS: Any of several tropical grasses yielding an aromatic oil used in perfumery and as flavoring.
LEVEL, WATER: The elevation of the free water or liquid surface of a body of water or liquid above or below a given datum line.
LICORICE: The root of the same plant used as a flavoring in candy, liquors, tobacco and medicines; synonym, glycyrrhiza.
LIGHT-SPOTS: Primitive light-sensitive organs, the forerunner of eyes.
LIMBIC: That area of the brain concerned with olfaction and gustation.
LIPOID: Cholesterins and phosphatides having the character of a lipid (fat).
LIPOIDS: Nitrogenous fats consisting of lecithins.
LIQUEFACTION: The changing of the organic matter in wastes from an insoluble to a soluble state effecting a reduction in the solid contents.
LIQUOR, MIXED: A mixture of activated sludge and sewage in the aeration tank undergoing activated sludge treatment.

LIQUOR, SUPERNATANT: The liquor overlying deposited solids: The liquid in a sludge digestion tank which lies between the sludge at the bottom and the floating scum at the top.
LOADING, BOD FILTER: The pounds of BOD in the applied liquid per unit of filterbed area or volume.
LOAD, POLLUTIONAL: The quantity of polluting material discharged into a body of water. The pollutional load imposed on sewage-treatment works is expressed as the equivalent population.
LOSS OF HEAD GAGE: A gage on a rapid sand filter which indicated the loss of head involved in the filtering operation whereby the operator is able to ascertain the need for filter backwashing.

MACROCYCLIC: A group of compounds with a large ring in the molecule.
MACROPORE: The pores in activated carbon which are larger (in diameter) than 1,000 angstroms.
MACROSMATIC: Possessed of exceptionally keen scent such as dogs or foxes.
MAKEUP CARBON: Fresh granular activated carbon which must be added to a column system after a regeneration cycle or when deemed necessary to bring the total amount of carbon to specification.
MALARIA: An infectious disease characterized by cycles of chills, fever, and sweating, transmitted by the bite of the infected female anopheles mosquito; obsolete definition: Foul or bad air.
MALASTHETIC: Unpleasant to the senses.
MALASTHETIC STENCH: Odors unpleasant sensorially but without the capacity to cause harm or damage to the environment and which, in fact, could even be beneficial.
MALODOR: Bad odors, ill-smelling odors.
MASK: The neutralization of two odors by each other.
MATRIX: A situation or surrounding substance within which somthing originates, develops, or is contained.
MATTER, SUSPENDED: Solids in suspension in wastes or effluent. Commonly, those which can be removed readily by laboratory methods or filtering.
MEATUS: A body canal or passage, such as the opening of the ear or the urethral canal.
MECHANO-RECEPTOR: Receptors actuated by pressure differences such as those of touch and hearing.
MEDIAN SEPTUM: The middle division in the nose, between the two nostrils.
MEDULLA OBLONGATA: The nervous tissue at the bottom of the brain that controls respiration, circulation and certain other bodily functions.
MEDULLATED: Sheathed; having a marrow.
MEPHITIS: An offensive smell; stench.
MERCURY: A silvery-white poisonous metallic element, liquid at room temperature. Forms alloys with most metals (except iron): Hg.
MEROSMIA: Normal odor perception for some odors but impairment for others.
MESH SIZE (activated carbon): The particle size of granular activated carbon as determined by the U.S. Sieve series.
METABOLIC: Of or pertaining to the complex of physical and chemical processes involved in the maintenance of life.
METALLIC ATOMS: Any of a category of electropositive elements that are usually whitish, lustrous, and, in the transition metals, typically ductile and malleable with high tensile strength.
METHYLENE BLUE NUMBER (activated carbon): The methylene blue number is the milligrams of methylene blue adsorbed by one gram of carbon in equilibrium with a solution of methylene blue having a concentration of 1.0 mg/l.

METHYL MERCAPTAN: A water white liquid when below boiling point, or colorless gas with a powerful unpleasant odor; highly flammable, toxic: $CH_3SH$.
MIASMA: A poisonous atmosphere formerly thought to arise from swamps and putrid matter and cause disease; a thick, vaporous atmosphere.
MICROPORE: The pores in activated carbon which range in size (in diameter) from 10 to 1,000 angstroms.
MICROSMATIC: Not possessed of exceptionally keen scent (man).
MIDDLE CONCHA: One of the three nearly horizontal folds of cartilaginous material on the inside lateral walls of the nose.
MINIMUM STIMULUS: The smallest stimulus that just evokes sensation such as the lowest concentration of a gas detectable by odor.
MID: Minimal identifiable odor.
MIXER, FLASH: A device for dispersing chemicals quickly and uniformly throughout a liquid.
MODALITY: Differentiation of a sense, partly or fully emerged.
MOLASSES NUMBER (activated carbon): The molasses number is calculcated from the ratios of the optical densities of the filtrate of a molasses solution treated with a standard activated carbon and the activated carbon in question.
MOLECULAR CONTACT: Actual contact between a molecule and the receptor.
MONOKYMATIC: A single vapor pressure range.
MONORHINE: Having only one nasal orifice.
MONORHINICALLY: Through one nostril.
MOTOR AXONE: Efferent nerve fiber.
MOVING BED (activated carbon): A unique application with Filtrasorb granular carbons in which a single carbon column offers the efficiency of several columns in series. This is accomplished by the removal of spent carbon from one end of the carbon bed and the addition of fresh carbon at the other end, with little or no interruption in the process.
MUCIDONE: An odorous volatile (extremely musty) resulting from certain waterborne Streptomyces. Similar but more odorous than geosmin: $C_{12}H_{18}O$.
MUCOUS: The viscous suspension of mucin, water, cells, and inorganic salts secreted as a protective lubricant coating by glands in the mucous membrane; the discharge of the goblet cells.
MUGUET: Lily-of-the-valley.
MUSC BAUR: Artificial musk (toluene or xylene).
MUSC AMBRETTE: A fine artificial musk.
MUSCONE: The odorous principle of musk: $CH_3C_{15}H_{27}O$.
MUSK: An unctuous brownish semi-liquid when fresh; dried, in grains or lumps with color resembling dried blood. Used as a fixative.

NARES: The openings in the nasal cavities of vertebrates; nostrils.
NARES VESTIBULES: The inside of the nostrils.
NASAL CAVITIES: The internal parts of the nose.
NASAL SEPTUM: The median septum.
NASCENT OXYGEN: A colorless gas; an extremely active form of oxygen: $O_3$.
NASOLACRYMAL DUCT: The canal which carries tears from the eye to the nose.
NASOPHARYNX: The portion of the pharynx directly behind the nasal cavity and above the soft palate.
NEPHRITIS: Any of various acute or chronic inflammations of the kidneys.
NERVE FIBER: The link between the peripheral receptors and the central nervous system.
NERVE LADDER: Two strand-like concentrations of nerve cells with cross connections; typical of some invertebrates.

NERVE NET: Concentration of nerve cells in the form of a ring or net.
NEURON: A nerve cell with all its processes.
NEUTRALIZE: To make ineffective, to counterbalance, as odors.
NIOBE OIL: (methyl benzoate) A colorless, transparent liquid with a pleasant odor: $C_6H_5COOCH_3$.
NITRIFICATION: The conversion of nitrogenous matter into nitrates by bacteria; the oxidization into nitric acid, nitrous acid, or any nitrate or nitrite, as by the action of nitrobacteria; to treat or combine with nitrogen or compounds containing nitrogen.
NITROSAMINES: Carcinogenic substances formed from nitrite breakdowns, especially sodium nitrite and amines resulting from protein degradation.
NOTOCHORD: A flexible, rod-like structure in some lower vertebrates that provides corsal support; the primitive background.
NUBILE: Ready for marriage or mating.
NUMBER, INDICATED (N): In the testing of bacterial density by the dilution method, the number obtained by taking the reciprocal of the highest possible dilution (smallest quantity of sample) in a decimal series.

OAK MOSS RESIN: A lichen growing on trees, used as a fixative.
OBJECTIFICATION: The presenting (something) as an object; the imparting of reality to.
OBOSMIC: The perception of an odor imperceptible to normal people or to people under normal circumstances. Often associated with metabolic disorders such as hormone imbalances, menopause, etc.
OCTAVOID: Events experienced in a distinct series; octave-like.
ODOR: The property or quality of a thing that affects, stimulates, or is perceived by the sense of smell; a scent.
ODORANT: An odorous substance.
ODORIFEROUS: Carrying an odor.
ODORIMETER: An instrument for measuring the intensity of odors.
ODORIPHORE: An odor-producing group (outdated, see osmogene).
ODOROSITY: The property of having an odor; odorousness.
ODOR VECTOR: (also odorivector) Any substance (odorous or inodorous) which by various forces collects and stores osmogenes.
OLFACID: Smell evoking.
OLFACTIE: A unit of smell. (now obsolete)
OLFACTION: The sense of smell. The action of smelling.
OLFACTISM: A sensation of smell produced by other than olfactory stimuli.
OLFACTOLOGY: The science of smell.
OLFACTOMETER: An instrument for measuring odor intensity; synonym: osmometer.
OLFACTORY: Of or contributing to the sense of smell.
OLFACTORY APPARATUS: The olfactory cells, hairs and nerves.
OLFACTORY BULB: The part of the brain into which the olfactory nerve leads.
OLFACTORY CELLS: Long narrow cells furnished with hairs which are smell-receptors.
OLFACTORY CLEFT: Part of nasal cavities, high up and to the back, in which the olfactory cells are situated.
OLFACTORY COEFFICIENT: The smallest volume of vapor of a substance necessary for the indentification of its odor.
OLFACTORY EPITHELIUM: The membranous tissue, composed of closely arranged cells separated by very little intercellular substance which forms the internal covering of the nasal cavity.
OLFACTORY HAIRS: Fragile, protoplasmic filaments on the olfactory cells.

OLEAGINOUS: Of or pertaining to oil, oily; unctuous.

OLFACTORY-NEGATIVE: That which reduces odor such as the influence of an electropositive element in a compound.

OLFACTORY PIT: Elementary olfactory organ found in invertebrates and lower vertebrates.

OLFACTORY PRISM: A method, devised by Henning, of representing six fundamental odors as the corners of a prism.

OLFACTORY REGION: The seat of the smell receptors.

OMEGA FACTOR: A penetrating characteristic in odorants such as pyridine.

OPACITY: Impenetrability.

OPOPONAX: A resin.

ORGANOLEPTIC: Pertaining to or perceived by a sensory organ.

ORTICANT: Irritating to the skin.

OSMATIC: Having a normal sense of smell.

OSMESIS: The act of smelling.

OSMESTHAESIA: Olfactory sensibility; ability to perceive and distinguish odors.

OSMIC FREQUENCY: The Raman shift, described by Dyson as characteristic of any specific odor.

OSMICS: The science of smell; synonym: olfactology.

OSMOCEPTOR: An osmic receptor, a smell receptor.

OSMODYSPHORIA: Dislike of certain smells not generally considered to be objectionable.

OSMOGENE: Any substance which inherently exhibits as a part of its essential nature properties which give rise to characteristic olfactory perception.

OSMOMETER: An instrument for measuring the acuteness of the sense of smell.

OSMOPHOBIA: Fear or dread of odors.

OSMOPHORE: An odor carrier; a smell-inducing chemical group.

OSMOSCOPE: An instrument for measuring odor intensity.

OSMYL: An odor producing substance.

OSPHRESIOLOGY: The sum of knowledge regarding odors and the sense of smell.

OSPHRESIS: The sense of smell.

OSPHRETIC: Appertaining to the sense of smell.

OUTFALL: The point or location where sewage or drainage discharges from a sewer, drain, or conduit.

OVERFLOW RATE: A criterion for the design of settling tanks in treatment plants; expressed in gallons per day per square foot of the surface area in a tank.

OVERFLOW, STORM: A weir, orifice, or other device for permitting the discharge from a combined sewer of that part of the flow in excess of that which the sewer is designed to carry.

OXIDATION: Any process which increases the proportion of oxygen in a compound; a reaction in which the atoms in an element lose electrons and its valence is correspondingly increased.

OXIDATION, DIRECT: Oxidation of substances in sewage without the benefit of living organisms, by the direct application of air or oxidizing agents such as chlorine.

OXIDATION, SEWAGE: The process whereby, through the agency of living organisms in the presence of oxygen, the organic matter that is contained in sewage is converted into a more stable or a mineral form.

OXYGEN, AVAILABLE: The quantity of atmospheric oxygen dissolved in the water of a stream. It is the quantity of dissolved oxygen available for the oxidation of organic matter in sewage.

OXYGEN, CONSUMED: The quantity of oxygen taken up from potassium permanganate in solution by a liquid containing organic matter. Commonly regarded as an index of the carbonaceous matter present. Time and temperature must be specified.

OXYGEN, DISSOLVED: Usually designated as DO. The oxygen dissolved in sewage, water, or other liquid, usually expressed in parts per million or percent of saturation.

OZONE: A blue, gaseous allotrope of oxygen derived or formed naturally from diatomic oxygen by electric discharge or exposure to ultraviolet radiation. It is an unstable, powerfully bleaching, poisonous, oxidizing agent, with a pungent, irritating odor, used to purify and deodorize air, to sterilize water, and as a bleach: $O_3$.

OZONIZATION: The treating or impregnation of a substance with ozone.

PALATE: The roof of the mouth; the sense of taste.

PALPI: Sensitive organs near the mouths of insects.

PAPILLAE: Little projections on the tongue, which give roughness to the surface.

PARIETAL: The area of the brain concerned with skin sensation.

PAROSMIA: Disturbance of the sense of smell, only repulsive odors being perceived.

PAROTID GLAND: Either of the largest of the paired salivary glands located below and in front of each ear.

PARTICULATES (SUSPENDED): A nonuniform distribution of a solid in a liquid without the solid being dissolved in the dispersion medium.

PARTITION COEFFICIENT: (Nernst Distribution Law) The law that the ratio in which a dissolved substance distributes itself between two immiscible solvents (the coefficient of distribution or partition) is a constant at constant temperature.

PATCHOULI: A fragrant oil used in the manufacture of perfumes derived from any of several Asiatic trees.

PATHOLOGICAL: Pertaining to or caused by disease.

P.C.B.'s: Polychlorinated biphenols.

PEAKING: A phenomenon of some osmogenes wherein the threshold of perception and odor intensity are interdependent. As the concentration of odorant is increased, the intensity of odor remains nearly constant.

PENTALARM: A warning odorant, chiefly amyl mercaptans.

PERCEPTION: The becoming aware of through any of the senses.

PERCEPTIONS BRUTES: Sensations which are vague, diffuse or poorly-defined. This type of perception is common to lower animal life-forms such as the coelenterates. There is no differentiation in receptors, resulting in sensations which are "blooming buzzing confusions". Such receptions give rise to the responses necessary for the survival of the animal.

PERCEPTUAL PATTERN: The integrated result of a present sensation and a past experience.

PERIOD, AERATION: (1) The theoretical time, usually expressed in hours, that the mixed liquor is subjected to aeration in an aeration tank undergoing activated sludge treatment. It is equal to the volume of the tank divided by the volumetric rate of flow of wastes and return sludge. (2) The theoretical time that liquids are subjected to aeration.

PERIOD, DETENTION: The theoretical time required to displace the contents of a tank or unit at a given rate of flow (volume divided by a rate of discharge in gallons per hour or cubic feet).

PERSISTENCE: The duration of sensation.

PETITGRAIN: Essential oil from the leaves and twigs of the orange tree.

P FACTOR: The presence of the characteristic of persistence in an odor such as skatole.

pH: A measure of the acidity or alkalinity of a solution, numerically equal to 7 for neutral solutions, increasing with increasing alkalinity and decreasing with increasing acidity.

PHARYNX: The section of the digestive tract that extends from the nasal cavities to the larynx, there becoming continuous with the esophagus.

PHENOL: A caustic, poisonous, white, crystalline compound derived from benzene and used in various resins, plastics, disinfectants, and pharmaceuticals (also called carbolic acid): $C_6H_5OH$.

PHENOMENOLOGIES: The study of all possible appearances in human experience, during which considerations of objective reality and of purely subjective response are temporarily left out of account.

PHEROMONES: Airborne, super-charged hormones.

PHI FACTOR: The presence of a burning characteristic in odors such as that of benzaldehyde.

PHOTIC: Pertaining to light.

PHOTOTROPISM: Growth or movement in response to a source of light.

PHRENIC NERVE: The nerve which brings about the rhythmic contraction of the diaphragm.

PI FACTOR: The presence of a characteristic causing taste changes upon inhalation of an odor such as that of methyl mercaptan.

PIGMENTATION: The coloration of tissues.

PIPERONAL: A white powder having a floral odor used as flavoring and in perfume; synonym: heliotropin: $C_8H_6O_3$.

pO: An evaluation of the odor intensity; low pO indicates little odor.

POLAR ODOR MOLECULES: An odor molecule (osmogene) which causes a response as a result of the polar characteristics.

POLLUTANT: Any gaseous, chemical, or organic waste that contaminates air, water or soil.

POLLUTION: The contamination of soil, water, or the atmosphere by the discharge of noxious substances.

POLLUTION LOAD: A measure of the strength of a waste water in terms of its solids or oxygen-demanding characteristics and/or other objectionable physical and chemical characteristics, or in terms of harm to receiving waters.

POLOSMIC: Odor perception elicited by the chemical polar characteristics of the osmogene.

POLYELECTROLYTES: Used as a coagulant or a coagulant aid in water and waste water treatment. They are synthetic polymers having a high molecular weight.

POLYMERIZATION: The uniting of two or more monomers to form a polymer (any of numerous natural and synthetic compounds of usually high molecular weight consisting of up to millions of repeated linked units, each a relatively simple and light molecule).

POND, SEWAGE OXIDATION: A pond, either natural or artificial, into which partly treated sewage is discharged and in which natural purification processes take place under the influence of sunlight and air.

PONS VAROLII: Part of the brain, below the cerebellum.

POOLING, FILTER: The formation of pools or liquid on the surface of biologic filters caused by clogging of the filter medium.

PORE VOLUME (activated carbon): The pore volume is the difference in the volumetric displacement by granular activated carbon in mercury and in helium at standard conditions.

POSTERIOR NARES: The passages joining the back of the nose with the throat. Same as "choana".

POTENTIOMETRIC: Referring to the potential produced by the flow of current in a resistance network (see wheatstone bridge).

PREAERATION: A preparatory treatment of wastes comprising aeration to remove gases, add oxygen, promote flotation of grease, increase the buoyancy of light particles, or aid coagulation.

PRECHLORINATION: Chlorination of water prior to filtration; chlorination of sewage prior to treatment.

PRECIPITATION: The phenomenon that occurs when a substance held in solution in a liquid passes out of solution into solid form.

PRECIPITATION, CHEMICAL: Precipitation induced by addition of chemicals; the process of softening water by the addition of lime and soda ash as the precipitants

PREFONTAL LOBOTOMY: An operation in which the white fibers connecting the prefrontal and frontal lobes of the brain to the thalamus are severed.

PRESETTLING: The process of sedimentation applied to a liquid preceding subsequent treatment.

PRETREATMENT: Any waste water treatment process used to reduce pollution load partially before the waste water is introduced into a main sewer system or delivered to a treatment plant for substantial reduction of the pollution load.

PRIMARY ODORS: A predetermined number of odors from which all other odors are composed. Different theories suggest varying numbers and types of odors. Similar to primary colors.

PRIMARY TREATMENT: A process to remove substantially all floating and settleable solids in waste water and partially to reduce the concentration of suspended solids. This process can include screening, grit removal, sedimentation, sludge digestion, and sludge disposal.

PROCESS, ACTIVATED SLUDGE: A biological waste-treatment process in which a mixture of wastes and activated sludge is agitated and aerated. The activated sludge is subsequently separated from the treated wastes (mixed liquor) by sedimentation and wasted or returned to the process as needed. The treated wastes overflow the weir of the final settling tank in which separation from the sludge takes place.

PROCESS, BIOLOGICAL: The process by which the life activities of bacteria, and other microorganisms in the search for food, break down complex organic materials into simple, more stable substances. Self-purification of sewage polluted streams, sludge digestion, and all so-called secondary sewage treatments result from this process.

PROCESS, OXIDATION: Any method of sewage treatment for the oxidation of the putrescible organic matter; the usual methods are biological filtration, and the activated sludge process.

PROJICIENCE: The ability of the olfactory sense to take notice of, and locate, a source of smell a considerable distance from the observer.

PROPRIOCEPTORS: A sensory receptor, chiefly in muscles, tendons, and joints, that responds to stimuli arising within the organism.

PROTEINS: Any of a group of complex nitrogenous organic compounds of high molecular weight that contain amino acids as their basic structural units and that occur in all living matter and are essential for the growth and repair of animal tissue.

PROTOPLASM: A complex, jellylike colloidal substance conceived of as constituting the living matter of plant and animal cells, and performing the basic life functions.

PROTOZOA: Single-celled, usually microscopic organisms of the phylum or subkingdom Protozoa which includes the most primitive forms of animal life.

PSI FACTOR: Odors displaying an acrid characteristic such as glacial acetic acid.

PSUEDOSMOGENES: Volatiles which elicit olfactory sensations through reaction with tissues or nerves not specifically olfactory receptors.

PURGING: Freeing from impurities, purifying.

PURIFICATION, DEGREE OF: A measure of the completeness of destruction or removal of objectionable impurities, such as bacteria and hardness, from water by natural means (self-purification) or by treatment; a measure of the removal, oxidation, or destruction of solids, organic matter, bacteria, or other specified substance effected by sewage treatment processes.

PUTREFACTION: The partial decomposition of organic matter by microorganisms, producing foul-smelling matter.

PUTRESCENT: Becoming putrid, rotten.

PUTRESCIBILITY: The relative tendency of organic matter to undergo decomposition in the absence of oxygen; the susceptibility of waste waters, sewage, effluent, or sludge to putrefaction; a term used in water or sewage analysis to define stability of polluted water or raw or partially treated sewage.

PYRIDINE: A flammable, colorless or yellowish liquid base used to synthesize vitamins and drugs, as a solvent, and as a denaturant for alcohol; $C_5H_5N$.

PYTHOGENIC THEORY: The theorem that odors, especially foul odors cause illness and/or disease.

RADIORECEPTORS: Receptors activated by radiant energy, such as light and heat..

RAIES ULTIMES: Very strong lines in absorption spectra.

RAMAN EFFECT: Change of frequency of light on being scattered by a substance.

RAMAN SHIFT: A measure of the change of wavelength due to the Raman effect.

RATE, OXIDATION: The rate at which the organic matter in sewage is stabilized.

RATIO, DOSING: The maximum rate of application of sewage to a filter on any unit of area, divided by the average rate of application on that area.

REACTION TIME: The time interval between the application of a stimulus and the detection of a response.

REACTIVATION (activated carbon): The removal of adsorbates from spent granular activated carbon which will allow the carbon to be reused.

REAERATION, SLUDGE: The continuous aeration of sludge after its initial aeration in the activated sludge process.

RECEPTOR: A nerve ending specialized to sense or to receive stimuli.

RECIRCULATION: The return of all or a portion of the effluent in a high-rate trickling filter for the purpose of maintaining a uniform or nonuniform rate through the filter.

REDUCTION, OVERALL: The percentage reduction in the final effluent as compared with the raw sewage.

REFLEX ACTION: Involuntary action or response such as a sneeze, blink, or hiccup.

REFLEX ARC: The neural path of a simple reflex.

REFRACTORY PERIOD: The duration of time in which a neuron is in a refractory state.

REFRACTORY STATE: The state of the neuron immediately following an impulse, during which it is unable to send another impulse.

REIZSCHWELLE: The threshold of stimulation (German).

REMOVAL, HYDROSTATIC SLUDGE: The discharge of sludge from a tank by utilizing the pressure of the column of liquid above the sludge outlet.

REOXYGENATION: The replenishment of oxygen in a stream from dilution water entering the stream, biological oxygenation through the activities of certain oxygen producing plants, and atmospheric reaeration.

RESERVOIR: A body of water collected and stored in a natural or artificial lake; a receptable or chamber for storing a fluid.

RESIDUAL AFFINITY: The ease with which molecules of odorous compounds frequently form double or addition compounds.

RESIN ODOR: The residue left after evaporating the alcohol from an alcoholic extract of a resin.

RESOSMIC: Odor perception elicited by vibrational or resonant phenomenon.

RHINAESTHESIA: The sense of smell.

RHINENCEPHALON: The smell-brain; a rudimentary portion of the brain which has to do with the sense of smell; it consists of the olfactory lobe, the anterior perforated substance, the subcallosal gyrus (convolution), and the parolfactory area.

RHINITIS: Chronic infection of the nose.

RHINOLOGY: The study of the nose.

RHINOSCOPE: An instrument for examining the nose.

RINGER'S SOLUTION: Aqueous solution of potassium, sodium, calcium, and magnesium chlorides, the cations being present in approximately the same concentration as in the blood of an animal; used as a medium in which tissue slices are suspended to observe their metabolism apart from the body. The concentration varies according to the animal.

RIPARIAN: Of, on, or pertaining to the bank of a river, or of a pond or small lake.

SAMPLE, COMPOSITE: A combination of individual samples of wastes taken at selected intervals, generally hourly for 24 hours, to minimize the effect of the variations in individual samples.

SAPID: Pleasantly flavorful; savory.

SAPOPHORES: Sweet-producing groups.

SARCOPHAGIC: Flesh-devouring.

SATURATION, CHEMICAL: Containing all of the solute that can normally be dissolved at a given temperature.

SCAVENGING: Collecting and removing refuse from; expelling exhaust gases from a cylinder of an internal combustion engine.

SCHNEIDERIAN MEMBRANE: The mucous membrane lining the interior surfaces of the nose.

SCHIZOSMOGENE: An osmogene which exhibits more than one characteristic odor, normally as a result of different concentrations in air.

SCREENING: The removal of relatively coarse, floating, and suspended solids by straining through racks or screens.

SCREEN, MECHANICALLY CLEANED: A screen equipped with mechanical cleaning apparatus for removal of retained solids.

SECONDARY TREATMENT: A process to reduce the amount of dissolved organic matter and further reduce the amount of suspended solids in waste water. The effluent from the primary treatment process is given this additional treatment with processes such as activated sludge or trickling filter.

SEDIMENTATION: The act or process of depositing material that settles to the bottom of a liquid.

SEDIMENTATION, PLAIN: The sedimentation of suspended matter in a liquid unaided by chemicals or other special means and without provision for the decomposition of deposited solids in contact with the sewage.

SEDIMENTATION, FINAL: Settling of partly settled, flocculated or oxidized sewage in a final tank.

SEEDING, SLUDGE: The inoculation of undigested sewage or waste solids with sludge that has undergone or is undergoing decomposition, for the purpose of introducing favorable organisms, thereby accelerating the initial stage of digestion and shortening digestion time.

SENSATION: A perception associated with a stimulation of a sense organ or with a specific bodily condition.
SENSORY MECHANISM: The receptors, nerve fibers and central connections.
SEWAGE, COMBINED: A sewage containing both sanitary sewage and surface or storm water with or without industrial wastes.
SEWAGE, DILUTE: Sewage containing less than 150 PPM of suspended solids and BOD (weak sewage).
SEWAGE, INDUSTRIAL: Sewage in which industrial wastes predominate.
SEWAGE, RAW: Sewage prior to receiving any treatment.
SEWAGE, SETTLED: Sewage from which most of the settleable solids have been removed by sedimentation.
SEWAGE, STORM: Liquid flowing in sewers during or following a period of heavy rainfall and resulting therefrom.
SEWER: An artificial, usually underground conduit for carrying off sewage or rainwater.
SEWER, INTERCEPTING: A sewer which receives dry-weather flow from a number of transverse sewers or outlets, and frequently, additional, predetermined quantities of storm water (if from a combined system), and which conducts such waters to a point for treatment or disposal.
SIGMA FACTOR: Odors exhibiting the characteristic of anesthetizing such as formalin.
SILVAN FISSURE: A furrow on the surface of the brain.
SINUS: A dilated channel for the passage of chiefly venous blood; any of various air-filled cavities in the cranial bones.
SKATOLE: A white, crystalline organic compound having a strong fecal odor, found naturally in feces, beets, and coal tar, and used as a fixative in the manufacture of perfume: C H N.
SLUDGE, ACTIVATED: Sludge floc produced in raw or settled sewage by the growth of zoogleal bacteria and other organisms in the presence of dissolved oxygen, and acculated in sufficient concentration by returning floc previously formed.
SLUDGE, DIGESTED: Sludge digested under anaerobic conditions until the volatile content has been reduced, usually by approximately 50 percent or more.
SLUDGE, DEWATERING: The process of removing a part of the water in sludge by any method, such as draining, evaporation, pressing, centrifuging, exhausting, passing between rollers, or acid flotation, with or without heat. It involves reducing from a liquid to spadable condition rather than merely changing the density of the liquid on the one hand or kiln drying on the other.
SLUDGE, EXCESS ACTIVATED: Excess activated sludge removed from the activated sludge system for ultimate disposal.
SOLIDS, DRY SUSPENDED: The weight of suspended matter in industrial wastes after drying for one hour at $103^{o}$ C.
SOLIDS, SUSPENDED: Solids that either float on the surface of, or are in suspension in, wastes or other liquids and which are largely removable by laboratory filtering.
SORPTION: The process of taking up, holding.
SPECIFIC SMELL STRENGTH: The reciprocal of the number of grams of a substance per liter that can just be smelled.
SPECIFICITY: A characteristic reaction or circumstance evoked only by precise components.
SPIKENARD: An aromatic plant of India having rose-purple flowers.
SPRAY ELECTRICITY: Electric charge formed by extruding through a fine nozzle various solutions, including those of odorants.
STACK FOGGER: An odor control device installed in a gas stream which superheats, atomizes, and fogs odor-active chemicals resulting in a more intimate

and reactive mixture of neutralizers and malodorants than otherwise possible.

STENCH: A strong and foul odor.

STERCORAL: Excrement-devouring.

STEREOCHEMICAL: A chemical system requiring a site-filling chemical and a reciprocal configured site receptor.

STEREOISOMER: Compounds whose molecules contain the same number and kind of atoms arranged in the molecule in an identical manner except for their relative positions in space. The isomerism is three dimensional.

STERNUTATORY: Causing or tending to cause sneezing.

STEROID: A group name for compounds that resemble cholesterol chemically and that contain also a hydrogenated cyclopentophenanthrene-ring system. Some substances included in this group are the sex hormones, cardiac aglycones, bile acids, sterols proper, toad poisons, saponins, and some of the cancerigenic hydrocarbons.

STIMULUS: Anything causing or regarded as causing a response; an agent, action, or condition that elicits or accelerates a physiological or psychological activity.

STOKE'S LAW: The maximum time a particle can stay in the air (float) varies with the size of it.

STORAX: A brownish, aromatic resin used in perfume and medicine and obtained from any of several trees of the genus Liquidambar.

STREPTOMYCES: A genus of microorganisms of the family Streptomycetaceae, order actinomycetales, separable into 150 different species, usually soil forms but occasionally parasitic on plants and animals, and notable as the source of various antibiotics, such as the tetracyclines.

SUBJECTIVE/EMPIRICAL: Personal experience reinforced by repetitive reoccurances of a situation or circumstance.

SUBLIMINAL: Below the threshold of conscious perception.

SUFFOCANT: A lung irritant.

SUPERIOR CONCHA: The last of the three nearly horizontal folds of cartilaginous material on the inside lateral walls of the nose.

SUSTENTACULAR CELLS: The main epithelial or supporting cells between which receptor cells are sandwiched.

SYNAESTHETIC REACTION: A phenomenon in which one type of stimulation evokes the sensation of another, as the hearing of a sound resulting in the sensation of the visualization of color.

SYNAPSE: The point at which a nerve impulse passes from an axon of one neuron to the dendrite of another.

SYNERGISTICALLY: The action of two or more substances, organs, or organisms to achieve an effect of which each is individually incapable.

TANK, SEDIMENTATION: A tank or basin in which wastes containing settleable solids are retained for a sufficient time and in which the velocity of flow is sufficiently low to remove a part of the suspended matter by gravity. Usually, in the treatment of decomposable wastes, the detention period must be short enough to avoid anaerobic decomposition.

TANK, SLUDGE DIGESTION: A tank in which the solids resulting from the sedimentation of wastes are stored for the purpose of permitting anaerobic decomposition to the point of rendering the product nonputrescible and inoffensive.

TANNIN: (Tannic acid) A lustrous yellowish to light-brown amorphous, powdered, flaked, or spongy mass derived from the bark and fruit of many plants and used in tanning, as a mordant, to clarify wine and beer, and as an astringent and styptic: $C_{76}H_{52}O_{46}$.

TASTE BLINDNESS: The inability to perceive certain tastes.
TASTE-BUDS: Any of numerous spherical or ovoid nests of cells distributed over the tongue embedded in the epithelium consisting of gustatory cells and supporting cells and constituting the end organs of the sense of taste.
TEMPERATURE, TACTILE: Primitive sensibility before differentiation into temperature sensibility and touch.
TEMPLATE: A pattern or gauge, such as a thin metal plate with a cut pattern, used as a guide in making something accurately, as in woodworking, or in replication of a standard object; a piece of stone or timber used to distribute weight or pressure, as over a door frame.
TERPENES: Any of various unsaturated hydrocarbons found in essential oils and oleoresins of plants such as conifers and used in organic synthesis: $C_{10}H_{16}$.
TERTIARY TREATMENT: A process to remove practically all solids and organic matter from waste water. Granular activated carbon filtration is a tertiary treatment process. Phosphate removal by chemical coagulation is also regarded as a step in tertiary treatment.
THEOBROMINE: A bitter, colorless alkaloid that occurs in chocolate products, is derived principally from the cacao bean, and is used as a diuretic and a nerve stimulant: $C_7H_8N_4O_2$.
THERMAL OXIDATION: Oxidation caused by heat.
THERMODYNAMICS: The physics of the relationships between heat and other forms of energy.
THETA FACTOR: The presence of the characteristic of duality in an odor such as that of indole.
THICKENER, SLUDGE: A type of sedimentation tank in which sludge is permitted to settle, usually equipped with scrapers traveling along or around the bottom of the tank to push the settled sludge to a sump. In one form, the mechanism is equipped with a set of vertical fingers or risers which pass through the sludge, releasing occluded water and thickening the mass.
THRESHOLD CONCENTRATION: The minimum concentration which will arouse sensation.
TINCTURE: An alcohol solution of a nonvolatile medicine; a component of a substance extracted by means of a solvent.
TOTAL ORGANIC CARBON (TOC): A measure of the amount of carbon in a sample originating from organic matter only. The test is run by burning the sample and measuring the carbon dioxide produced.
TOTAL SOLIDS: The total amount of solids in a waste water in both solution and suspension.
TOXOPHORE: A group which in the presence of another group, an autotox, gives toxicity to a substance.
TRANSLOCATION: The change from one location or position to another.
TRANS-3-METHYL-2-HEXENOIC ACID: The schizophrenic odor factor isolated and identified by Thompson and Koster in 1969.
TREATMENT, PRELIMINARY: The conditioning of an industrial waste at its source prior to discharge to remove or neutralize substances injurious to sewers and sewage-treatment processes or to effect a partial reduction in the load on the treatment processes. Unit operations which prepare the liquid for subsequent major operations.
TREATMENT, PRIMARY: The first major treatment and sometimes the only treatment in a waste-treatment works, usually sedimentation and/or flocculation and digestion. The removal of a moderate percentage of suspended matter but little or no colloidal or dissolved matter.
TRIGEMINAL: The chief facial sensory nerve and the motor nerve of the masticatory muscles, largely responsible for common chemical sensation.
TRIOXYGEN: Ozone.

TROPISM: The responsive growth or movement of an organism toward or away from an external stimulus.

TURBIDITY: A condition of a liquid due to fine visible material in suspension, which may not be of sufficient size to be seen as individual particles by the naked eye but which prevents the passage of light through the liquid; a measure of fine suspended matter in liquids.

UBIQUITOUS: Being or seeming to be everywhere at the same time.

ULTRAVIOLET: Of or pertaining to the range of radiation wavelengths from about 4,000 angstroms, just beyond the violet in the visible spectrum, to about 40 angstroms, on the border of the x-ray region.

UNDULATORY: Moving in a smooth, wave-like motion; having a wavy outline or appearance.

UNLOADING, FILTER: The periodic sloughing or unloading of the film on the stones of a trickling filter.

UNSATURATED, CHEMICALLY: Of or pertaining to a compound, especially carbon, containing atoms that share more than one valence bond; capable of dissolving more of a solute at a given temperature.

URIDOSIS or URHIDROSIS (ur+hidros=sweat): The presence in the sweat of urinous materials, such as uric acid, urea, etc.

UTILIZATION: The use of the gas produced in the digestion of sludge for heating the sludge-digestion tanks, for heating buildings about the plant, as a fuel in engines for the generation of power, for the incineration of screenings and sludge, and in drying sludge for the production of fertilizer.

VAGUS: The tenth and longest of the cranial nerves, passing through the neck and thorax into the abdomen and supplying sensation to part of the ear, the larynx, and the pharynx, motor impulses to the vocal-cord muscles, and motor and secretory impulses to the abdominal and thoracic viscera.

VALENCY: The capacity of an atom or group of atoms to combine in specific proportions with other atoms or groups of atoms.

VAN DER WAAL'S FORCES: Small forces of attraction between molecules which determine whether a substance is a solid, liquid or gas.

VANILLIN: A white or yellowish crystalline compound found in vanilla beans and certain balsams and resins and used in perfumes, flavorings, and pharmaceuticals: $C_8H_8O_3$.

VAPOR PHASE: The state of a substance that exists below its critical temperature and that may be liquified by application of sufficient pressure.

VAPOR PRESSURE: The pressure exerted by a vapor in equilibrium with its solid or liquid phase.

VECTOR: A carrier.

VENTURI: Flumes with convergent/divergent channels (Bernoulli principle) with parallel sides and a sharp drop near the throat position.

VESTIBULE: The inside of the nostrils.

VETIVERT: Oil distilled from the odorous roots of khaskhas grass, used as a fixative in perfumes.

VOIDS: The percent by volume of the interstices to total bed volume.

VOMER: The bone which forms the lower rear part of the median septum in the nose.

VOMERO-NASAL ORGAN: Olfactory receptors present in many animals; degenerated in man. They connect by a pore to the nasal cavity.

WASTES, INDUSTRIAL: The liquid wastes from industrial processes as distinct from domestic or sanitary sewage.

WATER, POTABLE: Water which is considered satisfactory for domestic consumption.

WAVEFRONT: The wavefront is the capacity gradient that exists in the critical bed depth. It outlines the gradual transition of the carbon from fresh to spent.

WEBER-FECHNER LAW: A change in intensity is not recognizable unless the alteration is sufficient to constitute a definite functional increment of the acting concentration or stimulus. Odor responses as well as all sense organs conform to this psychophysical law.

WEIR, PERIPHERAL: The outlet weir in a settling tank, extending around the perimeter and over which the effluent discharges.

XI FACTOR: The presence of the peaking characteristic in an odor such as that in vanilla.

ZETA FACTOR: The presence of the suffocating characteristic in an odor such as that in carbon tetrachloride.

ZOOGLEA: Any of various bacteria of the genus Zoogloea, forming colonies in a jelly-like secretion.

ZWAARDEMAKER PAIRS: Pairs of odorants which neutralize or cancel each other's respective odors.

# BIBLIOGRAPHY


Adrian, E. D. (1946). 'The Physical Background of Perception.' New York: Oxford University Press.

Adrian, E. D. (1951). 'Olfactory adaptation.' J. Physiol., 112:38.

Adrian, E. D. (1953). 'Sensory messages and sensation.' Acta Physiol. Scand., 29:4-14.

Adrian, E. D. and Zotterman, Y. (1926). 'The impulses produced by sensory nerve endings, part III.' J. Physiol., 61:465-483.

Airkem, Inc. (1951). 'Odours and sense of smell.' New York: Airkem.

Air Pollution Industries, Inc., 95 Cedar Lane, Englewood, New Jersey 07631.

Air Preheater Company, Inc., subsidiary of Combustion Engineering, Inc., Wellsville, New York, 14895.

Airwick Industries, Inc., 380 North Street, Teterboro, New Jersey 07608.

Allen, W. F. (1928). 'Effect of respiration, blood pressure, and carotid pulse of various inhaled and insufflated vapors when stimulating one cranial nerve and various combinations of cranial nerves.' Amer. J. Physiol., 87:319-325.

Allen, W. F. (1929). 'Effect of respiration, blood pressure, and carotid pulse of various inhaled and insufflated vapors when stimulating one cranial nerve and various combinations of cranial nerves, III: Olfactories and trigeminals stimulated.' Amer. J. Physiol., 88:117-29.

Altschuller, A. P. and Lange, L. J. (1963). Analyt. Chem., 35:1541.

American Chemical Society. 'Aspirins, Enzymes, and Fragrant Redheads, An Essay Report.' American Chemical Society Radio Series: Cassette Number 553.

American Chemical Society. 'The Damaged Air, Part I, Part II.' American Chemical Society Radio Series: Cassette Number 606, 607.

American City (June, 1967). 'How to trace bad odors.' P. 144.

American Water Works Association (1970). 'Research on Tastes and Odors.' P. 59-62.

Amoore, J. E. (1970). 'The Molecular Basis of Odor.' Springfield: C. C. Thomas Publishing Co.

Amoore, J. E. (1971). 'Olfactory genetics and anosmia.' In Beidler, L. M. (Editor) 'Handbook of Sensory Physiology.' Berlin: Springer-Verlag, p. 245-256.

Amoore, Johnston and Rubin (1964). 'The stereochemical theory of odor.' Sci. Amer., 210:42-49.

Amoore, Venstrom and Nutting (January-February, 1972). 'Sweaty odor in fatty acids: measurements of similarity, confusion and fatigue.' Journal of Food Sci., p. 33-34.

Analytical Chemistry (August, 1959). 'Odor control is challenging scientific frontier.' Vol. 31, No. 8:63A-65A.

Analytical Instrument Development, Inc., Route 41 and Newark Road, Avondale, Pennsylvania 19311.

Angino, Waugh and Bredfeldt (April, 1970). Science, 168:389-390.

Arnold, D. L. B. (March 12, 1974). 'Chemical oxidation of odours by ozone.' In Chemical Engineering Group of the SCI 'Odour and fume control,' papers presented at a symposium.

Arnold, G. D. (March 12, 1974). 'The destruction of fumes and odours by thermal oxidation.' In Chemical Engineering Group of the SCI 'Odour and fume control,' papers presented at a symposium.

Atlantic Ultraviolet Corporation, 24-10 40th Avenue, Long Island City, New York 11101.

Babbitt, H. E. and Joland, J. J. (1955). 'Water Supply Engineering.' New York: McGraw-Hill Book Company, Inc.

Bak, B. (1954). 'Elementary Introduction to Molecular Spectra.' New York: Interscience Publishers, Inc.

Baker, et al. (August, 1973). 'Recovering p-cresol from process effluent.' Ch. Engin. Prog., vol. 69, no. 8:77-78.

Bannister, L. H. and Cuschieri, A. (1972). 'The fine structure and enzyme histochemistry of vomeronasal receptor cells.' In Schneider, D. (Editor) 'Olfaction and Taste, IV.' Stuttgart: Wissenschaftliche verlagsgessellschaft, MBH, p. 27-33.

Baradi, A. F. and Bourne, G. H. (1951). 'Localization of gustatory and olfactory enzymes in the rabbit, and the problems of taste and smell.' Nature, 168:977.

Bassi, M. and Manci, F. (1940). 'Le reazioni vegatative agli stimuli odorosi IV L'influenza degli odori non-alimentari sulla secrezione salivare: Sull' esistenza di un riflesso diretto olfatto salvare.' Rassigna di Neurologia Vegeratica (Florence), 3:57-67.

Bassi, M. and Pascucci, F. (1942). 'Le reazioni vegatative agli stimuli odorosi.' Rass. Neurol. Veg., 3:68-93.

Baumgartner, W. H. (1934). 'Effect of temperature and seeding on hydrogen sulfide formation in sewage.' Sew. Works. Jour., 6:399.

Beardsley, C. W., et al. (1958). 'Removal of sewer odors by scrubbing with alkaline solution.' Sew. and Ind. Wastes, 30:220.

Bedichek (1969). 'The Sense of Smell.' New York: Doubleday and Company.

Beets, M. G. J. (1957). 'Molecular structure and organoleptic quality.' SCI Monograph No. 1, Society of Chem. Ind., London.

Beets, M. G. J. (Editor)(1964). 'Molecular Pharmacology.' New York: Academic Press.

Beets, M. G. J. (1971). 'Olfactory response and molecular structure.' In Beidler, L. M. (Editor) 'Handbook of Sensory Physiology, Vol. IV.' Berlin: Springer-Verlag, p. 257-321.

Benarie, M. M. (1973). 'Language as a model relating to odour quality.' At. Envir., Pergamon Press, 7:369-371.

Berg, Pangborn, Roessler and Webb (1963). 'Influence of hunger on olfactory acuity.' Nature, 197:4862.

Bernard, H. 'The Oil Mystery.' American Chemical Society Radio Series: Cassette Number 580.

Besselievre, E. B. (1952). 'Industrial Waste Treatment.' New York: McGraw-Hill Book Company, Inc.

Bethea, Murthy and Carey (June, 1973). 'Odor controls for rendering plants.' Environmental Sci. and Tech., p. 504-510.

Biederman, N. P. (May, 1970). 'Odortron: a better nose.' Pipeln. and Gas J., p. 90.

Blackburn, E. K. (1957). 'The breath in acute leukemia.' Brit. M. J., 1:146.

Bloom, G. (1954). 'Studies on the olfactory epithelium of the frog and the toad with the aid of light electron microscopy.' Z. Zellforsch., 41:89-100.

Boch, R. and Shearer, D. A. (1962). 'Identification of geraniol as the active component in the Nassanoff pheromone of the honey bee.' Nature, 194:704-706.

Boch, Shearer and Petrasovits (1969). 'Efficacies of two alarm substances of the honey bee.' J. Insect. Physiol., 16:17-24.

Boffey, P. M. (September 12, 1969). 'The environment: ACS report is practical anti-pollution guide.' Science, 165:1104-1107.

Bohn, Dr. H. L. (1971). 'Production of methane from anaerobic digestion of wastes.' Environment.

Brady, Dr. R. O. 'A Richness of Lipids.' American Chemical Society Radio Series: Cassette Number 463.

Brandt, A. D. (1947). 'Industrial Health Engineering.' New York: John Wiley and Sons, Inc.

Braverman, Hochheiser and Jacobs (1957). American Industrial Hygiene Association Quarterly, 18:132.
Briegleb, G. (1961). 'Elektronen-donator-acceptor-komplexe.' Berlin: Springer.
Brooks Technical Bulletins, Brooks Chemicals, Inc., 3302 East 87th Street, Cleveland, Ohio 44127.
Bryan, A. C. (1956). 'Experience with odor control at Houston, Texas.' Sew. and Ind. Wastes, 28:1512.
Burgenborg, Dejong and Saubert (1937). 'Models for the stimulation of the organ of smell.' Amsterdam: Weutch, 40:302-306.
Business Week (May 25, 1968). 'Mechanical noses sniff success.' P. 62-64.
Buswell, A. M. (1939). Ind. Eng. Chem., 31:1349.
Caniggia, A. and Brogi, B. (1947). 'Sulle modificazioni da stimuli sensoreali nell'vomo.' Rass. Studi Psichiat., 36:592.
Capital Controls Company, Division of Dart Chemicals, Advance Lane, Colmar, Pennsylvania 18915.
Champion, R. A. and Field, R. K. (1963). 'Human performance and short term food deprivation.' Aust. J. Psychol., 15, 3:187-190.
Care, M. R. and Maller, O. (Editors)(1967). 'The Chemical Senses and Nutrition.' Baltimore: John Hopkins Press.
Carter, L. J. (January 23, 1970. Science, 167:360-361.
Chamberlin, N. S. (1930). New Jersey Agr. Expt. Sta. Bull., 500:3.
Chauncey, Feller and Shannon (1963). 'Effect of acid solutions on human gustatory chemoreceptors as determined by parotid gland secretion rate.' RSEB, 112:917-923.
Chemical Bond Approach Project (Group)(1964). 'Chemical Systems.' St. Louis: Webster Division of McGraw-Hill Book Company.
Chemical Engineering (October 4, 1971). 'Stop-odor incinerator has built in safeguards.' P. 42.
Chemical Engineering (February 5, 1973). 'Service helps control mists and odors.' P. 48.
Chemical Engineering News (September 23, 1968). 'New light shed on chemoceptor systems.' P. 38-39.
Chemical Engineering News (August 17, 1970). 'Fragrances: mixing the primaries.' P. 15.
Chemical Engineering News (March 27, 1972). P. 41-42.
Chemical Week (March 14, 1973). 'Putting the nose to the test.' P. 35-36.
Clarenburg, L. A. (1973). 'Penalization of the environment due to stench.' Atmos. Env., Pergamon Press, 7:333-351.
Consumer Bulletin (August, 1971). 'Room deodorizers.' P. 38-40.
Consumer Reports (January, 1972). 'Should genital deodorants be used.' P. 39-41.
Cormack, Dorling and Lynch (March 12, 1974). 'Comparison of techniques for organoleptic odour-intensity assessment.' In Chemical Engineering Group of the SCI 'Odour and fume control,' papers presented at a symposium.
Cox, J. P. (1973-1974). 'Odor panel evaluations of colored paper adsorbancy specificity and intensity in the blind.' (Unpublished paper).
Crawford, B. (October, 1953). 'Chemical analysis by infrared.' Scien. Amer., p. 257-263.
Cross, F. L., Jr. (1973). 'Air Pollution Odor Control Primer.' Westport, Connecticut: Technomic Publishing Company, Inc.
Cunningham, E. (1910). 'Proceedings of the Royal Society.' (London), series A, 83:357.
Dague, R. R. (April, 1972). 'Fundamentals of odor control.' J. Water Pol. Con. Fed., vol 44, no. 4:583-594.
Danielson, J. A. (Editor) (1967). 'Air Pollution Engineering Manual.' Los Angeles: Los Angeles County Air Pollution Control District.

Daval, et al. (1972). 'Studies on local EOG and single receptor responses to multiple odour stimulation in the frog.' In Schneider, D. (Editor) 'Olfaction and Taste, IV.' Stuttgart: Wissenschaftliche verlagsgesellschaft MBH, p. 109+.
Davies, C. and Jenkins, G. N. (1964). 'The effects of different stimuli on the composition of saliva in man.' J. Physiol., 170:86-100.
Davies, J. T. (1953). 'L'odour et la morphologie des molecules.' Ind. Parf., 8:74-79.
Davies, J. T. (1953). 'Olfactory stimulation.' Int. Perfum., 3:17
Davies, J. T. (1962). 'The mechanism of olfaction.' Symposia of the Society for Experimental Biology, 16:170.
Davies, J. T. (1965). 'A theory of the quality of odors.' J. Theor. Biol., 8:1.
Davies, J. T. (1969). 'The penetration and puncturing theory of odor.' J. Colloid and Interface Science, Schulman Memorial Volume, 29:296.
Davies, J. T. (1971). 'Olfactory theories.' In Beidler, L. M. (Editor) 'Handbook of Sensory Physiology, Vol. IV.' Berlin: Springer-Verlag, p. 322-350.
Davis, J. C. (May 14, 1973). 'Taking malodor's measure.' Chem. Engineering, p. 86-88.
Davson, H. (1964). 'Textbook of General Physiology.' J. A. Churchill, Ltd.
Dethier, V. G. (1958). 'Anatomy and physiology.' AMA Archives of Ind. Health, p. 535-536.
Deutsch, W. (1922). Ann. Phys. Lpz., 68:335.
Deutsch, W. (1931). Ann. Phys. Lpz., 9:249.
Deutsch, W. (1931). Ann. Phys. Lpz., 10:847.
Digiesi, Palchetti and Tortoli (1963). 'Influenza di odori non alimentari sull' accrescimento corporeo del ratto.' Rass. Neurol. Veg., 17:56.
Disher, D. R. (1934). 'The reactions of newborn infants to chemical stimuli administered nasally.' In Dockeray, F. C. 'Studies of Infant Behavior, Vol. 12.' Columbus: Ohio State University Press, p. 1-52.
Dodd, E. E. (1953). J. Applied Phys., 24:73.
Dodson, Dressler, Hills, Adams and Williams (1969). 'Biologically active compounds in orchid fragrances.' Science, 164:1243.
Doolittle, Beroza, Keisler,and Schneider (1968). 'Deuteration of the melon fly attractant, Cue-lure and its effect on olfactory response and infra-red adsorption.' J. Insect Physiol., 14:1697-1712.
Dravnieks, A. (1966). 'Current status of odor theories.' Advanc. Chem. Ser., 56:29.
Dravnieks, A. (October 21, 1974). 'Measuring industrial odors.' Chem. Engin. Deskbook Issue, p. 91.
Dravnieks, A. and Gaynor, A. J. (November, 1974). 'Odor Survey of M.S.D. Land Reclamation Project Located in Fulton County, Illinois.' Report, p. 3-4.
Dravnieks, A. and Prokop, W. H. (January, 1975). 'Source emission odor measurement by a dynamic forced-choice triangle olfactometer.' J. Air Poll. Con. Assoc., vol. 25, no. 1:28-35.
Drinker, P. and Hatch, T. (1954). 'Industrial Dust.' New York: McGraw-Hill Publishing Company.
Driskell, T. 'Bones, Teeth and Ceramics.' American Chemical Society Radio Series: Cassette Number 576.
Duclos, R. (May, 1975). 'Impervious Covering for Lagoons and Method of Collecting and Using Off-gases.' Report on an invention owned by Monitor Corp.
Duncan, R. B. and Briggs, M. (1962). 'Treatment of uncomplicated anosmia by vitamin A.' Arch. Otolaryng., 67:116-124.
Dyson, G. M. (1937). 'Raman effect and the concept of odour.' Perf. Ess. Oil Rec., 28:13-19.
Dyson, G. M. (1938). 'The scientific basis of odour.' Chem. and Ind., 16:647-651.

Edwards, F. R. (July 8, 1971). 'Oxidation processes for controlling fumes and odors.' Plant Engin.
Eliassen, R., et al. (1949). 'The effect of chlorinated hydrocarbons on hydrogen sulfide production.' Sew. Works Jour., 21:457.
Elliott, F. C. (June, 1971). 'Odor control: its time is coming.' Power, p. S12-S13.
Elsberg, Spotnitz and Strongin (1940). 'The effect of stimulation by odorous substances upon the amount of secretion of the parotid glands.' J. Exp. Psychol., 27:58-65.
Engen, T. (1971). 'Olfactory psychophysics.' In Beidler, L. M. (Editor) 'Handbook of Sensory Physiology, Vol. IV.' Berlin: Springer-Verlag, p. 216-244.
Engen, Lipsitt and Kaye (1963). 'Olfactory response and adaptation in the human neonate.' J. Comp. Physiol. Psychol., 56:73-77.
Engineering Science, Inc., 7903 Westpark Drive, McLean, Virginia 22101.
Enos, Dr. H. 'PCB's: The Accidental Pollutants.' American Chemical Society Radio Series: Cassette Number 597.
Environmental Science and Technology (January, 1973). 'Are you drinking biorefractories, too?' Env. Sci. and Tech., vol. 7, no. 1:14-15.
Epstein, Dr. S. 'Chemicals in the Environment.' American Chemical Society Radio Series: Cassette Number 593.
Evans, Moser, List, Dutton and Cowan (November, 1971). 'Edible oil evaluation by room odor tests: a preliminary report.' J. of the Amer. Oil Chem. Soc., 48:711-714.
Fair, G. M. and Geyer, J. C. (1954). 'Water Supply and Waste Water Disposal.' New York: John Wiley and Sons.
Faith, W. L. (1959). 'Air Pollution Control.' New York: John Wiley and Sons, Inc, p. 179-187.
Faith, Keyes and Clark (1950). 'Industrial Chemicals.' New York: John Wiley and Sons, Inc.
Federal Register (August 14, 1971). Appendix B, section 4.6, vol. 36, no. 158: 15497.
Fieandt, K. von (1966). 'The World of Perception.' Illinois: Dorsey Press, p. 49-60.
Field, R. (September 2, 1972). The Saturday Review, p. 45-48.
Fink, E. (1965). 'Geruchsorgan und Riechvermogen bei Vogeln.' Zool. Jb. Physiol., 71:429-450.
Food Engineering (May, 1971). 'Celentano Bros. eliminates smoke and offensive odors.' Food. Engin., p. 119.
Food Engineering (September, 1971). 'Science tackles taste and smell.' Food Engin., p. 82.
Food Processing (September, 1974). '$O_2$ injection doubles/triples biological waste treatment activity.' Food Proc.
Foulds, J. M. (December, 1972). 'Oxidation pond as an advanced treatment unit.' Water and Sew. Wrks., p. 56-58.
Freedman, Dr. R. (October 18, 1973). 'How do you recognise that smell?' New Scientist, p. 190-191.
Freeman, Dr. S. 'The Language of Odors.' American Chemical Society Radio Series: Cassette Number 579.
Friedman, L. and Miller, J. G. (1971). 'Odor incongruity and chirality.' Science, 172:1044-1046.
Fuchs, N. (1950). Usp. Khim., 19:175.
Furchtgott, E. and Friedman, M. P. (1960). 'The effects of hunger on taste and odor RLs.' J. Comp. Physiol. Psychol., 53:576-587.
Gamow, G. (July, 1959). 'The exclusion principle.' Scientific American, p. 264-273.

Garcia, J. and Koelling, R. A. (1971). 'The use of ionizing rays as a mammalian olfactory stimulus.' In Beidler, L. M. (Editor) 'Handbook of Sensory Physiology, Vol. IV.' Berlin: Springer-Verlag, p. 449-464.

Genzmer, A. (1873). 'Untersuchungen uber die sinneswahrnehmungen des neugeborenen meushen.' Inaugural Dissertation, Halle.

Gesteland, R. C. (1971). 'Neural coding in olfactory receptor cells.' In Beidler, L. M. (Editor) 'Handbook of Sensory Physiology, Vol. IV.' Berlin: Springer-Verlag, p. 132-150.

Gesteland, Lettvin, Pitts and Rojas (1963). 'Odor specificities of the frog's olfactory receptors.' In Zotterman, Y. (Editor) 'Olfaction and Taste, Vol. I.' Oxford: Pergamon Press, p. 19-34.

Glasstone, S. (1957). 'Physical Chemistry.' Van Nostrand.

Gleason, G. H., et al. (1933). Sewage Works Jour., vol. 5, no. 1:61-73.

Gleason, G. H., et al. (1934). Sewage Works Jour., vol. 6, no. 3:450-468.

Goetzl, F. R. and Stone, F. (1947). 'Diurnal variations in acuity of olfaction and food intake.' Gastroenterology, 9:444-453.

Goetzl, Abel and Ahokas (1950). 'Occurence in normal individuals of diurnal variations in olfactory acuity.' J. Appl. Physiol., 2:553-562.

Goldenson, R. M. (1970). 'The Encyclopedia of Human Behavior: Phychology, Psychiatry and Mental Health.' New Jersey: Doubleday and Company, Inc.

Gorman, W. (1964). 'Flavor, Taste and the Psychology of Smell.' Illinois: C. C. Thomas Publishing Company.

Grant, J. (1946). 'Hack's Chemical Dictionary.' Philadelphia: Blakiston Company.

Graziadei, P. P. C. (1971). 'The olfactory mucosa of vertebrates.' In Beidler, L. M. (Editor) 'Handbook of Sensory Physiology, Vol. IV.' Berlin: Springer-Verlag, p. 27-58.

Green, D. E. (January, 1954). 'The metabolism of fats.' Scientific American, p. 16-20.

Green, D. E. (February, 1960). 'The synthesis of fats.' Scientific American, p. 67-73.

Green, H. L. and Lane, W. R. (1957). 'Particulate Clouds, Dusts, Smokes and Mists.' Jew Jersey: D. Van Nostrand Company, Inc.

Greenberg, D. S. (October 10, 1969). 'Pollution control: Sweden sets up an ambitious new program.' Science, 166:200-201.

Hamaker, H. C. (1937). Physica. 4:1058.

Hamburg, Pribram and Stunkard (1970). 'Perception and Its Disorders.' Baltimore: Williams and Wilkins Company.

Hammer, F. J. (1951). 'The relations of odor, taste and flicker fusion thresholds to food intake.' J. Comp. Physiol. Psychol., 44:403-411.

Harper, Bate Smith and Land (1968). 'Odor Description and Odor Classification.' New York: American Elsevier Publishing Company, Inc.

Harper, Bate Smith, Land and Griffiths (1968). 'A glossary of odour stimuli and their qualities.' Perfum. Essent. Oil Rec., 59:22-37.

Hauser, T. R. and Cummins, R. L. (1964). Analyt. Chem., 36:679.

Heilman, W. (January 30, 1970). 'Study of costs of non-condensable fume incinerators for rendering plants.' Report for National By-products.

Hellman, T. M. and Small, F. H. (1974). 'Characterization of the odor properties of 101 petrochemicals using sensory methods.' Jour. A. Pol. Cont., vol. 24, no. 10:979-982.

Hemeon, W. C. L. (December, 1971). 'Malodors--a basis for regulations.' J. of A. Pol. Cont., vol. 21, no. 12:770-773.

Henkelekian, H. (1943). 'Effect of the addition of sodium nitrate to sewage on hydrogen sulfide formation in sewage.' Sew. Works Jour., 15:255.

Henkin, R. I. (1965). 'Hypogonadism associated with familial hyposmia.' Clin. Res., 13:244.

Henkin, R. I. and Bartter, F. C. (1964). 'Increased sensitivity of taste and smell in patients with congenital adrenal hyperplasia.' Clin. Res., 12:270.
Henkin, R. I. and Bartter, F. C. (1966). 'Studies on olfactory thresholds in normal man and in patients with adrenal cortical insufficiency: the role of adrenal cortical steroids and of serum sodium concentration.' J. Clin. Invest., 45:1631.
Henkin, Christiansen and Bosma (1966). 'Impairment of recognition of oral sensation and familial hyposmia in patients with facial hypoplasia and growth retardation; a new syndrome.' Clin. Res., 14:236.
Henkin, R. I. and Kopin, I. J. (1964). 'Abnormalities of taste and smell thresholds in familial dysantonomia; improvement with methacholine.' Life Sciences, 3:1319-1325.
Henkin, R. I. and Powell, G. F. (1962). 'Increased sensitivity of taste and smell in cystic fibrosis.' Science, 138:1107-1108.
Herzberg, G. (1950). 'Molecular Spectra and Molecular Structure.' New Jersey: D. Van Nostrand Company, Inc.
Heuss, J. M. and Glasson, W. A. (December, 1968). Env. Science and Tech., 2:1109.
Hodgkin, A. L. and Katz, B. (1949). J. Physiol., 108:37.
Hogewind, F. and Zwaardemaker, H. (1920). Proc. Acad. Sci., Amsterdam, 22:429-437.
Holldobler, B. (November, 1969). "Host finding by odor in the myrmecophilic beetle Atemeles pubicollis bris. (staphylinidae).' Science, 166:757-758.
Honeywell.. 'Theory and Fundamentals of Odor Control.' Honeywell, Inc., Honeywell Plaza, Minneapolis, Minnesota 55408.
Hoppitt, H. B. (March 12, 1974). 'Filtration.' In the Chemical Engineering Group of the SCI 'Odour and fume control.' Papers presented at a symposium organized by the Chemical Engineering Group in London.
Horn-Shafer (1965). 'The Air Conservation Commission.' Maryland: The Horn-Shafer Company.
Hughes, E. E. and Lias, S. H. (1960). Anal. Chem., 32:707.
Ishizaki, C. and Cookson, J. T. Jr. (March, 1973). J. Water Pol. Cont. Fed., vol. 45, no. 3:515-522.
Issac, G. W. (June, 1971). 'Low cost odor control.' The Amer. City., p. 14.
Jacobs, M. B. (1960). 'The Chemical Analysis of Air Pollutants.' New York: Interscience Publishers.
Jacobson, A. R. (December, 1972). 'Peroxide treatment eliminates rotten egg odor.' Public Works, p. 84.
Jacobson, M. (1969). 'Sex pheromone of the pink bollworm moth. Biological masking by its geometrical isomer.' Science, 163:190-191.
Jacobson, M. and Beroza, M. (1964). 'Insect attractants.' Scientific American, 211:20-28.
Janowitz, H. D. and Grossman, M. I. (1949). 'Gusto-olfactory thresholds in relation to appetite and hunger sensations.' J. Appl. Physiol., 2:217-222.
Jensen, K. (1932). 'Differential reactions to taste and temperature stimuli in newborn infants.' Genet. Psychol. Monog., 12:361-479.
Johnston, J. W. (March 12, 1974). 'Odour and fume control by wet scrubbing processes.' In the Chemical Engineering Group of the SCI 'Odour and fume control.' Papers presented at a symposium organized by the Chemical Engineering Group in London.
Jones, H. R. (1974). 'Pollution Control in Meat, Poultry and Seafood Processing.' New Jersey: Noyes Data Corporation.
Journal of the Air Pollution Control Association (1969). 'Product Guide, 1969.' J. Air Pol. Cont. Assoc.
Kaissling, K. (1971). 'Insect olfaction.' In Beidler, L. M. (Editor) 'Handbook of Sensory Physiology, Vol. IV.' Berlin: Springer-Verlag, p. 351-420.

Kalmus, H. (May, 1952). 'Inherited sense defects.' Scientific American, p. 406.
Kalmus, H. (1955). 'The discrimination by the nose of the dog of individual human odors and in particular of the odours of twins.' Brit. J. Animal. Behav., 3:25-31.
Katz, M. (1969). 'Measurement of Air Pollutants.' Geneva: World Health Organization.
Keane, J. R. and Fisher, E. M. R. (1967). Report AERA-R-5366 (Harwell).
Keller, R. A. (October, 1961). 'Gas chromatography.' Scientific American, p. 276-287.
Kempner, S. K. (March, 1970). 'Dealing with odor pollution.' Building Syst. Des., p. 21-22.
Kessler, K. O. and Carlisle, N. (1965). 'The Successful Inventor's Guide.' New Jersey: Prentice-Hall, Inc.
Kistiakowskyi, G. B. (1950). 'On the theory of odors.' Science, 112:154.
Kleerekoper, H. (1969). 'Olfaction in Fishes.' Bloomington, Indiana: Indiana University Press.
Klopping, H. L. (1971). 'Olfactory theories and the odors of small molecules.' J. Agr. Food Chem., vol. 19, no. 5:999-1004.
Kneese, A. V. and Bower, B. T. (1968). 'Managing Water Quality: Economics, Technology, Institutions.' Maryland: Johns Hopkins Press.
Kondo, et al. (March, 1973). 'Some problems on the joint treatment of industrial waste and sewage in the Ukima treatment plant.' Wat. Res., Pergamon Press, 7:375-384.
Kopplin, J. O., et al. (1960). J. Amer. Pharm. Assoc., Sci. Ed., 48:427, 521.
Laboon, J. F. (1961). 'Construction and operation of the Pittsburgh Project.' J. W. Poll. Cont. Fed., 33:758.
Lahmoun, E. (December, 1966). Staub., 26:24-29.
Lange, N. A. (1961). 'Handbook of Chemistry.' New York: McGraw-Hill.
Larson, D. M. (1972). Metal Finishing.
Laughlin, J. E. (1964). 'Studies in force main aeration.' J. San. Eng. Div. Proc. Amer. Soc. Civil Engin., 90:SA6-13.
LeMagnen, J. (1971). 'Olfaction and nutrition.' In Beidler, L. M. (Editor) 'Handbook of Sensory Physiology.' Springer-Verlag Berlin, p. 465-482.
Leonardos, G. (May 13, 1970). 'The Profile Approach to Odor Measurement.' Cambridge, Massachusettes: Arthur D. Little, Inc.
Leonardos, G. (May, 1974). 'A critical review of regulations for the control of odors.' J. Air Poll. Cont. Assoc., vol. 24, no. 5.
Levy, A. 'Puzzles of Air Pollution.' American Chemical Society Radio Series: Cassette Number 577.
Lewis, H. R. (1965). 'With Every Breath You Take.' New York: Crown Publishers, Inc.
Libby, W. F. (February 5, 1971). 'Promising catalyst for auto exhaust.' Science, 171:499-500.
Lindvall, T. (August, 1973). 'Sensory measurement of ambient traffic odors.' J. Air Pol. Cont. Assoc., vol. 23, no. 8:697-700.
Lo Cicero, P. M. and Sjolseth, D. E. (January, 1973). Tappi vol. 56, no. 1: 76-82.
Long, G. 'Antidote to the Energy Crisis.' American Chemical Society Radio Series: Cassette Number 594.
Lue-Hing, Dr. C. (April 9, 1975). 'Small Balls Repel Smells.' An evaluation report for the MSDGC.
Lund, H. F. (Editor)(1971). 'Industrial Pollution Control Handbook.' New York: McGraw-Hill Book Company.
Maarse, H. and Ten Noever de Brauw, M. C. (January 5, 1974). 'Another catty odour compound causing air pollution.' Chem. and Ind., p. 36-37.

MacLeod, P. (1971). 'Structure and function of higher olfactory centers.' In Beidler, L. M. (Editor) 'Handbook of Sensory Physiology, Vol. IV.' Berlin: Springer-Verlag, p. 182-204.

Macrides, F. and Chorover, S. L. (January, 1972). 'Olfactory bulb units: activity correlated with inhalation cycles and odor quality.' Science, 175: 84-87.

Magill, Holden and Ackley (1956). 'Air Pollution Handbook.' New York: McGraw-Hill Publishing Company.

Magos, L. (1966). Brit. J. Ind. Med., 23:230-236.

Malinovskii (1940). J. Gen. Chem. (U.S.S.R.), 10:1918-1922.

Mallette, F. S. (Editor)(1955). 'Problems and Control of Air-Pollution.' New York: Reinhold Publishing Corp.

Mast Development Company, 212 East 12th Street, Davenport, Iowa 52803.

Matthews, D. F. (1972). 'Rat olfactory nerve responses to qualitatively similar stimuli.' In Schneider, D. (Editor) 'Olfaction and Taste, Vol. IV.' Stuttgart: Wissenschaftliche Verlagsgesellschaft, p. 129-133.

Mayrsohn, H. and Hyman, M. H. 'The Lead Issue.' American Chemical Society Radio Series: Cassette Number 542.

McCaldin, Johnson and Stephens (October 17, 1969). Science, p. 381-382.

McCartney, W. (1968). 'Olfaction and Odours.' London: John Wiley and sons.

McCord, C. P. and Witheridge, W. N. (1949). 'Odours: Physiology and Control.' New York: McGraw-Hill Book Company, Inc.

McDermott, W. (October, 1961). 'Air pollution and public health.' Scientific American, 205:49-57.

McGraw-Hill (1971). 'McGraw-Hill Encyclopedia of Science and Technology.' Vol. 12, p. 435-436.

McKinney, R. E. (1956). 'The role of chemically combined oxygen in biological systems.' J. San. Eng. Div. Proc. Amer. Soc. Civil Engin., 82:SA4-1053.

McWhirter, K. (January-February, 1971). 'A simple procedure for obtaining virus-free strains of freesia.' The J. of Hered., p. 52-53.

Meetham, A. R. (1956). 'Atmospheric Pollution.' London: Pergamon Press, Ltd.

Mercer, B. M., et al. (1960). Chem Abst., vol. 71, no. 12, ref. 116322b.

Metropolitan Sanitary District of Greater Chicago (1973). 'Implementing the Prairie Plan.' MSDGC.

Moncrieff, R. W. (1946). 'The Chemical Senses.' London: John Wiley and Sons.

Moncrieff, R. W. (1963). 'Psycho-galvanic reflexes to odors.' Perf. and Essen. Oil. Rec., 54:313-316.

Moncrieff, R. W. (1966). 'Odour Preferences.' New York: John Wiley and sons.

Morrison, P. (April, 1957). 'The overthrow of parity.' Scientific American, p. 231-242.

Morrison, R. R. and Ludvigson, H. W. (1970). 'Discrimination by rats of conspecific odors of reward and non-reward.' Science, 167:904-905.

Mosier, Andre and Viets, Jr. (July, 1973). 'Identification of aliphatic amines volatized from cattle feedyard.' Env. Science and Tech., vol. 7, no. 7:642-644.

Moulton, D. G. (1967). 'The interrelations of the chemical senses.' In Kare, M. R. and Maller, O. (Editors) 'The Chemical Senses and Nutrition.' Baltimore: John Hopkins Press.

Moulton, D. G. (1970). Brain Research, 21:138.

Moulton, D. G. (1971). 'The olfactory pigment.' In Beidler, L. M. (Editor) 'Handbook of Sensory Physiology, Vol. IV.' Berlin: Springer Verlag, p. 59-74.

Moulton, Celebi and Fink (1970). 'Olfaction in mammals--aspects: proliferation of cells in the olfactory epithelium and sensitivity to odours.' In Wolstenholme, G. E. W. and knight, J. (Editors) 'Taste and Smell in Vertebrates.' London: J. and A. Churchill, p. 227-245.

Mozell, M. M. (1971). 'Spatial and temporal patterning.' In Beidler, L. M. (Editor) 'Handbook of Sensory Physiology, Vol. IV.' Berlin: Springer-Verlag, p. 205-215.

Mozell, M. M. and Jagodowicz, M. (September, 1973). 'Chromatographic separation of odorants by the nose: retention times measured across in vivo olfactory mucosa.' Science, 181:1247-1249.

Mullins, L. J. (1955). 'Olfaction.' Ann. Y. Y. Acad. Sci., 62:247-276.

Nader, J. S. (May, 1958). 'Current techniques of odor measurement.' AMA Arch. of Ind. Health, p. 537-541.

Natanson, G. L. (1949). J. Phys. Chem. (U.S.S.R.), 23:305.

Nature (September 22, 1972). 'Correlation of ant alarm pheromone activity with molecular vibration.' Nature, 239:225.

Nelson, M. K. (1963). 'Sulfide odor control.' J. Water Poll. Cont. Fed., 35: 1285.

Nesselson, E. J. (1954). 'Removal of Inorganic Nitrogen from Sewage Effluent.' Ph.D. thesis, University of Wisconsin.

Neuhaus, W. (1963). 'On the olfactory sense of birds.' In Zotterman, Y. (Editor) 'Olfaction and Taste, Vol. I.' New York: MacMillan

Newsweek (January 31, 1966). 'The war on smell.' P. 23-24.

Ohloff, G. (1972). 'Odorous properties of enantiomeric compounds.' In Schneider, D. (Editor) 'Olfaction and Taste, Vol. IV.' Stuttgart: Wissenschaftliche Verlagsgesellschaft.

Ottoson, D. (1971). 'The electro-olfactogram.' In Beidler, L. M. (Editor) 'Handbook of Sensory Physiology, Vol. IV.' Berlin: Springer-Verlag, p. 95-113.

Ouchakov, A. A. (1930). 'L'adsorption des substances odorantes et l'odorat.' Acta. Otolaryngol., 14:470-511.

Padfield, J. H. (January, 1973). 'Control of odor from recovery units by direct contact evaporative scrubbers with oxidized black liquor.' Tappi, vol. 56, no. 1:83-86.

Pake, G. E. (August, 1958). 'Magnetic resonance.' Scientific American, p. 233-242.

Parry, E. J. (1908). 'The Chemistry of Essential Oils and Artificial Perfumes.' London: Scott, Greenwood and Sons.

Parsons, T. S. (1971). 'Anatomy of nasal structures from a comparative viewpoint.' In Beidler, L. M. (Editor) 'Handbook of Sensory Physiology, Vol. IV.' Berlin: Springer-Verlag, p. 1-26.

Pateman, S. G. (September, 1969). 'Oxnard sewage plant solves odor control problem.' Water and Sew. Works, p. 352-353.

Pfaffman, C. (Editor)(1969). 'Olfaction and Taste, Vol III.' New York: Rockefeller University Press.

Pfaffman, C. and Engen, T. (May, 1958). 'Psychology: absolute judgements of odor.' AMA Arch. of Ind. Health, 17:544-545.

Pitman, G. B. (November, 1969). 'Pheromone response in pine bark beetles: influence of host volatiles.' Science, 166:905-906.

Pitts, Dr. J. 'Smog: an Environmental Dilemma.' American Chemical Society Radio Series: Cassette Number 546.

Pitts, J. N. and Metcalf, R. L. (Editors)(1969). 'Advances in Environmental Sciences, Vol. I.' New York: Wiley Interscience.

Polandus, A. (1948). 'Sur l'influence de substances odorantes sur le cocur du lapin.' Acta. Brevia Neerland., 16:15-22.

Pollio, F. X., et al. (May, 1969). Hydrocarbon Processing, p. 124-126.

Pomeroy, K. and Bowlus, F. D. (1946). 'Progress report on sulfide control research.' Sew. Works Jour., 18:597.

Porter, R. D. and Wiemeyer, S. N. (July 11, 1969). Science, 165:199-200.

Powell, S. T. (1965). 'Water Conditioning for Industry.' Maryland: McGraw-Hill Book Company.

Power Engineering (July, 1972). 'Sniffers help identify main causes of odor in diesel exhaust smoke.' Power Engin.
Product Engineering (July 14, 1969). 'Artificial nose will sniff odor intensity.' Prod. Engin., p. 18.
Ramparts, the editors of (1970). 'Eco-catastrophe.' New York: Harper and Row Publishers.
Randebrock, R. E. (1968). 'Molecular theory of odor.' Nature, 219:503.
Randebrock, R. E. (1971). 'Molecular theory of odor with the α-helix as potential perceptor.' In Ohloff, G. and Thomas, A. F. (Editors) 'Gustation and Olfaction.' New York: Academic Press, p. 111-125.
Raspail, M. X. (June 30, 1899). 'On the sense of smell in birds.' Annual report of regents of the Smithsonian Institution, p. 367-373.
Regnier, F. E. and Wilson, E. O. (April 16, 1971). 'Chemical communication and propaganda in slave-maker ants.' Science, 172:267-269.
Roberts, J. B. (September, 1973). 'Solving the process wastes problem.' Chem. Eng. Prog., vol. 69, no. 9:27-32.
Rocket Dispensers and Fluids, Inc., 636 North Lancaster Avenue, Aurora, Illinois 60507.
Roelofs, W. L. and Arn, H. (1968). 'Sex attractant of the red banded leaf roller moth.' Nature, 219:513.
Roelofs, W. L. and Comeau, A. (1968). 'A sex pheromone perception.' Nature, 220:600-601.
Roelofs, W. L. and Comeau, A. (July 25, 1969). 'Sex pheromone specificity: taxonomic and evolutionary aspects in Lepidoptera.' Science, 165:398-400.
Roelofs, W. L. and Comeau, A. (1971). 'Sex pheromone perception: synergists and inhibitors for the red banded leaf roller moth.' J. Insect Physiol., 17: 1043-1055.
Roelofs, W. L. and Tette, J. P. (1970). 'Sex pheromone of the oblique banded leaf roller moth.' Nature, 226:1172.
Rorvik, D. M. (October, 1971). 'Present shock.' Esquire Magazine, p. 68+.
Rudinsky, J. A. (1969). 'Masking of the aggregation pheromone in Dendroctonus pseudotsugae Hopk.' Science, 166:884-885.
Rudolfs, W. (1932). Sewage Works J., 4:782.
Russell, G. F. and Hills, J. (1971). 'Odor differences between enantiomeric isomers.' Science, 172:1043-1044.
Ruzicka, L. (1919). 'Uber die henningshen geruchsklassen.' Dtsch. Parf., Ztg., 5:173-175.
Ruzicka, L. (1920). 'Die grundlagen der geruchschemie.' Chemiker, Ztg., 44: 93-94, 173-175.
Saltzman, B. E. (1965). 'Selected methods for the measurement of air pollutants.' Pub. Mo., 999-AP-11.
Saltzman, B. E. and Wartburg, A. F. (1965). Anal. Chem., 37:779.
Sarkadi, D. S. (September, 1958). 'Laboratory deodorizer with a vaporization efficiency of unit.' J. Amer. Oil Chem. Soc., 35:472.
Sawyer, C. N. and Kahn, P. A. (1960). 'Temperature requirements for odor destruction in sludge incineration.' J. Water Poll. Cont. Fed., 32:1274.
Sawyer, C. N. and McCarthy, P. L. (1967). 'Chemistry for Sanitary Engineers.' New York: McGraw-Hill Book Company.
Sax, N. I. (1957). 'Dangerous Properties of Industrial Materials.' New York: Reinhold Publishing Corporation.
Schiffmann, S. S. (July 12, 1974). 'Physicochemical correlates of olfactory quality.' Science, 185:112-117.
Schrantz, J. (July, 1972). 'Chicago's approach to effluent discharge violations.' Ind. Fin., p. 9-14.
Schutz, H. G. (1964). A matching standards method for characterizing odor qualities.' Ann. N. Y. Acad. Sci., 116:517-526.

Schutz, Hilldenbrand and Ray (1964). 'Relations of odor to physicochemical properties of compounds.' ASTIA document 237834, contract no. DA19-129-qm-1500.
Schutz, H. G. and Pilgram, F. J. (1953). 'Psycholophysiology in food acceptance research.' J. Amer. Diet. Assoc., 29:1127-1128.
Science News (June 11, 1966). 'Center established for research in odor.' Sci. N., 89:463.
Scientific American (July, 1971). 'Attack by pheromone.' Scientific American, p. 45.
Scientific American (August, 1971). 'Left and right-handed odors.' Scientific American, p. 46-47.
Scientific American (September, 1971). 'Knowing noses.' Scientific American, p. 76.
Scott, R. P. W. (June 21, 1969). 'Recent techniques in flavour analysis.' Chem. and Ind., p. 797-803.
Searles, R. A. (March 12, 1974). 'Clean air through catalysis.' In Chemical Engineering Group of the SCI 'Odour and fume control,' papers presented at a symposium organised by the Chemical Engineering Group in London.
Seiyama, T. and Kagawa, S. (1966). Anal. Chem., 38:1069.
Shaheen, E. I. (1974). 'Environmental Pollution: Awareness and Control.' Illinois: Engineering Technology, Inc.
Sharman, R. U. (1963). 'Vibrations and Waves.' London: Butterworths Publishing, Ltd.
Sherwood, P. W. (November, 1962). 'Needed? Smelling machines.' Drug and Cos. Ind., vol. 91, no. 5:565+.
Shibuya, T. and Tucker, D. (1967). 'Single unit responses of olfactory receptors in vultures.' In Hayashi, T. (Editor) 'Olfaction and Taste, Vol. II.' Oxford: Pergamon Press, p. 219-233.
Siegel, R. D. (November, 1972). 'Measurement of aircraft engine pollutant emissions.' J. Air Poll. Cont. Assoc., vol. 22, no. 11:845-853.
Singer, R. (February, 1974). 'Odor modification: the good neighbor policy.' Amer. Dyestuff Rep., p. 57+.
Smith, K. and Sines, J. O. (1960). 'Demonstration of a peculiar odor in the sweat of schizophrenic patients.' AMA Arch. of Gen. Psychiat., 2:184.
Smith, Thompson and Koster (October 17, 1969). 'Sweat in schizophrenic patients: identification of the odorous substance.' Science, p. 398-399.
Smoluchowski, M. von (1912). Phys. Z., 73:1069.
Snarski, A. T. (1901). 'Analiz nornrolnikh vsloviy raboti slycenikj zhelyoz u sobaki.' Unpublished thesis, St. Petersburg.
Soucie, G. (September, 1972). 'How you gonna keep it down on the farm?' Audobon, p. 113-115.
Sproull, W. T. (1972). 'Air Pollution and its Control.' New York: Exposition Press, Inc.
Stahl, W. H. (Editor)(1973). 'Compilation of Odor and Taste Threshold Values Data.' Philadelphia: ASTM.
Standen, A. (Editor)(1967). 'The Kirk-Othmer Encyclopedia of Chemical Technology.' New York: Interscience Publishers.
Stecher, P. G. (Editor)(1968). 'The Merck Index.' New Jersey: Merck and Company, Inc.
Stokes, G. (1901). Mathematical and Physical Papers, 3:1.
Stoll, M. (1965). 'De l'effet important de differences chimiques minimes sur la perception de l'odeur.' France et ses Parfums, 8:227-232.
Sullivan, J. L. and Roberts, R. J. (April, 1975). 'Expert witnesses and environmental litigation.' J. Air Poll. Cont. Assoc., vol. 25, no. 4:353-361.
Summer, W. (1963). 'Methods of Air Deodorization.' Amsterdam: Elsevier Publishing Company.

Summer, W. (1971). 'Odour Pollution of Air.' Cleveland: CRC Press.
Svericenko, P. A. (1954). 'The searching by rodents for food in fields, and their conditioned reflexes to non-food odors.' Zool. Zh., 33:876-887.
Swets, J. A. (1961). 'Is there a sensory threshold?' Science, 134:168-177.
Swets, J. A. (1964).. 'Signal Detection and Recognition by Human Observers.' New York: John Wiley.
Swets, Tanner and Birdsall (1961). 'Decision processes in perception.' Psychol. Rev., 68:301-340.
Syrotuck, W. E. (1972). 'Scent and the Scenting Dog.' Arner Publishers, Inc.
Tagliamonte, et al. (December 12, 1969). 'Compulsive sexual activity induced by p-chlorophenylamine in normal and pinealectomized male rats.' Science, 166:1433-1435.
Takagi, S. F. (1971). 'Degeneration and regeneration of the olfactory epithelium.' In Beidler, L. M. (Editor) 'Handbook of Sensory Physiology, Vol. IV.' Springer-Verlag Berlin, p. 75-94.
Tauber, H. (1950). 'The Chemistry and Technology of Enzymes.' New York: John Wiley and Sons.
Thewlis, J. (Editor)(1962). 'Encyclopaedic Dictionary of Physics.' New York: MacMillan Company.
Thomson, Sir St. Clair and Negus, V. E. (1937). 'Diseases of the Nose and Throat.' New York: D. Appleton-Century Company.
Thornhill, R. A. (1967). 'The ultra structure of the olfactory epithelium in the lamprey.' J. Cell Sci., 2:591-602.
Time Magazine (November, 1971). 'S.M.E.L.L.S. v. smells.' Time, p. 84.
Timmermans, J. (1954). 'Odour and chemical constitution.' Nature, 174:235.
Todd, J. H. (May, 1971). 'The chemical languages of fishes.' Scientific American, p. 12, 98-106.
Treiman, S. B. (March, 1959). 'The weak interactions.' Scientific American, p. 247-258.
Tucker, D. (1971). 'Nonolfactory response from the nasal cavity: Jacobson's organ and the trigeminal system.' In Beidler, L. M. (Editor) 'Handbook of Sensory Physiology, Vol. IV.' Berlin: Springer-Verlag, p. 151-181.
Tucknott, O. G. and Williams, A. A. (October 5, 1974). 'A simple method for obtaining more reliable information on the odours of components eluting from gas chromatographic columns.' Chem. and Ind., p. 784.
Tumlinson, et al. (November 21, 1969). 'Sex pheromones produced by male boll weevil.' Science, 166:1010-1012.
Turk, A. (May 1958). 'Control.' AMA Arch. of Ind. Health, 17:542-544.
Turk, A. (November 3, 1969). 'Industrial odor and its problems.' Chem. Eng., p. 71-78.
Turk, A. (April 27, 1970). 'Industrial odor control.' Chem. Eng., Deskbook Issue, p. 199-204.
Turk, Haring and Okey. 'Odor control technology.' Env. Sci. and Tech., vol. 6, no. 7:602-607.
Underwood, E. J. (1971). 'Trace Elements in Human and Animal Nutrition.' New York: Academic Press.
U. S. Department of Agriculture (1955). 'Water.' Washington, D. C.: U. S. Government Printing Office.
U. S. Department of Public Health (1968). 'Consumer Bulletin Annual.' U. S. Government Printing Office.
Versage, F. J. (April, 1970). 'Ozone and electronic air cleaners.' Air Conditioning, Heating and Refrigeration News.
Vic Manufacturing Company. 'Control of Organic Solvent Emissions by Activated Carbon.' Vic Mfg. Co., 1620 Central Avenue, Northeast, Minneapolis, Minnesota 55413.

Vic Manufacturing Company. 'Energy Recovery from Solvent Vapors.' Vic Mfg. Co., 1620 Central Avenue, Northeast, Minneapolis, Minnesota 55413.

Vierling, J. S. and Rocks, J. (1967). 'Variations in olfactory sensitivity during the menstrual cycle.' J. Appl. Physiol., 22:311-315.

Viets, F. G. Jr. (1970). 'The Mounting Problem of Cattle Feedlot Production.' U.S.D.A. Report.

Volk, W. (1958). 'Applied Statistics for Engineers.' New York: McGraw-Hill, p. 319.

Wallach, H. (January, 1963). 'The perception of neutral colors.' Scientific American, p. 474-484.

Waller, G. (March 12, 1974). 'Adsorption.' In Chemical Engineering Group of the SCI 'Odour and fume control,' papers presented at a symposium in London.

Walther, J. E. and Amberg, H. R. (March, 1970). 'Odor control in the kraft pulp industry.' Chem. Engin. Prog., vol. 66, no. 3:73-80.

Water and Wastes Engineering (March, 1974). 'Small Balls Repel Smells.' Water and Wastes Engin.

Weast, R. C. (1965). 'Handbook of Chemistry and Physics.' Cleveland: CRC Press.

Weinaug, R. J. Jr. (January, 1973). 'Early experiences with a low-odor recovery system.' Tappi, vol. 56, no. 1:80-82.

Wenzel, B. M. (1971). 'Olfaction in birds.' In Beidler, L. M. (Editor) 'Handbook of Sensory Physiology, Vol. IV.' Berlin: Springer-Verlag, p. 432-448.

Westenberger, J. A. and Mermelstein, N. H. (February, 1973). 'Solving air pollution problems.' Food Tech., p. 44-47.

Whitten, W. K. (1965). J. Endocrin., 14:160-163.

Wilson, E. O. (May, 1963). 'Pheromones.' Scientific American.

Wilson, E. O. and Regnier, F. E. (April, 1971). 'Chemical communication and propaganda in slave-maker ants.' Science.

Winslow, C. E. A. and Greenberg, R. (1918). Am. J. Pub. Health, 8:759.

Winslow, C. E. A. and Herrington, L. P. (1936). 'Influence of odors on appetite.' Am. J. Hyg., 23:143.

Winslow, C. E. A. and Palmer, R. (1915). 'The effects of ventillation on health.' Proc. Soc. Exp. Biol. Med., 21:141.

Wolnak, B. (July, 1973). 'Potential industrial application of immobilized enzymes.' Unpublished paper.

Wood, D. L., et al. (1968). 'Response of Ips confusus to synthetic sex pheromones in nature.' Science, 159:1373-1374.

Wright, R. H. (1954). 'Odor and molecular vibration. I. Quantum and thermodynamic considerations.' J. Appl. Chem., 4:611-615.

Wright, R. H. (1954). 'Odor and chemical constitution.' Nature, 173:831.

Wright, R. H. (1957). 'Odor and molecular vibration.' Soc. Chem. Indust., Monograph no. 1, p. 91-102.

Wright, R. H. (1957). 'Molecular structure and organoleptic quality.' SCI monograph no. 1, Society of Chem. Ind., London, p. 100.

Wright, R. H. (1963). 'Odor and Molecular vibration.' Nature, 198:782.

Wright, R. H. (1964). 'The Science of Smell.' George Allen and Unwin, Ltd.

Wright, R. H. (January, 1971). 'Molecular vibration and the green odour.' J. Appl. Chem. Biotech., 21:10.

Wright, R. H. (1971). 'Correlation of far IR spectra and Mediterranean fruit fly.' Can. Ent., 103(2):284-285.

Wright, R. H. (September 22, 1972). 'Stereochemical and vibrational theories of odour.' Nature, 239:226.

Wright, R. H. and Burgess, R. E. (December 6, 1969). 'Musk odour and far infrared vibration frequencies.' Nature, 224:1033-1035.

Wright, Chambers and Keiser (April, 1971). 'Insect attractants, anti-attractants and repellents.' The Can. Ent., 103:627-630.

Wright, Hughes and Hendrix (October 28, 1967). 'Olfactory coding.' Nature, 216:404-406.
Wright, R. H. and Robson, A. (April 19, 1969). 'Basis of odour specificity: homologues of benzaldehyde and nitrobenzene.' Nature, 222:290-292.
Yokuchi, C. (1971). 'The Photographic Anatomy of the Human Body.' University Park Press.
Zilstorff-Pedersen, K. (1955). 'Olfactory threshold determination in relation to food intake.' Acta-Oto-Laryng. (Stockh.), 45:86-90.
Zurn Industries, Inc., Air Systems Div., Box 2206, Birmingham, Alabama 35201.
Zwaardemaker, H. (1895). 'Die Physiologie des Geruchs.' Berlin.

## Contributors

Air Pollution Industries, Inc.
95 Cedar Lane
Englewood, New Jersey 07631
(201) 871-3855

Air-Preheater Company, Inc.
Wellsville, New York 14895
(716) 593-2700

Airwick Industries, Inc.
380 North Street
Teteroboro, New Jersey 07608
(201) 933-8200

Analytical Instrument Development, Inc.
Route 41 and Newark Road
Avondale, Pennsylvania 19311
(215) 268-3181

Capital Controls Company
Advance Lane
Colmar, Pennsylvania 18915
(215) 822-2901

Mast Development Company
2212 East 12th Street
Davenport, Iowa 52803
(319) 326-0141

Pace National Corporation
500 7th Avenue South
Kirkland, Washington 98033
(206) 827-8711

Edw. Renneburg and Sons Company
2639 Boston Street
Baltimore, Maryland 21224
(301) 732-1665

Vic Manufacturing Company
1620 Central Avenue Northeast
Minneapolis, Minnesota 55413
(612) 781-6601

Zurn Industries, Inc.
One Clarage Place
Kalamazoo, Michigan 49001
(616) 349-1541

# INDEX

To: POLLUTION SCIENCES PUBLISHING COMPANY
P. O. Box 175
Lynden, Washington 98264

Dear Sirs:

I would like to suggest the following for improvement or updating of the compilation of Odor Control and Olfaction:

1. New Data: Journal reference — Reprint included ☐

2. Errata — Reprint included ☐

3. "Missed" data — Reprint included ☐

4. Disagreements

5. Observations and/or questions

6. Contributions: Credit given to:

7. Suggestions for overall improvement of the compilation

FOLD

ODOR CONTROL and OLFACTION

PLACE
STAMP
HERE

POLLUTION SCIENCES PUBLISHING COMPANY

P.O. Box 175

Lynden, Washington 98265

FOLD

CUT

To: POLLUTION SCIENCES PUBLISHING COMPANY
P. O. Box 175
Lynden, Washington 98264

Dear Sirs:

I would like to suggest the following for improvement or updating of the compilation of Odor Control and Olfaction:

1. New Data: Journal reference — Reprint included ☐

2. Errata — Reprint included ☐

3. "Missed" data — Reprint included ☐

4. Disagreements

5. Observations and/or questions

6. Contributions: Credit given to:

7. Suggestions for overall improvement of the compilation

ODOR CONTROL and OLFACTION

FOLD

PLACE
STAMP
HERE

POLLUTION SCIENCES PUBLISHING COMPANY

P.O. Box 175

Lynden, Washington 98265

FOLD

CUT

To: POLLUTION SCIENCES PUBLISHING COMPANY
P. O. Box 175
Lynden, Washington 98264

Dear Sirs:

I would like to suggest the following for improvement or updating of the compilation of Odor Control and Olfaction:

1. New Data: Journal reference — Reprint included ☐

2. Errata — Reprint included ☐

3. "Missed" data — Reprint included ☐

4. Disagreements

5. Observations and/or questions

6. Contributions: Credit given to:

7. Suggestions for overall improvement of the compilation

ODOR CONTROL and OLFACTION

FOLD

PLACE
STAMP
HERE

CUT

POLLUTION SCIENCES PUBLISHING COMPANY

P.O. Box 175

Lynden, Washington 98265

FOLD

To: POLLUTION SCIENCES PUBLISHING COMPANY
P. O. Box 175
Lynden, Washington 98264

Dear Sirs:

I would like to suggest the following for improvement or updating of the compilation of Odor Control and Olfaction:

1. New Data: Journal reference — Reprint included ☐

2. Errata — Reprint included ☐

3. "Missed" data — Reprint included ☐

4. Disagreements

5. Observations and/or questions

6. Contributions: Credit given to:

7. Suggestions for overall improvement of the compilation

ODOR CONTROL and OLFACTION

FOLD

PLACE
STAMP
HERE

POLLUTION SCIENCES PUBLISHING COMPANY

P.O. Box 175

Lynden, Washington 98265

FOLD

CUT

To: POLLUTION SCIENCES PUBLISHING COMPANY
P. O. Box 175
Lynden, Washington 98264

Dear Sirs:

I would like to suggest the following for improvement or up-dating of the compilation of Odor Control and Olfaction:

1. New Data: Journal reference — Reprint included ☐

2. Errata — Reprint included ☐

3. "Missed" data — Reprint included ☐

4. Disagreements

5. Observations and/or questions

6. Contributions: Credit given to:

7. Suggestions for overall improvement of the compilation

FOLD

ODOR CONTROL and OLFACTION

PLACE
STAMP
HERE

POLLUTION SCIENCES PUBLISHING COMPANY

P.O. Box 175

Lynden, Washington 98265

FOLD

CUT

To: POLLUTION SCIENCES PUBLISHING COMPANY
P. O. Box 175
Lynden, Washington 98264

Dear Sirs:

I would like to suggest the following for improvement or updating of the compilation of Odor Control and Olfaction:

1. New Data: Journal reference — Reprint included ☐

2. Errata — Reprint included ☐

3. "Missed" data — Reprint included ☐

4. Disagreements

5. Observations and/or questions

6. Contributions: Credit given to:

7. Suggestions for overall improvement of the compilation

ODOR CONTROL and OLFACTION

FOLD

PLACE
STAMP
HERE

POLLUTION SCIENCES PUBLISHING COMPANY

P.O. Box 175

Lynden, Washington 98265

FOLD

CUT